PHYSICAL ORGANIC CHEMISTRY

Physical Organic Chemistry

JACK HINE

Professor of Chemistry
Georgia Institute of Technology

McGRAW-HILL BOOK COMPANY, INC.

New York   Toronto   London

1956

PHYSICAL ORGANIC CHEMISTRY

Library of Congress Catalog Card Number 55-7280

VI

PREFACE

A broad definition of the term "physical organic chemistry" might include a major fraction of existing chemical knowledge and theory. As the title for the present book, the term is used in a considerably narrower sense to refer to the mechanisms of organic reactions and the effect of changing reaction variables, particularly reactant structures, on reactivity in these reactions. In order to facilitate consideration of the latter topic certain aspects of structural theory are discussed in Chap. 1. More than half of the book deals with polar reactions, but space is allotted to free-radical reactions in reasonable accord with their importance and with the extent to which they are presently understood. Four-center-type reactions are also treated separately. Despite the tremendous practical importance of heterogeneous reactions, their consideration is largely omitted both because of space limitations and because they are in general more poorly understood than homogeneous processes.

Of the vast amount of research in the area thus selected it is possible to mention only a small fraction. The investigations discussed have been chosen because of their relation to the principles the author believes to be most important, but, even so, their choice has often been necessarily arbitrary. Certain topics have been chosen for discussion in some detail, both for their own sake and because it is believed that detailed discussions give the reader viewpoints that could never be gained in any other way. The experimental evidence for reaction mechanisms and the logical methods by which these mechanisms are formulated from experimental data are emphasized throughout.

This book is written primarily for graduate students and advanced undergraduates. The unpublished manuscript has been used by the author as lecture notes for a one-year graduate course. It is hoped that the book will be useful to others in need of a survey of physical organic chemistry. Only a good knowledge of the standard undergraduate courses in organic and physical chemistry is assumed. While no more knowledge of mathematics and physical chemistry is required than may be expected of the student at this level, the knowledge he has is not ignored but used where needed.

v

I gratefully acknowledge my indebtedness to Dr. P. K. Calaway and Dr. R. L. Sweigert for valuable encouragement in the early phases of this work; to Dr. Erling Grovenstein and Dr. W. H. Eberhardt for many helpful discussions; to A. I. Turbak, N. W. Burske, L. H. Zalkow, P. E. Robbins, Dr. A. M. Dowell, Jr., and the other graduate students who have read and criticized parts of the manuscript; and above all to my wife for help at every step of the way.

JACK HINE

CONTENTS

PART I. BASIC PRINCIPLES

PART III. FREE-RADICAL REACTIONS

PART I

BASIC PRINCIPLES

CHAPTER 1

THE STRUCTURE OF ORGANIC MOLECULES

The representation of electronic structures of organic molecules most commonly used in discussions of reaction mechanisms is that developed by G. N. Lewis,[1] in which only the outer shell of electrons is shown. We shall use a common variation of Lewis's notation, letting the usual line drawn between two atoms represent the bonding electron pair and denoting unshared electron pairs by lines parallel to the sides of the atomic symbols. Unpaired electrons are shown by a dot. Some electronic formulas of this type are shown below.

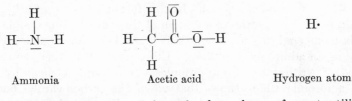

| Ammonia | Acetic acid | Hydrogen atom |

1-1. Resonance. Structural formulas have been of great utility to organic chemists because of the large amount of information they compress into a small space. For example, on seeing the structure

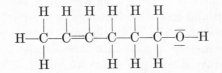

the chemist recognizes a compound which would be expected to add bromine (since most compounds with carbon-carbon double bonds do) and to react with acetic anhydride to yield an ester (a characteristic of compounds with the —CH₂OH grouping). The properties of various atomic groupings vary, of course, from compound to compound but often remain within a small enough range for a wide enough variety of compounds to permit the prediction of chemical and physical properties to be made with confidence. Often, however, the properties of com-

---

[1] G. N. Lewis, "Valence and the Structure of Atoms and Molecules," Reinhold Publishing Corporation, New York, 1923.

pounds containing certain groups differ so widely from those which have
become associated with those groups that ordinary structural formulas
become of little value. For example, from a knowledge of aliphatic
chemistry there is little way of understanding why the formula

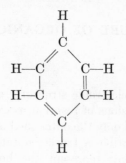

should represent a compound of relatively great stability, which does
not add bromine or reduce permanganate under ordinary conditions.
While the reason for this unexpected behavior has been the subject of a
great deal of discussion since the Kekule formula was proposed in 1865,
the "aromatic" properties of a system of three alternating double bonds
in a six-membered ring were essentially grafted onto the organic structure
theory as an additional postulate. Unfortunately, neither the classical
method of writing structural formulas nor its improvement by Lewis
yields a formula which shows that *all* of the carbon-carbon bonds in
benzene are quite equivalent to each other. Because of shortcomings of
this type it became desirable to introduce a new method of representing
the structure of molecules, or at least to modify the old method suitably.
The resonance method of describing structures is a modification of the
classical method and has the advantage of retaining most of its useful
and familiar aspects. The molecular orbital method (see Sec. 1-2) of
describing the structure of molecules is essentially a new method which,
while having many advantages of its own, uses much less of the familiar
terminology of classical organic chemistry.

The theory of resonance originated independently from quantum-
mechanical calculations on the hydrogen molecule and from the early
theory of the English school of physical organic chemists.[2] We shall
discuss only *valence-bond resonance, the description of organic molecules
in terms of Lewis electronic structures.* In this method of representation,

[2] A much more complete discussion of resonance is given in G. W. Wheland, "The
Theory of Resonance and Its Application to Organic Chemistry," John Wiley &
Sons, Inc., New York, 1944.

the Lewis structures in terms of which the molecule is to be described are joined by double-headed arrows, e.g.,

The two formulas and the arrow between them are taken together as a description of the benzene molecule. The double-headed arrow should not be confused with the two half arrows ($\rightleftharpoons$) signifying equilibrium, since the benzene molecule does *not* oscillate between the two structures shown but instead has a definite structure of its own. Certain other methods of notation have been used such as

which probably make clearer the fact that only one type of molecule is involved, but the use of the "resonance arrow" is probably the most common.

1-1a. *Rules for Resonance.* The resonance description of a molecule in terms of Lewis structures is governed by the following rules:

1. Any compound for which more than one Lewis structure may be written is accurately described by none but is said to be a *resonance hybrid* of them all. The various structures are called *contributing structures*. The *extent* to which a contributing structure is said to contribute to the total structure of a resonance hybrid is measured by the extent to which the hybrid has the properties which would be expected from the given structure. However, the properties of a resonance hybrid are not just an average of the properties of the contributing structures.

2. In addition, *the stability of a resonance hybrid is greater than that which would be expected of any of the contributing structures.* The energy content of a resonance hybrid is lower than that of the most stable contributing structure by an amount which is referred to as the *resonance energy.* The hybrid is therefore said to be *stabilized by resonance.*

Note that the actual molecule would be expected to assume the most stable configuration. From X-ray, electron-diffraction, and spectroscopic determinations of structure in the case of benzene, for example, it is clear that the actual structure is not that which would be expected of a contributing Kekule structure. Hence the resonance hybrid is more stable than any contributing structure.

3. The greater the number of important contributing structures, and the more nearly equal their contributions, the greater the resonance energy.

4. The greater the stability, i.e., the lower the energy content, to be expected of a contributing structure, the greater will be its contribution to the total structure of the hybrid.

5. *A structure will not contribute if it has a different number of unpaired electrons from the actual molecule.* According to quantum mechanics, it is not possible to specify the position and velocity of any electron. However, it is possible to obtain a mathematical function, called the wave function, whose square (the *probability-density function*) indicates the probability of finding an electron within any given volume element of the system. For a given position of the atomic nuclei in space and a given energy content the electrons of the molecule will move in harmony with a certain definite probability-density function. In valence-bond resonance we are, in effect, describing this function in terms of certain others (of whose properties we know more) in accord with which the electrons could (in theory only) be caused to move. This is not the same as a description in terms of a distribution function for the electrons when some have been paired or unpaired. Furthermore, the pairing or unpairing would change the energy content of the system. For instance, structure I is not a contributing structure for ethylene (II). It is,

rather, a different type of molecule, an excited state of ethylene.

Since the relative contributions of various Lewis structures to the total electronic structure of a system of atomic nuclei in space (a molecule), and hence the resonance stabilization, depend on the stability to be expected for the various structures, it is desirable to have a set of rules for estimating this stability.

A. Other things being equal, the greater the number of covalent bonds, the greater the stability. This follows from the known generalization that covalent bonds stabilize a system. The fact that the union of two hydrogen atoms to form a hydrogen molecule causes the liberation of 103.4 kcal/mole,

$$2H\cdot \rightarrow H_2 \qquad \Delta H = -103.4 \text{ kcal/mole}$$

shows that the system H—H containing a covalent bond is 103.4 kcal more stable than the system 2H·. Exceptions to this rule are known, e.g., the oxygen molecule has two unpaired electrons which could be written as paired to give an additional bond.

For the rule to hold rigorously, it would be necessary for all covalent bonds to have the same bond energy. This is not the case, but in estimating the relative stability of contributing structures the rule is still very useful. One reason for this is that in comparing two structures A and B with n and $n + x$ covalent bonds, it is found that all, or almost all, of the n covalent bonds of A are also present in B, so that most of the differences in individual bond energies cancel when the total energy content of A is compared with that of B.

B. *Other things being equal, a structure with a negative charge on the most electronegative element will be more stable.* This rule predicts which of several Lewis structures of the type

$$X^+ \ |Y^- \quad \text{and} \quad X^-| \ Y^+$$

will be the more stable and hence contribute more to the total structure of the molecule. This relative stability is a measure of the electron-attracting power or *electronegativity* of X and Y and might be expected to be related to their ionization potentials and electron affinities.[3] Thus it is not surprising that in this prediction we shall use electronegativities, since they are roughly proportional to the average of the ionization potentials and the electron affinities of the various elements. Electronegativities for some elements of common occurrence in organic molecules, on the most widely used scale, that of Pauling,[4] are shown in Table 1-1.

TABLE 1-1. ELECTRONEGATIVITIES OF VARIOUS ELEMENTS[4]

Fluorine	4.0	Selenium	2.4
Oxygen	3.5	Phosphorus	2.1
Chlorine	3.0	Hydrogen	2.1
Nitrogen	3.0	Arsenic	2.0
Bromine	2.8	Boron	2.0
Iodine	2.5	Silicon	1.8
Sulfur	2.5	Magnesium	1.2
Carbon	2.5	Sodium	0.9

The molecule X—Y *could* be described in terms of the structures

$$\overset{\oplus}{X} \ |\overset{\ominus}{Y} \ \leftrightarrow X\text{—}Y \leftrightarrow X| \ \overset{\ominus \ \oplus}{Y}$$
$$A \qquad\qquad B \qquad\qquad C$$

[3] The ionization potential is the energy required to remove an electron from a neutral atom; the electron affinity is the energy liberated by the combination of a neutral atom with an electron.

$$X\cdot \rightarrow X^+ + \text{electron} \qquad \Delta E = \text{ionization Potential of X}$$
$$X\cdot + \text{electron} \rightarrow X^- \qquad \Delta E = -\text{electron Affinity of X}$$

[4] L. Pauling, "The Nature of the Chemical Bond," 2d ed., pp. 58–75, Cornell University Press, Ithaca, N.Y., 1945.

but it is more convenient to make the description in terms of a covalent structure (III), which is really a resonance hybrid of B and equal amounts of A and C, and of that ionic structure which contributes more.   Thus, by writing a covalent structure, we may *imply* equal contributions of ionic structures and reserve the representation

$$X—Y \leftrightarrow X| \overset{\ominus}{} \overset{\oplus}{Y}$$

$$\text{III} \qquad \text{IV}$$

for cases in which X is more electronegative than Y and IV is therefore the more highly contributing ionic structure.   Since the contribution of IV will increase with the electronegativity difference between X and Y, the contribution of the two structures will simultaneously become more nearly equal up to the point (when the electronegativities differ by about two or more) where the contribution of IV reaches that of III.   An increase in the electronegativity difference would therefore be expected to increase the resonance stabilization (the extent to which the molecule is more stable than would be expected from a purely covalent structure). Since the bonds in X—X and Y—Y *must* be purely covalent, it might be expected that the bond in X—Y should have a strength halfway between X—X and Y—Y if the bond in X—Y is entirely covalent.   This is indeed found to be very nearly true for molecules in which the electronegativity difference is very small.   However, bonds between elements with considerably different electronegativities are definitely stronger than would be expected, due to the resonance stabilization arising from the contribution of structure IV.   In fact, the numerical electronegativity values shown in Table 1-1 were based on bond-energy data, as described in Sec. 1-3c.

C. *Other things being equal, the more closely the bond lengths and bond angles to be expected of the contributing structure resemble those of the actual resonance hybrid, the greater the stability.*

An example of the application of this rule may be found in the case of ethane.

$$\begin{array}{ccccc}
\text{H} & & \text{H} & \text{H}\text{———————}\text{H} \\
\ \diagdown & & \diagup & \\
\text{H—C—C—H} & \leftrightarrow & \text{H—C}{=}\text{C—H} \\
\ \diagup & & \diagdown & \\
\text{H} & & \text{H} & \text{H} \qquad\quad \text{H} \\
& \text{V} & & \text{VI}
\end{array}$$

Studies of the actual geometrical configuration of the ethane molecule show that hydrogen atoms on different carbon atoms may not come closer together than about 2.25 A.   The fact that the bond distance in the hydrogen molecule is 0.74 A shows that the hydrogen-hydrogen bond is most stable at this length.   It therefore seems likely that a hydrogen-

hydrogen bond more than three times as long would be very unstable. From similar data it may be shown that bond angles in ethane are very unfavorable for a structure of the type of VI. These and several other points indicate that VI would be very unstable and should contribute negligibly to the structure of ethane.

D. *Other things being equal, the greater the separation of like charges, the greater the stability.* This follows from the simple physical principle that work is required to bring two like charges closer together. Therefore, any structure with like charges close together, having had work done upon it, will have a high energy content and lower stability.

This rule usually acquires importance only when the two charges are very close together. That is, structures with like charges on adjacent atoms or especially those with a double charge on one atom tend to be unstable. Among the structures which can be written for an alkyl azide are

$$R\overline{\text{---}N}\overset{\oplus}{=}N\overset{\ominus}{=}\overline{N}| \qquad R\text{---}\overset{\ominus}{\overline{N}}\text{---}\overset{\oplus}{N}\equiv N| \qquad R\text{---}\overset{\oplus}{N}\equiv\overset{\oplus}{N}\text{---}\overset{\ominus\ominus}{\overline{N}}|$$
$$\text{VII} \qquad\qquad\qquad \text{VIII} \qquad\qquad\qquad \text{IX}$$

There is reason to believe that structure IX does not contribute appreciably to the hybrid. This structure would not be expected to be stable because of the double negative charge on one atom and the positive charges on adjacent atoms.

E. *Other things being equal, the greater the separation of unlike charges, the less the stability.* This follows from the same coulombic principle that was stated under rule D. The converse of this rule—the less the separation of unlike charges, the greater the stability—reaches its logical extreme in the case where both of the unlike charges are on the same atom, or, in other words, the charges do not exist.

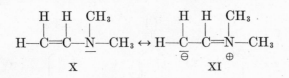

In the above resonance structures for dimethylvinylamine, XI has the destabilization caused by charge separation. It is, however, stabilized by permitting nitrogen to share its electron pairs (see rule F).

F. *Other things being equal, structures in which basic atoms coordinate their unshared electron pairs with adjacent atoms to form double bonds will be more stable than those in which this is not done.*

Just as basic atoms may be stabilized in intermolecular reactions by coordination through their unshared electron pair with another atom to form a covalent bond, so may contributing structures be similarly stabilized intramolecularly. While structures of this type are *most* important with the more basic elements, they are still of importance with elements whose basicity is often too small to detect in intermolecular reactions. For example, the contribution of structures XIV, XV, and XVI to the total structure of aniline is well evidenced by a number of data. Due to the contributions of these structures, the hybrid has a smaller density of unshared electrons on the nitrogen atom, which therefore is less basic than in aliphatic amines or ammonia (see Sec. 1-1*c*). Also, the contributions of these structures increase the electron density in the ortho and para positions of the molecule and thus increase its reactivity (in these positions) toward aromatic substituting reagents (Sec. 16-3*a*).

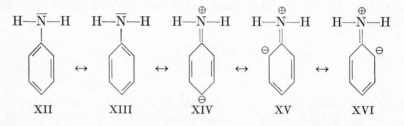

Although the contributions of structures XIX, XX, and XXI to the total structure of chlorobenzene are considerably less than those of the analogous structures of aniline, they are believed responsible for the observed ortho-para aromatic substitution because the carbon-chlorine bond is definitely shorter than in alkyl chlorides. That is, since double bonds are always shorter than the corresponding single bonds, the admixture of double-bond character should result in a shorter bond in the resonance hybrid (see Sec. 1-3*a*).

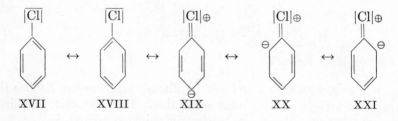

G. Structures with more than two electrons in the outer shell of hydrogen, more than eight in the outer shell of first-row elements, more than twelve in the outer shell of second-row elements, etc., will be unstable. This is a simple extension of the observation that hydrogen never forms a covalent bond with more than one other atom, first-row elements never with more than four, second-row elements six, etc. For instance, valence-bond structures of the type

are considered too unstable to contribute significantly.

Unfortunately, in most comparisons of the stabilities of several valence-bond structures "other things" are not equal. Thus, in comparing structures XXII and XXIII

$$H-\overline{Cl}| \leftrightarrow \overset{\oplus}{H} \,\, \overset{\ominus}{|\overline{Cl}|}$$
$$\text{XXII} \qquad \text{XXIII}$$

for hydrogen chloride, it may be seen that XXII has the advantage of one more covalent bond (rule A) and of less charge separation (rule E), while XXIII is stabilized by having a negative charge on the most electronegative element (rule B). Since we have no quantitative yardstick for the operation of these rules, we cannot judge the relative stability, and hence the relative contributions, of the two structures. However, since the dipole moment of a molecule is equal to the distance between the centers of positive and negative charge multiplied by the magnitude of this charge (Sec. 1-1c), if we assume that the covalent structure XXII has a dipole moment of zero[5] and that the ionic structure XXIII has a dipole moment equal to the product of the charge on an electron and the interatomic distance in HCl (4.8×10^{-10} esu $\times 1.28 \times 10^{-8}$ cm $= 6.15$ D); from the observed dipole moment of hydrogen chloride, 1.03 D, we can state that the contribution of structure XXIII is $1.03/6.15 \times 100 = 16.7$ per cent. (1 D [Debye] $= 10^{-18}$ esu.) Having determined the percentage contribution of the ionic structure in hydrogen chloride, we might predict that because of the greater electronegativity of fluorine, an ionic structure should contribute more to hydrogen fluoride. In agreement with the prediction a 43 per cent contribution is found. Conversely, ionic structures contribute 11.5 per cent and 4.9 per cent to hydrogen bromide and hydrogen iodide, respectively. The figures quoted, of course, relate to a definition of *percentage contribution* of a structure in terms of dipole moments and need not equal the values obtained from some other definition, e.g., one based on the bond length.

This method of describing a bond as a resonance hybrid of a purely covalent and a purely ionic bond is often very useful, but since most bonds have at least some ionic character, the method can become quite

---

[5] It has been argued, however, that even a purely covalent molecule will have a dipole if the atoms involved are not identical and especially if they differ greatly in size (C. A. Coulson, "Valence," p. 145, Oxford University Press, London, 1952).

tedious for molecules with many bonds. For this reason molecules are ordinarily described not in terms of entirely covalent and ionic bond structures but in terms of the typically partial covalent bond. For example, in describing the resonance stabilization of the propionate anion (responsible for the acidity of propionic acid) we write the structures

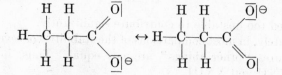

and by each we mean a structure having carbon-hydrogen bonds with their characteristic percentage of ionic character. That is, we *imply* the contributions of the purely covalent and purely ionic structures in the case where we do not specifically state it.

The question is sometimes raised as to whether the electrons do not move back and forth, sometimes assuming the positions characteristic of one valence-bond structure and sometimes of another. To this it may be answered that while the electrons do move, they do not ever assume a position characteristic of one valence-bond structure since *there is no such position.* No particular position of electrons can be said to be characteristic of a carbon-carbon single bond or double bond; only a certain type of probability-density function is characteristic. The probability-density function for the benzene molecule is not like that which would be expected from either Kekule structure, nor does it change back and forth from one such function to the other.

The atomic nuclei are free to vibrate (although usually with only a relatively small amplitude), and therefore any structural formula showing the exact positions will, in reality, show only the centers around which they vibrate. The electronic probability-density distribution will change somewhat as the nuclei move, but for a given molecule with a given energy content, these centers around which the nuclei vibrate have definite relative positions in space.

1-1b. *A Graphic Treatment of Resonance.* Among other valence-bond structures for *o*-dichlorobenzene we may write

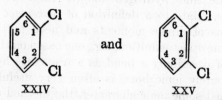

Since ordinary carbon-carbon single bonds are about 1.54 A in length, we should expect that a molecule which was adequately described by structure XXIV would have C_1—C_2, C_3—C_4, and C_5—C_6 bonds of about

this length, with C_2—C_3, C_4—C_5, and C_6—C_1 bonds of about 1.33 A, like most other double bonds. For XXV these bond lengths should be reversed. Unlike either of these structures, the actual o-dichlorobenzene molecule is thought to have six carbon-carbon bonds of very nearly equal length (about 1.39 A). Thus there are actually not two different

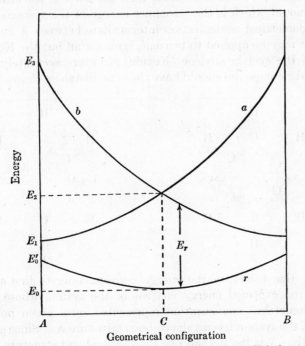

FIG. 1-1. Graphic representation of resonance between two Kekule structures for benzene.

kinds of molecules corresponding to XXIV and XXV but only one type of molecule, a resonance hybrid of these two structures.

On the other hand, we are well aware not only that we may write valence-bond structures for n-butane and isobutane but also that there are two different types of molecules corresponding to these two different structures. This raises the question of how we may tell, in general, when, for two or more isomeric valence-bond structures, there will be two or more different kinds of molecules and when there will be only one resonance hybrid. This question is usually, but not always, an easy one to answer and will be discussed in terms of a graphic treatment of resonance.[6]

Let the left end of the abscissa of Fig. 1-1 represent the geometrical configuration of atoms corresponding to structure A, and the right end

[6] This discussion is similar to one by G. E. K. Branch and M. Calvin, "The Theory of Organic Chemistry," p. 74, Prentice-Hall Inc., New York, 1941.

represent the configuration corresponding to valence-bond structure B, where the energy is plotted as the ordinate. Line *a*, then, represents the expected energy of the system if it is considered to be in valence-bond structure A, and line *b* represents the energy of the system considered as valence-bond structure B. The actual energy of the system, represented by line *r*, is in all cases lower than the lower of the other two lines (by an amount which is the resonance energy of the system). C represents a geometrical configuration intermediate between A and B. This treatment may be applied to benzene, ignoring all but the Kekule structures. If the cyclohexatriene (Kekule) structure accurately represents benzene, the compound should have the bond distances shown in formulas A and B.

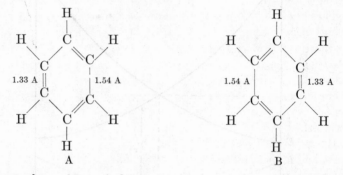

To get the values of the energy corresponding to line *a*, we must estimate the expected energy content of the system whose atoms are in the geometrical configuration represented by a given point on the abscissa if the system has a valence-bond structure A. Since geometrical configuration A is the normal one for valence-bond structure A, it must represent an energy minimum (E_1 in Fig. 1-1). On the other hand, if geometrical configuration B were represented as having valence-bond structure A, the stability would be less and the energy content higher, since the single bonds are 0.21 A shorter than their optimum length, and

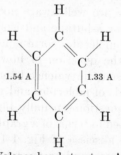

Valence bond structure A
with geometrical configuration B

the double bonds are stretched a like amount. Thus, the energy will have a value E_3, greater than E_1. The exact shape of line a cannot be predicted, but E_1 will be its lowest value and E_3 its highest. It seems likely that the line will be concave upward; i.e., a large change in the geometric configuration will cause an increase in the energy content more than proportional to the increase produced by a small change of configuration. By similar reasoning, line b is readily constructed. The actual energy of the system in its various geometrical configurations is represented by line r. This will be lower than the lower of lines a and b by an amount equal to the resonance energy of the system. Since the resonance energy E_r will be greater the more nearly equal the energy content of the contributing structures, it will be at a maximum for geometrical configuration C, where lines a and b cross. It happens, in the case of benzene, that upon going from configuration A (or B) to C, the resonance energy increases more rapidly than the energy content plotted on line a (or b). Therefore, the true energy curve r has one minimum at the intermediate configuration C, and in benzene we do not have an equilibrium mixture of forms A and B; we have merely the resonance hybrid C. This resonance hybrid is halfway between structures A and B in that it is as close to one as it is to the other. However, C does not have its various atomic nuclei lying at the mid-point of the line joining the position of the nucleus in structure A and its position in structure B. And although the length of a given bond may be 1.54 A in structure A and 1.33 A in B, the bond in C does not have the average length 1.43 A but instead is 1.39 A. Since the bonds in the resonance hybrid are shorter than the average of those in A and B, and shorter bonds are in general stronger, this is evidence for the increased stability of benzene. That is, while having the properties of A and B in equal amounts it has additional properties all its own, such as lower energy content.

Other specific examples of this general case do not necessarily give the same result as in the case of benzene. For example, it is known that carboxylic acid dimers exist not only in certain solvents but also in the vapor phase. In these dimers the two carboxyl groups are joined by hydrogen bonds. We shall discuss a specific example, formic acid, in the same manner that we have discussed benzene. The two forms A and B are

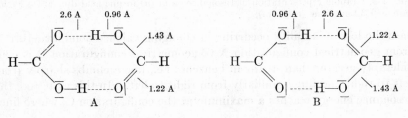

The O—H, C—O, and C=O bond distances are set equal to those found in most compounds with these bonds. The O---H distance is set equal to the sum of the van der Waals radii (the distance at which atoms appear to "touch" other atoms to which they are not bonded [see Sec. 1-3a]) of oxygen and hydrogen. The energy content expected of valence-bond structure A in geometrical configuration B would appear to be relatively high.

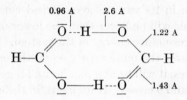

In addition to smaller distortions of the C—O and C=O bonds, the O—H bonds are stretched 1.6 A beyond their optimum length. Hence in this

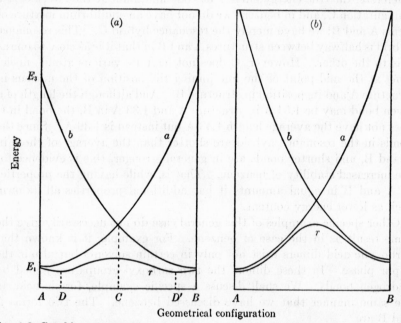

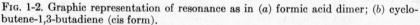

Fig. 1-2. Graphic representation of resonance as in (a) formic acid dimer; (b) cyclobutene-1,3-butadiene (cis form).

case the loss of stability occurring in changing valence-bond structure A from geometrical configuration A to geometrical configuration B is considerably greater than it was in benzene; i.e., line a climbs sharply from left to right and line b similarly from right to left. In this case, too, the resonance energy reaches a maximum at the configuration C, where lines *a* and *b* cross (Fig. 1-2*a*).   However, this increase in resonance energy is not sufficient to offset the increase in energy shown on lines *a* and *b*. Therefore it is seen that we have in the present case not a single energy minimum corresponding to one resonance hybrid with two equally contributing structures but two energy minima: D, a resonance hybrid with A the most important contributing structure, and D′, a hybrid toward whose structure B is the more important contributor.

The possibility that formic acid dimer might exist as a resonance hybrid with the hydrogen atoms equidistant between two oxygen atoms and with two equivalent contributing structures could not have been ruled out in advance.   In fact, it was early thought that this was the case.   How-

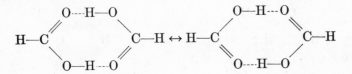

ever, more recent work has shown that the oxygen atoms are not equidistant from the carbon atoms to which they are attached, as they should be if such a resonance hybrid existed.[7]   Also, the hydrogen atoms are considerably closer to one of the oxygen atoms than to the other.[8]   From these data the bond distances in formic acid dimer are approximately as shown below.

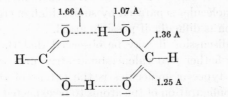

That is, the —C=O is longer since it now has more single-bond character, and the —C—O, with some double-bond character, is shorter.   These changes are due to the contributions of B to D and of A to D′.   On the whole, the average bond lengths are shorter and hence stronger, as would be expected of a resonance-stabilized structure.   The most striking feature is that the oxygen and hydrogen atoms which were merely touching in structure A are now joined by a linkage with some covalent-bond character.   This type of linkage is called a hydrogen bond and will be discussed in more detail later.   It is the opinion of some that most of the stability of the hydrogen bond is better described as an interaction of dipoles than in terms of resonance (see Sec. 1-4).

[7] J. Karle and L. O. Brockway, *J. Am. Chem. Soc.*, **66**, 574 (1944).
[8] R. Hofstadter, *J. Chem. Phys.*, **6**, 540 (1938).

Since in the present case the energy barrier separating the two forms is not a large one, it is very easily surmounted, and the forms are in tautomeric equilibrium with each other. In many cases, however, this energy barrier may be much larger. An example of such a system follows.

For structure A we shall choose cyclobutene, and for structure B a molecule corresponding to one of the possible configurations of 1,3-butadiene.

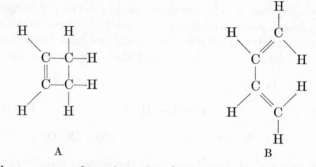

A   B

The student can see why valence-bond structure A would be expected to be very unstable in geometrical configuration B. In addition to the differences in bond lengths, all of the atoms in B lie in the plane of the paper, while the four right-hand hydrogen atoms of A are above and below this plane. Therefore, an energy diagram of the type shown in Fig. 1-2b would be expected. In this case there are seen to be two different types of molecules separated by such a high energy barrier that their interconversion is difficult, if possible at all.

From this discussion it may be observed that the principal factor in determining whether two valence-bond structures will represent one or two different types of molecules is the extent of the difference in the geometrical configuration of the atoms to be expected from the structures. If the positions of the atoms in geometrical configuration A differ from their positions in configuration B by only a few tenths of an angstrom, then only one type of molecule, a resonance hybrid, will exist.[9] However, if this difference amounts to several angstroms and if there are also

[9] On the basis of these criteria, such data as those obtained by J. M. Robertson [*J. Chem. Soc.*, 1222 (1951)] on the structure of cupric tropolone (of which one resonance structure is shown below)

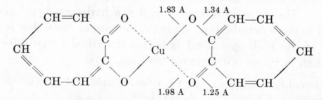

are surprising, since the molecule might be expected to be symmetrical (have all Cu—O

considerable differences in bond angles, there will be two types of molecules, and valence-bond structure A will contribute only slightly to the resonance structure of the molecules in geometrical configuration B. We cannot state however just where, between several angstroms and a few tenths, a line can be drawn. Fortunately, intermediate cases are not very common. Nevertheless, it is possible to draw any number of r curves varying continuously from the one in Fig. 1-1 to that in Fig. 1-2. Therefore, theoretically at least, there is a gradual and continuous change in going from a resonance hybrid to two forms in tautomeric equilibrium.

Thus whenever two different valence-bond structures (having the same number of unpaired electrons) predict very nearly the same arrangement of atomic nuclei in space, there will be only one type of compound, a resonance hybrid of the two or more structures. In most cases where the resonance itself is not being discussed it is the most common and simplest procedure to write merely the valence-bond structure thought to contribute most and to assume the reader will realize that the actual molecule will be a resonance hybrid.

1-1c. *Data from Dipole-moment Measurements.* The dipole moment of a molecule is equal to the *distance* between the centers of positive and negative charge multiplied by the size of the charge, and, since the distances are commonly on the order of 10^{-8} cm and the charges 10^{-10} esu, is expressed in Debyes (see Sec. 1-1a). Having a positive and a negative end, as well as magnitude, the dipole may be seen to be a vector and is often written with the positive end crossed and the arrow at the negative end.

$$\overset{+\longrightarrow}{\text{H}-\text{Cl}}$$

It is convenient to define a *bond moment* as that part of the dipole moment of a molecule which is due to an individual bond. For a diatomic molecule the bond moment is equal to the dipole moment, but for a polyatomic molecule the dipole moment is equal to the vector sum of the various bond moments. The dipole moment of water, for example, is 1.84 D. Since the angle H—O—H is known to be about 105°, the bond moments must be 1.51 D.

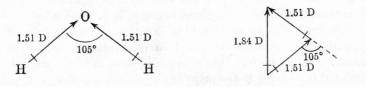

bond distances equal). However, the above dimensions were measured in the crystal lattice, where the molecule was subjected to the distorting influence of other molecules in an unsymmetrical manner. This fact, coupled with the experimental error in the structure determination, may account for this lack of symmetry.

The magnitude of the dipole moment of chlorobenzene has been cited as evidence for the contribution of structures of the type of XIX. Dipole moments of saturated aliphatic chlorides do not vary widely from 2.0 D. The negative end of this dipole is almost certainly in the direction of the more electronegative chlorine atom. Therefore any contribution of structure XIX would tend to decrease this value, and indeed chlorobenzene is found to have the considerably lower dipole moment of 1.56 D.

The dipole moment of nitrobenzene is 3.97 D, while that of *p*-chloronitrobenzene is 2.57 D. Since this is much nearer the difference between the values of chlorobenzene and nitrobenzene than it is to their sum, the dipole of the nitro group, like that of the chlorine atom, must be directed *away* from the ring.

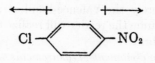

Since the dipole moments of typical saturated aliphatic nitro compounds are around 3.3 D, the larger value for nitrobenzene is evidence for the contributions of structures like XXVIII and XXIX, for which there are no analogs with the aliphatic derivatives. It should be noted that

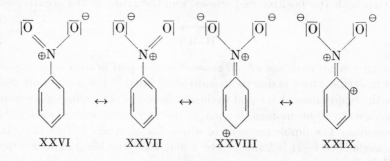

structures XXVIII and XXIX will have their greatest stability when all of the atoms are in the same plane, because, in general, when two atoms (of the first row of the periodic table at least) are joined by a double bond, they, and all of the atoms attached directly to them, are preferentially coplanar. Thus, the fact that nitromesitylene, in which the nitro group is hindered from lying in the plane of the ring by the size of the *o*-methyl groups, has a dipole moment of only 3.65 D (the effects of the three methyl groups should approximately cancel) is added evidence that the exaltation of the dipole moment of nitrobenzene is due to the contribution of structures like XXVIII and XXIX. Considerable other data have been obtained on the steric inhibition of resonance by dipole-moment

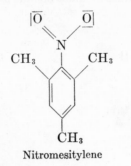

Nitromesitylene

measurements, spectral studies, determinations of the strengths of acids and bases, and studies of the effect of structure on reactivity.[10]

1-1*d*. *Hyperconjugation.* Regardless of the direction or magnitude of the C—H bond dipole,[11] the dipole moment of methane would be expected to be zero since, because of the symmetry of the methane molecule, the bond moments would cancel each other. Because the methane molecule may be represented as methyl hydride,

$$H_3C—H$$

it may be seen that the moment of the methyl group must exactly equal that of the C—H bond. Since any saturated aliphatic hydrocarbon may be represented as being formed by the successive replacement of hydrogen atoms with methyl groups, starting with methane, all of these hydrocarbons, like methane, should have a dipole moment of zero. This has been found to be the case. For this reason, it is of interest to learn that toluene has a dipole moment of 0.4 D, which is shown by the dipole moment of *p*-chlorotoluene (1.90 D) to be oriented toward the ring. This fact has been correlated with the contribution of structures like XXX to the total structure of toluene. The resonance contributions of structures of this type, in which no covalent bond is written to a hydrogen atom, is called *no-bond resonance*, or *hyperconjugation*. Much other evi-

[10] Wheland, *op. cit.*, pp. 136, 160, 185, 272.
[11] The hydrogen has been taken as the positive end because of its smaller electronegativity, and the magnitude has been estimated at 0.4 D (Pauling, *op. cit.*, pp. 67–68), but it has been claimed that because of the smaller size of hydrogen the bond has the opposite direction, although about the same size [W. L. G. Gent, *Quart. Revs. (London)*, **2**, 383 (1948)].

dence for resonance of this type has been given.[12] We are aware that if we attempt to describe the molecule in terms of purely covalent and purely ionic bond structures, we must include a definite contribution from a structure like **XXXI**.

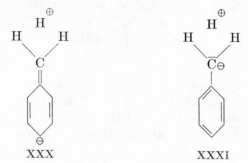

XXX   XXXI

Therefore it is not surprising that structure **XXX** should contribute significantly, since it should be only slightly less stable than **XXXI**, having a slightly less favorable geometrical configuration of atoms and somewhat more separation of charge.

Hyperconjugation is also important for olefins.

The stabilization that is due to added hyperconjugative resonance is believed to be responsible for the increased stabilization of nonterminal over terminal olefins; i.e., it explains why the former are favored in equilibria.

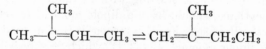

Added evidence for hyperconjugation has come from studies by Kistiakowsky and coworkers[13] on the heats of hydrogenation of a number of olefinic hydrocarbons. The heats of hydrogenation were found to decrease as the number of alkyl groups attached to the doubly bound carbons increased (see Table 1-2). The fact that the less-alkylated olefins add hydrogen considerably more exothermically suggests the

---

[12] J. W. Baker, "Hyperconjugation," Oxford University Press, London, 1952.

[13] G. B. Kistiakowsky, H. Romeyn, Jr., J. R. Ruhoff, H. A. Smith, and W. E. Vaughan, *J. Am. Chem. Soc.*, **57**, 65 (1935); G. B. Kistiakowsky, J. R. Ruhoff, H. A. Smith, and W. E. Vaughan, *J. Am. Chem. Soc.*, **57**, 876 (1935); **58**, 137, 146 (1936); M. A. Dolliver, T. L. Gresham, G. B. Kistiakowsky, and W. E. Vaughan, *J. Am. Chem. Soc.*, **59**, 831 (1937).

stabilizing influence of alkyl groups on the double bond (although other factors are also at work). The relative stabilities, of course, are not related to the heat contents, or enthalpies, H, but to the free energy, $F = H - TS$. However, the entropies S of these closely related substances differ so little that differences in ΔH of the size observed ensure that ΔF's will vary in the same order. This is also known to be true from the greater stability of more highly alkylated olefins, demonstrated in equilibrium experiments. It should be mentioned, though, that the heats of *bromination* of monoolefins *increase* with the extent of alkylation of the double bond. This is related to the fact that the stability of alkyl halides decreases in the order: tertiary > secondary > primary.

1-1e. *Resonance Energy.* From thermochemical measurements of the type just described, numerical estimates of the stabilization due to

TABLE 1-2. HEATS OF HYDROGENATION OF OLEFINS AT 80°[13]

Compound	$-\Delta H$, kcal/mole	Compound	$-\Delta H$, kcal/mole
Ethylene.................	32.8	Cyclohexene...............	28.6
Propylene.................	30.1	Cyclopentene..............	26.9
1-Heptene.................	30.1	1,3-Butadiene.............	57.1
Isobutylene...............	28.4	1,4-Pentadiene............	60.8
cis-2-Butene..............	28.6	Allene....................	71.3
trans-2-Butene.............	27.6	Benzene..................	49.8
Trimethylethylene...........	26.9	1,3-Cyclohexadiene.........	55.4
Tetramethylethylene........	26.6	1,3-Cyclopentadiene........	50.9

resonance have been made. Since the heat of hydrogenation of cyclohexene is 28.6 kcal/mole, the heat of hydrogenation of benzene might be expected to be 85.8 kcal/mole if the compound was accurately described by a cyclohexatriene valence-bond structure, in which the character of the double bonds is like that of cyclohexene. Actually, the hydrogenation of benzene to cyclohexane gives off only 49.8 kcal/mole. For this reason, benzene has been said to be stabilized by 36 kcal/mole of resonance energy. However, the assumption that the double bonds in a cyclohexatriene structure (A or B, Sec. 1-1b) should be identical (in heat of hydrogenation) to those of cyclohexene might very well be challenged. For cyclohexene we might expect stabilization by hyperconjugation (unlikely in a cyclohexatriene structure), and the heat of hydrogenation of this compound is indeed 4.2 kcal/mole lower than that of ethylene. Calculations based on a cyclohexatriene valence-bond structure with ethylenelike double bonds would give a resonance energy of 48.6 kcal/mole. Here it might be argued that the mere replacement of two of the hydrogens of ethylene by carbon without hyperconjugation might change the nature of the double bond, and that the double bonds of a cyclo-hexatriene structure would not be expected to be identical to those of ethylene either.   Upon further thought, it may be seen that there is *no* obvious and logical olefin whose double bond should serve as a standard for those in a cyclohexatriene valence-bond structure.   Therefore, while it is obvious that the "double bonds" in benzene are considerably more resistant to addition than those in most olefins, no quantitative calcula-tion of the resonance energy can have any significance unless the double bonds in terms of which the cyclohexatriene structures are described are clearly defined.   Furthermore, any such definitions will necessarily be arbitrary.

It should be understood that the "resonance energy" discussed above, the stabilization of benzene with respect to structure A (or B) in its most stable geometrical configuration, is not the resonance energy E_r of Fig. 1-1 (which has the value $E_2 - E_0$ for benzene) but rather $E_1 - E_0$. The quantity $E_2 - E_0$, the stabilization of benzene relative to valence-bond structure A (or B) when in the geometrical configuration of benzene, has been estimated (from the energy required to stretch and compress typical double and single bonds) to be about 35 kcal/mole higher than $E_1 - E_0$.[14]

Calculations of resonance energies have also been based on heats of combustion, both directly and by use of bond energies calculated from heat-of-combustion data; they have also been calculated theoretically.[15]

1-2. Atomic and Molecular Orbitals.[16]   From quantum mechanics, it may be shown that the probability-density function for the electron in a hydrogen atom depends upon its energy level (by quantum theory, there are only certain definite amounts of energy possible, so that the energy increases in steps rather than gradually).   The seven lowest types of energy levels, which are the only ones commonly of interest in organic chemistry, are the $1s$, $2s$, $2p$, $3s$, $3p$, $3d$, and $4s$ levels, in the order of their increasing energy content.   Electrons in any of the s levels have prob-ability-density functions which are independent of the direction from the nucleus, i.e., they are spherically symmetrical.   For the lowest level, $1s$, the function may be represented by shading the areas with a darkness proportional to the probability of finding an electron there (Fig. 1-3a) or by a contour map (Fig. 1-3b).   In each case, the three-dimensional representation must be obtained by rotating the two-dimensional repre-sentation in Fig. 1-3 about a line through its center.   Alternately, we

[14] R. S. Mulliken, C. A. Rieke, and W. G. Brown, *J. Am. Chem. Soc.*, **63**, 41 (1941). D. F. Hornig [*J. Am. Chem. Soc.*, **72**, 5772 (1950)] has estimated the value $E_2 - E_1$ at 30 kcal and $E_0' - E_0$ at 25 to 27 kcal.

[15] Wheland, *op. cit.*, chap. 3.

[16] A much more complete, but still fairly nonmathematical, treatment of this topic and much of the other material in this chapter is given in Coulson, *op. cit.*

may plot the probability of finding an electron at a given distance r from the nucleus against this distance (Fig. 1-4).

It is interesting to see that although the probability of finding an electron within a given volume increment increases steadily as the volume increment nears the nucleus, the probability of finding an electron at a given distance is maximum at a distance of about 0.53 A (of course, the number of volume increments at a given distance from the nucleus

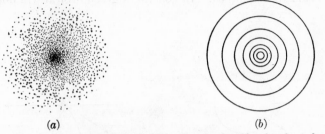

(a)   (b)

FIG. 1-3. Two representations of the probability-density function for the 1s level of the hydrogen atom. (a) Probability proportional to darkness of shading; (b) contour lines connecting points of equal probability.

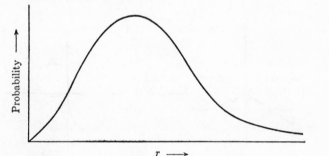

FIG. 1-4. Probability of finding an electron as function of distance r from nucleus (for a hydrogen atom in the 1s state).

increases with the distance). The probability-density function for an electron is called its "orbital" and is most commonly depicted by a line corresponding to a single probability contour (Fig. 1-3b). An outer contour is chosen to ensure a high probability of finding the electron within the orbital. For the spherically symmetrical s orbitals this contour is simply a sphere (Fig. 1-5a). There are three of each type of p levels. These are referred to as the p_x, p_y, and p_z orbitals and are shown in Figs. 1-5b, c, and d. The boundary surfaces like those shown in Fig. 1-5 have the same shape for all orbitals of a given letter (s or p) and increase in size with the number describing the orbital. By reasonable, but approximate, calculations it may be shown that in atoms containing many electrons these electrons fill the various orbitals described in the order of their decreasing stability in accordance with certain rules. One of these rules depends upon the fact that in addition to mass and charge an electron has a quality known as *spin*. This spin may be represented as a vector having only one definite magnitude but capable of being oriented in either a positive or negative direction. According to the Pauli exclusion principle, a given orbital cannot contain more than one electron whose spin is oriented in a given direction, and the orbital is therefore filled when occupied by two electrons with opposite spins (the electrons are then said to be paired). In general, a given orbital will not be filled

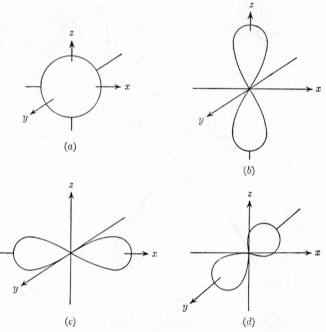

FIG. 1-5. Atomic orbitals of the s and p type. (a) s; (b) p_z; (c) p_x; (d) p_y.

until all of the more stable orbitals have been filled. When filling orbitals of equal stability, electrons enter according to Hund's rules: (1) Electrons tend to avoid being in the same orbital. (2) They tend to have identical spins, when possible. Thus, for atoms of the first 10 elements the configurations of the electrons in the atomic orbitals are as shown in Fig. 1-6, where each electron is represented by an arrow pointed up or down to show the direction of spin. It may be seen that this formulation offers an explanation for the great stability possible with 2 electrons, as in helium, or 10 as in neon, etc.

In all cases common in organic chemistry, a chemical bond between two atoms is represented as resulting from two electrons' filling an orbital which includes both of the nuclei being bound together. Orbitals of this type are called *molecular orbitals* in contrast to the *atomic orbitals*, surrounding only one nucleus, which we have been discussing. The characteristics of that part of such an orbital nearest an individual nucleus are determined largely by that nucleus, and therefore in this region the orbital will resemble the familiar atomic orbital, only somewhat influ-enced (perturbed) by the presence of the other nucleus.

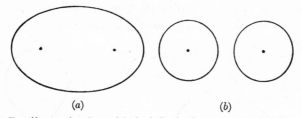

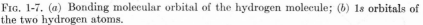

FIG. 1-6. Most stable electronic configurations for the atoms of the first ten elements.

FIG. 1-7. (a) Bonding molecular orbital of the hydrogen molecule; (b) 1s orbitals of the two hydrogen atoms.

FIG. 1-8. (a) Bonding molecular orbital formed by coaxial p orbitals; (b) coaxial p orbitals.

For this and other reasons, it is useful to regard this bonding orbital as the modified result of the combination or overlap of two atomic orbitals. Thus the bonding orbital in the hydrogen molecule (Fig. 1-7a) may be thought of in terms of the overlap of the two 1s orbitals of the two atoms. Bonding may also occur by the overlap of p orbitals, an s and a p orbital, etc. Bonds formed between p orbitals with a common axis (Fig. 1-8), like those between s orbitals or an s and a p orbital, are called *sigma bonds*. Another type of bond is called the *pi bond* and is produced by the overlap of a *p* orbital (only) with another *p* orbital having a parallel axis (Fig. 1-9). Since pi bonds are usually weaker than sigma bonds, they are formed only when a *p* orbital is forced to be noncoaxial by the presence of a sigma bond formed from other orbitals.

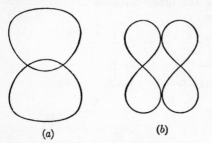

Orbital hybridization is an additional important factor which we shall discuss in its application to the valence of carbon. Instead of forming four bonds with its 2*s* and three 2*p* orbitals, tetravalent carbon *mixes* these orbitals to get four equivalent orbitals. The four resultant orbitals are known as sp^3 orbitals, their wave functions being a combination of those for the *s* and the three *p* orbitals. They have the shape shown in

FIG. 1-9. (*a*) Bonding molecular orbital (pi orbital) formed from parallel *p* orbitals; (*b*) *p* orbitals with parallel axes.

Fig. 1-10 and are oriented at angles of 109°28′ from each other (a regular tetrahedral configuration). The use of orbitals of this sort for bonding is probably related to the fact that there appears to be a definite correlation between the extent to which the two atomic orbitals overlap and the strength of the bond formed thereby. The carbon atom tends not to

FIG. 1-10. An sp^3 orbital.

FIG. 1-11. The three sp^2 orbitals.

form bonds with its *s* orbital, which, because of its concentration near the nucleus, may not overlap extensively with other orbitals, but it may hybridize this *s* orbital with *p*'s to yield orbitals which are very effective at overlapping. The sp^3 hybridization occurs when carbon is bound to four other atoms. When it is bound to only three, the result is a hybrid of the 2*s* and two of the 2*p* orbitals to give three sp^2 orbitals. These are coplanar and at 120° angles (Fig. 1-11), while the remaining unhybridized *p* orbital is perpendicular to this plane. Thus in ethylene each carbon is joined to two hydrogen atoms by sigma bonds formed by the overlap of one of the sp^2 orbitals on carbon and the s orbital of hydrogen. In addition, the two carbon atoms are joined by a sigma bond due to sp^2 orbital overlap *and* by a pi bond due to p orbital overlap. Carbon atoms attached to two other atoms hybridize one s and one p orbital to give two coaxial sp orbitals, which form sigma bonds, and to leave two p orbitals at right angles to form pi bonds. Triple bonds may thus be seen to consist of one sigma and two pi bonds.

It is of interest to apply these principles to a few simple molecules. In the water molecule the oxygen atom has available to it one $2s$ and three $2p$ orbitals. Two orbitals are required for bonding and two for the four unshared electrons of oxygen. Since electrons in an s orbital are more stable than those in a p orbital, we should expect that a nonbonding orbital (in which the oxygen has two electrons) will be s in character, rather than a bonding orbital (whose electrons spend only part of their time around the oxygen atom). Furthermore, the p orbitals should be preferred for bond formation since they overlap more effectively. Because the three p orbitals are perpendicular to each other, we might expect an H—O—H bond angle of 90°. The observed bond angle is about 104°31'. This deviation is believed to be due to repulsion between the partially positive hydrogen atoms and is much smaller with hydrogen sulfide (92° bond angle), where the hydrogen atoms are further apart and less positive. This increase in the bond angle lends s character to the bonding orbitals[17] and hence p character to the nonbonding orbitals. The addition of s character to the bonding orbitals increases their ability to overlap, and the resultant stronger bonds partially compensate for the energy required to place the unshared electrons in an orbital with more p character. Similar considerations may be applied to ammonia (107° valence angle), phosphine (93°), and arsine (92°).

In the molecular orbital description of benzene we should expect each carbon atom to be bonded through sp^2 orbitals to two adjacent carbon atoms and a hydrogen atom. This leaves one electron in a p orbital which may overlap to form a pi bond with a similar orbital on an adjacent carbon atom. However, it may be seen that because of the symmetrical arrangement of the atoms, each p orbital will overlap as much with the p orbital on one adjacent carbon as with that on the other. Thus the atomic orbitals will combine to form molecular orbitals which resemble two doughnuts, one on each side of the plane of the atomic nuclei (Fig. 1-12).

1-3. Some Properties of Bonds. 1-3a. *Bond Distances.* Pauling and Huggins have pointed out that to a fair degree of accuracy the length of covalent bonds is equal to the sum of what are called the *covalent bond*

[17] Note that p orbitals (0 per cent s) give 90° bond angles, sp^3 (25 per cent s) 109°28', sp^2 (33 per cent s) 120°, and sp (50 per cent s) 180°.

radii of the two atoms involved.[18] The numerical values of covalent bond radii may be simply chosen so as to give the best general agreement with determinations of bond distances by X rays, electron diffraction, and spectroscopic studies. Since multiple bonds are shorter than the corresponding single bonds, it is necessary to have double and triple as well

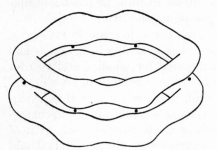

FIG. 1-12. The pi molecular orbital for benzene.

as single bond radii. A number of covalent bond radii compiled by Pauling are shown in Table 1-3.[19] By use of the values in this table, we may predict the length of various bonds. For example, the carbon-chlorine bond distance in methyl chloride should be equal to the sum of the covalent bond radii of carbon and chlorine: 0.77 + 0.99 = 1.76 A. The distance actually found is 1.78 A. The predicted bond lengths are usually within a few hundredths of an angstrom of those found experimentally, although in the case of the hydrogen molecule an error as large as 0.14 A is found. The contribution of ionic structures to the total

TABLE 1-3. COVALENT BOND RADII AND VAN DER WAALS RADII, ANGSTROMS[19]

Element	Single bond radius	Double bond radius	Van der Waals radius
Hydrogen	0.30	.....	1.2
Carbon[a]	0.77	0.665	[b]
Nitrogen[c]	0.70	0.60	1.5
Oxygen	0.66	0.55	1.4
Fluorine	0.64	0.54	1.35
Phosphorus	1.10	1.00	1.9
Sulfur	1.04	0.94	1.85
Chlorine	0.99	0.89	1.8
Bromine	1.14	1.04	1.95
Iodine	1.33	1.23	2.15

[a] Triple bond radius is 0.60.
[b] Radius of a methyl group, 2.0; half thickness of aromatic ring, 1.85.
[c] Triple bond radius is 0.55.

structure of a molecule usually leads to a bond length which is shorter than if the bond were purely covalent. Schomaker and Stevenson have therefore suggested an equation for predicting bond lengths in which the

[18] L. Pauling and M. L. Huggins, *Z. Krist.*, **87 A**, 205 (1934).
[19] Pauling, *op. cit.*, pp. 164, 189.

difference in electronegativity of the atoms involved is used as an added parameter.[20]

Within a distance of a few angstroms, all molecules exert significant attractive forces (van der Waals forces) on each other. If these forces are sufficient to overcome their thermal motion, the molecules are held relatively closely together as a liquid or a solid. From the finite volume of such matter, it is obvious that at sufficiently small distances these van der Waals attractive forces are balanced by repulsive forces due to the interpenetration of the outer electronic orbitals of the atoms involved. As a measure of the equilibrium distances thus possible between atoms in adjacent molecules and between contiguous atoms attached to different parts of the same molecule, the van der Waals radii shown in Table 1-3 are used. Thus, the value 1.8 A listed for chlorine shows that "touching" chlorine atoms in adjacent carbon tetrachloride molecules should have an internuclear distance of about 3.6 A. This would also be expected to be the equilibrium distance between the two chlorine atoms in 2,2'-dichlorobiphenyl (when the molecule is rotated so that those two atoms touch). When attached to the same or adjacent atoms, however, two atoms may approach each other more closely, two chlorine atoms in the same molecule of carbon tetrachloride being less than 3.0 A apart. Van der Waals radii often vary by 0.1 A from the values listed.

1-3b. *Bond Angles.* As described in Sec. 1-2, when carbon is attached to four other atoms, it forms bonds with sp^3 orbitals, which have their maximum stability in a regular tetrahedral configuration with bond angles of 109°28'. In addition to the stability of the bonding orbitals the bond angles are also affected by interactions between the various groups attached. When the four groups attached to carbon are not identical, the angles would not be expected to be exactly those of a regular tetrahedron. In this connection, it is of interest that, despite dipolar repulsions, the F—C—F bond in methylene fluoride is about 108°17',[21] somewhat smaller than the tetrahedral angle. With the larger chlorine atoms, the Cl—C—Cl angle of methylene chloride is about 111°47'.[21] By far the greatest deviations occur with cyclic systems, the bond angles in cyclopropane and cyclobutane being, of course, 60 and 90°, respectively. When three atoms or groups are attached to carbon, their interaction may lead to analogous deviations from the 120° bond angles normal for sp^2 orbitals, while carbon attached to two other atoms tends toward a linear configuration (180° bond angles). Nitrogen has bond angles analogous to those of carbon when all of its outer electrons are involved in bonding, as in ammonium compounds,

[20] V. Schomaker and D. P. Stevenson, *J. Am. Chem. Soc.*, **63**, 37 (1941).
[21] D. R. Lide, Jr., *J. Am. Chem. Soc.*, **74**, 3548 (1952).

nitro compounds, etc. For bond angles in amines, alcohols, ethers, sulfides, etc., the unshared electrons have the effect discussed in Sec. 1-2.

1-3c. *Bond Energies*. In a diatomic molecule the bond energy is customarily defined as the energy required to bring about the fission of the molecule into atoms. For the reaction

$$A\text{—}B(g) \rightarrow A\cdot(g) + B\cdot(g)$$

in the vapor phase, we shall define the value of ΔE at $0°K$ as the bond energy. Frequently, values of ΔH at $291°$ or $298°$ are used. The ΔH_{298} values are often obtainable from the experimental data in cases where the ΔE_0's are not, but the former values relate to further differences in energies of vibration, rotation, and translation, and to a pressure-volume term in addition to the energy dependent upon the bond strengths. The errors introduced by using ΔH_{298} values, however, are often no larger than the uncertainty in the ΔH (or analogous ΔE) value.

For polyatomic molecules there are two alternate methods of defining the bond energy. By one definition it is an aliquot part of the energy required to dissociate the molecule completely into atoms. Thus for water, we might define the O—H bond energy as one-half of the energy required to dissociate the water molecule into hydrogen and oxygen atoms.

$$H_2O(g) \rightarrow 2H(g) + O(g) \qquad \Delta E_0 = 218.9 \text{ kcal/mole}$$

The O—H bond energy defined in this way (109.4 kcal) is called the *average bond energy*. On the other hand, the O—H bond energy in water may be thought of simply as the energy required to break an O—H bond in water to give a hydroxyl radical and a hydrogen atom. While we know that the ΔE's for the two reactions

$$H_2O(g) \rightarrow H(g) + OH(g) \qquad \Delta E_0 = 118.6 \text{ kcal/mole}$$
$$OH(g) \rightarrow H(g) + O(g) \qquad \Delta E_0 = 100.3 \text{ kcal/mole}$$

must total 218.9 kcal, there is no reason why they should be identical, and indeed, as shown, they are not. The bond energies defined in this manner are called *bond-dissociation energies*. Hereafter average bond energies will usually be referred to simply as bond energies, while the complete name will be used for bond-dissociation energies.

The types of experimental data[22] from which average bond energies

---

[22] Most of the thermochemical data used herein are taken from Selected Values of Chemical Thermodynamic Properties, *Natl. Bur. Standards Misc. Publ. Ser.* III.

may be calculated are illustrated below for methane.

$$CH_4(g) + 2O_2(g) \rightarrow CO_2(g) + 2H_2O(g) \qquad \Delta E_0 = -192.2 \text{ kcal}$$
$$CO_2(g) \rightarrow C \text{ (graphite)} + O_2(g) \qquad = \qquad 94.0$$
$$2H_2O(g) \rightarrow 2H_2(g) + O_2(g) \qquad = \qquad 114.2$$
$$2H_2(g) \rightarrow 4H(g) \qquad = \qquad 206.4$$
$$C \text{ (graphite)} \rightarrow C(g) \qquad = \qquad 170.4$$
$$\overline{CH_4(g) \rightarrow C(g) + 4H(g) \qquad \Delta E_0 = \qquad 392.8 \text{ kcal}}$$

Therefore the C—H bond energy in methane is 392.8/4 = 98.2 kcal

A source of considerable disagreement among workers in the field is the value of 170.4 kcal shown for the transformation of graphite into monatomic carbon vapor. Values around 125 and 141 kcal have also been used rather widely. However, since we shall be most commonly concerned with *differences* in bond energies, the particular value chosen is not of such great importance.

Since methane has four equivalent C—H bonds, it is obvious that its heat of atomization should be divided by 4 in order to get the average C—H bond energy. However, for ethane there is no fundamentally correct way of subdividing the heat of atomization into that due to the C—C and that due to the C—H bonds. For this reason the C—C bond energy in ethane is usually arbitrarily defined as that which is calculated on the assumption that the C—H bonds have the same energy that they do in methane. The value thus obtained is 77.7 kcal. Analogous calculations yield average C—C bond energies approaching 80.5 kcal for higher normal paraffins. This increase in bond energy has no necessary relation to the dissociation energies of the C—C bonds, since it is based on the arbitrary assumption that the C—H bond energy is constant and that only the C—C energy varies. In fact, the thermodynamic data may be explained rather well by assuming that the C—C bond energy has the constant value 84.9 kcal (that in diamond) and that C—H bond energies are 98.2 kcal in methane, and 96.9 kcal for primary, 96.2 kcal for secondary, and 95.6 kcal for tertiary C—H bonds, respectively. Some bond energies of interest are listed in Table 1-4. Most of those in the right-hand column were calculated on the basis of an assumption like that described above for the C—C bond energy. In these cases the value of the bond energy will depend upon the compound on which the calculation is based. Nevertheless such variations are usually small enough for the bond energy calculated from data on one compound to be useful in predicting the properties of another compound with the same type of bond.

Bond-dissociation energies for diatomic molecules are identical to the average bond energies. For polyatomic molecules, however, they may

TABLE 1-4. SOME AVERAGE BOND ENERGIES OF INTEREST IN ORGANIC CHEMISTRY[a]

Bond	Energy, kcal	Bond	Compound	Energy, kcal
H—H	103.2	O—O	H_2O_2	34
F—F	~37	N—N	N_2H_4	37
Cl—Cl	57.1	C—C	C_2H_6	77.7
Br—Br	45.4	C—C	C_3H_8	79.0
I—I	35.6	C—C	n-C_4H_{10}	79.6
N≡N	225.2	C—C	i-C_4H_{10}	80.1
H—F	~135	C—C	Diamond	84.9
H—Cl	102.1	C=C	C_2H_4	140.0
H—Br	86.7	C=C	C_6H_6	123.8
H—I	70.6	C≡C	C_2H_2	193.3
O—H	109.4	C—O	CH_3OH	78.3[b]
N—H	92.2	C=O	CH_2O	163.3[b]
C—H	98.2	C=O	CH_3CHO	174.4[b]
S—H	81.1[b]	C=O	CH_3COCH_3	185.6[b]
C—F	~102[b]	C—N	CH_3NH_2	66.3[b]
C—Cl	78	C—S	CH_3SH	56.7[b]
C—Br	65			
C—I	57	C≡N	CH_3CN	215.0[b]

[a] Many of these values are from a table in K. S. Pitzer, *J. Am. Chem. Soc.*, **70**, 2140 (1948).
[b] Calculated from ΔH_{298} data.

be considerably different, as has been pointed out in the case of water. Spectroscopic and *electron-impact* methods and studies of the kinetics and equilibria of bond-dissociation processes have been used to determine bond-dissociation energies.[23] While these are often more useful in physical organic chemistry than the average bond energies, much fewer pertinent data are available.

In general, the bond energy between two different atoms A and B is the mean of that for A—A and B—B plus an additional amount due to the resonance contribution of ionic structures (see Sec. 1-1a) and dependent upon the electronegativity difference between A and B. In fact, Pauling's electronegativities (Table 1-1) are numbers chosen to give as good a general fit as possible to the relation

$$x_B - x_A = 0.208 \sqrt{BE_{A-B} - \frac{BE_{A-A} + BE_{B-B}}{2}}$$

where x_A and x_B are electronegativities and BE's are bond energies in kcal/mole.

Wrinch and Harker have pointed out that, in general, for a bond

[23] M. Szwarc, *Quart. Revs. (London)*, **5**, 22 (1951).

between two given atoms the bond length decreases as the bond energy increases.[24]

1-4. Hydrogen Bonding. It has long been observed that hydroxy compounds have considerably higher boiling points than their non-hydroxylic isomers. Ethanol, for example, boils 103° higher than dimethyl ether. This has been explained by the formation of a bond between the hydroxylic hydrogen atom of one molecule and the oxygen atom of another. This bond is called a hydrogen bond, and while it is much stronger than the van der Waals attractive forces between molecules, it is much weaker than ordinary covalent bonds, rarely having bond energies above 9 kcal. These bonds form between a hydrogen atom and an atom containing an unshared electron pair. The strength of the bond formed is best correlated with the acidity of the hydrogen atom and the basicity of the atom with the unshared electron pair (the *acceptor* atom).[25] Unless the acceptor atom is at least as basic as nitrogen, oxygen, and fluorine atoms are in uncharged molecules, and unless the hydrogen atoms are much more acidic than those in saturated hydrocarbons, any hydrogen bonds which may form are usually too weak to be of significance. Of course, if the hydrogen atom is too acidic and the acceptor atom too basic, the hydrogen will be transferred as a proton to form a covalent bond with the acceptor atom in a simple acid-base reaction. Hydrogen bonds are usually represented by a broken or dotted line. Thus we shall represent the hydrogen bonded complex formed between an alcohol and an amine in the following manner:

$$R—\overline{\underline{O}}—H\text{---}N—R$$
$$\begin{array}{c}R\\ |\\ \phantom{R—\overline{\underline{O}}—H\text{---}}N—R\\ |\\ R\end{array}$$

The discussion of formic acid dimer in Sec. 1-1b is an explanation of hydrogen bonding in terms of resonance. The objection has been raised that hydrogen bonding cannot be due to resonance because the hydrogen is usually not halfway between the bonded atoms. However, this merely gives the information that the two resonance structures do not contribute equally. Indeed, in the case of the F---H---F⁻ ion, the hydrogen has been shown to be equidistant from the two fluorine atoms,[26] suggesting resonance stabilization by two equally contributing

[24] D. Wrinch and D. Harker, *J. Chem. Phys.*, **8**, 502 (1940). See also H. A. Skinner, *Trans. Faraday Soc.*, **41**, 645 (1945); G. Glockler, *J. Chem. Phys.*, **16**, 842 (1948); **19**, 124 (1951).

[25] W. Gordy and S. C. Stanford, *J. Chem. Phys.*, **8**, 170 (1940); L. P. Hammett, *J. Chem. Phys.*, **8**, 644 (1940); S. C. Stanford and W. Gordy, *J. Am. Chem. Soc.*, **63**, 1094 (1941); C. Curran, *J. Am. Chem. Soc.*, **67**, 1835 (1945).

[26] E. F. Westrum, Jr. and K. S. Pitzer, *J. Am. Chem. Soc.*, **71**, 1940 (1949); S. W. Peterson and H. A. Levy, *J. Chem. Phys.*, **20**, 704 (1952).

structures. Hydrogen bonding has been depicted as an electrostatic interaction, and Coulson has described some of the evidence for this representation.[27] However, although electrostatic interactions must contribute to hydrogen bonding, a representation solely on this basis might be expected to yield a correlation of hydrogen-bonding ability with electronegativity. That is, one would expect alkyl fluorides to be better hydrogen-bond acceptors than alcohols and ethers and these latter to be better than amines. The actual order appears to be the reverse of this, with the more basic atoms leading to stronger hydrogen bonds,[25] as might be expected from a resonance interpretation of hydrogen bonding (in which the hydrogen is covalently bonded to the basic atom in one contributing structure). The unusually stronger bond in the HF_2^- is no exception to this generalization, since in this case the fairly strongly acidic HF is forming a bond not to an electrically neutral fluoride but to the much more strongly basic fluoride anion.

The formation of intramolecular hydrogen bonds is called *chelation* and is often of interest because of its effect on the properties of compounds involved. For example, the chelated compound salicylaldehyde

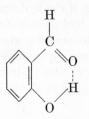

boils at 196° and may be steam-distilled readily, while the meta and para isomers, whose hydrogen-bonding tendencies must be satisfied intermolecularly, boil above 240° and are not appreciably volatile in steam.

1-5. Rotation around Carbon-Carbon Single Bonds. Although it was assumed for many years that rotation around carbon-carbon single bonds is entirely free, the resolution of 2,2'-dinitrobiphenyl-6,6'-dicarboxylic acid[28] and the large amount of subsequent work on the stereochemistry of biphenyl derivatives[29] demonstrated that sufficiently bulky groups may prevent this rotation. In 1937, by measurements of the entropy of ethane, Kemp and Pitzer showed that there is even considerable resistance to rotation around the carbon-carbon single bond in this compound.[30]

[27] Coulson, *op. cit.*, pp. 298–307.

[28] G. H. Christie and J. Kenner, *J. Chem. Soc.*, **121**, 614 (1922).

[29] R. L. Shriner, R. Adams, and C. S. Marvel in H. Gilman, "Organic Chemistry," 2d ed., vol. I, pp. 347–382, John Wiley & Sons, Inc., New York, 1943.

[30] J. D. Kemp and K. S. Pitzer, *J. Am. Chem. Soc.*, **59**, 276 (1937).

The entropy of a substance, a direct function of its heat capacity, may be calculated by the methods of statistical mechanics if the geometry of the molecule and the strength with which it resists certain distortions are known. The temperature of the substance depends only on the average kinetic energy due to the mass and velocity of the molecule as a whole, i.e., translational energy, but the rate at which the substance absorbs heat depends also upon the extent to which this energy may appear in the form of rotational and vibrational motions. At low temperatures the heat capacity of ethane was smaller than would be calculated on the assumption of complete freedom of rotation around the carbon-carbon bond. The heat capacity varied with temperature in a

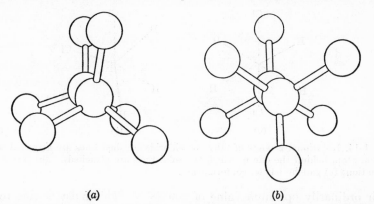

(a)   *(b)*

FIG. 1-13. Rotational forms of ethane. (*a*) Eclipsed conformation; (*b*) staggered conformation.

manner most nearly explained by assuming a barrier to rotation of about 3 kcal/mole.

Since this work, hindered rotation around carbon-carbon single bonds has been studied by X-ray and electron-diffraction determinations of molecular structure, by measurements of dipole moments and of infrared, Raman, and ultraviolet spectra, and by a number of other techniques, including heat-capacity measurements. Some of these studies have yielded further evidence for the nature of this restricted rotation. Since the restriction may reasonably be attributed only to some sort of interaction between the atoms (or groups) attached to the two carbons in question and/or the bonds by which they are attached, it seems likely that these atoms attain their most stable configuration either when they are as near as possible to, or as far as possible from, an atom on the adjacent carbon. That is, of the eclipsed, or opposed, conformation, Fig. 1-13*a*, and the staggered conformation, Fig. 1-13*b* (the different forms of a molecule produced by rotation around single bonds are known as its various *conformations*) one should be the most and the other the least stable form producible by rotation around the bond. Considerable evidence has accumulated that it is the staggered conformation which is the most stable, not only in the case of ethane but for most single bonds. Pertinent data have been obtained in studies of the structure of cyclopentane. If the carbon atoms in this molecule were all coplanar, the bond angles would be 108°, only 1°28′ below the optimum value for tetrahedral carbon, and all of the hydrogen atoms would be opposed (eclipsed). The structure should be stable if Fig. 1-13a represents the stable structure of ethane. It is observed, however, that cyclopentane has a nonplanar arrangement of its carbon atoms, even though such an arrangement decreases the C—C—C bond angles even further below

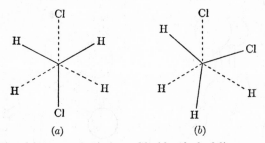

(a)   (b)

Fig. 1-14. Rotational isomers of ethylene chloride (dashed lines are attached to the carbon atom behind the one to which the solid lines are attached). (a) Trans conformation; (b) gauche (skew) conformation.

their ordinarily optimum value of 109°28′.[31] This must be due to the tendency of the hydrogens to get "between" those on adjacent bonds in a staggered conformation. The fact that cyclohexane exists in the chair form (see Sec. 1-6) is further evidence for the stability of structures in which the valence bonds of adjacent tetrahedral carbon atoms are staggered. It is also noteworthy that in the diamond crystal the carbon atoms are arranged so that all valence bonds on adjacent atoms are staggered.

Electron-diffraction studies have shown that hexachloroethane, pentachloroethane, and 1,1,1,2-tetrachloroethane all have the staggered conformation.[32] By the same technique, ethylene chloride has been shown to consist of a mixture of two staggered conformations, the *trans* (Fig. 1-14a) and the *gauche*, or skew (Fig. 1-14b), containing about 75 per cent of the former in the vapor phase at room temperature.[33,34]

[31] J. E. Kilpatrick, K. S. Pitzer, and R. Spitzer, *J. Am. Chem. Soc.*, **69**, 2483 (1947).

[32] S. Mizushima and coworkers, *J. Chem. Soc. Japan*, **65**, 131 (1944); *Sci. Papers Inst. Phys. Chem. Research (Tokyo)*, **42**, Chemistry 5 (1944).

[33] S. Mizushima and coworkers, *Sci. Papers Inst. Phys. Chem. Research (Tokyo)*, **40**, 417 (1943); *J. Chem. Phys.*, **17**, 591 (1949); **21**, 1411 (1953).

[34] J. Ainsworth and J. Karle, *J. Chem. Phys.*, **20**, 425 (1952).

The vapor-phase dipole moment of ethylene chloride has been found to increase by more than 37 per cent between 33 and 270°C.[33,35] Since the dipole moment of the trans form should be zero, this increase is largely due to the shift of the equilibrium toward the less stable and more polar gauche form. From the change in the dipole moment the trans is found to be the more stable isomer by 1.2 kcal/mole. Rotational isomerism in ethylene bromide, acetylene tetrachloride, 1,1,2-trichloroethane, several polyhalopropanes, and many other compounds has been

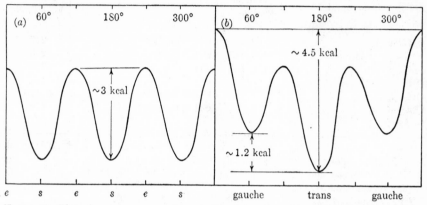

FIG. 1-15. Plot of energy vs. angular rotation from cis and/or eclipsed conformation. (a) Ethane (e, eclipsed; s, staggered); (b) ethylene chloride.

studied by dipole-moment measurements.[36] It should be noted that the 3.0 kcal energy difference mentioned for ethane is between the staggered and the eclipsed forms, while the 1.2 kcal for ethylene chloride is between two staggered forms. This may be represented by plotting energy content against angular rotation, as in Fig. 1-15.

Rotation around aliphatic carbon-carbon single bonds has also received considerable study by spectral methods. From the number, wave lengths, and intensities of absorption bands in the Raman spectrum of solid ethylene halides, it has been found that only the trans conformation is present.[37] In the liquid and vapor phases, however, the number of absorption bands for these compounds is much larger than in the solid, due to the establishment of equilibrium between the trans form and the

[35] C. T. Zahn, *Phys. Rev.*, **38**, 521 (1931); E. W. Greene and J. W. Williams, *Phys. Rev.*, **42**, 119 (1932).

[36] J. R. Thomas and W. D. Gwinn, *J. Am. Chem. Soc.*, **71**, 2785 (1949); R. W. Crowe and C. P. Smyth, *J. Am. Chem. Soc.*, **72**, 4009 (1950); R. A. Oriani and C. P. Smyth, *J. Chem. Phys.*, **16**, 930 (1948); **17**, 1174 (1949).

[37] S. Mizushima and coworkers, (a) *Sci. Papers Inst. Phys. Chem. Research* (*Tokyo*), **29**, 188 (1936); **39**, 387 (1942); (b) *ibid.*, **42**, 51 (1946); (c) *J. Chem. Phys.*, **17**, 591 (1949); (d) *ibid.*, **18**, 754 (1950).

gauche form, which has a different spectrum. For compounds like pentachloroethane and 1,1,1,2-tetrachloroethane, where rotation produces no isomerism, the Raman spectrum is almost the same for the liquid and solid materials.[33] The rate at which the intensity of the absorption bands due to the two forms changes with the temperature may be used to calculate their relative stabilities. By vapor-phase infrared

TABLE 1-5. BARRIERS TO ROTATION AROUND SINGLE BONDS

Compound	Barrier kcal/mole	Compound	Barrier, kcal/mole
CH_3—CH_3[a]	2.9	CH_3—OCH_3[a]	2.7
$(CH_3)_3C$—CH_3[a]	4.3–4.8	CH_3—SCH_3[a]	2.0
$(CH_3)_3Si$—CH_3[a]	1.1–1.5	CH_3—CH_2CH_3[a]	3.4
CH_3—CF_3[b]	3.0	CH_3—OH[a]	1.3
CH_3—SiF_3[c]	1.2	C_6H_5—CH_3[f]	0–1.0
Cl_3C—CCl_3[d]	10–15	CH_2=CH—CH=CH_2[g]	4.9
Cl_3Si—$SiCl_3$[e]	~0		

[a] From tables in K. S. Pitzer, *Discussions Faraday Soc.*, **No. 10,** 71 (1951) and J. G. Aston, *Discussions Faraday Soc.*, **No. 10,** 74 (1951).

[b] H. S. Gutowsky and H. B. Levine, *J. Chem. Phys.*, **18,** 1297 (1950).

[c] J. Sheridan and W. Gordy, *Phys. Rev.*, **77,** 719 (1950).

[d] Y. Morino and M. Iwasaki, *J. Chem. Phys.*, **17,** 216 (1949).

[e] M. Katayama, T. Shimanouchi, Y. Morino, and S. Mizushima, *J. Chem. Phys.*, **18,** 506 (1950).

[f] K. S. Pitzer and D. W. Scott, *J. Am. Chem. Soc.*, **65,** 803 (1943). Note that in this case there will be not three but six energy maxima per rotation.

[g] J. G. Aston, G. J. Szasz, H. W. Wooley, and F. G. Brickwedde, *J. Chem. Phys.*, **14,** 28 (1946). In this case it is the eclipsed forms (all carbons coplanar) that are stable, due to contributions of structures of the type $\oplus CH_2$—CH=CH—$CH_2\ominus$.

measurements of this sort the trans form has been found to be about 1.0 kcal/mole more stable than the gauche, in reasonable agreement with the value 1.2 kcal found from dipole-moment determinations.[37b] From measurement in the liquid state, however, very little difference in the energy content of the two forms is found.[37c,38] This has been attributed to the fact that in ethylene chloride, a solvent with a dielectric constant around 10, the more polar gauche form should be stabilized more than the trans form.[37d]

No theory explaining hindered rotation in cases of the type described appears to have received general acceptance, although the matter has been discussed from several points of view.[39] It seems, however, that

[38] D. H. Rank, R. E. Kagarise and D. W. E. Axford, *J. Chem. Phys.*, **17,** 1354 (1949).

[39] E. Gorin, J. Walter, and H. Eyring, *J. Am. Chem. Soc.*, **61,** 1876 (1939); J. G. Aston, S. Isserow, G. J. Szasz, and R. M. Kennedy, *J. Chem. Phys.*, **12,** 336 (1944); E. N. Lassettre and L. B. Dean, Jr., *J. Chem. Phys.*, **16,** 151 (1948); **17,** 317 (1949).

steric hindrance is, frequently at least, of importance. It has been estimated that the barrier to rotation in Cl_3C—CCl_3 is 10 to 15 kcal/mole, while in Cl_3Si—$SiCl_3$, where the chlorine atoms are more widely separated, the barrier is almost nonexistent, despite the fact that the Si—Cl bond dipole is probably considerably larger than that of C—Cl.   Data on these and other barriers to internal rotation are given in Table 1-5.   A major drawback to the development of a theory for restricted rotation lies in the considerable quantitative uncertainty in many of the existent data.

1-6. Structure of Cyclohexane and Its Derivatives.   While it was realized for many years that cyclohexane could be written in two conformations, the "boat" form and the "chair" form, it remained for

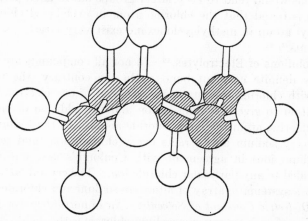

FIG. 1-16. Chair form of cyclohexane.

Hassel to show by electron-diffraction structure determinations that cyclohexane actually has (very predominantly, at least) the chair form[40] (Fig. 1-16).   Pitzer has pointed out that this would be expected, since in this form all the valences attached to adjacent carbon atoms are staggered, while in the boat form there are six pairs of opposed valences on adjacent carbon atoms, a fact which might render this form less stable by around 6 kcal/mole.[41]   Hassel has also pointed out that substituents on the cyclohexane ring may be of two different types (see Fig. 1-16).   Three valences are directed straight up from the plane of the ring (actually, two parallel planes, each containing three carbon atoms) and three more directed straight down.   These, Hassel called the ϵ

[40] O. Hassel, *Tidsskr. Kjemi, Bergvesen Met.*, **3**, 32 (1943); *Chem. Abstr.* **39**, 2244 (1945); and earlier articles.   See also R. S. Rasmussen, *J. Chem. Phys.*, **11**, 249 (1943), where evidence is presented for the chair structure from the Raman spectrum.

[41] K. S. Pitzer, *Science*, **101**, 672 (1945); C. W. Beckett, K. S. Pitzer, and R. Spitzer, *J. Am. Chem. Soc.*, **69**, 2488 (1947).

bonds, but Pitzer and Beckett suggested the term *polar* (or *p*) bonds,[42] which has also been widely used. Recently, several of the most active workers in the field have agreed upon the term *axial*, symbolized *a*, for these bonds (which are parallel to the molecule's axis of symmetry).[43] The other six valence bonds alternate somewhat up and down around the ring but are nearly in the plane of the ring. These were originally called *κ* bonds but are now known as equatorial, or *e*, bonds.[43] It may be noted that each carbon atom contains one axial and one equatorial bond. Examination of molecular models shows that adjacent axial groups of a given size are definitely closer to each other than are adjacent equatorial groups. For this reason it might be expected that steric interactions would tend to keep larger groups out of axial positions, and indeed it is found that the chlorine atom in cyclohexyl chloride[44] and the methyl group in methylcyclohexane exist very largely as equatorial substituents.[41,42]

1-7. Solutions of Electrolytes.[45] In not all compounds are the atoms joined by definite covalent bonds. On the contrary, the reaction of sodium with chlorine consists of the removal of one electron from each sodium atom to give a sodium cation and the addition of one electron to each chlorine atom to give a chloride anion. In the sodium chloride crystal every sodium ion attracts every chloride ion (and repels every other sodium ion) in agreement with Coulomb's law, but no sodium ion is bonded to any particular chloride ion. The crystal lattice consists merely of a systematic array of alternate sodium and chloride ions.

1-7a. Dielectric Constant of Solvents. An important factor permitting the solution of an ionic salt like sodium chloride is the dielectric constant of the solvent (the factor by which the interactions between electrical charges is reduced). That is, in a solution with a dielectric constant of 80, e.g., water, two oppositely charged ions separated by a given distance will have only one-eightieth the attraction for each other that they would in a vacuum and will therefore have a much smaller tendency to recombine to form a crystal. A representative list of dielectric constants for various compounds is given in Table 1-6.

1-7b. Solvation of Ions. Many facts, including the much more general solubility of ionic substances in water ($\epsilon = 80$) than in hydrogen cyanide ($\epsilon = 115$), show that there is an additional factor operating in solutions

[42] K. S. Pitzer and C. W. Beckett, *J. Am. Chem. Soc.*, **69**, 977 (1947).

[43] D. H. R. Barton, O. Hassel, K. S. Pitzer, and V. Prelog, *Science*, **119**, 49 (1954).

[44] O. Hassel and H. Viervoll, *Tidsskr. Kjemi, Bergvesen Met.*, **3**, 35 (1943); *Chem. Abstr.*, **39**, 2244[7] (1945).

[45] For a much more complete treatment see R. W. Gurney, "Ionic Processes in Solution," McGraw-Hill Book Company, Inc., New York, 1953; H. S. Harned and B. B. Owen, "The Physical Chemistry of Electrolyte Solutions," 2d ed., Reinhold Publishing Corporation, New York, 1950.

TABLE 1-6. DIELECTRIC CONSTANTS, ϵ, OF VARIOUS COMPOUNDS[a,b]

Compound	ϵ	Compound	ϵ
N-Methylformamide	190.5[c]	Ethanol	25.1
Hydrogen cyanide	115	Acetone	21.2
Sulfuric acid	~110[d]	Acetic anhydride	20
Formamide	109	n-Butyl alcohol	17.8
Water (at 0°C)	88.3	Ammonia	17.3
Water (at 20°C)	80.4	Sulfur dioxide	14.1
Water (at 100°C)	55.1	t-Butyl alcohol (at 30°C)	10.9
Hydrogen fluoride (at 0°C)	84	Ethylene chloride	10.65
Formic acid	57.9	Acetic acid	6.15
Hydrazine	53	Chlorobenzene	5.71
N,N-Dimethylformamide	37.6[c]	Ethyl ether	4.34
Nitromethane	37.5	Benzene	2.28
Acetonitrile	37.5	Carbon tetrachloride	2.24
Nitrobenzene	35.7	Cyclohexane	2.07
Methanol	33.6	n-Hexane	1.89

[a] Largely from A. A. Maryott and E. R. Smith, Table of Dielectric Constants of Pure Liquids, *Natl. Bur. Standards Circ.* 514, 1951.

[b] At 20°C unless otherwise stated.

[c] G. R. Leader and J. F. Gormley, *J. Am. Chem. Soc.*, **73**, 5731 (1951).

[d] J. C. D. Brand, J. C. James, and A. Rutherford, *J. Chem. Phys.*, **20**, 530 (1952).

of electrolytes which is probably even more important than the dielectric constant. This is a specific interaction between solvent molecules and the dissolved ions called *solvation*. The attraction of a charge for a dipole must account for part of this interaction. In the presence of a sodium ion, a dipolar water molecule would be expected to be oriented with its negative (oxygen) end toward the sodium. Since the negative charge on the oxygen is equal to the sum of the positive charges on the hydrogens and is also closer to the sodium ion, there will be a net attraction. Thus a sodium ion in an aqueous solution will be surrounded by the oxygen atoms of water molecules held as closely as the balance between the attractive forces and steric repulsive forces permits.

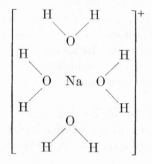

Although four molecules are shown above, the exact number in the primary solvation shell immediately surrounding the sodium ion is not definitely agreed upon.[46] Also there are secondary, more weakly held solvation shells of water molecules outside the primary one. An anion would be expected to attract the positive end of a polar solvent molecule,

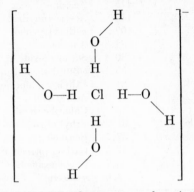

so that for suitable solvents (such as water, above) the solvation interaction is a type of hydrogen bonding. In this connection, sometimes there is utility in considering resonance contributions of structures with covalent bonds between solvent and ion (with cations as well as anions).

The extent to which an ion tends to be stabilized by solvation, as described above, depends, among other things, on the size of the ion. Since the potential energy associated with a given charge is an inverse function of the volume over which the charge is spread, large ions tend to be more stable than small ions. On the other hand, since the charge on small ions is more concentrated, it interacts more strongly with the solvent.

1-7c. Ion-pair Formation. In dilute aqueous solutions (<0.01 N) most salts are almost completely dissociated. In poorer solvating media, however, this is not the case. In acetone solution, lithium bromide has a dissociation constant of about 4×10^{-4}. It should not be thought, however, that the undissociated lithium bromide exists as a covalent compound: it consists of a lithium ion and a bromide ion held together by electrostatic attraction, the acetone not having sufficient solvating power to free the ions from each other. This complex made up of the two ions is called an *ion pair*. In poorly solvating solvents most salts exist as ion pairs (and triplets and higher aggregates) even at fairly low concentrations. The phenomenon occurs even in water at higher concentrations.

It is not always easy to distinguish between the association of two ions to form an ion pair and an association to form a covalent compound,

[46] J. O'M. Bockris, *Quart. Revs. (London)*, **3**, 173 (1949).

and indeed it is quite likely that the types of bonds formed may vary gradually and continuously from highly ionic to highly covalent ones. Nevertheless, it has been found in several cases that the absorption spectrum (in the visible and ultraviolet) is almost the same for an ion whether it is part of an ion pair or completely dissociated. This is because the formation of an ion pair does not greatly affect the electronic structure of the ion. For example, it is known that many picrates form ion pairs under certain conditions. It has been found that the absorption spectrum of these ion pairs is very similar to that of the picrate ion. On the other hand, the formation of a covalent bond to give picric acid gives a colorless compound rather than a yellow one (the yellow color of ordinary picric acid is said to be due to impurities).

Many of the organic reaction mechanisms which we shall discuss in terms of ions are actually reactions of ion pairs, especially in the poor ion-solvating media and high concentrations common in synthetic organic chemistry. Brady and Jakobovits have recently demonstrated the importance of this fact in connection with several organic reactions.[47]

[47] O. L. Brady and J. Jakobovits, *J. Chem. Soc.*, 767 (1950).

CHAPTER 2

ACIDS AND BASES

2-1. Definitions of Acids and Bases. While the Arrhenius definition of acids (substances that ionize in aqueous solution to produce hydrogen ions) and of bases (those that ionize to produce hydroxide ions) is still widely used, e.g., especially in relation to nomenclature, certain other definitions are more useful in theoretical chemistry.

2-1a. Lowry-Brønsted Acids and Bases. According to the definitions of Lowry and Brønsted,[1] an acid is a *proton donor* and a base is a *proton acceptor.* These definitions may be illustrated by the following equilibria:

(1) Acid		(2) Base		(3) Acid		(4) Base
H_2SO_4	$+$	H_2O	$\rightleftharpoons$	H_3O^+	$+$	HSO_4^-
$(C_6H_5)_3CH$	$+$	NH_2^-	$\rightleftharpoons$	NH_3	$+$	$(C_6H_5)_3C^-$
HSO_4^-	$+$	NH_3	$\rightleftharpoons$	NH_4^+	$+$	$SO_4^=$
HBr	$+$	$H_3\overset{+}{N}-NH_2$	$\rightleftharpoons$	$H_3\overset{+}{N}-\overset{+}{N}H_3$	$+$	Br^-
H_3O^+	$+$	OH^-	$\rightleftharpoons$	H_2O	$+$	H_2O

From these equilibria it is seen that acids and bases may have either positive or negative charges or be neutral and that a given molecule or ion may act as an acid in one reaction and as a base in another. It should also be noted that when an acid has donated a proton, it becomes a base. This base is known as the conjugate base of the acid in question. Analogously, each base has its conjugate acid. The acids in columns 1 and 3 above are the conjugate acids of the bases in 4 and 2, respectively.

2-1b. Lewis Acids and Bases. According to Lewis's definition,[2] acids are molecules or ions capable of coordinating with unshared electron pairs, and bases are molecules or ions having unshared electron pairs available for sharing with acids. Since a reagent must have an unshared electron pair in order to accept a proton, the same reagents may act as bases in either the Lowry-Brønsted or the Lewis sense. All Lowry-Brønsted acids are also Lewis acids, since the proton from any proton

---

[1] T. M. Lowry, *Chemistry & Industry,* **42,** 43 (1923); J. N. Brønsted, *Rec. trav. chim.,* **42,** 718 (1923).

[2] G. N. Lewis, *J. Franklin Inst.,* **226,** 293 (1938).

donor coordinates with an unshared electron pair. In addition, however, the Lewis definition includes many reagents, such as boron trifluoride, sulfur trioxide, aluminum chloride, etc., which may also neutralize bases.

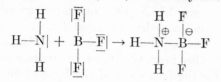

While it is therefore true that Lowry-Brønsted acids merely form a special class of Lewis acids, this class is so important and has been so extensively studied that a separate name is useful. For this reason, following common usage, we shall use the terms acid and base in the Lowry-Brønsted sense and call aprotic acids Lewis acids or electrophilic reagents (the respective conjugate terms being Lewis bases and nucleophilic reagents).

2-2. Ionization as an Acid-Base Reaction. *2-2a. Oxonium Ions.* The "ionization" of hydrogen bromide, a covalent compound, that occurs upon solution in water (and many other solvents) involves the action of water as a base in accepting a proton from the acid hydrogen bromide. The hydronium ions (H_3O^+, sometimes called oxonium ions) and bromide ions thus formed are, of course, solvated, as are all ions in solution; but since the over-all process also involves the formation of ions from a covalent molecule, it may be seen to differ from the solution of sodium chloride in water, in which the ions that are solvated already existed as ions in the solute. It should be noted that in the solvation of any cation water may be said to act as a base in the Lewis sense in so far as covalent bonds are formed between the cation and solvent. Similarly, the solvation of an anion, involving hydrogen bonding, may be related to solvent acidity.

The basicity of water was not recognized much earlier than it was principally because of the relative weakness of this basicity. Evaporation of a solution of hydrogen bromide in liquid ammonia leaves the solid salt ammonium bromide behind because the equilibrium

$$NH_3 + HBr \rightleftharpoons NH_4^+ + Br^-$$

lies so far to the right at room temperature (but not at elevated temperatures). However, the equilibrium constant for the reaction

$$H_2O + HBr \rightleftharpoons H_3O^+ + Br^-$$

is considerably smaller, so that at equilibrium appreciable amounts of water and hydrogen bromide are present. When the solution is evaporated, these volatile components are continuously removed and replaced by a shift of equilibrium from the salt, hydronium bromide. However, it was shown that water will form stable hydronium salts if sufficiently strong acids are used. The explosive liquid perchloric acid forms a relatively stable solid salt, hydronium perchlorate, formerly written as $HClO_4 \cdot H_2O$ but shown by X-ray,[3] nuclear-magnetic-resonance,[4] and infrared-spectral[5] studies to have a crystal lattice consisting of H_3O^+ and ClO_4^- ions. The crystalline hydrates of boron trifluoride[6] and nitric acid[4,5] have also been shown to be hydronium salts. Striking further evidence for the formation of the hydronium ion was obtained by Bagster and Cooling in a study in liquid sulfur dioxide solution.[7] In this solvent, water is almost insoluble, and hydrogen bromide is soluble but not ionized. A solution of hydrogen bromide in sulfur dioxide, however, dissolves 1 mole of water per mole of hydrogen bromide to give an ionic solution, which upon electrolysis liberates at the cathode 1 mole of water per faraday. All these facts are explained by the equilibrium

$$H_2O + HBr \rightleftharpoons H_3O^+ + Br^-$$

In addition to the simple H_3O^+ ion, substituted oxonium ions are known. Meerwein and coworkers have isolated $(CH_3)_3O^+\ BF_4^-$ and several other solid oxonium salts.[8] A number of oxonium salts of the general type of the methylpyrone hydrobromide shown below are also known.

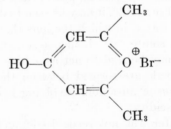

From the similarity of the behavior of acids in alcoholic and in aqueous solutions, there is little doubt that ROH_2^+ ions are present in the former.

2-2b. *Leveling Effects of Solvents.* The compounds commonly referred to as "strong acids" are those for which the equilibrium

$$HA + H_2O \rightleftharpoons H_3O^+ + A^-$$

[3] M. Volmer, *Ann.*, **440**, 200 (1924).

[4] R. E. Richards and J. A. S. Smith, *Trans. Faraday Soc.*, **47**, 1261 (1951); Y. Kakiuchi, H. Shono, K. Komatsu, and K. Kigoshi, *J. Chem. Phys.*, **19**, 1069 (1951).

[5] D. E. Bethell and N. Sheppard, *J. Chem. Phys.*, **21**, 1421 (1953).

[6] L. J. Klinkenberg and J. A. A. Ketelaar, *Rec. trav. chim.*, **54**, 959 (1935).

[7] L. S. Bagster and G. Cooling, *J. Chem. Soc.*, **117**, 693 (1920).

[8] H. Meerwein, G. Hinz, P. Hofmann, E. Kroning, and E. Pfeil, *J. prakt. Chem.*, **147**, 257 (1937).

in dilute aqueous solution is so far to the right that the amount of H_3O^+ formed differs from the amount of HA added by less than the experimental error. The fact that two acids are found to be completely ionized in dilute aqueous solution by present methods of measurement does not, of course, mean they are necessarily equal in strength. For instance, if the ionization constants of HX and HY are 10^4 and 10^2, the hydrogen-ion concentration of their 0.1 N aqueous solutions will be 0.099999 N and 0.0999 N, respectively. Thus, equal concentrations of the two acids yield equal concentrations of hydrogen ions, within experimental error. In a solvent 10^6 times less basic than water,[9] HX and HY should have ionization constants of 10^{-2} and 10^{-4} and hydrogen-ion concentrations (in 0.1 N solutions) of 0.027 and 0.0031, respectively, and should thus be easily distinguishable in strength. This tendency of a solvent to make all acids whose strength is greater than a certain amount appear equal is called the *leveling effect*.

The strength of bases is also subject to the leveling effect. The basicity of dimethylamine in water is due to the existence of the equilibrium

$$(CH_3)_2NH + H_2O \rightleftharpoons (CH_3)_2NH_2^+ + OH^-$$

The amine is said to be a weak base because not all of it is transformed to its conjugate acid even in fairly dilute aqueous solution. Aniline, which is converted to an even lesser extent into the anilinium ion, is said to be a weaker base. The positions of these equilibria are as much due to the weakness of water as a proton donor as to the proton-accepting ability of the amine. In a more strongly acidic solvent, such as formic acid, both amines would be strong bases and their strengths probably indistinguishable, since both would be transformed entirely (within experimental error) into the corresponding substituted ammonium ions.

2-2c. Very Weak Acids. The strengths of acids may be studied only by measurements on equilibria involving at least two acids.

$$HA + B \rightleftharpoons A + HB$$

(In order to make the above equation general we have omitted electrical charges, since in the general case we can say only that the charge on an acid is one unit more positive than that on its conjugate base.) Commonly the solvent acts as one of the acids or bases in equilibria of this type. For fairly strong acids, measurable concentrations of A

---

[9] It is not possible in practice to find a solvent which differs from water *only* in basicity, and therefore we have no definite assurance that the relative acidities of HX and HY will remain unchanged. However, experimental data show that the relative acidity of closely related acids of the same electrical charge type does not vary greatly from solvent to solvent (see Sec. 2-3).

(and hence a quantitative measurement of the equilibrium constant) are obtained when the base B is the solvent.   For weaker acids, however, the conjugate base of the solvent must be used as B in order to transform a measurable concentration of HA to A.   In this case, as well as in the former case, success depends upon the basicity of B and hence the acidity of HB.   In studies of very weak acids it is necessary that HB also be very weak so that B will be very strongly basic.   For this reason, the solvent liquid ammonia is often used in studying very weak acids. Even many hydrocarbons, such as diphenylmethane, react as acids toward potassium amide.

$$(C_6H_5)_2CH_2 + NH_2^- \rightleftharpoons (C_6H_5)_2CH^- + NH_3$$

Another technique that has been used in the study of very weak acids involves a direct comparison of two acids by establishment of equilibrium between one and the conjugate base (as the sodium or potassium salt) of the other in a solvent of negligible acidity.   Comparisons of this sort have been made by Conant and Wheland and by McEwen using ether and benzene as solvents.[10]   By these comparisons, the following order of acidity (in the solvents used) was obtained: t-butyl alcohol $\sim$ acetophenone > phenylacetylene $\sim$ indene > diphenylamine > fluorene > acetylene[11] > aniline > xanthane > triphenylmethane > diphenylmethane > ammonia > toluene > benzene[11] > pentane.[11]   Thus a tertiary alcohol, one of the most weakly acidic hydroxy compounds, is more strongly acidic than any of the hydrocarbons studied.

2-2d. *Very Weak Bases.*   Very weak bases may be studied only by their reactions with very strong acids.   Sulfuric acid is the most acidic solvent in which it is convenient to make measurements.   Many compounds that are too weakly basic to be measured in water are strong bases in this solvent.   The ionization of bases in sulfuric acid solution has been studied most usefully by cryoscopic measurements.   These measurements were pioneered by Hantzsch[12], greatly improved by Hammett and coworkers,[13] and further refined by Gillespie, Hughes,

[10] J. B. Conant and G. W. Wheland, *J. Am. Chem. Soc.*, **54**, 1212 (1932); W. K. McEwen, *J. Am. Chem. Soc.*, **58**, 1124 (1936).

[11] Acetylene has been placed in this series by N. S. Wooding and W. C. E. Higginson [*J. Chem. Soc.*, 774 (1952)].   The positions of benzene and pentane followed from the ability of phenylsodium to metalate toluene and of amylsodium to metalate benzene [A. A. Morton and F. Fallwell, Jr., *J. Am. Chem. Soc.*, **60**, 1429, 1924 (1938)].

[12] A. Hantzsch, *Z. physik. Chem.*, **61**, 257 (1907); *Ber.*, **63B**, 1782, 1789 (1930); and intervening papers.

[13] L. P. Hammett and A. J. Deyrup, *J. Am. Chem. Soc.*, **55**, 1900 (1933); H. P. Treffers and L. P. Hammett, *J. Am. Chem. Soc.*, **59**, 1708 (1937).

and Ingold.[14] Cryoscopic measurements in sulfuric acid are made convenient by its freezing point (10.36°, relatively near room temperature) and fairly high cryoscopic constant (6.12° mole^{-1} kg).[15] The purity of sulfuric acid solutions may be established better by freezing-point measurements than by chemical analysis.   In Fig. 2-1, the molality of water and of $H_2S_2O_7$ (the principal form in which a little SO_3 dissolved

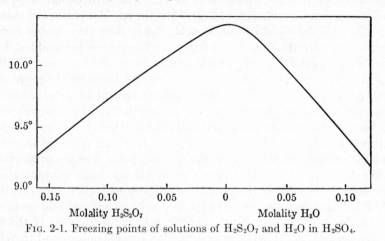

Fig. 2-1. Freezing points of solutions of $H_2S_2O_7$ and H_2O in H_2SO_4.

in H_2SO_4 is believed to exist) is plotted for solutions whose compositions are in the vicinity of that of pure H_2SO_4.   From the nature of the curve obtained—straight lines leading to a rounded maximum—it may be seen that after the solution has become about 0.05 molal in H_2O (or $H_2S_2O_7$), the lowering of the freezing point produced by the addition of further H_2O (or $H_2S_2O_7$) is directly proportional to the amount added. The addition of small concentrations of H_2O or $H_2S_2O_7$, however, does not lower the freezing point nearly so much as would be expected.   This is explained by the considerable self-ionization of sulfuric acid occurring both by autoprotolysis

$$2H_2SO_4 \rightleftharpoons H_3SO_4^+ + HSO_4^- \tag{2-1}$$

and by a process called *ionic self-dehydration*

$$2H_2SO_4 \rightleftharpoons H_3O^+ + HS_2O_7^- \tag{2-2}$$

It is complicated by such further equilibria as

$$H_3SO_4^+ + HS_2O_7^- \rightleftharpoons H_2SO_4 + H_2S_2O_7 \tag{2-3}$$

[14] (a) R. J. Gillespie, E. D. Hughes, and C. K. Ingold, *J. Chem. Soc.*, 2473 (1950); (b) R. J. Gillespie, *J. Chem. Soc.*, 2493, 2537, 2542 (1950).
[15] R. J. Gillespie, *J. Chem. Soc.*, 1851 (1954).

The addition of water may produce two foreign particles by the reaction

$$H_2O + H_2SO_4 \rightarrow H_3O^+ + HSO_4^- \tag{2-4}$$

but the bisulfate ion thus produced may react with some of the approximately 0.013 molal sulfuric acidium ions ($H_3SO_4^+$) present in pure sulfuric acid to reverse equilibrium (2-1). The hydronium ions may similarly reverse equilibrium (2-2). Thus the net increase in the number of foreign particles will be considerably lower than the number formed from water. By the time about 0.05 molal water has been added, however, the concentrations of sulfuric acidium ions and hydrogen disulfate ions ($HS_2O_7^-$) left are negligible and so cannot be reduced significantly further. For this reason it is often most convenient to make cryoscopic measurement not on pure sulfuric acid but on that to which enough water has been added to repress the self-ionization. One of the most striking features of sulfuric acid as a solvent is the fact that for ionic as well as nonionic solutes, the lowering of the freezing point remains proportional to the concentration added, even to relatively large concentrations. (For most ionic solutes, this ideality continues to higher concentrations only if it is assumed that some of the ions take on sulfuric acid molecules of solvation.) This fact shows that the activity coefficients of the ions involved remain constant to unusually high concentrations and therefore that the ion-solvating ability of sulfuric acid is probably greater than that of any other known solvent.

Cryoscopic measurement may lead in the present case, as it does in general, to information about the number of moles of foreign (nonsolvent) particles (ions and/or molecules) per formula weight of material added. We shall use the term "ν factor" for this number, in agreement with Gillespie, Hughes, and Ingold,[14] although earlier workers have used the term "i factor."

If water had a ν factor of two, i.e., if it yielded two particles per molecule by acting as a strong base according to Eq. (2-4), and if its solutions in sulfuric acid were ideal, the slope of the straight part of the right branch of the curve in Fig. 2-1 would be equal to twice the cryoscopic constant of sulfuric acid, or $12.24°$ mole^{-1} kg. The actual slope is significantly less, being $11.21°$ mole^{-1} kg, according to Gillespie.[14b] From his data Gillespie has calculated a value for the basicity constant of water in sulfuric acid (using a somewhat different cryoscopic constant for sulfuric acid from that now accepted).

$$K_b = \frac{[H_3O^+][HSO_4^-]}{[H_2O][H_2SO_4]} = 0.12 \text{ mole/kg}$$

His data led to a constant value for K only if it was assumed that hydronium bisulfate takes on one molecule of sulfuric acid of solvation. Deno and Taft[16] have presented a strong argument that K_b is about 50, while a calculation based on the acidity function (Sec. 2-3d) leads to a value of about 10^6. By determining ν values at various concentrations, Gillespie has determined the basic ionization constants of a number of weak bases such as sulfones, sulfonic acids, sulfates, and nitro compounds.[14b] By analogous methods the acidic ionization constants for sulfuric, disulfuric, and perchloric acids have been determined and found to vary in the order $H_2S_2O_7 > HClO_4 > H_2SO_4$, showing disulfuric acid to be considerably stronger than perchloric (sometimes claimed to be the strongest acid known). Higher polysulfuric acids, such as $H_2S_3O_{10}$, are probably even stronger than disulfuric.

The ν factors that have been determined for a number of other substances are also of considerable interest.[12-14] Acetic acid gives a ν factor of two, due to its reaction as a strong base.

$$CH_3CO_2H + H_2SO_4 \rightarrow CH_3C(OH)_2^+ + HSO_4^-$$

Other compounds that appear to be strong bases in sulfuric acid solution, as judged from their ν factors of two, are 2,4-dinitroaniline, azobenzene, benzalacetophenone, anthraquinone, benzophenone, benzoic acid, trimethylacetic acid, acetone, diethyl ether, ethyl acetate, acetaldehyde, benzamide, acetonitrile, and chloroacetic acid. Dichloroacetic acid gives a ν factor between one and two, showing that it is a weak base, and trichloroacetic acid is a still weaker base, its ν factor being indistinguishable, by earlier workers, from unity. Certain compounds react in a more complicated manner. Methanol and ethanol give ν factors of three by the reaction

$$ROH + 2H_2SO_4 \rightarrow ROSO_3H + H_3O^+ + HSO_4^-$$

Triphenylcarbinol gives a yellow solution and a ν factor of four. Among the evidence that this is due to the reaction

$$(C_6H_5)_3COH + 2H_2SO_4 \rightarrow (C_6H_5)_3C^+ + H_3O^+ + 2HSO_4^-$$

is the fact that the yellow solution has the same absorption spectrum as the yellow solution of triphenylmethyl chloride in liquid sulfur dioxide (in which triphenylmethyl cations are believed to be present).[17]

Liquid hydrogen fluoride is another solvent in which very weak bases may be studied, and the basicities of aromatic hydrocarbons in this solvent have received considerable attention.[18]

[16] N. C. Deno and R. W. Taft, Jr., *J. Am. Chem. Soc.*, **76**, 244 (1954).

[17] A. Hantzsch, *Ber.*, **54B**, 2573 (1921).

[18] D. A. McCaulay and A. P. Lien, *J. Am. Chem. Soc.*, **73**, 2013 (1951); H. C. Brown and J. D. Brady, *J. Am. Chem. Soc.*, **74**, 3570 (1952); M. Kilpatrick and F. E. Luborsky, *J. Am. Chem. Soc.*, **75**, 577 (1953).

2-3. Effect of Solvents on the Strength of Acids and Bases. The strength of an acid HA in the solvent S is usually defined as being proportional to its *acidity constant*, i.e., the equilibrium constant K_a for the equilibrium

$$HA^n + S \rightleftharpoons A^{n-1} + SH^+$$
$$K_a = \frac{[A^{n-1}][SH^+]}{[HA^n]}$$

the constant concentration of the solvent being included in K_a. For an electrically neutral acid ($n = 0$) the acidity constant is the same as the ionization constant, but the acidity constant for an acid with a unit positive charge is not reasonably called an ionization constant, since it is a measure of an equilibrium in which there are as many ions in the reactants as in the products.

2-3a. Effect of the Ion-solvating Powers of the Solvent. The acidity constant of an acid is, as implied in Sec. 2-2b, directly proportional to the basicity of the solvent. However, there are other factors which may affect the acidity constant, and it is not possible to change the solvent basicity without also changing these factors. One of the most important is the ion-solvating power of the solvent. Its influence may be noticed particularly when comparing the effect of solvent changes on the acidity constants of acids of different electrical-charge types. For example, while the ionization constants of carboxylic acids are usually from 10^5 to 10^6 times as large in water as in absolute ethanol, the acidity constants of substituted ammonium ions are, on the average, less than 10 times as large in water as in ethanol. In the latter case

$$R_3NH^+ + H_2O \rightleftharpoons R_3N + H_3O^+ \qquad (2\text{-}5)$$
$$R_3NH^+ + EtOH \rightleftharpoons R_3N + EtOH_2^+ \qquad (2\text{-}6)$$

Equilibrium (2-5) usually lies slightly further to the right than (2-6), probably because water is a stronger base then ethanol.[19] This factor has an effect on the equilibria

$$RCO_2H + H_2O \rightleftharpoons RCO_2^- + H_3O^+$$
$$RCO_2H + EtOH \rightleftharpoons RCO_2^- + EtOH_2^+$$

but in addition it must be noted that we are now dealing with equilibria between two neutral molecules and two ions and that the production of ions will be greatly favored by the much better ion-solvating medium, water. Hence the acidity constants for electrically neutral acids should

---

[19] Water is a strong enough base to be measured in absolute ethanol solution and has been found to be 15 to 20 times as strong a base as ethanol [H. Goldschmidt, *Z. physik. Chem.*, **89**, 129 (1914); I. I. Bezman and F. H. Verhoek, *J. Am. Chem. Soc.*, **67**, 1330 (1945); E. A. Braude and E. S. Stern, *J. Chem. Soc.*, 1976 (1948)].

increase more on going from ethanol to water than those for positively charged acids. The principles used here may even be applied to comparisons of acids of the same charge type. For example, the ionization constant of picric acid increases only about 1,500-fold between ethanol and water. Since the charge on the picrate anion is so spread out by resonance, the ion is not so strongly solvated. For this reason its stability does not change so greatly with the ion-solvating power of the solvent as does that of a carboxylate anion, in which the negative charge is largely on two atoms. By analogous reasoning we may explain why the acidity of p-nitrobenzamide relative to ethanol increases on going from ethyl to isopropyl alcohol solution and why that of nitroaniline derivatives increases even more.[20] The ionization of bases may be discussed similarly in terms of the acidity of the solvent and the ion-solvating power of the medium.

2-3b. *Solvent Effects in Terms of Activity Coefficients.* While many useful correlations result from qualitative arguments of the type used above, further discussion of the subject is made more convenient by the use of activities and activity coefficients. Although the equilibrium constants, expressed in terms of concentrations, that we have used heretofore have definite values only in a particular medium, it is possible by substituting activities for concentrations to obtain equilibrium constants whose values are independent of the medium. These are called thermodynamic equilibrium constants. The activity of a molecule or ion X is written a_x and is equal to the concentration of X times its activity coefficient γ_x.[21] It is often useful to ignore the solvent in writing the equilibrium equation for an acid (in a mixed solvent, such as aqueous ethanol, we may not know the relative extent to which the proton coordinates with water and ethanol).

$$HA \rightleftharpoons H^+ + A$$

The thermodynamic equilibrium constant for this equation may be written in terms of activities

$$K_a = \frac{a_{H^+} a_A}{a_{HA}} \tag{2-7}$$

or in terms of concentrations and activity coefficients,

[20] J. Hine and M. Hine, *J. Am. Chem. Soc.*, **74**, 5266 (1952).

[21] Discussion of activities, activity coefficients, and their use in equilibrium expressions are given in most beginning physical chemistry texts. See F. Daniels, "Outlines of Physical Chemistry," chap. XII, John Wiley & Sons, Inc., New York, 1952, and L. P. Hammett, "Introduction to the Study of Physical Chemistry," pp. 245–247, 312–325, McGraw-Hill Book Company, Inc., New York, 1952.

$$K_a = \frac{[\mathrm{H^+}]\gamma_{\mathrm{H^+}}[\mathrm{A}]\gamma_{\mathrm{A}}}{[\mathrm{HA}]\gamma_{\mathrm{HA}}} = \frac{[\mathrm{H^+}][\mathrm{A}]}{[\mathrm{HA}]}\frac{\gamma_{\mathrm{H^+}}\gamma_{\mathrm{A}}}{\gamma_{\mathrm{HA}}}$$

If we define the activity coefficients so that they approach unity at infinite dilution in aqueous solution, the thermodynamic acidity constant K_A is (in dilute aqueous solution) equal to the concentration-acidity constant, which we shall call $K_A{}^W$. If, then, γ_x's are activity coefficients in solvent S, referred to dilute aqueous solution,

$$K_a = K_A{}^S \frac{\gamma_{\mathrm{H^+}}\gamma_{\mathrm{A}}}{\gamma_{\mathrm{HA}}} = K_A{}^W \tag{2-8}$$

Analogously, for another acid HB

$$K'_a = K_A{}^{S'} \frac{\gamma_{\mathrm{H^+}}\gamma_{\mathrm{B}}}{\gamma_{\mathrm{HB}}} = K_A{}^{W'} \tag{2-9}$$

Dividing (2-8) by (2-9),

$$\frac{K_A{}^S \gamma_{\mathrm{A}}\gamma_{\mathrm{HB}}}{K_A{}^{S'} \gamma_{\mathrm{B}}\gamma_{\mathrm{HA}}} = \frac{K_A{}^W}{K_A{}^{W'}}$$

or

$$K_A{}^S = K_A{}^{S'} \frac{K_A{}^W}{K_A{}^{W'}} \frac{\gamma_{\mathrm{B}}\gamma_{\mathrm{HA}}}{\gamma_{\mathrm{A}}\gamma_{\mathrm{HB}}} \tag{2-10}$$

That is, the acidity constant of an acid HA in any solvent S may be calculated from its acidity constant in water, the acidity constants of some other acid HB in water and S, and the activity-coefficient term shown. For electrically neutral acids HA and HB, this term will have the form $\gamma_{\mathrm{B}}\cdot\gamma_{\mathrm{HA}}/\gamma_{\mathrm{A}}\cdot\gamma_{\mathrm{HB}}$. The γ_{HA} and γ_{HB} terms may often be evaluated readily from the solubilities, partial pressures, distribution coefficients, etc., of HA and HB in water and solvent S. The ratio of ionic activity coefficients, $\gamma_{\mathrm{B^-}}/\gamma_{\mathrm{A^-}}$, may be determined from the solubilities of salts, potentiometrically or otherwise. Values of $K_A{}^{S'}$ calculated in this manner from various types of experimental data have been found in reasonable agreement with those determined experimentally.[22]

2-3c. *Determination of Acidity Constants in Certain Mixed Solvents.* Remembering that $pK = -\log K$, Eq. (2-7) may, for a singly charged cationic acid, be rewritten in the form

$$pK_a = -\log \frac{a_{\mathrm{H^+}}a_{\mathrm{A}}}{a_{\mathrm{AH^+}}} = \log \frac{a_{\mathrm{AH^+}}}{a_{\mathrm{A}}} - \log a_{\mathrm{H^+}} \tag{2-11}$$

Since in sufficiently dilute aqueous solution concentrations may be

[22] N. Bjerrum and E. Larsson, *Z. physik. Chem.*, **127**, 358 (1927); J. O. Halford, *J. Am. Chem. Soc.*, **53**, 2939 (1931); I. M. Kolthoff, J. J. Lingane, and W. D. Larson, *J. Am. Chem. Soc.*, **60**, 2512 (1938).

equated to activities,

$$pK_a = \log \frac{[AH^+]}{[A]} + pH$$

the pK_a for AH^+ may be determined from a measurement of the relative concentrations of AH^+ and A in a solution of known pH. In cases where either AH^+ or A absorb at suitable wave lengths, this may often be done conveniently by spectrophotometric measurements. If the base A is too weak, however, it may not be possible to produce from it, in a dilute aqueous solution, an accurately measurable concentration of AH^+. While a relatively strongly acidic solution may produce enough AH^+ to measure, we have no assurance that activities may be equated to concentrations in such a solution. The problem of determining the value of pK_a under such conditions has been treated successfully by Hammett and Deyrup[23] by use of the following method.

For another acid BH^+ of the same electrical-charge type as AH^+, an equation analogous to (2-11) may be written.

$$pK_a' = \log \frac{a_{BH^+}}{a_B} - \log a_{H^+} \tag{2-12}$$

Subtracting (2-12) from (2-11),

$$pK_a - pK_a' = \log \frac{a_{AH^+}}{a_A} - \log \frac{a_{BH^+}}{a_B}$$

or, in terms of concentrations and activity coefficients,

$$pK_a - pK_a' = \log \frac{[AH^+]}{[A]} - \log \frac{[BH^+]}{[B]} + \log \frac{\gamma_{AH^+}\gamma_B}{\gamma_A\gamma_{BH^+}} \tag{2-13}$$

Since pK_a and pK_a' are defined in terms of activities their values are independent of the medium. Measurements of

$$\log \frac{[AH^+]}{[A]} - \log \frac{[BH^+]}{[B]}$$

have been made for a number of pairs of compounds in various mixtures of water and sulfuric acid, and for each pair the values obtained have been almost independent of the composition of the medium over the range in which it was possible to make measurements (this range, however, was always a fairly small fraction of the total possible range). In so far as the value of this function for a given pair of compounds is independent of

[23] L. P. Hammett and A. J. Deyrup, *J. Am. Chem. Soc.*, **54**, 2721 (1932); L. P. Hammett, *Chem. Rev.*, **16**, 67 (1935); "Physical Organic Chemistry," chap. IX, McGraw-Hill Book Company, Inc., New York, 1940.

the solvent, we may be sure that the function $\log \gamma_{AH^+}\gamma_B/\gamma_A\gamma_{BH^+}$ is also independent of the solvent. Since this activity-coefficient term has the value zero in aqueous solution and since it is also independent of the nature of the sulfuric acid–water mixture, its value must be zero in all such mixtures. Obviously, if

$$\log \frac{\gamma_{AH^+}\gamma_B}{\gamma_A\gamma_{BH^+}} = \log \frac{\gamma_{AH^+}}{\gamma_A} - \log \frac{\gamma_{BH^+}}{\gamma_B} = 0$$

then
$$\log \frac{\gamma_{AH^+}}{\gamma_A} = \log \frac{\gamma_{BH^+}}{\gamma_B} \qquad (2\text{-}14)$$

That is, in sulfuric acid–water mixtures the ratio of the activity coefficient of an electrically neutral base to that of its conjugate acid is independent of the nature of the acid.[24] It appears that this generalization may also be extended to aqueous solutions of hydrochloric acid, nitric acid, and perchloric acid, to anhydrous formic acid, and to fairly strong solutions of sulfuric acid in acetic acid (although there are fewer data available for most of these solvent mixtures).

Thus, if we choose as the base A one which is barely strong enough to be measured in dilute aqueous solution, the ratio [AH+]/[A] will also be measurable in certain water–sulfuric acid mixtures. If B is a base that is not quite strong enough to be measured in aqueous solution, [BH+]/[B] will be measurable in some of the same water–sulfuric acid mixtures, and pK_a', the activity constant of BH+, may be determined from Eq. (2-13), which acquires the form

$$pK_a - pK_a' = \log \frac{[AH^+]}{[A]} - \log \frac{[BH^+]}{[B]}$$

when the activity-coefficient term vanishes. From B, the acidity constant of the conjugate acid of a still weaker base C may be determined. By such a stepwise process a value of pK_a can be determined for the conjugate acid of any base that is strong enough to be measured in a sulfuric acid–water mixture (provided that the base and conjugate acid have different absorption spectra or differ in some other way that permits their concentrations to be determined). Some pK_a values obtained in this way are listed in Table 2-1. Values of pK_a determined in the other solvent mixtures mentioned agree satisfactorily (rarely deviating by more than 0.1) with these values, as Eq. (2-14) requires, since for media for which (2-14) applies, *relative* basicities (of electrically neutral bases) do not change.

---

[24] This may be true only for somewhat related bases. (Practically all those tested contained nitrogen as the basic atom.) In fact, from the work of Deno and Taft (Ref. 16) the base water appears to deviate considerably.

TABLE 2-1. VALUES OF pK_a IN SULFURIC ACID–WATER MIXTURES FOR THE CONJUGATE ACIDS OF SOME WEAK BASES

Base	pK_a	Base	pK_a
p-Nitroaniline.................	$+1.11$	Benzalacetophenone.........	-5.61
o-Nitroaniline.................	-0.13	p-Benzoylbiphenyl..........	-6.19
p-Nitrodiphenylamine........	-2.38	Anthraquinone.............	-8.15
p-Nitroazobenzene...........	-3.35	2,4,6-Trinitroaniline........	-9.29
2,4-Dinitroaniline...........	-4.38		

2-3d. *Acidity Functions.*[23] Equation (2-11) may be rewritten in the form

$$pK_a = \log \frac{[\text{AH}^+]}{[\text{A}]} - \log \frac{a_{\text{H}^+}\gamma_\text{A}}{\gamma_{\text{AH}^+}} \qquad (2\text{-}15)$$

Since a_{H^+} and $\gamma_\text{A}/\gamma_{\text{AH}^+}$ both have a definite value in any solvent mixture and since this value is independent of the nature of the base A in solvents for which Eq. (2-14) holds, the term $-\log a_{\text{H}^+}\gamma_\text{A}/\gamma_{\text{AH}^+}$ must have a definite value for any such solvent mixture. It is seen that for a given pK_a the magnitude of this function determines how much of the base is present as its conjugate acid. Therefore the function is a quantitative measure of the ability of the solvent to donate protons to an electrically neutral base and is called the *acidity function*, H_0.

$$H_0 = - \log \frac{a_{\text{H}^+}\gamma_\text{A}}{.\gamma_{\text{AH}^+}} \qquad (2\text{-}16)$$

By substitution of Eq. (2-16) into (2-15), we get an equation which may be used in the experimental determination of H_0.

$$H_0 = pK_a + \log \frac{[\text{A}]}{[\text{AH}^+]} \qquad (2\text{-}17)$$

Using indicators such as those listed in Table 2-1, for which pK_a values are known, values of H_0 have been determined for mixtures of water with sulfuric, hydrochloric, nitric, perchloric, and trichloroacetic acids. Some of the values obtained for sulfuric acid–water mixtures are listed in Table 2-2. From the value of H_0 for a given medium and the value of $[\text{A}]/[\text{AH}^+]$ a value of pK_a may be calculated.

The antilogarithm of $-H_0$ has been given the symbol h_0 and is often a useful term.

$$\log h_0 = -H_0$$

therefore $\qquad\qquad h_0 = \dfrac{a_{\text{H}^+}\gamma_\text{A}}{\gamma_{\text{AH}^+}}$

TABLE 2-2. H_0 IN VARIOUS SULFURIC ACID–WATER MIXTURES

Wt. H_2SO_4, %	H_0	Wt. H_2SO_4, %	H_0	Wt. H_2SO_4, %	H_0
5	$+0.24$	40	-2.28	80	-6.82
10	-0.16	50	-3.23	85	-7.62
15	-0.54	60	-4.32	90	-8.17
20	-0.89	70	-5.54	95	-8.74
30	-1.54	75	-6.16	100	-10.60

Deno and Taft[16] have shown that the numerical value of the acidity function H_0 may be calculated in 83 to 99.8 per cent (by weight) sulfuric acid by assuming that the reaction

$$H_2O + H_2SO_4 \rightleftharpoons H_3O^+ + HSO_4^-$$

controls the acidity properties of the solution and that the equilibrium constant for this reaction has a value of about 50 (Sec. 2-2d). These assumptions also permit the calculation of the activity of water in 83 to 95 per cent sulfuric acid. From these facts it appears likely that the activity coefficients of the species involved in the equilibrium do not change between 83 and 99.8 per cent sulfuric acid.

Gold and Hawes have defined another acidity function J_0 by the equation[25]

$$J_0 = H_0 + \log a_{H_2O}$$

Since a_{H_2O} is defined as unity for pure water, J_0 approaches H_0, and both approach pH as the solvent approaches pure water. The ionization of compounds that react by the scheme

$$ROH + H^+ \rightarrow R^+ + H_2O$$

will follow J_0 in the same logarithmic way that the ionization of simple Brønsted bases follows H_0.

Gutbezahl and Grunwald have demonstrated that γ_{AH^+}/γ_A does not vary in the same manner for all bases in mixtures of ethanol and water (variations between two bases of as much as sixtyfold were noted) and that therefore the acidity function H_0 is too crude an approximation to be of much use in these mixtures.[26]

The subscript zero in the acidity function H_0 refers to electrical charge on the base. For mononegatively charged bases in equilibrium with uncharged acids, the acidity function H_- may be defined by equations analogous to (2-16) and (2-17).

[25] V. Gold and B. W. V. Hawes, *J. Chem. Soc.*, 2102 (1951); cf. V. Gold, *J. Chem. Soc.*, 1263 (1955).

[26] B. Gutbezahl and E. Grunwald, *J. Am. Chem. Soc.*, **75**, 559 (1953).

$$H_- = pK_{HA} + \log \frac{[A^-]}{[HA]} = \log \frac{\gamma_{HA}}{\gamma_{A^-}} - \log a_{H^+}$$

The acidity function H_- will be generally applicable for solvent changes over which the value of γ_{HA}/γ_{A^-} is essentially independent of the nature of HA. Deno has shown that this is the case for several nitroaniline and nitrotoluene derivatives used as indicators in water-hydrazine mixtures and has calculated values of H_- for these mixtures.[27] The deviation by one indicator and the fact that all the indicators used were rather closely related render it still somewhat uncertain that the values of H_- calculated may be applied to all electrically neutral acids with a reasonable degree of accuracy. The variations in the relative acidities of electrically neutral acids on going from water to ethanol[26,28] and from ethanol to isopropyl alcohol[20] show that H_- is not a generally useful approximation in these solvent mixtures, and indeed it seems likely that solvent mixtures in which it is useful are the exception rather than the rule.

Schwarzenbach and Sulzberger have described measurements in strong sodium hydroxide and potassium hydroxide solutions, but because of the limited number of types of indicators used and the uncertainty as to the exact nature of their color-change reaction, it cannot be stated whether or not H_- is a good approximation in these solutions.[29]

Correlations of the rates of acid- and base-catalyzed reactions with acidity functions are discussed in Sec. 8-2e.

Gutbezahl and Grunwald have suggested a more general rule for the variation of the activity coefficients of species that are closely related to each other and have used this rule, for which considerable evidence is presented, to evaluate the activity coefficients of individual ions.[25]

2-4. Effect of Structure on the Strength of Acids and Bases. 2-4a. *Effect of Structure on Equilibria.*[30] Let us use the reversible reaction below as a general example of an equilibrium involving organic molecules.

$$A + B \rightleftharpoons C + D \tag{2-18}$$
$$K_1 = \frac{[C][D]}{[A][B]}$$

A change in the nature of a substituent group of A to give A′ (which will also produce a change in the structure of at least one of the products, say C) will, in general, change the equilibrium constant.

$$A' + B \rightleftharpoons C' + D \tag{2-19}$$

[27] N. C. Deno, *J. Am. Chem. Soc.*, **74**, 2039 (1952).
[28] E. Grunwald and B. J. Berkowitz, *J. Am. Chem. Soc.*, **73**, 4939 (1951).
[29] G. Schwarzenbach and R. Sulzberger, *Helv. Chim. Acta*, **27**, 348 (1944).
[30] Hammett, "Physical Organic Chemistry," pp. 69–79.

$$K_2 = \frac{[C'][D]}{[A'][B]}$$

The magnitude of this change may be expressed as the equilibrium constant for a reaction involving the two molecules of differing structure.

$$K_3 = \frac{K_1}{K_2} = \frac{[C][A']}{[A][C']}$$
$$A + C' \rightleftharpoons A' + C \tag{2-20}$$

The equilibrium constant is related to the free-energy change occurring,

$$\Delta F^\circ = -RT \ln K$$

and by measurements of K and hence ΔF at several temperatures, the heat and entropy changes may be determined for the reaction. The free-energy change may be divided into two parts, the heat of reaction and the temperature-entropy term.

$$\Delta F^\circ = \Delta H - T\Delta S^\circ$$

It is desirable to relate these experimentally determinable quantities to the factors that govern equilibria.

These factors may usefully be divided into three categories: (1) potential energy, (2) kinetic energy, (3) probability. Potential-energy differences are those which would exist if all the molecules were completely deprived of their energy of motion. Potential-energy differences may be thought of as changes in bond energy due to resonance, to the electron-attracting and -repelling power of functional groups, to the interaction of ions, dipoles, etc. The kinetic energy is that due to the motions of the molecules—to the translational motion and rotational motion of a molecule as a whole and to the vibrational and rotational motions occurring within a molecule. Probability differences are due to the different number of ways in which a molecule (or group of molecules) can possess a given amount of energy. Our probability discussions will be limited almost entirely to cases involving a change in the number of identical functional groups in the molecule (as in comparisons of dicarboxylic and monocarboxylic acids) and in the number of "rotational isomers" possible.

Potential-energy differences will appear in the heat-of-reaction term (ΔH), and probability differences will appear in the temperature-entropy term ($T\Delta S$), but kinetic-energy differences may appear in either or both these terms. Hence, from experimentally determined values of ΔH and ΔS°, one can usually draw no definite conclusions about what combinations of changes in potential and kinetic energy are responsible for given changes in equilibrium constants. Measurements extrapolated to absolute zero are also useless for this purpose, since even at this temperature the molecules possess considerable kinetic energy. There is a useful special case in which potential-energy differences can be detected, however. This occurs when the entropy changes for two equilibria like (2-18) and (2-19) are the same, i.e., where the entropy change for (2-20) is zero. It can be shown that in such a case there is probably no change in the kinetic-energy terms and therefore that all changes in the equilibrium constant are due to potential-energy changes.[30]

2-4b. *Effect of the Identity of the Acidic or Basic Atom on Acidity and Basicity.* As just stated, it is not possible in most cases to determine experimentally whether given changes in equilibria are due to potential-energy or kinetic-energy differences. Nevertheless, in correlating the effect of structure on equilibria, including acidity and basicity, it is often useful to assume that certain electronic and polar changes in the molecule do produce certain changes in the potential energy. These correlations based on potential-energy factors fail occasionally. This may be due in some instances to an incorrect evaluation of the potential-energy factors (since many are based on data in which kinetic-energy terms may be important), so that the generalization will hold only when the potential-energy terms are overwhelmed by kinetic-energy terms. In other cases the potential energy may be evaluated correctly, and failures may be due to the intrusion of kinetic-energy factors. Indeed, no theory involving only the structures of the acids and bases concerned could hope to be infallible, since there are a number of examples known of inversions in relative orders of acidity produced by solvent changes. Nevertheless, generalizations of the type described are of the greatest importance to both the synthetic and theoretical organic chemist.

One of the most important factors governing the acidity or basicity of a molecule is the identity of the atom to which this acidity or basicity is due. Several generalizations may be based on the periodic table.

1. *Within a given period of the periodic table, the acidity of hydrides increases with increasing electronegativity.* Thus, as acids: $HCH_3 <$ $HNH_2 < HOH < HF$. This change is most often attributed to the increasing nuclear charge, but the decrease in the number of electropositive hydrogen atoms attached to the central atom must also be important. This generalization also applies to comparisons of ions of the same charge type, so that the acidity varies thus: $HNH_3^+ < HOH_2^+$ $< HFH^+$. These two orders of acidity are, of course, simply another way of stating the following two orders of basicity: $CH_3^- > NH_2^- >$ $OH^- > F^-$ and $NH_3 > H_2O > HF$. There is considerable evidence that *the attachment of a multiple linkage to an atom increases its effective electronegativity.* From this fact and the generalization given above, we should expect acetylene to be a stronger acid than ethylene or benzene

and these in turn to be more acidic than ethane. Similarly, pyridine is a much weaker base than saturated amines, and nitriles are still weaker.

2. Another generalization is that *the acidity of hydrides of elements within a given family increases with increasing atomic number.* That is, as acids HI > HBr > HCl > HF. This generalization may be correlated with the decrease in bond strengths that occurs with increasing atomic number. The stabilization of the heavier anions due to the spreading of the charge over a larger volume is probably of some importance but is apparently a secondary factor, since HF is the strongest base of the hydrogen halides despite the fact that the addition of a proton gives a relatively small ion. Similarly NH_3 is a stronger base than PH_3.

2-4c. Resonance Effects on Acidity and Basicity. Another factor of great importance in determining relative acidities is the degree of resonance stabilization of the acids and conjugate bases involved. For instance, in comparing the acidity of an alcohol and a carboxylic acid

$$RCO_2H \rightleftharpoons H^+ + RCO_2^-$$
$$ROH \rightleftharpoons H^+ + RO^-$$

the greater acidity of the carboxylic acid is almost undoubtedly due in part to the resonance stabilization of the carboxylate anion,

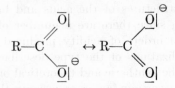

and the resultant spread of the negative charge over a larger volume. Resonance also occurs in the undissociated carboxylic acid, of course, but the resonance stabilization is less, since the principal contributing structures are not of equal energy content.

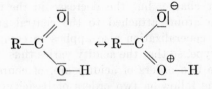

In addition to resonance, inductive effects must also be important in this case, since the double-bonded carbon and oxygen atoms are more electronegative than any atom in the hydrocarbon R group of the alcohol.

The acidity of phenols (relative to alcohols) is similarly attributed to

resonance stabilization of the anion,

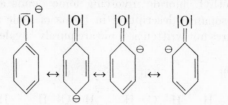

while in aniline the weak basicity (relative to aliphatic amines) is attributed to resonance in the base itself,

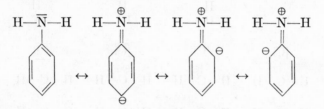

resonance of this type occurring only to a very much smaller extent in the anilinium ion. In the case of both phenol and aniline the electronegativity of the benzenoid carbon atoms must also be important.

Both effects similarly explain the decreased basicity of pyrrole

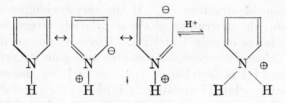

and increased acidity of cyclopentadiene,

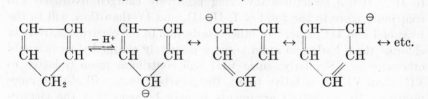

β-diketones,

$$R—\overset{O}{\overset{\|}{C}}—CH_2—\overset{O}{\overset{\|}{C}}—R \underset{}{\overset{-H^+}{\rightleftharpoons}} R—\overset{O}{\overset{\|}{C}}—\overset{\ominus}{C}H—\overset{O}{\overset{\|}{C}}—R \leftrightarrow R—\overset{\ominus}{\overset{O}{\overset{\|}{C}}}=CH—\overset{O}{\overset{\|}{C}}—R \leftrightarrow etc.$$

and related compounds.

2-4d. *Inductive Effects on Acidity and Basicity.* A number of resonance structures for ethyl chloride involving ionic bonds are written below. Note that a resonance description in terms of ionic structures implies that the structures not written as ionic are purely covalent (see Sec. 1-1a).

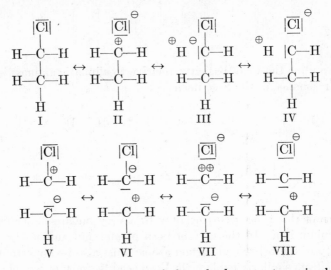

The relatively positive character of the α-hydrogen atoms is shown by the contribution of structure III. If the carbon-chlorine bond were purely covalent, the description of the α-carbon–hydrogen bond might be written in terms of only I and III. However, due to the electronegativity of chlorine we must also write the analogous structures II and IV. Now since III is destabilized (relative to I) by the existence of charge separation, while IV (relative to II) is not thus destabilized, the contribution of III (relative to I) will be less than that of IV (relative to II). Hence structures involving positively charged hydrogen will contribute more to the total of I, II, III, and IV than they will to the total of I and III alone. In other words, due to the electronegativity of chlorine the α-hydrogen atom is more positively charged than it would otherwise be. Similarly, since VIII will contribute more (relative to VII) than VI will (relative to V), the β-carbon atom will also be more positive. By analogous arguments it may be seen that the electronegative character of the chlorine atom would be expected to increase the positive (or decrease the negative) character of every other atom in the molecule, although the magnitude of the effect is expected to decrease with increasing distance. While this effect may be seen to be a result of the resonance contribution of ionic structures, it may be stated by a much less involved argument in terms of the inductive effect. According to this concept, an electron-withdrawing group may, by taking a larger share of the bonding electron pair, induce a positive charge on an atom to which it is attached. Since this positive charge will increase the electron-withdrawing power of the atom upon which it resides, the inductive effect will be relayed along a chain of atoms, although with decreasing intensity. The effect is commonly depicted by arrows pointing in the direction in which the electrons are induced.

$$H \rightarrow \overset{\overset{\displaystyle H}{\downarrow}}{\underset{\underset{\displaystyle H}{\uparrow}}{C}} \rightarrow \overset{\overset{\displaystyle H}{\downarrow}}{\underset{\underset{\displaystyle H}{\uparrow}}{C}} \rightarrow Cl$$

The extent to which atoms or groups withdraw electrons increases with increasing charge on the group,

$$-\overset{\oplus}{SR_2} > -SR > -\overset{\ominus}{S}$$

increases with the nuclear charge, for a given number of inner-shell electrons,

$$-F > -OR > -NR_2 > -CR_3$$

and decreases with the increasing number of inner electron shells.

$$-F > -Cl > -Br > -I$$

These series apply when R is a hydrocarbon radical or hydrogen. Other groups behave in predictable ways. For example, the nitro group, in which the nitrogen atom bears a positive charge in both of the important resonance structures, is a relatively strong electron-withdrawing group. As might be expected from the effect of multiple bonds on effective electronegativity,

$$-C{\equiv}CR > -CR{=}CR_2 > -CR_3$$

In acid-base equilibria,

$$ROH + OH^{\ominus} \rightleftharpoons RO^{\ominus} + H_2O$$
$$RNH_3^{\oplus} + OH^{\ominus} \rightleftharpoons RNH_2 + H_2O$$

the atom bearing the acidic proton will possess a relative deficiency of electrons in the acid and an excess in the conjugate base. Since an electron-withdrawing group will increase the deficiency (destabilizing the acid) and relieve the excess (stabilizing the conjugate base), it will in general increase the strength of acids and decrease that of bases. The extent to which the inductive effect changes the strength of acids has been expressed as an empirical equation by Branch and Calvin.[31] These

[31] G. E. K. Branch and M. Calvin, "The Theory of Organic Chemistry," chap. VI. Prentice-Hall, Inc., New York, 1941.

workers give methods for calculating and list values of *inductive constants* which result in the following order:

$$-SO_2R > -\overset{\oplus}{N}R_3 > -NO_2 > -CN > -F > -Cl > -Br > -CO_2H$$
$$> -I > -COR > -OR > -SR > -C_6H_5 > -NR_2 > -H > -R,$$

where —R is a saturated aliphatic radical. This correlation gives fairly good results but was not intended for cases in which the substituent is conjugated with the acidic functional group (—OH or —CO₂H, etc.), because in these cases resonance is also an important factor. Branch and Calvin's equation includes the generalization that the effect of a group decreases by a factor of about 2.8 for every additional atom that separates it from the acidic hydrogen. The general magnitude of the effect produced may be seen from the ionization constants listed in Table 2-3.

TABLE 2-3. IONIZATION CONSTANTS OF ACIDS IN WATER

Acid	pK_a	Acid	pK_a
CH_3CO_2H	4.7	$ClCH_2CH_2CH_2CO_2H$	4.5
FCH_2CO_2H	2.7	$C_6H_5CH_2CO_2H$	4.3
$ClCH_2CO_2H$	2.8	$O_2NCH_2CH_2CO_2H$	3.8
$BrCH_2CO_2H$	2.9	$CH_2{=}CHCH_2CO_2H$	4.4
ICH_2CO_2H	3.0	$\overset{\oplus}{H_3}NCH_2CO_2H$	2.3
Cl_2CHCO_2H	1.3	$HO_2CCH_2CO_2H$	2.8
$CH_3CH_2CH_2CO_2H$	4.9	HCO_2H	3.8
$CH_3CH_2\underset{\mid}{C}HCO_2H$ Cl	2.9	$CH_3COCH_2CO_2H$	3.6
		$HOCH_2CO_2H$	3.8
$CH_3\underset{\mid}{C}HCH_2CO_2H$ Cl	4.1	HOH	15.7
		CH_3CH_2OH	~15.8
		CF_3CH_2OH	~12

Instead of the above correlation, in which the effect of an electronegative group is depicted as operating along the atomic chain, it is possible to consider an interaction through space of the dipole resulting from the electronegative group and the carboxylate group or ion. A mathematical treatment based on a model of this sort has been carried out by Kirkwood and Westheimer.[32a] Since the positive end of the carbon-chlorine dipole in the chloroacetate anion is nearer the carboxylate anion than is the negative end, there will be a net attraction and stabilization of this anion. The extent of this stabilization depends upon the magnitude of the dipole, its distance from the carboxylate anion, and

[32] (a) J. G. Kirkwood and F. H. Westheimer, *J. Chem. Phys.*, **6**, 506, 513 (1938); F. H. Westheimer and M. W. Shookhoff, *J. Am. Chem. Soc.*, **61**, 555 (1939); (b) J. D. Roberts and W. T. Moreland, Jr., *J. Am. Chem. Soc.*, **75**, 2167 (1953).

the dielectric constant of the medium through which the interacting lines of force must pass. Kirkwood and Westheimer's treatment was an improvement over earlier studies (in which this dielectric constant was taken as either a rather high value equal to that of the solvent or a low value characteristic of a hydrocarbon group) in that they used a model consisting of a cavity (spherical or ellipsoidal for mathematical convenience) of low-dielectric constant surrounded by a medium of high dielectric constant. Using reasonable values for their various estimated parameters, they obtained fairly good agreement with experimental data on acids with dipolar *and* with electrically charged substituents. Roberts and Moreland, however, report that with 4-substituted bicyclo[2,2,2]-octane-1-carboxylic acids, calculations by the Kirkwood-Westheimer method predict that substituents should have only about half as large an effect as they are actually found to.[32b] This suggests that it is necessary to consider the inductive effect in addition to the direct electrostatic effect.

2-4e. *The Hammett Equation.* It is not possible to tell whether the changes in the free energy of an individual equilibrium produced by various substituents are proportional to some property (such as electron-withdrawing power) of the substituents, except in the rare cases in which there is some other way of measuring this property. However, if the changes in free energies of more than one equilibrium are proportional to the change in the same property of the substituents, this fact will automatically be shown by a proportionality between the effects of substituents on the free energies of the several equilibria. Such a proportionality is known as a *linear free-energy relationship* and will, of course, result in a similar linear relationship between the logarithms of the equilibrium constants. As one of the first of the major steps toward making organic chemistry a quantitative science, Hammett found that a proportionality of this type describes with reasonable accuracy the changes produced by meta and para substituents on almost all equilibria involving phenyl-substituted compounds.[33] That is, if for each substituent a point is plotted whose abscissa is log K for the appropriately substituted compound in one equilibrium and whose ordinate is log K for the analogously substituted compound in the other equilibrium, the resultant points should describe a straight line. One reason for the generality of this relationship for meta- and para-substituted phenyl compounds is that the substituents very often have no effect on the entropy change for the reaction. Therefore (see Sec. 2-4b and Ref. 30)

[33] L. P. Hammett, *Chem. Rev.*, **17**, 125 (1935); *Trans. Faraday Soc.*, **34**, 156 (1938); "Physical Organic Chemistry," pp. 184–207; see also G. N. Burkhardt, *Nature*, **136**, 687 (1935); G. N. Burkhardt, W. G. K. Ford, and E. Singleton, *J. Chem. Soc.*, 17 (1936).

the effects noted are due to potential-energy differences.[34]   Since the
substituent group in most cases is too far from the reaction center for the
effect to be steric, it must be electronic.   In Fig. 2-2 the logarithms of
the ionization constants of various substituted benzoic acids are plotted

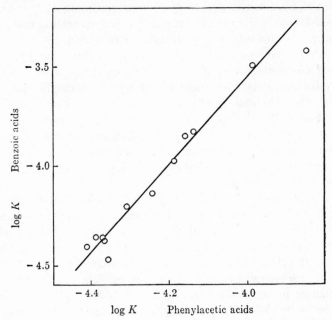

FIG. 2-2. Proportionality of effect of substituents on the acidity of benzoic and
phenylacetic acids.

against the logarithms of the ionization constants of the corresponding
substituted phenylacetic acids.   The points lie reasonably near a straight
line whose equation is

$$\log K = \rho \log K' + C \qquad (2\text{-}21)$$

where K and K' are the two equilibrium constants for a given substituent, ρ is the slope of the line, and C is the intercept.   This equation
is applicable for any substituent in any two of the large number of
equilibria that obey this linear free-energy relationship.   If the equilibrium constants for the unsubstituted compounds are denoted by K_0
and K_0', then

$$\log K_0 = \rho \log K_0' + C \qquad (2\text{-}22)$$

Equation (2-22) may be subtracted from the equation (2-21) for the

[34] This entropy relationship, however, is not required by the Hammett equation
and is not found for all reactions that obey the equation (see Sec. 13-5c).   The equation merely requires that ΔS changes be proportional to ΔH changes.

same pair of equilibria to give

$$\log \frac{K}{K_0} = \rho \log \frac{K'}{K'_0} \qquad (2\text{-}23)$$

From this equation, applicable to any two of the equilibria, it may be seen that any equilibrium may be selected as a standard with which to compare all of the rest. Because of the large number of accurate data available, the ionization of benzoic acids in aqueous solution at 25° has been chosen as this standard equilibrium, and a new constant σ characteristic of a given substituent has been defined as $\log K'/K'_0$, where K' is the ionization constant of the substituted benzoic acid itself under the conditions specified. This definition reduces Eq. (2-23) to

$$\log \frac{K}{K_0} = \rho\sigma \qquad (2\text{-}24)$$

where σ (as stated, the substituent constant) is reasonably interpreted as being a measure of the ability of the substituent to change the electron density at the reaction center, and ρ, the reaction constant, is a measure of the sensitivity of the equilibrium in question to a change in electron density. From Eq. (2-24) and the definition of σ it may be seen that ρ has been defined as unity for the standard reaction, ionization of benzoic acids. The value of σ may be obtained from its definition if the ionization constant of the appropriately substituted benzoic acid has been determined in water at 25°. In the case of any reaction for which data on a reasonable number of meta- and para-substituted phenyl derivatives are available, ρ is simply the slope of the best line through the values of $\log K$ plotted against σ. If data are available for this reaction for any substituent whose σ is unknown from ionization constants, the value may be obtained from Eq. (2-24). One of the most striking facts about the generality of the Hammett equation is that it correlates the *rates* of reactions involving meta- and para-substituted phenyl compounds in an entirely analogous manner, rate constants being used in place of the equilibrium constants of Eq. (2-24). This fact has made possible the use of the Hammett equation in studying reaction mechanisms and the effect of structure on reactivity, a use we shall describe repeatedly.

Jaffé[35] has compiled and recalculated a large number of data on the Hammett equation published since Hammett's[33] most recent compilation. Some representative substituent constants are listed in Table 2-4. From the definition of ρ and σ it may be seen that groups with negative substituent constants are electron-donating groups, while those with positive substituent constants are electron-withdrawing. Further confirmation of the interpretation of substituent constants as measures of the effect

[35] H. H. Jaffé, *Chem. Rev.*, **53**, 191 (1953).

TABLE 2-4. SUBSTITUENT CONSTANTS[a]

Substituent	σ	Substituent	σ
p-O⊖[b]	−1.00[d]	m-I	+0.352[c]
m-O⊖[b]	−0.71	m-CO₂H	+0.355
p-NH₂	−0.660	m-Cl	+0.373[c]
p-(CH₃)₂N	−0.600	m-Br	+0.391[c]
p-OH	−0.357	m-CO₂Et	+0.398
p-CH₃O	−0.268[c]	m-CF₃	+0.415[c]
m-(CH₃)₂N[d]	−0.211	p-B(OH)₂	+0.454
p-(CH₃)₃C	−0.197[c]	p-C₆H₅CO[e]	+0.459
p-CH₃	−0.170[c]	p-CH₃CO[e]	+0.516
m-NH₂	−0.161	p-CO₂Et	+0.522
p-C₂H₅	−0.151[c]	p-CF₃[e]	+0.551
p-(CH₃)₂CH	−0.151[c]	m-CH₃SO	+0.551
m-(CH₃)₃Si	−0.121	p-CH₃SO[e]	+0.567
m-(CH₃)₃C	−0.120	p-CN[e]	+0.628
p-(CH₃)₃Si	−0.072	m-CH₃SO₂	+0.647[c]
m-CH₃	−0.069[c]	m-CN	+0.678
p-CH₃S	−0.047	m-IO₂	+0.700[c]
p-C₆H₅O	−0.028	m-NO₂	+0.710[e]
p-NHCOCH₃	−0.015	p-CH₃SO₂[e]	+0.728
m-OH	−0.002	p-IO₂[e]	+0.760[c]
None	0.0000[c]	p-NO₂[e]	+0.778[c]
p-C₆H₅	+0.009	p-(CH₃)₃N⊕[b]	+0.86
p-F	+0.062[c]	m-(CH₃)₃N⊕[b]	+0.90
m-CO₂⊖[b]	+0.10	For anilines, phenols, and thiophenols:	
p-I	+0.276[c]	p-CH=CHC₆H₅	+0.62
m-CH₃O	+0.115[c]	p-CO₂Et	+0.68
p-CO₂⊖[b]	+0.13	p-CO₂H	+0.73
m-CH₃S	+0.144	p-CF₃[f]	+0.74
m-C₆H₅	+0.218	p-CH₃CO	+0.87
p-Cl	+0.226[c]	p-CN	+1.00
p-Br	+0.232[c]	p-CH₃SO₂	+1.05
m-CH₃CO	+0.306	p-NO₂	+1.27
m-F	+0.337[c]		

Substituent Constants for Fused-ring Substituents

Substituent	Radical[g]	σ	Substituent	Radical[g]	σ
3,4-(CH₂)₄	5-Indanyl	−0.477	3,4-(CH)₄	β-Naphthyl	+0.17
3,4-(CH₂)₃	6-Tetralyl	−0.259	3,4-(CH)₃N	6-Quinolyl	+0.23[c]
3,4-CH₂O₂	3,4-Methylenedioxyphenyl	−0.159	3,4-N(CH)₃	7-Quinolyl	+0.24[c]
			3-aza-4,5-(CH)₄	3-Quinolyl	+0.52[c]

[a] Substituent constants are from the compilation by Jaffé[35], except as noted. Those based on the ionization constant of a benzoic acid are also noted.

[b] Although the Hammett equation does not fit electrically charged groups very well, this value is probably within 0.3 of a satisfactory one.

[c] Based on the ionization constant of a substituted benzoic acid.

[d] E. Berliner and L. C. Monack, J. Am. Chem. Soc., 74, 1574 (1952).

[e] This value is not to be used on anilines, phenols, or thiophenols.

[f] J. D. Roberts, R. A. Clement, and J. J. Drysdale, J. Am. Chem. Soc., 73, 2181 (1951).

[g] Formed by attachment of substituent to phenyl group.

of groups on electron density is found in the correlation of σ constants with the electron density on the halogen atom of fluorobenzene and chlorobenzene derivatives as determined by studies of the nuclear-magnetic and nuclear-quadripole-resonance spectra.[36] It is useful to divide the causes of these electronic effects into two categories, tautomeric, or resonance, effects and inductive effects. As stated in Sec. 2-4d, inductive effects can be discussed in terms of resonance, but are more conveniently discussed separately. Resonance in the acidic (or basic) functional group has already been discussed but not that in substituents. The resonance, or tautomeric, effect is called the T effect by British workers. Groups such as —NR$_2$, —OR, and to a lesser extent halogen and alkyl groups, which tend to donate electrons when attached to an unsaturated system, are said to have a $+T$ effect while those like —NO$_2$, —CO$_2$H, —COR, —CN, —SO$_2$R, etc., which tend to withdraw electrons, have a $-T$ effect.[37] Groups withdrawing electrons inductively have a $-I$ effect, while those which donate electrons have a $+I$ effect.[38] The substituent constants in Table 2-4 have many features that might be predicted from a combination of two such effects. For example, it is seen that in the meta position the methoxy and methylmercapto groups and all of the halogens have positive σ constants, since in the meta position only the inductive effect operates well. Since all of these groups have the power to feed electrons to the para position by a resonance effect,

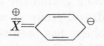

the σ constants in this position would be expected to contain a negative component due to this resonance. It is accordingly found that the

[36] H. S. Gutowsky, D. W. McCall, B. R. McGarvey, and L. H. Meyer, *J. Am. Chem. Soc.*, **74**, 4809 (1952); H. C. Meal, *J. Am. Chem. Soc.*, **74**, 6121 (1952); P. J. Bray, *J. Chem. Phys.*, **22**, 1787 (1954); P. J. Bray and R. G. Barnes, *J. Chem. Phys.*, **22**, 2023 (1954).

[37] The T effect is further subdivided into the mesomeric, or M, effect, which is the T effect in normal molecules, and the electromeric, or E, effect, which is the change in the T effect that takes place during a reaction. The usage of plus and minus signs given here in connection with I, T, M, and E effects is that of Ingold and coworkers; an opposite convention has been used by others. For a much more complete discussion of these effects see C. K. Ingold, "Structure and Mechanism in Organic Chemistry," sec. 7, Cornell University Press, Ithaca, N.Y., 1953, or A. E. Remick, "Electronic Interpretations of Organic Chemistry," 2d ed., chap. V, John Wiley & Sons, Inc., New York, 1949.

[38] This inductive effect in the normal molecule is sometimes called the I_s effect to distinguish it from the inductomeric, or polarizability, effect (I_d) occurring during a reaction.

groups mentioned have σ's from 0.076 to 0.383 units more negative in the para position than in the meta. The change found is greatest for the first-row elements oxygen and fluorine because of their greater ease of double-bond formation. It is also seen that σ for p-amino is much more negative than that for m-amino. It is somewhat surprising that m-amino has a negative σ, but this may be due to the ortho and para positions' being made so electron-rich by the powerful amino group that they in turn increase the meta electron density by an inductive effect. A hypothesis of this sort might also be used to explain the fact that the σ's of the meta halogens do not increase with electronegativity (although the differences are within the probable errors). Similarly, —COR, —CO$_2$R, —SOCH$_3$, —CH=CHCO$_2$H, —CN, —SO$_2$CH$_3$, and —NO$_2$, groups capable of tautomeric electron withdrawal, have σ's more positive in the para than in the meta position. The small negative σ for m-CH$_3$ and the larger one for p-CH$_3$ suggests that the methyl group supplies electrons to all positions by an inductive effect and donates still more to the ortho and para positions by hyperconjugation.

A given σ constant may be used for a wide range of reactions, showing that the extent to which a group supplies or withdraws electrons is independent of the nature of the reaction, over this range. However, if the group at the reaction center interacts too strongly with the substituent, then a reaction requiring a large change in this interaction will not follow the unmodified Hammett equation. This occurs most often when a group capable of strong tautomeric electron withdrawal is conjugated with a phenolic hydroxyl group or with the amino group of an aniline derivative. The problem has been solved by use of two σ constants for such electron-withdrawing substituents, one for reactions involving amines and phenolate anions and a smaller one for all other cases. Gilman and Dunn have pointed out that a larger substituent constant than that used in other cases should be used for the p-dimethylamino group in reactions of strongly tautomeric electron-withdrawing groups conjugated with the substituent.[39] For cases of the latter type the value they suggest (-0.41) gives better results than the value listed in the table for either the p-dimethylamino or p-amino group. Similar considerations apply, to a smaller extent, to the hydroxyl and alkoxyl groups. Groups such as p-C$_6$H$_5$, capable of both tautomeric electron withdrawal and supply, give deviations in the expected direction depending on whether they are conjugated with an electron-donating or -withdrawing group. Agreement with the Hammett equation must also be somewhat dependent upon solvent changes, since, among other things, these may alter the extent of hydrogen bonding and hence the actual

[39] H. Gilman and G. E. Dunn, *J. Am. Chem. Soc.*, **73**, 3404 (1951); cf. D. E. Pearson, J. F. Baxter, and J. C. Martin, *J. Org. Chem.*, **17**, 1511 (1952).

nature of hydroxyl, amino, and other groups. Changes in the reaction media so affect electrically charged substituents—both by changing the extent of their solvation and by changing the dielectric constant of part of the space through which their interaction with the reaction center occurs—that the Hammett equation holds only rather poorly for substituents of this type. Solvation effects on hyperconjugation have also been reported.[40] Other deviations relating more to reaction-rate data are discussed in the review by Jaffé[35] and in a number of the references there cited.

2-4f. *Discussion of Acidity and Basicity in Terms of the Hammett Equation.* The effect of meta and para substituents in the benzene ring on the strength of aromatic acids and bases is conveniently discussed in terms of the reaction constants listed in Table 2-5.

TABLE 2-5. REACTION CONSTANTS FOR ACID-BASE EQUILIBRIA[a]

No.	Acidity Constants of	$-\log K_0{}^b$	ρ
1	Benzoic acids in water at 25°	4.203	+1.000
2	Benzoic acids in methanol at 25°	6.514	+1.537
3	Benzoic acids in ethanol at 25°	7.206	+1.957
4	Phenylacetic acids in water at 25°	4.297	+0.489
5	β-Phenylpropionic acids in water at 25°	4.551	+0.212
6	Cinnamic acids in water at 25°	4.447	+0.466
7	p-Phenylbenzoic acids in 50% butyl cellosolve at 25°	5.636	+0.482
8	Phenylboronic acids in 25% ethanol at 25°	9.700	+2.164
9	Benzeneselenic acids in water at 25°	4.740	+0.905
10	Phenols in 95% ethanol at 20-22°	12.572	+2.364
11	Thiophenols in 95% ethanol at 20-22°	9.211	+2.847
12	Anilinium ions in water at 25°	4.557	+2.767

[a] From H. H. Jaffé, *Chem. Rev.*, **53**, 191 (1953).

[b] These are the values of $\log K_0$ that give an equation $\log K = \log K_0 + \rho\sigma$ best fitting the experimental data (the one for which the sum of the squares of the deviations is a minimum). In some cases the K's are not true thermodynamic equilibrium constants but are "apparent" equilibrium constants.

From reactions 1 through 7, it may be seen that increasing the number of atoms between the carboxyl group and the substituent decreases the effect of the substituent on the acidity. From reactions 1, 4, and 5 it is seen that successive methylene groups cause a decrease of 2.04, (1.00/0.489)-fold, and 2.31, (0.489/0.212)-fold, factors not too far from the 2.8 used in the empirical equation of Branch and Calvin[31] (Sec. 2-4d). The effect of a substituent is conducted much better through a vinyl (reaction 6) or a phenyl group (reaction 7) than through a saturated

[40] H. Kloosterziel and H. J. Backer, *J. Am. Chem. Soc.*, **74**, 5806 (1952); W. A Sweeney and W. M. Schubert, *J. Am. Chem. Soc.*, **76**, 4625 (1954).

chain with the same number of carbon atoms. The acidity of phenols, thiophenols, and anilinium ions is much more sensitive to substituents than that of carboxylic acids, at least partially because the acidic hydrogen atom is nearer the substituents.

It should be noted that the Hammett equation does not apply to ortho substituents or to aliphatic derivatives. In Fig. 2-3 the logarithms of

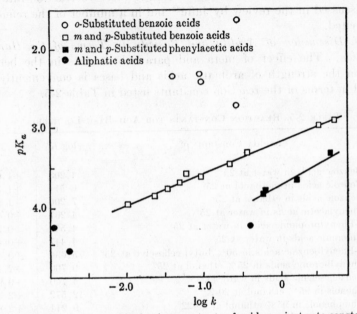

FIG. 2-3. Plot of logarithms of ionization constants of acids against rate constants for alkaline hydrolysis of their ethyl esters.

the ionization constants of a number of acids are plotted against logarithms of the rate constants for alkaline hydrolysis of their ethyl esters in 87.83 per cent ethanol.[41] The points for meta- and para-substituted benzoic acids describe a straight line, while those for meta- and para-substituted phenylacetic acids approximate a quite different line, and ortho-substituted derivatives and aliphatic compounds do not necessarily lie on either line. This lack of a simple free-energy relationship is quite often found for ortho-substituted and aliphatic compounds. Somewhat less simple quantitative correlations of reaction rates and equilibria will be described in Secs. 6-1, 8-1c, and 12-3c.

[41] Ionization constants from J. F. J. Dippy, *Chem. Rev.*, **25**, 151 (1939); rate constants from K. Kindler, *Ann.* **450**, 1 (1926); **452**, 90 (1927); **464**, 278 (1928); *Ber.*, **69B**, 2792 (1936); and by a short extrapolation from data in 85 per cent ethanol by D. P. Evans, J. J. Gordon, and H. B. Watson, *J. Chem. Soc.*, 1439 (1938).

2-4g. Steric Effects on Acidity and Basicity. Steric effects on acidity and basicity have received considerable attention both in regard to their effect on the action of resonance and in their own right. A particularly striking case of the former is illustrated by the basicity of benzoquinuclidine.

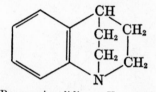

Benzoquinuclidine, $pK = 6.21$

Wepster has shown that this compound is a much stronger base than ordinary dialkylaniline derivatives (dimethylaniline, pK 8.94; diethylaniline, pK 7.44; N-phenylpiperidine, pK 8.80).[42] This basicity is not due to the bicyclic ring system in itself, since quinuclidine (pK 3.35) is a weaker base than piperidine (pK 2.87). It seems likely that one important contributing factor is steric inhibition of resonance. The bicyclic ring system greatly decreases the contributions of structures of the type

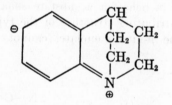

because the two atoms attached directly to the nitrogen atom cannot lie in the plane of the ring. Since less resonance of this type exists, less can be lost upon formation of the conjugate acid. The fact that benzoquinuclidine is still a much weaker base than quinuclidine is probably due to the increased electronegativity of the aromatic carbon atoms, although small contributions of resonance structures of the type shown above may still be important. Wheland has pointed out one case in which this electronegativity rather than resonance must be important.[43] Triphenylboron is a much stronger Lewis acid toward ammonia than is trimethylboron, although triphenylboron gains no resonance in forming the addition compound.

An example of a more common type of steric inhibition of resonance

[42] B. M. Wepster, *Rec. trav. chim.*, **71**, 1171 (1952).
[43] G. W. Wheland, "The Theory of Resonance," p. 176, John Wiley & Sons, Inc., New York, 1944.

has been described by Wheland, Brownell, and Mayo.[44] These workers found that although 3,5 dimethylation decreases the acidity of phenol by 0.19 and that of *p*-cyanophenol by 0.26 *pK* units, the effect on *p*-nitrophenol is a decrease of 1.09 *pK* units.

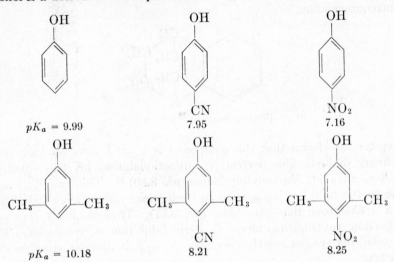

$$pK_a = 9.99 \qquad 7.95 \qquad 7.16$$

$$pK_a = 10.18 \qquad 8.21 \qquad 8.25$$

This large difference in behavior is most reasonably explained by the suggestion that a contributing structure of the type of IX, which does much to stabilize the *p*-nitrophenolate, cannot contribute nearly so

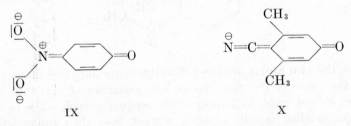

much to the total structure of the 3,5-dimethyl-4-nitrophenolate anion, since the oxygen atoms of the nitro group are hindered from lying in the plane of the aromatic ring. The cyano group being linear, there is no analogous inhibition of the contribution of structure X. Similar reasoning explains why *N,N* dimethylation increases the basicity of 2,4,6-trinitroaniline by 40,000-fold,[45] while it merely triples the basicity of aniline.

Other types of steric effects on acidity and basicity have been extensively investigated by Brown and coworkers. As expected from the

[44] G. W. Wheland, R. M. Brownell, and E. C. Mayo, *J. Am. Chem. Soc.*, **70**, 2492 (1948).

[45] L. P. Hammett and M. A. Paul, *J. Am. Chem. Soc.*, **56**, 827 (1934).

electron-donating ability of alkyl groups, methylamine is a considerably stronger base than ammonia. Dimethylamine, however, is only slightly stronger than methylamine, and trimethylamine is actually considerably weaker. Brown, Bartholomay, and Taylor have suggested the following explanation of these data.[46] Trigonal nitrogen might be expected to form bonds by use of its p orbitals (Sec. 1-2) and therefore to have 90° valence angles. Actually, however, the three groups attached to nitrogen usually appear to repel each other and to produce somewhat larger angles. It is postulated that in trimethylamine these angles have become larger than tetrahedral. When the amine has accepted a proton to yield the tetragonal ammonium ion, the shift toward a tetrahedral bond angle produces strain by compressing the groups on the "back" of the molecule (away from the added proton) against the action of their repulsive forces. This "back strain" is called B strain and is distinguished from "front," or F, strain, which will be discussed later. Bell and coworkers have suggested that the diminished basicity of tertiary amines in aqueous solution might be due to diminished solvation of their conjugate acids because of the decreased number of hydrogen atoms available for hydrogen bonding to water.[47] In agreement with this suggestion they find

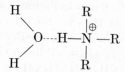

tri-n-butylamine to be a stronger base than mono- or di-n-butylamine in chlorobenzene solution.[47b] The solvation hypothesis also appears to offer a better explanation than the B-strain concept for the fact that piperidine is a stronger base than quinuclidine.[47c] Spitzer and Pitzer have stated that B strain could not produce an effect of the magnitude claimed.[48] The extrapolation of the B-strain hypothesis to a consideration of the relative basicities of water, alcohols, and ethers does not require the unproved postulate of bond angles greater than 109°28′, because in this case the conjugate acids, oxonium ions, are trigonal.[49] Thus, since an ether is already more strained than an alcohol, the addition

[46] H. C. Brown, H. Bartholomay, Jr., and M. D. Taylor, *J. Am. Chem. Soc.*, **66**, 435 (1944).

[47] (a) R. P. Bell and A. F. Trotman-Dickenson, *J. Chem. Soc.*, 1288 (1949); A. F. Trotman-Dickenson, *J. Chem. Soc.*, 1293 (1949); (b) R. P. Bell and J. W. Bayles, *J. Chem. Soc.*, 1518 (1952); (c) R. G. Pearson and F. V. Williams, *J. Am. Chem. Soc.*, **76**, 258 (1954).

[48] R. Spitzer and K. S. Pitzer, *J. Am. Chem. Soc.*, **70**, 1261 (1948). For the reply of H. C. Brown and E. A. Fletcher see Abstracts of Papers, ACS meeting, Mar. 23–27, 1952, Buffalo, N.Y., p. 10N.

[49] J. Hine and M. Hine, *J. Am. Chem. Soc.*, **74**, 5266 (1952).

of a proton produces even more added strain, and ethers appear to be weaker bases than alcohols. Dioxane, where the valence angles are held down to about 109° by the six-membered ring, is a considerably stronger base than an open-chain ether like di-n-butyl ether.[50] Water has been shown to be a considerably stronger base than methanol or ethanol.[51] This same effect would tend to make alkoxide ions weaker bases than hydroxide ions, i.e., to make alcohols stronger acids than water, and indeed methanol has been shown to be a stronger acid than water in isopropyl alcohol solution.[49] With ordinary unsubstituted primary alcohols, however, and to an increasing extent with secondary and tertiary alcohols, the inductive effect cannot be overruled by B strain, and these compounds are weaker acids than water. The introduction of electron-withdrawing groups, as expected, may increase the acidity of alcohols greatly, the acidity of trifluoroethanol being easily measurable in aqueous solution.[52] Hydrogen bonding also is probably important with these oxygen acids and bases.

Brown and coworkers have accumulated a large amount of excellent evidence that basicity toward reasonably bulky Lewis acids is greatly affected by steric hindrance. For example, the relative stability of addition compounds with trimethylboron varies as follows: $NH_3 < CH_3NH_2 < (CH_3)_2NH > (CH_3)_3N$, the steric effect becoming predominant only when the amine is trimethylated.[46] With tri-t-butylboron, however, the stability of the addition compounds with the ethylamines varies as follows: $NH_3 > C_2H_5NH_2 > (C_2H_5)_2NH > (C_2H_5)_3N$, showing that the steric factor is controlling in all cases.[53] One of the largest F-strain effects that has been observed occurs in the case of 2,6-di-t-butylpyridine, which utterly fails to coordinate with the usually powerful Lewis acid boron trifluoride and even shows diminished basicity toward the hydrogen ion.[54]

[50] H. Lemaire and H. J. Lucas, *J. Am. Chem. Soc.*, **73**, 5198 (1951).

[51] H. Goldschmidt et al., *Z. physik. Chem.*, **60**, 728 (1907); **81**, 30 (1912); **89**, 129 (1914); **108**, 121 (1924); I. I. Bezman and F. H. Verhoek, *J. Am. Chem. Soc.*, **67**, 1330 (1945); E. A. Braude and E. S. Stern, *J. Chem. Soc.*, 1976 (1948).

[52] E. T. McBee, W. F. Marzluff, and O. R. Pierce [*J. Am. Chem. Soc.*, **74**, 444 (1952)] report a pK_a of 12.3, while A. L. Henne and R. L. Pelley [*J. Am. Chem. Soc.*, **74**, 1426 (1952)] obtained a value of 11.4.

[53] H. C. Brown, *J. Am. Chem. Soc.*, **67**, 1452 (1945).

[54] H. C. Brown and B. Kanner, *J. Am. Chem. Soc.*, **75**, 3865 (1953).

CHAPTER 3

KINETICS[1]

3-1. Kinetics of Consecutive Reactions. *3-1a. The Steady-state Treatment.* The *steady-state treatment*, sometimes called the *method of the reactive intermediate*, is a very useful approximation that greatly simplifies the kinetic equations for a number of types of consecutive and reversible reactions. The method involves the assumption that a given intermediate(s) is so reactive that it is consumed almost as soon as it is formed. When the intermediate is sufficiently reactive, its concentration is always negligible in comparison to the changes in concentrations of reactants and products during the reaction. This means, of course, that the rate of formation of the intermediate is essentially equal to its rate of reaction, or that its net rate of formation is zero. If the intermediate is reactive enough, the approximation is quite precise.

We shall illustrate the principle by applying it to the reaction scheme

$$A + B \underset{k_{-1}}{\overset{k_1}{\rightleftharpoons}} C + D$$
$$C + E \overset{k_2}{\to} F$$

where C is the reactive intermediate. By the rate of reaction we mean the rate of formation of F. Since F is formed only in the second step

$$\frac{dF}{dt} = k_2 CE \qquad (3\text{-}1)$$

---

[1] In this chapter it is assumed that the reader has a knowledge of the fundamentals of kinetics as presented in most elementary textbooks of physical chemistry. See (a) L. P. Hammett, "Introduction to the Study of Physical Chemistry," chap. IX, McGraw-Hill Book Company, Inc., New York, 1952; (b) F. Daniels, "Outlines of Physical Chemistry," chap. XIV, John Wiley & Sons, Inc., New York, 1948. More detailed treatments may be found in (c) K. J. Laidler, "Chemical Kinetics," McGraw-Hill Book Company, Inc., New York, 1950; (d) A. A. Frost and R. G. Pearson, "Kinetics and Mechanism," John Wiley & Sons, Inc., New York, 1953; (e) S. Glasstone, K. J. Laidler, and H. Eyring, "The Theory of Rate Processes," McGraw-Hill Book Company, Inc., New York, 1941.

81

According to the steady-state approximation for C

$$k_1AB = k_{-1}CD + k_2CE$$

therefore
$$C = \frac{k_1AB}{k_{-1}D + k_2E} \qquad (3\text{-}2)$$

Substituting into Eq. (3-1),

$$\frac{dF}{dt} = \frac{k_1k_2ABE}{k_{-1}D + k_2E}$$

In a given case it may be that $k_{-1}D \gg k_2E$. If so,

$$\frac{dF}{dt} = \frac{k_1k_2}{k_{-1}} \frac{ABE}{D}$$

If $k_2E \gg k_{-1}D$, then

$$\frac{dF}{dt} = k_1AB$$

Reaction schemes of this general type are quite common and important in organic chemistry.

3-1b. *The Christiansen Method.* For many rather complicated reaction schemes the steady-state treatment is somewhat cumbersome. A fairly general treatment of systems involving the reversible formation of unstable intermediates has been devised by Christiansen.[2] If in the system

$$A + B \underset{k_{-1}}{\overset{k_1}{\rightleftharpoons}} X_1 + C$$

$$X_1 + D \underset{k_{-2}}{\overset{k_2}{\rightleftharpoons}} X_2 + E$$

$$\cdots \cdots \cdots \cdots \cdots$$

$$X_{n-1} + L \underset{k_{-n}}{\overset{k_n}{\rightleftharpoons}} M + N$$

$X_1, X_2, \ldots, X_{n-1}$ are the unstable intermediates, we may define a series of quantities w as the rate of a given step divided by the concentration of any reacting unstable intermediate. That is, letting v's represent the velocities of the various steps,

$$w_1 = v_1 = k_1[A][B]$$

$$w_{-1} = \frac{v_{-1}}{[X_1]} = k_{-1}[C]$$

$$w_2 = \frac{v_2}{[X_1]} = k_2[D]$$

$$w_{-2} = \frac{v_{-2}}{[X_2]} = k_{-2}[E] \qquad \text{etc.}$$

---

[2] J. A. Christiansen, *Z. physik. Chem.*, **33B**, 145 (1936); **37B**, 374 (1937); L. P. Hammett, "Physical Organic Chemistry," p. 107, McGraw-Hill Book Company, Inc., New York, 1940.

Since the concentration(s) of material present as reactive intermediate(s) is negligible compared to [A], [B], [M], and [N], the over-all rate of reaction is equal to the rate of any step. Thus

$$v = w_1 - w_{-1}[X_1] = w_2[X_1] - w_{-2}[X_2] = w_3[X_2] - w_{-3}[X_3] = \text{etc.}$$

This set of n simultaneous equations with unknowns $[X_1]$, $[X_2]$, . . . , $[X_{n-1}]$, and v may be solved for v, the over-all reaction velocity, and the answer expressed as the difference between the forward (v_+) and reverse (v_-) rates.

$$v = v_+ - v_-$$

with
$$\frac{1}{v_+} = \frac{1}{w_1} + \frac{w_{-1}}{w_1 w_2} + \frac{w_{-1}w_{-2}}{w_1 w_2 w_3} + \cdots \frac{w_{-1}w_{-2} \cdots w_{-(n-1)}}{w_1 w_2 w_3 \cdots w_n} \quad (3\text{-}3)$$

and
$$\frac{1}{v_-} = \frac{1}{w_{-n}} + \frac{w_n}{w_{-n}w_{-(n-1)}} + \cdots \frac{w_n w_{n-1} \cdots w_2}{w_{-n}w_{-(n-1)} \cdots w_{-1}} \quad (3\text{-}4)$$

3-2. Effect of Reaction Medium on Rate. *3-2a. Effect of Solvents on Reaction Rates.* While a number of equations have been proposed for the quantitative correlation of the rates of reactions with the nature of the solvent, none appears to have anywhere near complete generality.[3] We shall therefore content ourselves here with describing the useful, though still not entirely general, qualitative theory of solvent effects of Hughes and Ingold.[4] According to this theory *an increase in the ion-solvating power of the medium will accelerate the creation and concentration of charges and inhibit their destruction and diffusion.* Thus the reaction of two like-charged ions involves the concentration of two (or more) charges onto one molecule, the transition state. Therefore the rate of this reaction, as well as that of an ionization reaction, will be increased by an increase in ion-solvating power. A reaction between oppositely charged ions or a reaction in which the charge is on one atom in the reactant but spread out over several in the transition state will go slower in a better ion-solvating solvent.

3-2b. Effect of Ionic Strength on Reaction Rates. While the rates of most polar reactions are influenced by the ionic strength of the reaction medium, reactions between ions are most strongly influenced. This is to be expected since activity coefficients of ions are more sensitive to the ionic strength than are those of most neutral molecules. An equation relating the ionic strength and the rate constant for a reaction between ions may be derived fairly readily from the Debye-Hückel equation and the transition-state theory. According to the latter, the rate constant k_0 in some standard solution is related to k, the rate constant in

---

[3] See Sec. 6-1 and also Laidler, *op. cit.*, chap. 5; Frost and Pearson, *op. cit.*, chap. 7; Glasstone, Laidler, and Eyring, *op. cit.*, chap. VIII.

[4] E. D. Hughes and C. K. Ingold, *J. Chem. Soc.*, 244 (1935).

another solution, by the equation

$$k = k_0 \frac{\gamma_A \gamma_B \cdots}{\gamma_\ddagger} \tag{3-5}$$

where $\gamma_A \gamma_B \cdots$ are the activity coefficients of the reactants and $\gamma_\ddagger$ that of the transition state, in the given solution, referred to the standard solution. According to the Debye-Hückel theory the activity coefficient of an ion in dilute solution, referred to the pure solvent, follows the equation

$$-\log \gamma = Z^2 \alpha \sqrt{\mu} \tag{3-6}$$

where Z is the charge on the ion, μ is the ionic strength, and α is a constant having the value 0.509 in dilute aqueous solution at 25°. The combination of Eqs. (3-5) and (3-6) gives[5]

$$\log k = \log k_0 - Z_A^2 \alpha \sqrt{\mu} - Z_B^2 \alpha \sqrt{\mu} + (Z_A + Z_B)^2 \alpha \sqrt{\mu}$$

or

$$\log \frac{k}{k_0} = 2 Z_A Z_B \alpha \sqrt{\mu} \tag{3-7}$$

Thus reactions between like-charged ions proceed more rapidly as the ionic strength increases, while those between oppositely charged ions proceed more slowly. These effects may be rationalized qualitatively in terms of the Hughes-Ingold theory of solvent action when it is realized that ions may be stabilized in a manner analogous to solvation by being surrounded by ions of opposite charge.

Equation (3-7) is applicable to what is known as a primary salt effect. Also of importance is the secondary salt effect. This pertains to the effect of salts on the rates of acid- and base-catalyzed reactions due to their effects on the ionization constants of the acids and bases involved. Since the ionization of an electrically neutral acid or base, e.g.,

$$HA \rightleftharpoons H^+ + A^-$$

consists of an equilibrium between ions and a neutral molecule, and since the activity coefficient of the neutral molecule is little affected by small changes in the ionic strength, the equilibrium will be shifted to the right by increasing ionic strength in dilute solution.

3-3. Effect of Structure on Reactivity. Most of our discussions of the effect of structure on reactivity will be in terms of the transition-state theory.[1] In such discussions the reactants are treated as being in equilibrium with the "activated complex," or "transition state," so that the rate at which molecules pass over a given energy barrier depends upon the free-energy change involved. For this reason it is necessary

[5] J. N. Brønsted, Z. physik. Chem., **102**, 169 (1922); **115**, 337 (1925); N. Bjerrum, Z. physik. Chem., **108**, 82 (1924); **118**, 251 (1925).

to have some idea about the properties of the activated complex. Stated in other words, *the effect of structure on reactivity in any reaction must be discussed in terms of the reaction mechanism.* The free energy and heat and entropy of activation are related to the potential-energy, kinetic-energy, and probability changes occurring in the same way as described for ordinary equilibria in Sec. 2-4a. That is, even for related compounds undergoing the same reaction by the same mechanism, we cannot say in general that the more reactive one (the one with the lower free energy of activation) necessarily requires a smaller increase in potential energy to pass through the transition state. Neither can we base such a statement on a smaller heat of activation. However, it is often useful to postulate increased reactivity or decreased heat of activation as being due to certain effects that would lower the potential-energy barrier to reaction, even though the increased reactivity or decreased heat of activation does not even prove that the operative cause is acting through a potential-energy change. Of course, in the special case where related compounds undergoing the same reaction by the same mechanism have the same entropy of activation it can be shown to be very likely that the observed changes in rate are due to potential-energy differences.[6] This is commonly, but not invariably, the case for meta- and para-substituted benzene derivatives. The fact that it does occur in a number of cases lends support to the belief that the σ constants of the Hammett equation are indeed measures of electron-donating and -withdrawing power. Reaction series that obey the Hammett equation but in which the entropy of activation varies significantly (e.g., see Sec. 13-5c) must be those in which the changes in the entropy of activation are proportional to the electron-donating or -withdrawing power of the substituents. There are several ways in which such a proportionality might reasonably be brought about.

[6] Hammett, "Physical Organic Chemistry," pp. 118–120.

CHAPTER 4

ORGANIC REACTION MECHANISMS

The mechanism of a reaction is simply the path the molecule(s) follows in going from reactant to product. The complete elucidation of a reaction mechanism might be expected to include a stereochemically complete description of the movements of every atom throughout the reaction and also a description of the stability, or energy content, of the system in every intermediate configuration, so that transition states, reactive intermediates, stable intermediates, etc., will be distinguishable. Such a description is probably an unattainable goal but one which may be approached as a limit.

We shall follow the common procedure of judging the correctness of a reaction mechanism, or indeed of any scientific theory, by the extent to which it correlates existing experimental data and predicts the results of new experiments. Of several mechanisms that are equal by this yardstick we shall prefer the simplest. The mechanism of a reaction is usually determined, then, by considering all of the mechanisms that may be devised in agreement with known data on reaction mechanisms in general and comparing their requirements to the experimental observations on the given reaction. A proposed mechanism in definite conflict with any experimental observation is ruled out. New experiments may then be carried out to distinguish between remaining possible mechanisms. If only one mechanism then remains it is often said to be the established reaction mechanism. A mechanism "proved" in this way may later be disproved by additional experimental evidence. We may then modify it or substitute for it a mechanism that had been more complicated than the previously existing experimental data demanded. We may not, in all cases, be sufficiently ingenious to devise a mechanism in agreement with all of the experimental evidence. The fact that we cannot guarantee that a given proved reaction mechanism will be in complete agreement with all future experiments does not in itself make the reaction mechanism less true than any other class of theories or laws of experimental science, since there are none for which we can make such a guarantee.[1]

[1] For a short discussion of scientific method and references to more complete treatments see E. B. Wilson, Jr., "An Introduction to Scientific Research," chap. 3, McGraw-Hill Book Company, Inc., New York, 1952.

In the study of organic reaction mechanisms it has been found that many diverse reactions proceed by a number of simple steps and that the number of different types of steps that occur is actually relatively small. In this connection it has been found very useful to divide organic reaction mechanisms into several classes.

4-1. Classes of Reaction Mechanisms. *4-1a. Polar Reactions.* Representatives of one type of organic reaction mechanism are called *polar, ionic,* or *electron-sharing reactions.* These reactions involve Lewis acids (electrophilic reagents), Lewis bases (nucleophilic reagents), and their addition compounds.[2] The driving force for these reactions is the affinity of electrophilic reagents for electron pairs and of nucleophilic reagents for nuclei with which to coordinate. Reactions of this class include:

1. Addition reactions between electrophilic and nucleophilic reagents (and their reversal), e.g.,

$$\underset{\underset{\overset{|}{\text{CH}_3}}{|}}{\overset{\overset{\text{CH}_3}{|}}{\text{CH}_3\text{—N}|}} + \underset{\underset{\overset{|}{\text{CH}_3}}{|}}{\overset{\overset{\text{CH}_3}{|}}{\text{B—CH}_3}} \rightleftharpoons \underset{\underset{\overset{|}{\text{CH}_3}}{|}}{\overset{\overset{\text{CH}_3}{\oplus|}}{\text{CH}_3\text{—N}}}\underset{\underset{\overset{|}{\text{CH}_3}}{|}}{\overset{\overset{\text{CH}_3}{|\ominus}}{\text{—B—CH}_3}}$$

2. Displacement reactions in which

   a. One nucleophilic reagent displaces another from its union with an electrophilic reagent, e.g.,

   $$(\text{CH}_3)_3\overset{\ominus}{\text{B}}\text{—}\overset{\oplus}{\text{N}}(\text{CH}_3)_3 + \text{NH}_3 \rightleftharpoons (\text{CH}_3)_3\overset{\ominus}{\text{B}}\text{—}\overset{\oplus}{\text{N}}\text{H}_3 + \text{N}(\text{CH}_3)_3$$

   b. One electrophilic reagent displaces another from its union with a nucleophilic reagent, e.g.,

   $$(\text{CH}_3)_3\overset{\oplus}{\text{N}}\text{—}\overset{\ominus}{\text{B}}(\text{CH}_3)_3 + \text{BF}_3 \rightleftharpoons (\text{CH}_3)_3\overset{\oplus}{\text{N}}\text{—}\overset{\ominus}{\text{B}}\text{F}_3 + \text{B}(\text{CH}_3)_3$$

We shall see that a reaction whose over-all result is a nucleophilic displacement (2a) may occur in one simple step or may consist of two steps, each of the type of 1. For example, reaction 2a may be written as proceeding by the mechanism

$$(\text{CH}_3)_3\overset{\ominus}{\text{B}}\text{—}\overset{\oplus}{\text{N}}(\text{CH}_3)_3 \rightleftharpoons (\text{CH}_3)_3\text{B} + \text{N}(\text{CH}_3)_3$$

$$(\text{CH}_3)_3\text{B} + \text{NH}_3 \rightleftharpoons (\text{CH}_3)_3\overset{\ominus}{\text{B}}\text{—}\overset{\oplus}{\text{N}}\text{H}_3$$

Polar reactions usually involve ions and, at the least, formal charges (see the examples above); in fact they are frequently called ionic reac-

[2] For definitions of these terms see Sec. 2-1b.

tions. Many examples involving ions may be given. The fluoride ion, a nucleophilic reagent, will combine with the electrophilic reagent boron trifluoride

$$\overset{\ominus}{F} + BF_3 \rightleftharpoons \overset{\ominus}{BF_4}$$

The hydroxide ion, a nucleophilic reagent, will displace the nucleophilic reagent ammonia from combination with the electrophilic reagent hydrogen ion (unknown in the uncombined state)

$$\overset{\ominus}{OH} + \overset{\oplus}{NH_4} \rightleftharpoons H_2O + NH_3$$

In fact, all acid-base reactions (in the Lowry-Brønsted sense) involve nucleophilic displacements on hydrogen (the displacement by one nucleophilic reagent of another from combination with the hydrogen ion). The ionization of perchloric acid in methanol solution involves a nucleophilic displacement on hydrogen of perchlorate ion by methanol.

$$CH_3OH + HClO_4 \rightleftharpoons \overset{\oplus}{CH_3OH_2} + \overset{\ominus}{ClO_4}$$

Of great importance in organic chemistry are nucleophilic displacements *on carbon* (Chap. 5); e.g.,

$$\overset{\ominus}{OH} + CH_3I \rightleftharpoons CH_3OH + \overset{\ominus}{I}$$

the displacement by hydroxide ion of iodide ion from its combination with the electrophilic reagent CH_3^+ (unknown in the uncombined state).

Many reactions may be written as combinations of several steps, each of which is a simple polar reaction.

In accordance with a suggestion of Swain and Scott,[3] we shall use the terms *nucleophilicity* and *electrophilicity* in connection with the *rate* of polar reactions, reserving the terms *acidity* and *basicity* for *equilibria*. For instance, the fact that the reaction

$$I^- + C_2H_5OSO_2C_6H_4CH_3\text{-}p \rightarrow C_2H_5I + p\text{-}CH_3C_6H_4SO_3^-$$

has a higher rate constant (in 61 per cent dioxane at 50°, at least) than the reaction[4]

$$OH^- + C_2H_5OSO_2C_6H_4CH_3\text{-}p \rightarrow C_2H_5OH + p\text{-}CH_3C_6H_4SO_3^-$$

will be denoted by the statement that iodide ion is more nucleophilic than hydroxide ion toward ethyl *p*-toluenesulfonate in 61 per cent dioxane

[3] C. G. Swain and C. B. Scott, *J. Am. Chem. Soc.*, **75**, 141 (1953).

[4] H. R. McCleary and L. P. Hammett, *J. Am. Chem. Soc.*, **63**, 2255 (1941).

at 50°. On the other hand, the fact that the equilibrium is further to the right in the latter reaction will be signified by stating that hydroxide ion is more basic than iodide ion toward ethyl p-toluenesulfonate in 61 per cent dioxane at 50°.

4-1*b*. *Free-radical Reactions.* *A free radical is a molecule or ion that contains one or more unpaired electrons,* and reactions in which electrons are paired or unpaired are called free-radical reactions. Included in this category are:

1. The formation of free radicals by the dissociation of a nonradical and the converse combination of two free radicals by the pairing of their unpaired electrons

$$(C_6H_5)_3C\!-\!C(C_6H_5)_3 \rightleftharpoons 2(C_6H_5)_3C\cdot$$

2. Radical-displacement reactions

$$CH_3\cdot + CCl_4 \rightarrow CH_3Cl + \cdot CCl_3$$

3. Radical additions and their reverse

$$R'\cdot + R_2C\!=\!CR_2 \rightleftharpoons R'\!-\!\overset{\displaystyle R}{\underset{\displaystyle R}{\overset{|}{\underset{|}{C}}}}\!-\!\overset{\displaystyle R}{\underset{\displaystyle R}{\overset{|}{\underset{|}{C}}}}\cdot$$

4-1*c*. *Other Types of Reaction Mechanisms.* While most organic reactions proceed by polar or free-radical mechanisms, there are two other types of mechanisms recognized. One is the *simple electron-transfer reaction*, e.g.,

$$Fe^{3+} + Cr^{++} \rightleftharpoons Fe^{++} + Cr^{3+}$$

This type of reaction is quite common in inorganic chemistry, but since it occurs more rarely with organic molecules, it will not be discussed in this book (in at least some cases it might be classed as a free-radical reaction).

Another category is the so-called *four-center-type reaction*, an inorganic example of which is the reaction of hydrogen iodide to form hydrogen and iodine and its reverse. It is believed that this reaction involves simply the approach of two molecules of hydrogen iodide to give a transition state that can be described as a molecule of hydrogen and one of iodine, followed by dissociation in one of the two possible ways.

$$\overset{\displaystyle H}{\underset{\displaystyle I}{\overset{|}{\underset{|}{}}}} + \overset{\displaystyle H}{\underset{\displaystyle I}{\overset{|}{\underset{|}{}}}} \rightleftharpoons \overset{\displaystyle H\cdots H}{\underset{\displaystyle I\cdots I}{\overset{\vdots}{\underset{\vdots}{}}}} \rightleftharpoons \overset{\displaystyle H\!-\!H}{\underset{\displaystyle I\!-\!I}{+}}$$

We shall define four-center-type reactions as those in which the atoms in the reactant(s) simply change their configuration to that of the product(s) without electron pairing or unpairing and without the formation or destruction of ions. There are four (or more) key atoms, each of which is simultaneously forming a new bond and breaking an old one in the transition state.

4-1*d*. *Characteristics of the Various Classes of Organic Reaction Mechanisms.* The extensive investigation of organic reaction mechanisms has made possible some useful generalizations about the various types of mechanisms.

Polar organic reactions, particularly those involving ions, rarely occur in the gas phase. They are very often catalyzed by acids and bases. They are usually not affected by light, traces of oxygen, or peroxides. They usually do not show induction periods or proceed by chain mechanisms. The rate of polar reactions is usually greatly affected by the ion-solvating ability of the reaction medium.

Free-radical reactions frequently occur in the gas phase, often show induction periods, and proceed by a chain mechanism. Many of these reactions are greatly affected by light, traces of oxygen, peroxides, and certain materials known as inhibitors. The reactions are rarely acid- or base-catalyzed, and their rate is not usually affected so greatly by the ion-solvating ability of the medium in which they proceed. Free-radical reactions are often brought about by much higher temperatures than those usually used for polar reactions.

Simple electron-transfer reactions always involve ions and therefore almost invariably take place in solution rather than in the vapor phase. The rate of four-center-type reactions is usually little affected by a change from the liquid to vapor phase.

It is not possible to draw a sharp boundary between the various classes of organic reaction mechanisms described. There are instead a few reactions whose mechanisms appear to be rather intermediate between two or more of the categories. In several cases it is possible to imagine, at least, a series of mechanisms with a gradual and continuous transition from one class to another.

PART II

POLAR REACTIONS

CHAPTER 5

MECHANISMS FOR NUCLEOPHILIC
DISPLACEMENTS ON CARBON

From a number of sources, including particularly a brilliant series of investigations by Hughes, Ingold, and coworkers, there is excellent evidence for the existence of two important mechanisms for nucleophilic substitution reactions at a saturated carbon atom. One, called the S_N2 (substitution, nucleophilic, bimolecular) mechanism,[1] consists of a one-step attack in which one nucleophilic reagent (X) displaces another (Y) from its attachment to a carbon atom. The attacking nucleophilic reagent combines with the carbon atom at the side opposite to that of the nucleophilic group being displaced, thus inverting its steric configuration, as shown in the following equation. No charges are written on X and Y since the mechanism may operate for reactants of a number of different charge types.

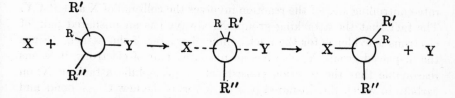

This has also been called the bimolecular-displacement mechanism, the Walden inversion mechanism, the direct, or one-step, mechanism, etc.

The other mechanism, termed S_N1 (substitution, nucleophilic, unimolecular),[1] consists of a preliminary cleavage to give a carbonium ion, which then reacts (usually quite rapidly) with a nucleophilic reagent.

$$R—Y \rightarrow R^+ + Y$$
$$R^+ + X \rightarrow R—X$$

This is also called the carbonium-ion, or two-step, mechanism.

[1] J. L. Gleave, E. D. Hughes, and C. K. Ingold, *J. Chem. Soc.*, 236 (1935).

It is seen that the S_N2 reaction would be first-order with respect to both [R₃CY] and [X], while the S_N1 reaction as written is first-order with respect to [RY] only. This is the principal difference between the two mechanisms. The rate of reaction of a compound by the S_N2 mechanism is directly proportional to the concentration of the entering nucleophilic reagent. The *true* rate of reaction of RY (this will be different from the *net* rate in those cases where R⁺ recombines with Y) by the S_N1 mechanism is independent of the concentration of the nucleophilic reagent X, which becomes attached to R in the product (although the extent to which R combines with X as compared to other nucleophilic reagents that are present may depend on the concentration of X). This is because the rate-controlling step precedes the product-controlling step in the S_N1 mechanism, while in the S_N2 mechanism the rate-controlling step *is* the product-controlling step. Unfortunately, the dependence of rate on the concentration of the nucleophilic reagent X is not always experimentally detectable. Thus in cases where X is present in considerable excess, e.g., as solvent, the reaction may be pseudounimolecular. For this reason it has not yet been possible to devise, for solvolysis reactions, experimentally applicable definitions of the S_N1 and S_N2 mechanisms that are entirely equivalent to those given above for nonsolvolytic nucleophilic displacements. This problem will be discussed in more detail in Sec. 5-2e.

5-1. The S_N2 Mechanism. The first-order dependence of reaction rate on both X and R₃CY concentrations supports the view that the rate-controlling step of the reaction involves the collision of X and R₃CY. The fact that the attacking group, X, always has an unshared pair of electrons is evidence for the nucleophilic character of the attack. Since the displaced group, Y, also has an unshared pair of electrons, it seems reasonable that the reaction consists of a nucleophilic attack of X on carbon, in which the unshared pair on X forms the new C—X bond and displaces Y with its electron pair. There are good theoretical as well as experimental reasons for believing that this attack occurs on the side of the carbon atom opposite to that to which the displaced group is attached.

5-1a. Racemization of Alkyl Halides by Halide Ions. Some of the best experimental evidence is based on the fact that in acetone solution optically active alkyl iodides are racemized by iodide ion, active alkyl bromides by bromide ion, etc. The rate of racemization is proportional to the concentration of the halide ion,[2] strongly suggesting that the racemization is due to inverting nucleophilic displacements of halogen from the alkyl halide by the halide ions in solution. It is certainly reasonable to expect nucleophilic substitutions to occur under these

[2] B. Holmberg, *J. prakt. Chem.*, [2], **88**, 553 (1913).

conditions, since reactions of the type

$$RBr + I^{\ominus} \xrightarrow{\text{acetone}} RI + Br^{\ominus}$$
$$RCl + I^{\ominus} \xrightarrow{\text{acetone}} RI + Cl^{\ominus}$$
$$RI + Br^{\ominus} \xrightarrow{\text{acetone}} RBr + I^{\ominus}$$

are well known.   In fact, reactions of the type

$$RI + I^{*\ominus} \rightarrow RI^{*} + I^{\ominus}$$
$$RBr + Br^{*\ominus} \rightarrow RBr^{*} + Br^{\ominus}$$

have definitely been shown to occur by the use of radioactive tracers. However, although it might be thus considered proved that inverting nucleophilic displacements are responsible for the observed racemization, it is still possible that only a very small percentage of the nucleophilic displacements occur with inversion, while most give retention of configuration.   Bergmann, Polanyi, and Szabo[3] have shown that this is not likely, since the rate constant for the racemization of sec-hexyl iodide by iodide ion in acetone solution is approximately equal to that predicted by extrapolation from the rates with the sec-hexyl fluoride, chloride, and bromide.

By studying simultaneously the rate of racemization of 2-octyl iodide by iodide ions in acetone solution and the rate of introduction of the iodide ions (which were labeled with radioactive iodine) into the organic iodide, Hughes and coworkers[4] were able to show that every replacement of organic iodide by an iodide ion produced inversion in the configuration of the compound.   To do so, it was necessary to assume that the radioactive iodide ions react at the same rate that ordinary iodide ions do. This is probably very nearly true in the present case, where the atomic weight of the radioactive iodine does not differ greatly from that of ordinary iodine, but it does not appear to be generally true in cases where there is a large percentage difference in the atomic weights of the two isotopes.   The differences in rates of reaction involving hydrogen and deuterium are frequently large, and those between C^{12} and C^{14} are large enough to detect.   The rate of inversion of 2-octyl iodide molecules may be determined by observing the rate of decrease of the optical rotation of the solution.   The rate of the nucleophilic substitution may be

[3] E. Bergmann, M. Polanyi, and A. L. Szabo, *Trans. Faraday Soc.*, **32**, 843 (1936).
[4] E. D. Hughes, F. Juliusberger, S. Masterman, B. Topley, and J. Weiss, *J. Chem. Soc.*, 1525 (1935).

calculated either by determining the rate of increase of radioactivity in the alkyl iodide or the rate of decrease in the radioactivity of the inorganic iodide used. This calculation is somewhat complicated by the fact that the rate of decay of the radioactive iodine used is comparable to the rate of reaction. The reaction of optically active α-phenylethyl bromide[5] and α-bromopropionic acid[6] with radioactive bromide ions was studied in an analogous manner. It was again found that the rate constants for inversion and for nucleophilic substitution by bromide ion differed by less than the experimental error. Data on the three reactions described are shown in Table 5-1.

TABLE 5-1. RATE CONSTANTS FOR SUBSTITUTION AND FOR INVERSION OF
ORGANIC HALIDES BY HALIDE IONS IN ACETONE SOLUTION

Compound	Temperature	$10^4 \times$ second-order rate constant for	
		Substitution	Inversion
2-Octyl iodide[4]................	30°	13.6 ± 1.1	13.1 ± 0.1
α-Phenylethyl bromide[5]........	30.2	8.72 ± 0.92	7.95 ± 0.12
α-Bromopropionic acid[6]........	22	5.15 ± 0.50	5.24 ± 0.05

5-1b. *Other Stereochemical Evidence for the Nature of the S_N2 Mechanism.* There is much more stereochemical evidence which points to this same conclusion—that the nucleophilic reagent attacks the carbon from the rear and inverts its configuration while displacing the nucleophilic group originally attached. The experiments with radioactive iodine put this conclusion on a somewhat firmer basis than the other data alone would, since, while we may be very nearly sure that d-2-octyl iodide has a configuration enantiomorphic to that of l-2-octyl iodide, we are somewhat less certain about the relationship between the configurations of the dextrorotatory isomer of 2-octyl bromide and the dextrorotatory isomer of 2-octyl alcohol (or any other 2-octyl derivative, except the levorotatory bromide). Nevertheless, the data that have been amassed by studying the transformation of RR'CHX compounds to RR'CHY derivatives are rather convincing in their own right, and when combined with the radioisotopic work, make it appear very likely that the mechanism accepted for these specific cases also applies in a very large number of other cases. From data of this type, in fact, Hughes and Ingold have

[5] E. D. Hughes, F. Juliusberger, A. D. Scott, B. Topley, and J. Weiss, *J. Chem. Soc.*, 1173 (1936).

[6] W. A. Cowdrey, E. D. Hughes, T. P. Nevell, and C. L. Wilson, *J. Chem. Soc.*, 209 (1938).

drawn the conclusion that "bimolecular substitutions (S_N2 . . .) are invariably accompanied by steric inversion."[7]

Among the experimental evidence of interest in this regard are the following: The series of reactions below accomplishes the transformation of d-benzylmethylcarbinol to its l isomer with very little racemization.[8]

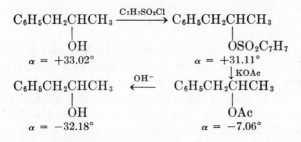

The over-all result, inversion, shows merely that during the process an odd number of inverting displacements occurred. However, since the result of the first step is the replacement of the alcoholic hydrogen atom by the p-toluenesulfonyl group ($C_7H_7SO_2$), it seems likely that none of the four valences of the asymmetric carbon atom are changed, and hence its configuration is unaffected. Similarly, it does not seem probable that any change in configuration would accompany the alkaline hydrolysis of the acetate, since (as will be shown in Sec. 12-1a) in the hydrolysis of ordinary esters the cleavage occurs between the oxygen and the *acyl* carbon atoms. Therefore it seems most likely that the inversion occurs during the replacement of the p-toluenesulfonate ion by the acetate ion, a simple example of a nucleophilic substitution reaction.

Similar results have been obtained with *sec*-butyl alcohol,[9a] ethyl lactate,[9b] lactamide,[9c] menthol,[9d] *sec*-octyl alcohol,[9d] *cis*- and *trans*-2-methylcyclohexanol,[9e] α-phenylethyl alcohol,[9f] and $C_6H_5CHOHCH_2$-CO_2H.[9g]

The effect of certain structural features on reactivity, e.g., the inertness of certain halides for which nucleophilic attack from the rear is impossible (see Sec. 6-3a), also constitutes evidence for the S_N2 mechanism.

5-1c. *Nature of the S_N2 Mechanism.* During an S_N2 displacement, the molecule passes through a state (I) in which carbon is pentavalent

[7] W. A. Cowdrey, E. D. Hughes, C. K. Ingold, S. Masterman, and A. D. Scott, *J. Chem. Soc.*, 1252 (1937).

[8] H. Phillips, *J. Chem. Soc.*, **123**, 44 (1923).

[9] (a) J. Kenyon, H. Phillips, and V. P. Pittman, *J. Chem. Soc.*, 1072 (1935); (b) J. Kenyon, H. Phillips, and H. G. Turley, *J. Chem. Soc.*, 399 (1925); (c) C. M. Bean, J. Kenyon, and H. Phillips, *J. Chem. Soc.*, 303 (1936); (d) H. Phillips, *J. Chem. Soc.*, 2552 (1925); (e) G. A. C. Gough, H. Hunter, and J. Kenyon, *J. Chem. Soc.*, 2052 (1926); (f) J. Kenyon, H. Phillips, and F. M. H. Taylor, *J. Chem. Soc.*, 173 (1933); (g) J. Kenyon, H. Phillips, and G. R. Shutt, *J. Chem. Soc.*, 1663 (1935).

and has the configuration of a triangular bipyramid.

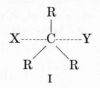

I

It seems reasonable that the partially broken and partially formed C—X and C—Y bonds should be the longer and weaker axial bonds. Gillespie has given arguments for the stability of carbon in this configuration,[10] which may be taken as arguments that a bimolecular nucleophilic attack would be expected to follow the path described, since the path taken will be that of the greatest stability.   The transition state for the S_N2 reaction is usually assumed to be represented by I, but there is no definite assurance that this is not a reactive intermediate preceding or following the transition state.

The *rearward* nature of the attack by the nucleophilic reagent is probably due to some such electronic effect as that described by Gillespie, since it does not appear to be due to an electrostatic cause.   This is shown by the observation of Snyder and Brewster that the nucleophilic attack of the acetate ion on the D-(+)-α-phenethyltrimethylammonium ion produced inversion of configuration.[11]

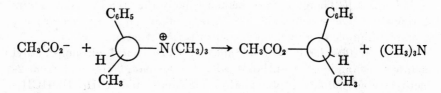

The attack of the bromide on the α-phenethyldimethylsulfonium ion has also been shown to produce inversion.[12]   If a coulombic effect had predominated, the anions would have been attracted by the positively charged nitrogen and sulfur atoms and attacked from the front side to give retention of configuration.

5-2. The S_N1 Mechanism.   *5-2a. Studies in Sulfur Dioxide Solution.* Bateman, Hughes, and Ingold have found that in liquid sulfur dioxide solution the initial rate of reaction of benzhydryl chloride is the same with each of the three different nucleophilic reagents: fluoride ion,

[10] R. J. Gillespie, *J. Chem. Soc.*, 1002 (1952); *J. Chem. Phys.*, **21**, 1893 (1953); cf. H. H. Jaffé, *J. Chem. Phys.*, **21**, 1893 (1953); M. J. S. Dewar, *J. Chem. Soc.*, 2885 (1953).

[11] H. R. Snyder and J. H. Brewster, *J. Am. Chem. Soc.*, **71**, 291 (1949).

[12] S. Siegel and A. F. Graefe, *J. Am. Chem. Soc.*, **75**, 4521 (1953).

pyridine, and triethylamine.[13] It was further shown that the reaction rate was not affected by changes in the concentration of the nucleophilic reagent (to any greater extent than might be attributed to the change in ionic strength). The most reasonable explanation for these data is that the rate is independent of the nature and concentration of the nucleophilic reagent because the rate-controlling step is the same in all of the reactions and does not involve the nucleophilic reagent. As shown below for reaction with fluoride, the benzhydryl chloride ionizes in the rate-controlling step, and the carbonium ion thus formed then rapidly combines with the fluoride ion.

$$RCl \rightarrow R^+ + Cl^-$$
$$R^+ + F^- \rightarrow RF$$

The independence of the nucleophilic reagent holds, of course, only for the initial stages of the reaction, because as the concentration of chloride ion increases, its ability to compete with the fluoride ion for combination with the carbonium ion (by reversal of the first step) becomes noticeable, and the kinetics become more complicated. The initial rate of reaction of m-chlorobenzhydryl chloride with fluoride ion was similarly found to be independent of the fluoride-ion concentration[14] and to proceed at the same rate as the reaction with iodide ion and with pyridine.[13] By supplying chloride ions to compete with the fluoride ions for the intermediate carbonium ions, the addition of tetramethylammonium chloride, it is found, slows the rate of transformation of the RCl to RF.[14] This effect is known as the *mass-law effect* and will be discussed in detail later. It has been suggested that, instead of involving carbonium ions, these reactions in sulfur dioxide solution all have as their rate-controlling step a nucleophilic attack by solvent[15] to give an intermediate that may then react rapidly with a nucleophilic reagent to give the final product.

$$RX + SO_2 \rightarrow R{-}OSO^+ + X$$
$$R{-}OSO^+ + Y \rightarrow RY + SO_2$$

This type of alternative to the S_N1 mechanism is discussed in more detail in the next section.

5-2b. *Solvolysis.* Solvolyses (nucleophilic substitution reactions in which the solvent is the nucleophilic reagent) have been responsible for much of the controversy that has occurred concerning the mechanism

---

[13] L. C. Bateman, E. D. Hughes, and C. K. Ingold, *J. Chem. Soc.*, 1011 (1940); cf. M. L. Bird, E. D. Hughes, and C. K. Ingold, *J. Chem. Soc.*, 634 (1954); C. A. Bunton, C. H. Greenstreet, E. D. Hughes, and C. K. Ingold, *J. Chem. Soc.*, 642, 647 (1954).

[14] L. C. Bateman, E. D. Hughes, and C. K. Ingold, *J. Chem. Soc.*, 1017 (1940).

[15] R. A. Ogg, Jr., *J. Am. Chem. Soc.*, **61**, 1946 (1939).

of nucleophilic displacements. Despite continued disagreement about the mechanisms of many solvolytic reactions, it will be necessary to devote considerable attention to reactions of this type since some of the most complete studies of the mechanism of nucleophilic substitution on carbon have involved solvolyses. In an investigation of this type Hughes, Ingold, and coworkers presented some of the first compelling evidence for the S_N1 mechanism when they studied certain deviations from purely first-order kinetics in solvolysis reactions.

The hydrolysis of t-butyl bromide in "90 per cent aqueous acetone" (90 per cent acetone by volume) is typical of that of a number of alkyl halides, since the hydrolysis of dilute solutions (less than 0.02 M) follows good first-order kinetics, while the kinetic study of the hydrolysis of more concentrated solutions, e.g., 0.1 M, shows that first-order rate "constants" increase as the reaction proceeds.[16] This result is attributed to the increase in ionic strength (from 0.00 to 0.10) resulting from the reaction and to the fact that a reaction of this type would be expected to have a positive ionic strength effect (see Sec. 3-2b). However, in the same solvent the rate "constants" for the hydrolysis of p,p'-dimethyl-benzhydryl chloride not only do not increase, they actually decrease (from 8.68×10^{-5} sec^{-1} at 8 per cent reaction to 6.7×10^{-5} sec^{-1} at 79.7 per cent reaction).[17] This fact is ascribed to the recombination of chloride ions with the carbonium ions by the reversal of the first step of the reaction. In the early part of the reaction no appreciable number of carbonium ions combine with chloride ion (step 2 in the scheme below), because the concentration of chloride ion is too small. However, later in the reaction this combination becomes important, and although the alkyl halide is ionizing even more rapidly than at the start (due to the increased ionic strength), so many of the carbonium ions are reverted to RCl that the rate of formation of ROH actually decreases. This effect is the result of the mass-law effect.

With regard to some of the quantitative aspects of the reaction of carbonium ions with nucleophilic reagents other than solvent, the investigation of the hydrolysis of p,p'-dimethylbenzhydryl chloride in 85 per cent aqueous acetone[17] is of interest. In this work, the effect of the addition of three types of salts was studied. (1) A "common-ion" salt, lithium chloride. This type would be expected to transform many carbonium ions back to RCl and thus slow the rate of disappearance of RCl and of formation of ROH. There would also be an ionic-strength effect working in the opposite direction. (2) Salts whose anions react with R$^+$ only to form compounds much more reactive than RCl. Two of these were used, lithium bromide and tetramethylammonium nitrate.

[16] L. C. Bateman, E. D. Hughes, and C. K. Ingold, *J. Chem. Soc.*, 960 (1940).
[17] *Ibid.*, 974 (1940).

It would be expected that, while the anions of these salts might combine with the carbonium ion, the products formed would be much more reactive than RCl and would rapidly re-form the carbonium ion. Hence the total effect would be much as if the salts did not react with the carbonium ion at all. The effect of adding these salts should be an ionic-strength effect. (3) A salt, sodium azide, whose anion may react with the carbonium ion to form a stable compound. On the rate of reaction of RCl this should have only an ionic-strength effect. However, any of the anion that reacted with carbonium ions would produce RN_3 rather than ROH as a final product of the reaction. Thus we arrive at the reaction scheme

$$RCl \underset{(2)}{\overset{(1)}{\rightleftharpoons}} R^+ + Cl^-$$

$$R^+ + H_2O \overset{(3)}{\rightarrow} ROH + H^+$$

$$R^+ + N_3^- \overset{(4)}{\rightarrow} RN_3$$

$$R^+ + Br^- \rightleftharpoons RBr$$

$$R^+ + NO_3^- \rightleftharpoons RNO_3$$

All of the salts were used in the same concentration, 0.051 N. When lithium bromide, sodium azide, and tetramethylammonium nitrate were used, it was found that the initial rate of reaction of RCl was, respectively, 1.46, 1.50, and 1.53 times the initial rate in the absence of any added salt. Thus it seems that this concentration of salt increases the initial reaction rate by about 50 per cent. When 0.051 N lithium chloride was used, however, it was found that the initial reaction rate was only 0.49 times that in the absence of added salt (and hence only about one-third of the reaction rate to be expected at this ionic strength). The explanation of Bateman, Hughes, and Ingold is that the alkyl chloride ionizes at the expected rate under these conditions but that two out of three of the carbonium ions combine with chloride ion to regenerate the starting material. Thus ROH is formed only one-third as fast as it would have been if no chloride ions were present.

As evidence for the combination of nucleophilic ions with the carbonium ions it is pointed out that although the RCl disappears at the expected rate in the presence of NaN_3, the product is not all alcohol but is 64 per cent RN_3, indicating that almost two-thirds of the carbonium ions combine with azide ions in this case. The explanation that this RN_3 is formed by an S_N2 attack of azide ion on RCl seems unlikely, since a reaction of this kind would not interfere with the solvolysis already occurring in the absence of NaN_3. Therefore the existence of this additional mode of reaction for RCl should cause a corresponding increase in the *rate* of reaction of RCl. Actually the rate in the presence of sodium azide does not differ beyond the experimental error from the rate in the presence of equal concentrations of lithium bromide or tetramethyl-ammonium nitrate.

When the alkyl chloride is hydrolyzing in the absence of added anions (other than chloride), the size of the mass effect is governed only by the concentration of chloride ions and by the *relative* magnitudes of k_2 and k_3, the rate constants for the combination of the carbonium ion with chloride ion and water, respectively. This may be seen from the following analysis.[18] If we assume that the carbonium ion is so highly reactive an intermediate that its concentration at any time is negligible compared to that of the alkyl chloride or alcohol, then the rate of reaction as measured by formation of chloride or hydrogen ions will simply be equal to the rate of step 3 in the reaction scheme above. Now the rate of step 3 will be the rate at which carbonium ions are formed—the rate of step 1—multiplied by the fraction of those carbonium ions that react with water.

$$\text{Rate} = k_1[\text{RCl}]F$$

where F is the fraction of carbonium ions reacting with water. This fraction will be equal to the rate of reaction of carbonium ions with water divided by their total rate of reaction. Since water is present in essentially constant excess, step 3 may be treated as a first-order reaction.

$$F = \frac{k_3[\text{R}^+]}{k_2[\text{R}^+][\text{Cl}^-] + k_3[\text{R}^+]} = \frac{1}{(k_2/k_3)[\text{Cl}^-] + 1}$$

Letting $\alpha = k_2/k_3$,

$$\text{Rate} = \frac{k_1[\text{RCl}]}{\alpha[\text{Cl}^-] + 1} \tag{5-1}$$

Values for α, the mass-law constant, have been obtained using a form of the above equation (modified in a somewhat complicated way to allow for ionic-strength effects) for several alkyl halides and are listed in Table 5-2.[18]

It may be noted that the values of α increase with the expected increasing stability of the carbonium ions. This agrees with the suggestion that the less stable and more reactive carbonium ions have a tendency to combine with one of the first molecules they meet, very probably a solvent molecule, while the more stable carbonium ions have a long enough average life to be able to show a preference for reacting with a more nucleophilic reagent.

In relation to an investigation of the mechanism of the hydrolysis of t-butyl nitrate, Lucas and Hammett suggested that the effect of dissolved salts may depend in part on their relative affinity for water

[18] L. C. Bateman, M. G. Church, E. D. Hughes, C. K. Ingold, and N. A. Taher, *J. Chem. Soc.*, 979 (1940).

molecules.[19] The retardation of the hydrolysis of an alkyl chloride produced by lithium chloride might thus be explained by the assumption that lithium chloride requires so much water for solvation that the solvent is rendered essentially less aqueous. Since it is well known that these hydrolysis reactions proceed more slowly in a solvent mixture containing less water, it appears possible that such an effect might override the positive ionic-strength effect also present. Benfey, Hughes, and Ingold have presented additional evidence to show that this explanation does not suffice for the data on benzhydryl halides, at least.[20] It may be

TABLE 5-2. VALUES OF THE MASS-LAW CONSTANT, α, FOR VARIOUS ALKYL HALIDES[18]

Alkyl halide	α
Triphenylmethyl chloride	$\sim 400^a$
p,p'-Dimethylbenzhydryl chloride	68–69
p-Methylbenzhydryl chloride	28–35
p-t-Butylbenzhydryl chloride	20–43
Benzhydryl chloride	10–16
Benzhydryl bromide	$50–70^b$
t-Butyl bromide	$1–2^{b,c}$

[a] C. G. Swain, C. B. Scott, and K. H. Lohmann, *J. Am. Chem. Soc.*, **75**, 136 (1953).

[b] With these two alkyl bromides, α is the rate constant for the reaction of the carbonium ion with bromide (rather than chloride) ion divided by the rate constant for its reaction with water. The fact that the value of α for benzhydryl bromide is about five times as large as for benzhydryl chloride shows that the bromide ion is about five times as adept at combining with the benzhydryl carbonium ion as the chloride ion is. This is in agreement with the generalization that bromide ion is usually more nucleophilic than chloride ion (see Sec. 6-2).

[c] This value is estimated from rather small deviations in reaction rate, which may be specific salt effects rather than mass effects. Hence α might even be zero in this case.

seen that the explanation supposes the effect of lithium chloride to be a general action on the solvent, while the mass-law explanation attributes it to a specific action on the compound being solvolyzed. According to the former explanation, if a certain alkyl chloride solvolyzes more slowly in the presence of lithium chloride than in the presence of the same concentration of lithium bromide, then so should the analogous alkyl bromide. It was found however that while 0.1 N lithium bromide speeded and 0.1 N lithium chloride slowed the hydrolysis of benzhydryl chloride in "80 per cent aqueous acetone," exactly the opposite result occurred with benzhydryl bromide. Here lithium bromide decreased and lithium chloride increased the rate. This, of course, is in agreement with the mass-law explanation, which requires that the decrease be the property of a common-ion salt.

[19] G. R. Lucas and L. P. Hammett, *J. Am. Chem. Soc.*, **64**, 1928 (1942).

[20] O. T. Benfey, E. D. Hughes, and C. K. Ingold, *J. Chem. Soc.*, 2488 (1952).

Actually, the existence of a mass-law effect primarily gives evidence that

1. The reaction proceeds in at least two steps, with the rate-controlling step preceding the product-controlling step.
2. The rate-controlling step is the same in all of the cases.
3. Some step earlier than the last produces halide ion and is reversible.

It might be argued that the mechanism

$$RCl + H_2O \overset{(1)}{\underset{(2)}{\rightleftharpoons}} ROH_2^+ + Cl^-$$

$$ROH_2^+ + H_2O \overset{(3)}{\underset{(5)}{\rightleftharpoons}} ROH + H_3O^+$$

$$ROH_2^+ + N_3^- \overset{(4)}{\rightarrow} RN_3 + H_2O$$

could explain the data if the various rate constants had suitable values. Actually, however, this mechanism requires k_5 to have what appears to be an unreasonable value. This may be shown by the following considerations. Treating steps 1 and 3 as first-order and neglecting ionic-strength effects, we may derive an expression for the rate of RCl hydrolysis analogous to Eq. (5-1).

$$\text{Rate of RCl hydrolysis} = \frac{k_1[RCl]}{1 + \alpha[Cl^-]}$$

Similarly,

$$\text{Rate of formation of RCl from ROH} = k_5[ROH][H_3O^+](1 - F)$$

$$\text{Rate of RCl formation} = \frac{k_5\alpha[ROH][H_3O^+][Cl^-]}{1 + \alpha[Cl^-]}$$

At equilibrium the rate of formation is equal to the rate of hydrolysis.

$$\frac{k_1[RCl]}{1 + \alpha[Cl^-]} = \frac{k_5\alpha[ROH][H_3O^+][Cl^-]}{1 + \alpha[Cl^-]}$$

or

$$\frac{k_1}{\alpha k_5} = \frac{[ROH][H_3O^+][Cl^-]}{[RCl]}$$

Bateman, Hughes, and Ingold state that at concentrations around 0.05 M this hydrolysis is irreversible, within the limits of their analysis.[17] From their data we may be sure that this means that equilibrium lies *at least* 98 per cent on the side of the ROH. Therefore

$$\frac{k_1}{\alpha k_5} > \frac{(0.05)(0.05)(0.05)}{(0.001)}$$

Substituting the values of α (74) and k_1 (4.7×10^{-4} sec^{-1}) obtained by these workers,

$$k_5 < 5 \times 10^{-5} \text{ liter mole}^{-1} \text{ sec}^{-1}$$

This means that the simple proton-transfer reaction from H_3O^+ to ROH would not be *half* completed after more than 4 days at the temperature (0°) and concentrations (0.05 M) employed.   This seems highly unlikely in view of the fact that in similar reactions, e.g., the ionization of acids containing oxygen-bound hydrogen,

$$HOAc + H_2O \rightleftharpoons H_3O^+ + OAc^-$$

the equilibrium is established so rapidly that no one has yet succeeded in measuring the reaction rate.   For this and a number of other reasons, the carbonium-ion mechanism offers the most plausible explanation for these and, as will be seen later, many other experimental data.

While the mass-law effect constitutes some of the most convincing evidence we have for the S_N1 mechanism, it is large enough to be detected only in the case of rather stable carbonium ions.   No mass-law effect has been definitely established for simple aliphatic tertiary halides in a hydroxylic solvent, although there are a number of reasons for believing that these compounds usually react by the S_N1 mechanism.   For this reason it is desirable to have other criteria for establishing the reaction mechanism, some of which will be described in the next two sections. While none of these criteria individually are based on compelling evidence, their sum often permits quite credible conclusions to be drawn.

5-2c. *Stereochemical Studies.*   The evidence that nucleophilic displacement reactions by halide ions in acetone solution proceed by an inverting mechanism has been given in Sec. 5-1a.   In order to learn whether this conclusion can be extended to other S_N2 reactions and to determine the stereochemical effect of the S_N1 reaction, Hughes and Ingold carried out an interesting series of investigations.   Since a number of important physical organic principles are involved, some of this work will be discussed in detail.   One of the compounds studied was a simple aliphatic secondary halide, 2-octyl bromide.[21]   The first problem involved was the determination of the relative configurations of the compounds to be used, since it is not *necessarily* true that two related compounds with the same direction of optical rotation will have the same stereochemical configuration; e.g., the optical isomer of lactic acid, which is levorotatory in acid solution, is dextrorotatory in alkaline solution.   Yet changing the pH of the solution does not change the configuration of the four groups around the asymmetric carbon atom. It merely changes the —CO_2H group to a —CO_2^- group.

[21] E. D. Hughes, C. K. Ingold, and S. Masterman, *J. Chem. Soc.*, 1196 (1937).

From a series of reactions[22] similar to that in Sec. 5-1b,

$$d\text{-}C_8H_{17}OH \rightarrow d\text{-}C_8H_{17}OSO_2R$$
$$\text{EtOH} \downarrow \text{OAc}^-$$
$$l\text{-}C_8H_{17}OH \leftarrow l\text{-}C_8H_{17}OAc$$

it appears most likely that the inversion which must have occurred did so in the transformation of the sulfonate to the acetate, since this is the only step in which a valence bond to the asymmetric carbon atom is changed. If this reaction produces inversion, it is reasonable to expect the similar reaction,

$$d\text{-}C_8H_{17}OSO_2C_7H_7 \xrightarrow[\text{EtOH}]{\text{Cl}^-} l\text{-}C_8H_{17}Cl$$

to do so also. An inversion in this reaction with chloride ion in ethanol might also have been predicted by analogy with the reaction of iodide ion in acetone with 2-octyl iodide, for which inversion has been rather well established. Since in the series[23]

$$d\text{-}C_8H_{17}OH \xrightarrow{\text{K}} C_8H_{17}OK \xrightarrow{\text{C}_2\text{H}_5\text{I}} d\text{-}C_8H_{17}OC_2H_5$$

none of the four valences of the asymmetric carbon atom are changed, it seems reasonable that the d-2-octyl ethyl ether has the same configuration as the d-alcohol. Therefore the reaction

$$d\text{-}C_8H_{17}Cl + NaOC_2H_5 \rightarrow l\text{-}C_8H_{17}OC_2H_5$$

must proceed with inversion. If it does, it seems probable that the corresponding reaction of the d-bromide to yield l-ether does also, and hence that the d-chloride and d-bromide have the same configuration. This same conclusion might have been reached from the fact that either the d-chloride or d-bromide can be produced by the action of the corresponding hydrogen halide on l-2-octanol.

The net result of these deductions is the conclusion that the d-2-octyl bromide, chloride, alcohol, and ethyl ether probably all have the same stereochemical configuration.

It was next necessary to estimate the specific rotation of the pure forms of some of the active compounds studied. For a compound dl-A resolved by crystallization of its diastereomeric compounds with an optically active compound d-B this is usually possible (if any separation at all can be obtained), because by a sufficient number of recrystallizations the less soluble product can be separated entirely from its diastereomer; but misleading results may be obtained if some such addition

[22] H. Phillips, *J. Chem. Soc.*, **127**, 2552 (1925).
[23] J. Kenyon and R. A. McNicol, *J. Chem. Soc.*, **123**, 14 (1923).

compound as $(d\text{-A})_2 \cdot l\text{-A} \cdot (d\text{-B})_3$ is formed.   If active A can be freed from this pure compound without racemization, its rotation can be determined. Furthermore, if A is a solid and can be obtained partially optically pure, its further recrystallization should lead to complete optical purity, unless d-A and l-A form solid solutions or some such compound as dl-A·d-A.

However, crystallization is a much more highly selective operation than fractional distillation, extraction, and the other ordinary methods of handling organic liquids, and for this reason partially resolved liquids may not usually be appreciably further resolved by techniques of the latter type.[24]   Therefore it is usually necessary to use indirect methods to determine the optical purity and hence the specific rotation (in the pure form) of a liquid compound if there is no crystalline solid from which the liquid can be generated with 100 per cent stereospecificity.

The resolution of 2-octanol is usually accomplished by use of the brucine salt of its monoester with phthalic acid.   This is a solid compound, and it can be recrystallized until optically pure.   The alkaline hydrolysis of the ester should yield optically pure 2-octanol, since the cleavage in cases of this type occurs at the acyl-oxygen bond (Sec. 12-1a) and since "no evidence of racemization has been observed with various types of saturated alcohols even on prolonged boiling with concentrated aqueous alkali."[25]   By the hydrolysis of an optically pure 2-octyl hydrogen phthalate, alcohol of specific rotation 9.9° is obtained, and for this reason 9.9° is believed to be the rotation of pure optically active 2-octanol.   From a sample of 2-octanol, $[\alpha]_D^{20°} = -9.07°$, treated with HBr, Hughes, Ingold, and Masterman obtained 2-octyl bromide, $[\alpha]_D^{20°} = +29.78°$.   Because the bromide is a liquid, its optical purity cannot be determined directly, but since no stereochemically specific processes were involved in purification, it can have no higher an optical purity than the alcohol from which it was made ($9.07/9.90 = 0.916$). Therefore the rotation of optically pure 2-octyl bromide must be at least $29.78/0.916 = 32.5°$.   If any racemization occurred during the transformation of the alcohol to the bromide, the fractional optical purity of the bromide is even lower than 0.916, and hence the rotation of pure bromide is even higher than 32.5°.   In addition to this minimum value, it is possible to obtain a maximum value for the specific rotation of optically pure 2-octyl bromide.

[24] M. E. Bailey and H. B. Hass [*J Am. Chem. Soc.*, **63**, 1969 (1941)] found that careful fractionation through a 60-plate column produced some separation of diastereomers.   One would expect much more difficulty in separating a partially resolved *dl* pair by this method.

[25] A. W. Ingersoll in R. Adams, "Organic Reactions," vol. II p. 397, John Wiley & Sons, Inc., New York, 1944.

The preparation of the ethyl ether of 2-octanol through its potassium derivative[23] yields presumably optically pure material of specific rotation, $[\alpha]_D^{20°} = 17.5°$ (in Ref. 21 this value, estimated from data at other wave lengths,[23] is taken as 17.1°). The possibility of racemization of the alcohol before reaction is ruled out because the unreacted alcohol was found to have the same rotation as that originally taken. Since a sample of 2-octyl bromide, $[\alpha]_D^{20°} = -24.54°$, reacted with sodium ethoxide to give ethyl 2-octyl ether of rotation $+12.41$ (70.9 per cent optically pure), the bromide of rotation $-24.54°$ must have been at least 70.9 per cent optically pure, and the rotation of the pure bromide can be no more than $24.54/0.709 = 34.6°$. Since the reaction with sodium ethoxide in absolute ethanol is known from kinetic studies to be almost purely second-order and should therefore give almost pure inversion (except for a small amount of racemization due to the bromide ions formed during the reaction), the optical purity of the ether formed must be very nearly equal to that of the bromide used, and the specific rotation of optically pure bromide must be close to 34.6°.

With estimates of this type, Hughes, Ingold, and Masterman have analyzed the data resulting from several reactions, as shown in Table 5-3. Optically active 2-octyl bromide was allowed to react in alkaline 60 per cent ethanol. Since both 2-octanol and its ethyl ether are formed, both hydroxylation and alkoxylation reactions were studied. The first-order reaction of 2-octyl bromide with solvent is so rapid in 60 per cent ethanol that even in the presence of $1.2~N$ alkali only 88 per cent of the bromide disappears via a second-order reaction with alkali, while the other 12 per cent reacts with solvent. Therefore, in order to learn the stereochemical result of the predominating second-order reaction, it is necessary to learn the stereochemical effect of the first-order reaction with solvent and to apply a suitable correction. This was done by solvolyzing a sample of the bromide in 60 per cent ethanol in the absence of added alkali (reaction 2 in Table 5-3). Octyl bromide, $[\alpha]_D^{20°} = -24.54$, yielded octanol, $[\alpha]_D^{20°} = +2.54$; hence bromide, $[\alpha]_D^{20°} = -34.6$, would have yielded octanol, $[\alpha]_D^{20°} = +3.58$ (36 per cent optical purity). Thus the over-all result is inversion of configuration, but it has been accompanied by a considerable amount of racemization. This racemization could have occurred in three ways: (1) The bromide could have been racemized before it reacted. (2) The alcohol could have been racemized after it was formed. (3) Racemization may have occurred during the hydrolysis reaction proper. A study of the reaction kinetics by polarimetric as well as analytical methods showed that the octyl bromide was indeed being racemized before reaction by the bromide ions formed in the solvolysis (by inverting displacements, just as bromide ions in acetone racemize optically active α-phenylethyl bromide, Sec. 5-1a). However, when this racemization is corrected for, it is found that optically pure 2-octyl bromide would have yielded alcohol of about 68 per cent optical purity.   It seems that it might have been desirable to consider the possibility of racemization of the alcohol produced under the reaction conditions (boiling for 3 days in a solution up to 0.3 M in acid), but no mention of this appears to have been made in Ref. 21.

TABLE 5-3. SOLVOLYSIS OF OPTICALLY ACTIVE 2-OCTYL BROMIDE IN 60 PER CENT ETHANOL AT 80°[a]

Acid or base concentration	Reaction order, %		Bromide	Alcohol, $[\alpha]_D^{20°}$		Retention of optical purity, %[b]	
	2nd	1st		Obs.	Cor.[c] to pure RBr	Un-cor.	Cor.
Hydrolysis:							
1. 1.23–0.91 N KOH	88	12	+29.78°	−7.73°	−8.98°	−91	−94
2. 0.00–0.31 N HBr	0	100	−24.54	+2.54	+3.58	−36	−68
3. Calcd. from 1 and 2	100	0	+34.6	−9.7	−9.7	−98	−98
Ethanolysis:				Ether, $[\alpha]_D^{20°}$			
4. 1.23–0.91 N KOH	95	5	−30.28	+13.93	+15.92	−91	−95
5. 0.00–0.31N HBr	0	100	−24.54	+4.90	+6.91	−39	−74
6. Calcd. from 4 and 5	100	0	+34.6	−15.98	−15.98	−94	−96

[a] This table is based on one in E. D. Hughes, C. K. Ingold, and S. Masterman, *J. Chem. Soc.*, 1196 (1937), except that the data have been recalculated on the basis of the estimate of 17.5° as the specific rotation of optically pure ethyl 2-octyl ether.

[b] A negative sign indicates inversion of configuration.

[c] Based on the estimate of 34.6° as the specific rotation of optically pure 2-octyl bromide.

The data for ethoxylation are similar to those for hydroxylation and are shown in Table 5-3.   From the results in Table 5-3 it seems very likely that some racemization occurred during the solvolysis.   However, in view of the neglect of the possibility of racemization of the alcohol and of such experimental uncertainties as those present in the correction for racemization by bromide ion, the establishment of this point may not be unequivocal.   We shall therefore defer any discussion of this point until after a consideration of the study of the solvolysis of α-phenylethyl chloride by Hughes, Ingold, and Scott,[26] who proved the occurrence of racemization during reaction beyond any reasonable doubt.   These workers studied the hydrolysis, methanolysis, and ethanolysis reactions with the results shown in Table 5-4.   These data were originally calculated on the basis of a rotation of 53.8° for the chloride, but since the

[26] E. D. Hughes, C. K. Ingold, and A. D. Scott, *J. Chem. Soc.*, 1201 (1937).

TABLE 5-4. REACTIONS OF α-PHENYLETHYL CHLORIDE[a]

Expt.	Conc. range of HCl, KOH, etc., N	Reaction order		Halide rotation	$\alpha_D^{20°}$ obs.	Cor. to RCl 109–126°	Optical purity, %
		2nd	1st				
Hydrolysis							
1a[b]	0.00–0.13 HCl	0	100	−11.60°	+2.00°	18.9–21.8	43–50
1b[b]	0.00–0.13 HCl	0	100	−47.12	+5.32	12.4–14.3	28–33
2a[b]	1.79–1.66 KOH	0	100	−39.20	+5.32	14.8–17.1	34–39
2b[b]	1.79–1.66 KOH	0	100	−47.12	+6.24	14.4–16.6	33–38
3[c]	0.00–0.04 HCl	0	100	−34.00	+1.32	4.3– 4.9	10–11
4[c]	0.05–0.01 KOH	0	100	−34.00	+1.72	5.5– 6.3	13–14
5a[d]	0.00–0.19 HCl	0	100	+11.76	−0.12	1.2– 1.4	2.7–3.2
5b[d]	0.00–0.15 HCl	0	100	−34.00	+0.72	2.2– 2.6	5–6
Methyl alcoholysis							
6[e]	0.00–0.14 HCl	0	100	+35.52	−10.24	31.4–36.4	25–28[f]
7[e]	3.6 –3.5 NaOMe	61	39	+35.52	−32.00	98–113	73–88[f]
Ethyl alcoholysis							
8a[g]	0.00–0.14 HCl	0	100	−32.60	+6.80	22.7–26.1	24–28[f]
8b[g]	0.00–0.14 HCl	0	100	−14.48	+2.72	20.4–23.6	22–25[f]
9a[g]	2.85–2.7 NaOEt	92.5	7.5	−32.60	+22.00	73–85	77–90[f]
9b[g]	2.85–2.7 NaOEt	92.5	7.5	−10.52	+7.00	72–84	76–89[f]

[a] Except for the last two columns, this table is from E. D. Hughes, C. K. Ingold, and A. D. Scott, *J. Chem. Soc.*, 1201 (1932).

[b] Solvent water, two liquid phases present.

[c] 60 per cent acetone, 70°.

[d] 80 per cent acetone.

[e] CH₃OH, 70°.

[f] Based on the rotations 128.3° for ROMe and 94.8° for ROEt, reported by K. Mislow, *J. Am. Chem. Soc.*, **73**, 4043 (1951).

[g] C₂H₅OH, 70°.

chloride has since been shown to have a rotation between 109 and 126°,[27] suitable recalculations have been made. It was found that the racemization of the α-phenylethyl chloride (by liberated chloride ions) before reaction was negligible. While no statement is made about the possibility of racemization of the alcohol after hydrolysis, there could have been no acid-catalyzed racemization in Expt. 4, where the solution was basic throughout the reaction. Hence it seems very likely that in this case some mechanism other than the S_N2 was operative, if it is assumed that racemization due to an S_N2 attack by acetone followed by a second

[27] R. L. Burwell, Jr., A. D. Shields, and H. Hart, *J. Am. Chem. Soc.*, **76**, 908 (1954).

nucleophilic displacement by water is improbable and that all proton transfers between oxygen atoms are rapid compared to reactions in which bonds to carbon are broken. Some mechanism other than the S_N2 also seems probable for Expt. 2, although the heterogeneous nature of the reaction mixture puts this evidence on a slightly weaker basis. If this is so, it is practically certain that the other reactions (Expts. 1 and 4) also proceed, at least in part, by mechanisms other than the S_N2. The S_N1 mechanism is certainly the most reasonable possibility (not because of this evidence alone, which would not exclude a nucleophilic front-side attack by solvent, but by the weight of a large amount of evidence from other sources).

The original conclusions reached by Hughes, Ingold, and coworkers[28] on the basis of these data on 2-octyl bromide and α-phenylethyl chloride are as follows: The S_N2 mechanism gives complete inversion in all cases. Since the first-order solvolysis was assumed to be entirely S_N1, it was necessary to suggest an explanation for the lack of complete racemization, in view of the fact that the most stable configuration of a carbonium ion is thought to be planar; hence any reaction proceeding via a carbonium ion might be expected to give complete racemization at the carbon atom involved. These workers pointed out that very reactive carbonium ions such as these may very well react with the solvent before the departing halide ion is more than a few molecular diameters away and will therefore be less likely to react at the front side because of the steric hindrance produced by this ion. This has been referred to as the "shielding effect."

Perhaps another way of describing this effect would be to point out that α-phenylethyl chloride, like α,α-dimethylallyl chloride (Sec. 5-5c) and other compounds (Sec. 14-1), may react initially to form an ion pair. The carbonium ion of this pair may then combine with solvent at the side opposite to the chloride ion. Since ion pairs appear to be intermediates in the solvolysis of those compounds whose structures render the ion-pair formation peculiarly detectable, it seems reasonable that they are also intermediates in the cases of other compounds thought to solvolyze by a carbonium-ion mechanism.

More recently, however, Hughes and Ingold have expressed the view that the first-order solvolysis of the 2-octyl bromide is more largely S_N2 than was originally believed,[29] implying that at least part of the inversion noted in reactions 2 and 5 of Table 5-3 is due to S_N2 attack by the solvent.

Doering and Zeiss have described the shielding action of the displaced

---

[28] W. A. Cowdrey, E. D. Hughes, C. K. Ingold, S. Masterman, and A. D. Scott, *J. Chem. Soc.*, 1252 (1937).

[29] I. Dostrovsky, E. D. Hughes, and C. K. Ingold, *J. Chem. Soc.*, 191 (1946).

group in terms of a weak bonding to the tertiary carbon atom through its vacant pi orbital.[30]

5-2d. *Other Criteria for Mechanism.* It has been suggested that solvolyses that are not speeded by the addition of small amounts of the conjugate base of the solvent must be S_N1, for if the solvent is performing nucleophilic displacements, its conjugate base should be capable of doing so much more effectively.[31] The validity and use of this criterion depend upon an at least semiquantitative knowledge of the relative nucleophilicities of the species involved toward the reactant in question, and discussion of this criterion will therefore be deferred until Sec. 6-2. Very useful discussions of mechanism have been based on the effect of solvent changes on the rate of solvolytic reactions and on the effect of the structure of the reacting molecules on their reactivity, but these will be discussed in Secs. 6-1 and 6-3.

5-2e. *Transition between the S_N1 and S_N2 Mechanisms.* Hughes, Ingold, and coworkers have stated that "no sharp line of demarkation exists between the two mechanisms"[32] and that "there must be degrees of collaboration by the reagent in the process of expelling the substituent that is to be replaced."[32b] That is, "the two mechanisms were regarded as the extremes of a graded range,"[32b] and "many molecules may react along paths which cannot be clearly classified as belonging to either mechanism."[32c] More recently these workers have discussed their viewpoint on "borderline" reactions in more detail.[33] They have emphasized the importance of the solvation of all ions taking part in a reaction and have discussed in considerable detail the solvation of carbonium ions and its influence on their ease of formation and on their further reaction.[34]

From discussions by Swain it may be seen that cationic solvation and nucleophilic attack are very closely related and that one may blend gradually into the other.[35] Swain states that there is therefore only one mechanism for nucleophilic substitutions, a termolecular "push-pull" mechanism in which one reagent pushes the halide (or other) ion off

---

[30] W. von E. Doering and H. H. Zeiss, *J. Am. Chem. Soc.*, **75**, 4733 (1953).

[31] E. D. Hughes and C. K. Ingold, *J. Chem. Soc.*, 244 (1935); E. D. Hughes, *Trans. Faraday Soc.*, **37**, 603 (1941).

[32] (a) E. D. Hughes, C. K. Ingold, and U. G. Shapiro, *J. Chem. Soc.*, 225 (1936); (b) J. L. Gleave, E. D. Hughes, and C. K. Ingold, *J. Chem. Soc.*, 236 (1935); (c) M. L. Dhar, E. D. Hughes, and C. K. Ingold, *J. Chem. Soc.*, 2058 (1948).

[33] M. L. Bird, E. D. Hughes, and C. K. Ingold, *J. Chem. Soc.*, 634 (1954); E. Gelles, E. D. Hughes, and C. K. Ingold, *J. Chem. Soc.*, 2918 (1954).

[34] L. C. Bateman, M. G. Church, E. D. Hughes, C. K. Ingold, and N. A. Taher, *J. Chem. Soc.*, 979 (1940).

[35] C. G. Swain, *J. Am. Chem. Soc.*, **70**, 1119 (1948); **72**, 2794, 4578 (1950); C. G. Swain and R. W. Eddy, *J. Am. Chem. Soc.*, **70**, 2989 (1948).

by cationic solvation of, or nucleophilic attack on, the carbon atom, and another reagent pulls it off by solvating it. In the sense that there is thus a striking point of similarity between S_N1 and S_N2 reactions in this regard, there may indeed be said to be only one mechanism. However, because of the useful correlations possible due to the differences in the S_N1 and S_N2 reactions, we shall not discuss nucleophilic substitutions in terms of only one mechanism, despite the existence of borderline cases whose mechanisms are less clearly understood and despite the fact that S_N1 and S_N2 reactions blend gradually into each other. Winstein, Grunwald, and Jones have stated that their equation (Sec. 6-1) correlating the effect of solvent changes on relative solvolysis rates better fits the data on borderline cases when they are treated as occurring by a single mechanism rather than partially by one and partially by the other mechanism.[36] Swain has also suggested equations for correlating solvolysis rates and has used the same equations for solvolyses of all types (Secs. 6-1 and 6-2). The limitations and generality of any of these equations have not yet been clearly established.

The following summary concerning the transition between the S_N1 and S_N2 mechanisms probably differs more in presentation than in actual content from several of the other discussions to which we have just referred. It seems most reasonable that for the reaction intermediate

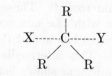

there will be a continuous gradation in the character of the C—X and C—Y bonds from the loose ionic "bonds" between a relatively stable carbonium ion and the two "solvating" molecules or ions on either side of it through bonds of intermediate strength to the rather covalent bonds present at the halfway point in a typical S_N2 reaction. In the former case the groups, X and Y, are so loosely attached to a relatively stable carbonium ion that they are easily replaced by other groups for which a positive charge may have an attraction. This rate of exchange of solvating groups is so fast compared to the rate at which the carbonium ion combines with X that it is very unlikely that the combination will occur before group Y, originally attached to C, has been replaced by a solvent molecule, X, to give a symmetrical intermediate. (Recombination with Y before its replacement is usually not experimentally detectable.) Therefore a racemic product is formed. However, if the R groups are less capable of supplying electrons to the carbon atom, it will attach itself more strongly to X and Y through their

[36] S. Winstein, E. Grunwald, and H. W. Jones, *J. Am. Chem. Soc.*, **73**, 2700 (1951).

unshared electron pairs and may often form an entirely covalent bond with X before Y has been replaced, giving a partially inverted and partially racemic product. In a typical S_N2 reaction X and Y are so tightly held that in the intermediate they are never exchanged for other groups, and a completely inverted product is obtained. A number of other changes cause, and are caused by, this continuous variation in the covalent character of the C—X and C—Y bonds and the change from complete racemization to complete inversion. Some of these changes, e.g., in the nature of the solvent and of the nucleophilic reagent and the effect of the structure of the R groups on the reaction rate, will be discussed in Chap. 6.

5-3. The S_Ni Mechanism. Optically active α-phenylethyl alcohol reacts with PCl_3, PCl_3 and pyridine, $POCl_3$, $POCl_3$ and pyridine, PCl_5, PCl_5 and pyridine, or HCl to give α-phenylethyl chloride of opposite rotation and configuration.[37a] In the presence of pyridine thionyl chloride gives the same result,[37b] but in its absence the product is α-phenylethyl chloride of the same configuration as the starting material.[37c] From qualitative observations of this sort, Hughes, Ingold, and coworkers have reasoned that in addition to the S_N1 and S_N2 mechanisms there is another mechanism for nucleophilic displacements on carbon which gives retention of configuration and which they call the S_Ni mechanism (substitution, nucleophilic, internal).[38] These workers suggest that all of the reactions of alcohols with the nonmetal halides described are initiated by the loss of hydrogen halide and the formation of an alkoxy derivative of the nonmetal. This intermediate may react further by either the S_N1 or S_N2 mechanism, as shown below for a chlorosulfite.

$$\overset{\diagdown}{\underset{\diagup}{C}}\text{—OSOCl} \xrightarrow{C_5H_5N} \overset{\diagdown}{\underset{\diagup}{C}}\text{—OSON}\overset{\oplus}{C_5H_5} + \overset{\ominus}{Cl} \rightarrow$$

$$Cl\text{—}\overset{\diagup}{\underset{\diagdown}{C}}\text{—} + C_5H_5N + SO_2$$

$$\overset{\diagdown}{\underset{\diagup}{C}}\text{—O}\overset{\oplus}{S}O \rightarrow SO_2 + \overset{\diagdown}{\underset{\diagup}{C}}\overset{\oplus}{} \overset{Cl^{\ominus}}{\longrightarrow} Cl\text{—}\overset{\diagup}{\underset{\diagdown}{C}}\text{—}$$
$$\underset{Cl^{\ominus}}{+}$$

(partially racemized)

[37] (a) A. McKenzie and G. W. Clough, *J. Chem. Soc.*, **97**, 1016, 2564 (1910), R. H. Pickard and J. Kenyon, *J. Chem. Soc.*, **99**, 45 (1911); (b) J. Kenyon, H. Phillips, and F. M. H. Taylor, *J. Chem. Soc.*, 382 (1931); (c) A. McKenzie and G. W. Clough, *J. Chem. Soc.*, **103**, 687 (1913).

[38] W. A. Cowdrey, E. D. Hughes, C. K. Ingold, S. Masterman, and A. D. Scott, *J. Chem. Soc.*, 1252 (1937); E. D. Hughes, C. K. Ingold, and I. C. Whitfield, *Nature*, **147**, 206 (1941).

Evidently in the case of the phosphorus halides the S_N2 reaction may proceed by attack of the chloride ion on some intermediate other than a pyridinium ion, since in these cases the absence of pyridine does not change the steric result. Under conditions where neither the S_N1 nor S_N2 reaction occurs too rapidly, reaction may occur by the S_Ni mechanism, in which the chlorosulfite rearranges directly to the observed products.

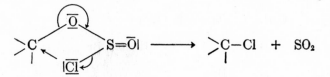

Cram has pointed out that since (1) the S_Ni mechanism best competes with other reaction paths when the alkyl group will form a relatively stable carbonium ion, and (2) the reaction proceeds more rapidly in better ion-solvating media, a close relationship between the S_Ni and the S_N1 reaction mechanisms is suggested.[39] In fact, Cram postulates that both reactions are initiated by the same rate-controlling step—an ionization to an ion pair—and that the only difference is that in the S_Ni reaction the anion is complex and may decompose to yield a new anion that can combine with the organic cation faster than the ion pair is successfully attacked by nucleophilic reagents. A particularly careful study of the reaction has been carried out by Lewis and Boozer. They were the first to prove the intermediacy of alkyl chlorosulfites in the S_Ni by actually decomposing compounds of this type and observing retention of configuration.[40] They also showed that the reaction is kinetically first-order, as demanded by the S_Ni mechanism. The decomposition in dioxane solution was found to give almost complete retention of configuration. This may result from back-side displacement of sulfur dioxide from the ion pair by dioxane, followed by a second back-side displacement of dioxane from the dioxane-solvated carbonium ion by chloride ion. The variation of the reaction rate and steric result with the nature of the solvent are also discussed.[41]

Phosgene reacts with alcohols in a manner somewhat analogous to that of thionyl chloride. Alkyl chloroformates are formed, which may decompose alone to give chlorides with retention of configuration or in the presence of pyridine to give inverted chlorides.[42] The reaction in

[39] D. J. Cram, *J. Am. Chem. Soc.*, **75**, 332 (1953).
[40] E. S. Lewis and C. E. Boozer, *J. Am. Chem. Soc.*, **74**, 308 (1952).
[41] C. E. Boozer and E. S. Lewis, *J. Am. Chem. Soc.*, **75**, 3182 (1953).
[42] M. B. Harford, J. Kenyon, and H. Phillips, *J. Chem. Soc.*, 179 (1933), and earlier references given therein.

the absence of pyridine may be an S_Ni reaction of the four-center type.[43]

The formation of a bromide with retained configuration in the reaction of hydrogen bromide with several phenylalkyl carbinols is another example of the S_Ni reaction,[44] probably involving a hydrogen-bonded complex between the acid and alcohol and an intermediate ion pair.

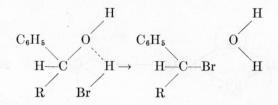

In addition to examples of the type described, there appears to be a somewhat different mechanism for substitution with retention of configuration due to the front-side attack. It bears the same relation to those S_Ni reactions proceeding by ionization to an ion pair that the S_N2 mechanism bears to the S_N1. Cases of this type proceed by a one-step mechanism involving a nucleophilic displacement by a group that is attached to the carbon atom attacked through the atom displaced. An example of this type is the Stevens rearrangement. In one example, phenacyl-α-phenethyldimethylammonium (II) salts rearrange to α-dimethylamino-β-phenylbutyrophenone (III) in the presence of alkali. The following mechanism[45]

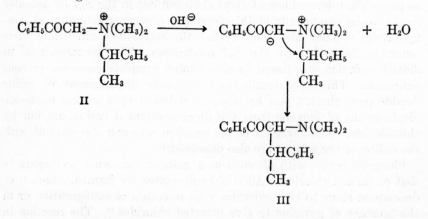

[43] See Sec. 24-1c. However cf. K. B. Wiberg and T. M. Shryne; *J. Am. Chem. Soc.*, **77**, 2774 (1955).

[44] P. A. Levene and A. Rothen, *J. Biol. Chem.*, **127**, 237 (1939).

[45] H. B. Watson, "Modern Theories of Organic Chemistry," 2d ed., p. 205, Oxford University Press, London, 1941; C. R. Hauser and S. W. Kantor, *J. Am. Chem. Soc.*, **73**, 1437 (1951)

is in agreement with the evidence of Stevens that the reaction is kinetically first-order in quaternary salt and intramolecular,[46] and has been
made very likely by the observation of Brewster and Kline that the
α-phenethyl group migrates with retention of configuration.[47] The
mechanism of reactions of this type has been discussed in some detail
by Hauser and Kantor.[45]

5-4. Participation of Neighboring Groups. We have discussed under
$S_N i$ reactions those nucleophilic displacements by groups that are connected to the carbon atom attacked only through the atom displaced.
There are probably a larger number of intramolecular displacements
in which the nucleophilic group is not connected through the atom displaced. Some examples of reactions of this type are

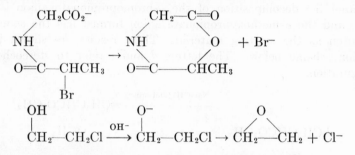

Intramolecular substitution reactions of this type usually occur much
more rapidly than the analogous intermolecular reactions, since a nucleophilic reagent located in the same molecule within five or six atoms of the
carbon atom at which displacement occurs will necessarily spend more
of its time in a position suitable for nucleophilic attack than if it were a
part of a different molecule. Like the two examples shown, many
"neighboring-group" displacement reactions are simply intramolecular
instances of reactions well known intermolecularly. However, because
of the great facility of cyclizations of this type, many neighboring-group
reactions have few, if any, intermolecular analogs. Some of the immediate products of neighboring-group displacements are stable compounds,
but others may be very reactive intermediates because of strain present
in their small rings. Even ethylene oxide, while capable of being isolated, is a vastly more reactive compound than a typical ether.

5-4a. *The Neighboring Carboxylate Anion.* The neighboring-group
participation of the carboxylate anion has been investigated considerably,
and some of the most interesting data have been obtained for cases in
which the carboxylate group is attached directly to the reaction center.

[46] T. Thomson and T. S. Stevens, *J. Chem. Soc.*, 55 (1932); T. S. Stevens, *J. Chem. Soc.*, 2107 (1930).

[47] J. H. Brewster and M. W. Kline, *J. Am. Chem. Soc.*, **74**, 5179 (1952).

Optically active α-bromopropionic acid and its derivatives have been studied by several investigators. Cowdrey, Hughes, and Ingold[48] found that the reactions of the methyl ester are normal, both the second-order reaction with methoxide ion and the first-order methanolysis giving inversion of configuration. In fact, when corrections are made for the racemization of the unreacted ester and the product by methoxide ion (probably due to carbanion formation) and for the racemization of the unreacted ester by inverting displacements by bromide ion, etc., the inversion appears to be complete. In concentrated methanolic sodium methoxide solution, the α-bromopropionic anion undergoes a second-order reaction with methoxide ion to give an α-methoxypropionate anion of inverted configuration. However, in dilute alkaline solution in methanol the decomposition of the α-bromopropionate anion is first-order, and the α-methoxypropionate anion formed has the same configuration as the starting material. These results are shown in the reaction scheme below. The letters d and l refer to stereochemical configuration.

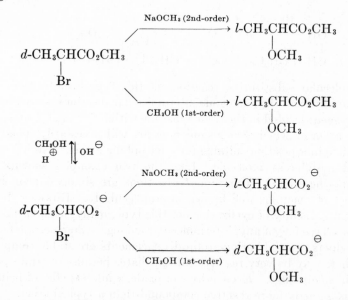

In the case of hydroxylation the results found are like those described for methoxylation above. The hydrolysis of the acid (in 0.5 N aqueous H_2SO_4 to suppress the ionization) gives inversion, as does the second-order reaction of the anion with hydroxide ion. However, the first order hydrolysis of the anion gives retention of configuration.

It appears that the most probable explanation for these results is

[48] W. A. Cowdrey, E. D. Hughes, and C. K. Ingold, *J. Chem. Soc.*, 1208 (1937).

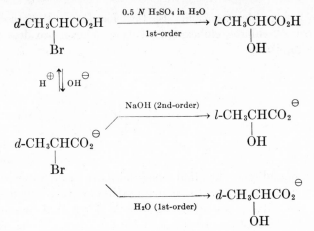

that all of the reactions proceed by the S_N2 mechanism except the first-order decompositions of the anions. The rate-controlling step in these cases appears to be the nucleophilic displacement of the bromide ion by the carboxylate anion of the same molecule.[49] Thus there is formed, with inversion of configuration, an α-lactone. This very reactive intermediate may then rapidly undergo a second nucleophilic displacement by solvent to give the final product with retention of configuration.

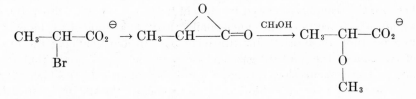

The formation of an intermediate of some sort is also indicated by Grunwald and Winstein's discovery of a mass-law effect in the reaction. That is, although the reaction is speeded by an inert salt such as perchlorate, it is slowed by a bromide, since bromide ions may react with the α-lactone reconverting it to α-bromopropionate ion.[50]

5-4b. *The Neighboring Hydroxyl Group.* The neighboring hydroxyl group as such has not been studied greatly, but reactions in alkaline solution due to its equilibrium transformation to an alkoxide anion have

[49] S. Winstein and H. J. Lucas, *J. Am. Chem. Soc.*, **61**, 1576 (1939); S. Winstein, *J. Am. Chem. Soc.*, **61**, 1635 (1939); the same mechanism was proposed for a different compound by C. M. Bean, J. Kenyon, and H. Phillips, *J. Chem. Soc.*, 303 (1936). Cowdrey, Hughes, and Ingold prefer to consider the reaction an ionization to a carbonium ion that is stabilized in a tetrahedral configuration by the negative charge of the carboxylate group.

[50] E. Grunwald and S. Winstein, *J. Am. Chem. Soc.*, **70**, 841 (1948).

received considerable attention. Bartlett has shown that the action of alkali on *trans*-2-chlorocyclohexanol yields cyclohexene oxide, apparently by the mechanism[51]

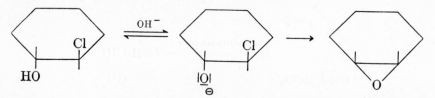

The cis compound reacts less than one-hundredth as rapidly with alkali,[52] although there is no reason to believe that its alkoxide anion should be formed significantly less readily. The lack of reactivity is almost certainly due to the inability of the alkoxide ion to attack the *rear* of the adjacent carbon atom without subjecting the molecule to considerable strain. Under the somewhat more vigorous conditions required for reaction *cis*-2-chlorocyclohexanol yields cyclohexanone.

5-4c. The Neighboring RS Group. One compound with a neighboring RS group that has received considerable study is mustard gas (β,β'-dichlorodiethyl sulfide).[53] The hydrolysis of this compound in its initial stages is purely first-order in mustard gas and independent of the concentration of added alkali. The rate constants decrease with time because the reaction is slowed by the chloride ions formed. When thiosulfate ions or certain other nucleophilic reagents are added to the reaction mixture, they react quantitatively but without changing the rate of reaction of the mustard gas. These data, of course, imply that the mustard gas reacts slowly to give a reactive intermediate which may react with (1) water, (2) chloride ion to regenerate the starting material, or (3) any other nucleophilic reagent present. The fact that the intermediate has the ability to react with small amounts of certain nucleophilic reagents in preference to the water, present in a much larger concentration, shows that the intermediate has some stability (see Sec. 5-2b). There is no reason to expect the primary carbonium ion, $ClCH_2$-$CH_2SCH_2CH_2{}^{\oplus}$, to have this much stability, or to be formed in a first-order solvolysis reaction at the rate found for mustard gas (*very* much faster than that for typical primary chlorides). However, an intramolecular attack by the sulfur atom (whose nucleophilicity in intermolecular reactions is well known) displacing the chloride ion seems a

[51] P. D. Bartlett, *J. Am. Chem. Soc.*, **57**, 224 (1935).

[52] T. Bergkvist, *Svensk Kem. Tidskr.*, **59**, 215 (1947).

[53] R. A. Peters and E. Walker, *Biochem. J.* (*London*), **17**, 260 (1923); A. G. Ogston, E. R. Holiday, J. St. L. Philpot, and L. A. Stocken, *Trans. Faraday Soc.*, **44**, 45 (1948); P. D. Bartlett and C. G. Swain, *J. Am. Chem. Soc.*, **71**, 1406 (1949).

reasonable rate-controlling step, especially since the three-membered-ring sulfonium ion might well be expected to be a reactive intermediate.[53,54]

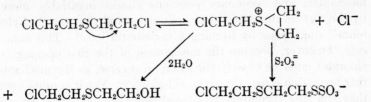

Intermediate substituted ethylene sulfonium ions seem to offer the most probable explanation for a number of rearrangements observed with hydroxy and halo sulfides. For example, Fuson, Price, and Burness[55] have found that the reaction of ethyl 1-hydroxy-2-propyl sulfide with hydrochloric acid yields a rearranged chloride.

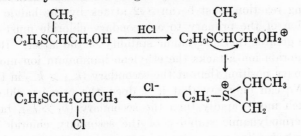

5-4d. *Neighboring Amino Groups.* In view of the fact that the nucleophilicity of the amino group is even more familiar than that of the sulfide group, it is not surprising that similar rearrangements have been found in the preparation and reactions of β-haloamines. Several workers[56] have reported the rearrangement of 1-chloro-2-dialkylaminopropanes to 1-dialkylamino-2-chloropropanes. Fuson and Zirkle have studied the following ring expansion, which probably proceeds by the mechanism shown.[57]

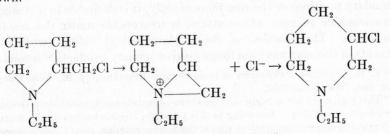

[54] Cf. F. E. Ray and I. Levine, *J. Org. Chem.*, **2**, 267 (1937).

[55] R. C. Fuson, C. C. Price, and D. M. Burness, *J. Org. Chem.*, **11**, 475 (1946).

[56] (a) J. F. Kerwin, G. E. Ullyot, R. C. Fuson, and C. L. Zirkle, *J. Am. Chem. Soc.*, **69**, 2961 (1947); (b) E. M. Schultz and J. M. Sprague, *J. Am. Chem. Soc.*, **70**, 48 (1948).

[57] R. C. Fuson and C. L. Zirkle, *J. Am. Chem. Soc.*, **70**, 2760 (1948).

In all of the cases mentioned a primary chloride rearranged to a secondary chloride. Since primary positions are usually more reactive by the S_N2 mechanism and secondary positions almost invariably more reactive by the S_N1 mechanism, it has been suggested that the "ethylene immonium" ring opens by forming a carbonium ion.[58] This cannot be the case, however, because the mechanism of the ring opening (to form a chloride) must be exactly the same, in reverse, as the mechanism of the ring formation (from the given chloride).[59] Yet it is quite unreasonable that the ring formation is an S_N1 ionization followed by cyclization, since the reaction proceeds thousands of times more rapidly than the hydrolysis of similar but unaminated halides (although there is certainly no reason to expect a β-amino group to stabilize a carbonium ion this much). This great reactivity of β-amino halides is almost certainly due to an internal S_N2 attack by the amino group, and therefore the ring-opening reaction must be an S_N2 attack by the halide ion. The isomerization of the primary to a secondary chloride must simply be due to the greater thermodynamic stability of the latter. It may well be that chloride ion attacks the ethylene immonium ion more rapidly at the primary position than at the secondary ($k_{-1} > k_{-2}$ in the scheme below). We can only say that if it does, the primary chloride must cyclize much more rapidly than the secondary ($k_1 \gg k_2$), because the greater thermodynamic stability of the secondary chloride shows us that $k_{-2}/k_2 > k_{-1}/k_1$.

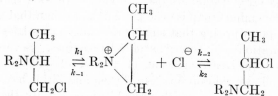

To learn whether nucleophilic reagents tend to attack the primary or secondary positions of the ring more rapidly, it is desirable to investigate a nucleophilic reagent whose attack is irreversible under the reaction conditions. The reaction of β-dialkylaminoalkyl halides with some reagents of this sort has been found to give primary products,[60] secondary

[58] E. R. Alexander, "Principles of Ionic Organic Reactions," p. 99, John Wiley & Sons, Inc., New York, 1950.

[59] This statement has a fairly obvious thermodynamic basis, called *the principle of microscopic reversibility*. According to this principle, the mechanism of any reaction is identical in microscopic detail to that of the reverse reaction, except that it proceeds in the opposite direction. For a fuller discussion see A. A. Frost and R. G. Pearson, "Kinetics and Mechanism," p. 202, John Wiley & Sons, Inc., New York, 1953.

[60] S. D. Ross, *J. Am. Chem. Soc.*, **69**, 2982 (1947); R. H. Reitsema, *J. Am. Chem. Soc.*, **71**, 2041 (1949); for a β-halosulfide example see R. C. Fuson and A. J. Speziale, *J. Am. Chem. Soc.*, **71**, 1582 (1949).

products,[56a] and mixtures,[56b,61] but in most of these studies only a fraction of the product was identified, and in no case was a kinetic study made to show that the nucleophilic reagent was reacting with an ethylene immonium ion rather than with uncyclized chloride.   Until these aspects of the problem have been studied, it is difficult to make any definite conclusions concerning the relative S_N2 reactivity of the primary and secondary positions of an ethylene immonium (or sulfonium) ion.

Kinetic investigations of certain reactions of β-haloamines also support the concept of the intermediacy of ethylene immonium ions.   Bartlett, Ross, and Swain have studied the cyclic dimerization of methyl-bis-β-chloroethylamine in aqueous acetone solution.[62]   Since the reaction involves several steps with comparable rate constants, and since the substituted ethylene immonium ion is stable enough under most conditions to accumulate in the solution to a considerable extent (rendering the steady-state approximation inapplicable), the kinetics of the reaction were complicated, and certain rate constants were obtained by use of a mechanical differential analyzer.   The mechanism of the dimerization is as follows:

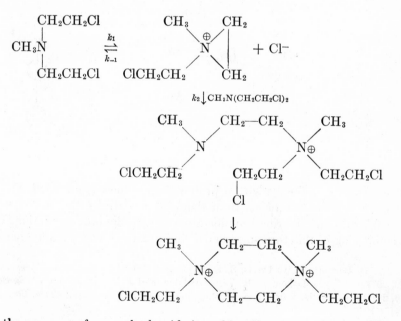

In the presence of excess hydroxide ion, thiosulfate ion, or triethylamine, the over-all course of the reaction becomes largely a replacement of

[61] E. M. Schultz, C. M. Robb, and J. M. Sprague, *J. Am. Chem. Soc.*, **69**, 188, 2454 (1947); W. R. Brode and M. W. Hill, *J. Am. Chem. Soc.*, **69**, 724 (1947).

[62] P. D. Bartlett, S. D. Ross, and C. G. Swain, *J. Am. Chem. Soc.*, **69**, 2971 (1947).

chloride ions by these nucleophilic reagents. As the reactivity and concentration of the nucleophilic reagent is increased, the reaction rate approaches but does not exceed $k_1[CH_3N(C_2H_4Cl)_2]$, the rate of ethylene immonium–ion formation. This shows that these reactions, too, are nucleophilic attacks not on the haloamine but on the cyclic immonium ion. As expected, the reactions may be slowed by chloride ion because of a mass-law effect. The reactions of other β-haloamines with nucleophilic reagents have also been studied kinetically.[63]

5-4e. *Neighboring Halogen Atoms.* Bromonium ions were first suggested as intermediates in the addition of bromine to olefins (Sec. 9-1a). Although analogous to no stable compounds known at the time,[64] the bromonium ion was the first intermediate investigated extensively in connection with the effect of neighboring groups on nucleophilic substitutions on carbon. Most of the pioneering work in this field was done by Winstein, Lucas, and colleagues. These workers found that upon reaction with fuming hydrobromic acid, optically active *erythro*-3-bromo-2-butanol (IV)[65] yielded *meso*-2,3-dibromobutane, while *threo*-3-bromo-2-butanol (VIII)[65] gave *dl*-2,3-dibromobutane.[66] The workers suggest that

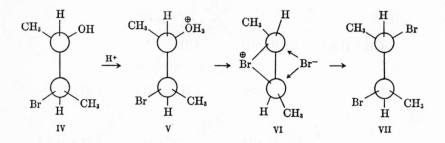

The alcohol coordinates with a proton to give the oxonium ion, **V**. A water molecule is displaced from this intermediate by the nucleophilic attack of the neighboring bromine atom to give the bromonium ion, **VI**. The opening of this three-membered ring by attack of a bromide ion on

[63] P. D. Bartlett, J. W. Davis, S. D. Ross, and C. G. Swain, *J. Am. Chem. Soc.,* **69,** 2977 (1947); B. Cohen, E. R. Van Artsdalen, and J. Harris, *J. Am. Chem. Soc.,* **70,** 281 (1948); P. D. Bartlett, S. D. Ross, and C. G. Swain, *J. Am. Chem. Soc.,* **71,** 1415 (1949).

[64] Although iodonium compounds had been long known, the first stable bromonium and chloronium salts appear to have been prepared by R. B. Sandin and A. S. Hay [*J. Am. Chem. Soc.,* **74,** 274 (1952)].

[65] The prefix erythro- means "having a configuration analogous to that of the aldotetrose erythrose"; threo- relates to the diastereomeric threose.

[66] S. Winstein and H. J. Lucas, *J. Am. Chem. Soc.,* **61,** 1576, 2845 (1939).

either carbon atom will yield the observed meso product, VII. With *three*-3-bromo-2-butanol, the mechanism is analogous.

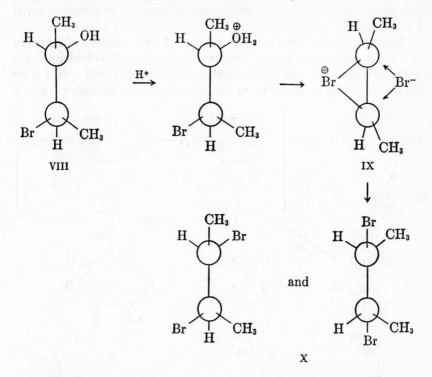

In this case the bromonium ion (IX) is symmetrical and therefore inactive; it will be attacked equally at carbon atoms 2 and 3 to yield a *dl* mixture (X). There appears to be no other reasonable mechanism to explain the experimental data. The reaction cannot be a simple S_N2 replacement of the protonated hydroxyl group, because such a mechanism would yield meso dibromide from threo bromohydrin rather than from erythro, as found. The mechanism cannot be of the S_Ni type, since the threo bromohydrin yields *dl* rather than the predicted optically active dibromide. An S_N1 reaction to give a planar carbonium ion capable of reacting on either side would produce a mixture of meso and active dibromides from either starting material. The objections to an S_N1 mechanism with inversion due to the shielding effect of the departing water molecule or with retention due to some effect of the adjacent bromine atom are the same as those to the S_N2 and S_Ni mechanisms, respectively. While we cannot definitely rule out the slight possibility that the specific rotation of the dibromide may be too small for its optical activity to be detected, it seems very unlikely that it should be fortuitously almost exactly zero. Although no experimental test was made, it is improbable that the isolation of a racemic product is due either to the racemization of the bromohydrin before reaction or racemization of the dibromide after its formation.

There is evidence for the intermediacy of an analogous chloronium ion in the transformation of 3-chloro-2-butanol to 2,3-dichlorobutane by thionyl chloride[67a] and in the reaction of stilbene dichlorides with silver acetate,[67b] as well as in the trans addition of chlorine to olefins. Many

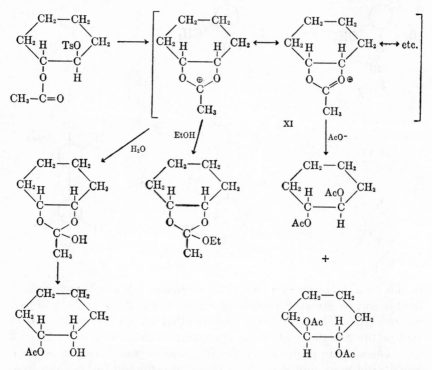

compounds with neighboring iodine atoms quite readily form cyclic iodonium ions. Some cases in which their importance has been mentioned include the transformation of *trans*-2-iodocyclohexanol to the bromide and chloride by hydrobromic and hydrochloric acid, respectively,[68a] and the solvolysis of *trans*-2-iodocyclohexyl *p*-bromobenzenesulfonate,[68b] 2-iodo-1-phenylethyl chloride,[68c] and β-iodo-*t*-butyl chloride.[68c]

5-4f. *Other Neighboring Groups.* A number of other neighboring

[67] (a) H. J. Lucas and C. W. Gould, Jr., *J. Am. Chem. Soc.*, **63**, 2541 (1941); (b) S. Winstein and D. Seymour, *J. Am. Chem. Soc.*, **68**, 119 (1946).

[68] (a) S. Winstein, E. Grunwald, R. E. Buckles, and C. Hanson, *J. Am. Chem. Soc.*, **70**, 816 (1948); (b) S. Winstein, E. Grunwald, and L. L. Ingraham, *J. Am. Chem. Soc.*, **70**, 821 (1948); (c) S. Winstein and E. Grunwald, *J. Am. Chem. Soc.*, **70**, 828 (1948).

groups have been found to participate in nucleophilic substitution reactions. The neighboring acetoxy group leads to the formation of an acetoxonium ion (such as XI), which may react in any of the ways shown on page 126 provided that it is produced in the proper environment.[69] The action of hydrocarbon radicals as neighboring groups is described under carbon-skeleton rearrangements in Sec. 14-1. Carbonium ions with the structure that would result from the neighboring-group participation of hydrogen are discussed in Sec. 9-2a. Neighboring-group participation also occurs with the methoxy[70] and the acylamino and related groups.[71]

5-5. Reactions of Allylic Halides. *5-5a. The S_N1 and S_N2 Mechanisms.* Nucleophilic substitution reactions of allylic halides may in some cases occur by mechanisms that are new or that at least represent a considerable modification of any of the mechanisms discussed so far. The S_N2 mechanism may proceed in essentially its normal manner, but in the case of the S_N1 mechanism, if a really free carbonium ion is formed, there will be two electrophilic carbon atoms and, if the allyl group is unsymmetrically substituted, two products may be formed.

$$R\!-\!CH\!=\!CH\!-\!CH_2X \rightarrow \quad \begin{array}{c} R\!-\!CH\!=\!CH\!-\!\overset{\oplus}{C}H_2 \\ \updownarrow \\ R\!-\!\overset{\oplus}{C}H\!-\!CH\!=\!CH_2 \end{array} \quad \overset{Y^-}{\rightarrow} \quad \begin{array}{c} R\!-\!CH\!=\!CH\!-\!CH_2Y \\ \text{and} \\ R\!-\!\underset{\underset{Y}{|}}{CH}\!-\!CH\!=\!CH_2 \end{array}$$

The formation of a rearranged product is, however, not regarded as sufficient evidence in itself for the intermediacy of a carbonium ion, since rearrangement could occur as a result of the so-called S_N2' mechanism, in which a bimolecular nucleophilic attack with allylic rearrangement occurs.

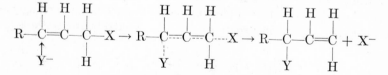

[69] S. Winstein, H. V. Hess, and R. E. Buckles, *J. Am. Chem. Soc.*, **64**, 2796 (1942); S. Winstein and R. E. Buckles, *J. Am. Chem. Soc.*, **64**, 2780, 2787 (1942); **65**, 613 (1943).

[70] S. Winstein and L. L. Ingraham, *J. Am. Chem. Soc.*, **74**, 1160 (1952); S. Winstein, C. R. Lindegren, and L. L. Ingraham, *J. Am. Chem. Soc.*, **75**, 155 (1953).

[71] G. E. McCasland, R. K. Clark, Jr., and H. E. Carter, *J. Am. Chem. Soc.*, **71**, 637 (1949); S. Winstein and R. Boschan, *J. Am. Chem. Soc.*, **72**, 4669 (1950).

In a number of instances the product of the solvolysis of an allylic halide has been found to be a mixture of the two possible allylic isomers. It seems reasonable that this is due to reaction by the S_N1 mechanism. Catchpole and Hughes found the first-order ethanolysis of α-methylallyl chloride to yield 82 per cent ethyl crotyl ether.[72] It does not seem likely that the nucleophilic attack of the ethanol solvent would have occurred at least 82 per cent by the S_N2' mechanism when it was demonstrated that the kinetically proved nucleophilic attack by ethoxide ion in the same solvent proceeded 100 per cent (within experimental error) by the normal S_N2 mechanism. Young and Andrews obtained mixtures in the first-order hydrolysis of crotyl chloride and α-methylallyl chloride despite the fact that they, too, detected no rearrangement in the reactions with ethoxide ion.[73] However, neither Young and Andrews nor Catchpole and Hughes found the solvolysis of both products yielding a mixture of the same composition, as it should have done if both reactions had proceeded entirely through the same free carbonium ion.

$$CH_3CH=\overset{\oplus}{C}HCH_2 \leftrightarrow CH_3\overset{\oplus}{C}HCH=CH_2$$

In each case the crotyl chloride yielded somewhat more crotyl derivative in the product than did the α-methylallyl chloride. Several explanations have been advanced for this formation of more than the expected amount of unrearranged products. It might be due to the intrusion of the S_N2 mechanism,[72] or it could be due to a lack of complete freedom for the intermediate carbonium ion. Because of the proximity of the chloride ion, the carbonium ion formed from crotyl chloride may have a larger positive charge induced on the number 1 carbon atom than would be there if the carbonium ion were entirely free of the chloride ion at the time of its combination with a nucleophilic reagent.[73]

It appears that many allylic rearrangements are simply S_N1 reactions in which the carbonium ion recombines (at a different carbon atom) with the anion to which it was originally attached. Catchpole and Hughes have suggested the following mechanism for the rearrangement of α-phenylallyl p-nitrobenzoate to cinnamyl p-nitrobenzoate.[74]

$$C_6H_5-CHCH=CH_2 \rightleftharpoons C_6H_5-\overset{\oplus}{C}HCH=CH_2$$
$$| \qquad\qquad\qquad\qquad\qquad\qquad\qquad$$
$$X \qquad\qquad\qquad \updownarrow \qquad\qquad + X^-$$

$$C_6H_5-CH=CHCH_2X \rightleftharpoons C_6H_5-CH=CH\overset{\oplus}{C}H_2$$

[72] A. G. Catchpole and E. D. Hughes, *J. Chem. Soc.*, 4 (1948).
[73] W. G. Young and L. J. Andrews, *J. Am. Chem. Soc.*, **66**, 421 (1944).
[74] A. G. Catchpole and E. D. Hughes, *J. Chem. Soc.*, 1 (1948).

where $X = p\text{-}O_2NC_6H_4CO_2^-$. The cinnamyl ester, in which the double bond is conjugated with the benzene ring, is the more stable of the two isomers. Compounds with terminal double bonds usually seem to be less stable, even if in the other isomer the double bond is merely stabilized by additional hyperconjugation.

5-5b. *The S_N2' Mechanism.* While a number of earlier investigations failed to detect the existence of the S_N2' mechanism[72-75] (bimolecular nucleophilic attack with allylic rearrangement), more recent studies have uncovered examples of its operation. The first good evidence for this mechanism appears to be due to Kepner, Winstein, and Young[76] in the case of the reaction of α-ethylallyl chloride with sodiomalonic ester. It was found that 23 per cent of the product of this reaction is the rearranged compound, XII.

$$C_2H_5\underset{\underset{Cl}{|}}{CH}CH{=}CH_2 + \overset{\ominus}{CH}(CO_2Et)_2 \rightarrow C_2H_5CH{=}CHCH_2CH(CO_2Et)_2$$

XII

Most of this compound must have been formed by the nucleophilic attack of the dicarbethoxymethyl anion, since kinetic studies show that at least 99 per cent of the reaction was of a second-order character, first-order in α-ethylallyl chloride and first-order in sodium dicarbethoxymethide. This attack must have been on α-ethylallyl chloride, since this chloride rearranges to γ-ethylallyl chloride much too slowly to explain these results. It was also shown that the isolation of the rearranged product could not have been due to a rearrangement of the normal product after its formation.

Young, Webb, and Goering have similarly shown that the reaction of diethylamine with α-methylallyl chloride in benzene, which yields at least 85 per cent crotyldiethylamine, also proceeds by the S_N2' mechanism,[77] as does the reaction of trimethylamine with α-methylallyl chloride.[78]

The S_N2' reaction of sodium thiophenolate with 3,3-dichloropropene-1 gives about as much cis as trans product.[79] With the 2,6-dichlorobenzoates of *trans*-6-alkyl-2-cyclohexenols, piperidine gives *trans*-3-(1-piperidyl)-6-alkylcyclohexenes by cis S_N2' attack.[80]

In the case of many allylic halides the S_N2 reaction occurs so rapidly

[75] J. D. Roberts, W. G. Young, and S. Winstein, *J. Am. Chem. Soc.*, **64**, 2157 (1942);
A. G. Catchpole, E. D. Hughes, and C. K. Ingold, *J. Chem. Soc.*, 8 (1948).
[76] R. E. Kepner, S. Winstein, and W. G. Young, *J. Am. Chem. Soc.*, **71**, 115 (1949).
[77] W. G. Young, I. D. Webb, and H. L. Goering, *J. Am. Chem. Soc.*, **73**, 1076 (1951).
[78] W. G. Young, R. A. Clement, and C. H. Shih, *J. Am. Chem. Soc.*, **77**, 3061 (1955).
[79] P. B. D. de la Mare and C. A. Vernon, *J. Chem. Soc.*, 3331 (1952); 3679 (1954).
[80] G. Stork and W. N. White, *J. Am. Chem. Soc.*, **75**, 4119 (1953).

that it is not possible to detect any reaction by the S_N2' mechanism. England and Hughes have ingeniously surmounted this difficulty by studying the reactions of crotyl bromide and α-methylallyl bromide with lithium bromide in acetone.[81]   The S_N2' mechanism may be studied in this case since reaction by the S_N2 mechanism leaves the allylic bromide chemically unchanged and hence does not render it unavailable for future S_N2' attack (as would an S_N2 attack by a foreign anion such as ethoxide). The lithium bromide is found to transform either allylic bromide into the equilibrium mixture of the two by a purely second-order process at a rate which is the rate of S_N2' attack.   The rate of S_N2 attack was measured simultaneously by use of radioactive bromide ions.   The rate constants shown in the accompanying table were obtained.

	Mechanism	$10^6 k_2$, 25°
Crotyl bromide...............	S_N2	141,000
	S_N2'	5
α-Methylallyl bromide..........	S_N2	879
	S_N2'	14.9

5-5c. *Ion Pairs in the Solvolysis of Allyl Halides.*   Young, Winstein, and Goering have shown that the acetolysis of α,α-dimethylallyl chloride involves simultaneous solvolysis and rearrangement to γ,γ-dimethylallyl chloride.[82]   This was shown by the fact that (1) the solvolysis rate constants fell from the initial high values that might be expected for the α,α-dimethyl isomer to the much lower values characteristic of γ,γ-dimethylallyl chloride, and (2) when the solvolysis of originally pure α,α-dimethylallyl chloride was interrupted after about 35 per cent completion, the unreacted halide was found to consist almost entirely of γ,γ-dimethylallyl chloride.   It was shown that the rearrangement is not due to a mass-law effect in which free carbonium ions combine with chloride ions to form γ,γ-dimethylallyl chloride.   Similar results have been obtained in the acetolysis of other compounds (Sec. 14-1).   The reaction could be considered as an internal rearrangement of the four-center type (Sec. 24-1), but if it is, we shall have to point out that the transition state is much more polar than the reacting molecule since the reaction increases with the ion-solvating power of the medium in much the same way that rates of carbonium-ion formation do.   For this reason, in fact, it is probably more useful to consider the reaction as an ionization

[81] B. D. England and E. D. Hughes, *Nature,* **168**, 1002 (1951).

[82] W. G. Young, S. Winstein, and H. L. Goering, *J. Am. Chem. Soc.,* **73**, 1958 (1951). For more recent information on ion pairs in solvolysis see S. Winstein, E. Clippinger, A. H. Fainberg, and G. C. Robinson, *J. Am. Chem. Soc.,* **76**, 2597 (1954); *Chemistry & Industry,* 664 (1954).

to an ion pair (XIII) that is transformed to a covalent chloride at a rate comparable with its dissociation to a carbonium ion able to combine with solvent.[82]

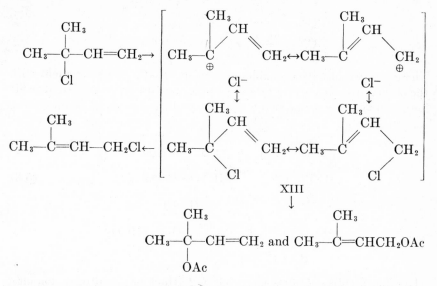

The discovery of this solvolysis through an ion-pair intermediate in the case of several different compounds makes it appear likely that ion pairs are intermediates in many, perhaps most, solvolyses, especially in poorly ion-solvating media. However, they have been detected so far only in the rather special cases in which certain types of rearrangements are possible. Of course, the rate at which the ion pair dissociates compared to its rate of reversion to starting material depends a great deal upon the nature of the solvent.

5-6. The Alpha-elimination Mechanism. There is good evidence for another mechanism for nucleophilic substitutions on carbon, which we shall call the alpha-elimination mechanism. It involves an initial removal of hydrogen and halide ions (in all the cases studied to date) attached to the *same* carbon atom, in contrast to the more common beta eliminations of hydrogen and halide ions (or other nucleophilic group) from *adjacent* carbon atoms (Sec. 7-1). This mechanism has at present been established only for the basic hydrolysis of some of the haloforms. In these cases the reaction is believed to involve a relatively rapid reversible formation of a trihalomethyl anion from the haloform and base, followed by an S_N1-type loss of halide ion from the trihalomethyl anion.[83] Under the reaction conditions the intermediate carbon

[83] J. Hine, *J. Am. Chem. Soc.*, **72**, 2438 (1950).

dihalide is then rapidly transformed into the observed products, carbon monoxide and formate ion.

$$CHX_3 + OH^- \overset{fast}{\rightleftharpoons} CX_3^- + H_2O$$
$$CX_3^- \overset{slow}{\longrightarrow} CX_2 + X^- \tag{5-2}$$
$$CX_2 \xrightarrow[fast]{OH^-,\ H_2O} CO \text{ and } HCO_2^-$$

There are two other reasonable mechanisms that are in agreement with the observed kinetics (first-order in haloform and first-order in hydroxide ion). In one the trihalomethyl anion undergoes an S_N2 attack by a water molecule.

$$CHX_3 + OH^- \overset{fast}{\rightleftharpoons} CX_3^- + H_2O$$

$$H_2O + CX_3^- \overset{slow}{\longrightarrow} H\overset{\oplus}{-}\underset{|}{\overset{|}{O}}\overset{\ominus}{-}\underset{|}{\overset{|}{C}}-Cl \tag{5-3}$$
$$\phantom{H_2O + CX_3^- \overset{slow}{\longrightarrow}} H\quad Cl$$

$$H\overset{\oplus}{-}\underset{|}{\overset{|}{O}}\overset{\ominus}{-}\underset{|}{\overset{|}{C}}-Cl \xrightarrow[fast]{OH^-,\ H_2O} CO \text{ and } HCO_2^-$$
$$H\quad Cl$$

The other involves a rate-controlling S_N2 attack of a hydroxide ion on a haloform molecule.

$$CHX_3 + OH^- \overset{slow}{\longrightarrow} CHX_2OH + X^-$$
$$CHX_2OH \xrightarrow[fast]{OH^-,\ H_2O} CO \text{ and } HCO_2^- \tag{5-4}$$

Chloroform undergoes a base-catalyzed deuterium exchange that is very much faster than its basic hydrolysis,[84] showing that the trichloromethyl anion is formed relatively rapidly, in agreement with mechanisms (5-2) and (5-3). This does not disprove mechanism (5-4). There are several strong arguments, however, for the intermediacy of trichloromethyl anions in the hydrolysis. Because methylene halides are much less reactive toward nucleophilic reagents than are methyl halides,[85] it is seen that the replacement of α-hydrogen atoms by halogens decreases reactivity by the S_N2 mechanism. It would therefore be expected that chloroform would be even less reactive than methylene chloride. This is found to be the case for nucleophilic reagents, such as piperidine and aqueous ethanol, but toward strongly basic nucleophilic reagents, such as sodium ethoxide and potassium hydroxide, the chloroform is much

[84] Y. Sakamoto, *J. Chem. Soc. Japan*, **57**, 1169 (1936); J. Horiuti and Y. Sakamoto, *Bull. Chem. Soc. Japan*, **11**, 627 (1936); J. Hine, R. C. Peek, Jr., and B. D. Oakes, *J. Am. Chem. Soc.*, **76**, 827 (1954).

[85] P. Petrenko-Kritschenko and V. Opotsky, *Ber.*, **59B**, 2131 (1926).

more reactive.[85] This correlation of the reaction rate with the ability of the nucleophilic reagent to coordinate with protons (its basicity toward hydrogen) is strong evidence against mechanism (5-4). Additional evidence was furnished by studying the reaction of chloroform with sodium thiophenolate. In neutral solution the reaction is very slow, but in the presence of sodium hydroxide the thiophenolate ions react hundreds of times more rapidly although the product, phenyl ortho-thioformate, does not contain the hydroxide catalyst.[83] This fact shows definitely that sodium thiophenolate and chloroform do not react by the S_N2 mechanism (5-4) and makes it very unlikely that the basic hydrolysis proceeds by this mechanism either. Studies on the effect of halide ions on the rate of the basic hydrolysis have made possible the unambiguous rejection of both mechanisms (5-4) and (5-3).[86] At concentrations where such anions as fluoride, nitrate, and perchlorate all had the same effect on the reaction rate, it was found that chloride, bromide, and iodide ions decreased the rate considerably. This is due to the combination of these ions with the carbon dichloride intermediate. Some intermediate that would otherwise have been hydrolyzed is thus changed back to haloform. Since the dichlorobromomethane and dichloroiodomethane formed (the latter was isolated) are more reactive than chloroform, the rate constants calculated by the acidimetric method of following the reaction were expected to climb during the reaction and were indeed found to do so. It was further shown that the relative amounts by which the three halide ions slowed the reaction were just those which would be predicted from the nucleophilicities of the ions determined in other reactions (see Sec. 6-2). The effect was found to increase with increasing halide-ion concentration in just the manner expected and was not found to be "swamped" by the addition of 1.5 N sodium perchlorate, as might be expected for a specific salt effect dependent on ionic radius, ion-pair-forming ability, etc. None of these data can be explained by mechanism (5-3) or (5-4). Preliminary data on $CHBr_3$, $CHBr_2Cl$, $CHBrCl_2$, $CHCl_2I$, $CHCl_2F$, and $CHBrClF$ suggest that these haloforms, too, undergo basic hydrolysis by the alpha-elimination mechanism.[87]

[86] J. Hine and A. M. Dowell, Jr., *J. Am. Chem. Soc.*, **76**, 2688 (1954).

[87] J. E. Singley, M.S. thesis, Georgia Institute of Technology, 1952; A. M. Dowell, Jr., Ph.D. thesis, Georgia Institute of Technology, 1953.

CHAPTER 6

REACTIVITY IN NUCLEOPHILIC
DISPLACEMENTS ON CARBON

6-1. Effect of Solvent on Reactivity in Nucleophilic Displacements.
The Hughes-Ingold theory of solvent effects was described in Sec. 3-2d.
According to this theory, the rate of solvolysis of electrically neutral
molecules by either the S_N1 or S_N2 mechanism would be expected to
increase with the ion-solvating power of the medium, since the reaction,
by either mechanism, involves charge formation in the transition state.
From the empirical observation that the solvolysis rate increases much
faster with compounds thought for other reasons to react by the S_N1
mechanism than with those thought to react by the S_N2 mechanism,
it may be rationalized that a larger or more concentrated charge is
formed in the S_N1 than in the S_N2 transition state. The magnitudes of
solvolysis effects, however, are not separated into two sharply defined
categories but vary continuously.

In addition to this qualitative theory, several quantitative correlations
of the rates of solvolysis reactions have been suggested. One of these
is due to Grunwald and Winstein, who have assigned to each of several
solvents a number, Y, which is a quantitative measure of its "ionizing"
power, as manifested in its effect on the rate of solvolyses by the S_N1
mechanism.[1] The relationship between Y and the solvolysis rate is
given by the equation

$$\log \frac{k_A}{k_B} = m(Y_A - Y_B) \tag{6-1}$$

where k_A and k_B are the rate constants for the S_N1 solvolysis in solvents A
and B, respectively, Y_A and Y_B are the "ionizing powers" of the two
solvents, and m is a constant characteristic (at a given temperature) of
the compound being solvolyzed. Obviously since the equation involves
only the difference in the Y values for the two solvents, the absolute
values of Y may be fixed in any way desired. In order to get values of a

---

[1] E. Grunwald and S. Winstein, *J. Am. Chem. Soc.*, **70**, 846 (1948); S. Winstein,
E. Grunwald, and H. W. Jones, *J. Am. Chem. Soc.*, **73**, 2700 (1951).

convenient order of magnitude, Y is defined by Eq. (6-2).

$$Y = \log k^{BuCl} - \log k_0{}^{BuCl} \tag{6-2}$$

where k^{BuCl} and $k_0{}^{BuCl}$ are the rate constants for the solvolysis of t-butyl chloride at 25° in the given solvent and in "80 per cent aqueous ethanol," respectively. This may be seen to be equivalent to defining m as 1.00 for t-butyl chloride at 25° and Y as 0.00 for the solvent "80 per cent aqueous ethanol." The general equation (6-1) is thus reduced to the form

$$\log \frac{k}{k_0} = mY \tag{6-3}$$

where k and k_0 are the rate constants for the solvolysis of the given compound at a certain temperature in the given solvent and in "80 per cent aqueous ethanol," respectively. Values of Y for various solvents, as calculated from Eq. (6-2) are listed in Table 6-1.

TABLE 6-1. Y VALUES FOR VARIOUS SOLVENTS[1]

Solvent[a]	Y	Solvent	Y
100% EtOH	−1.974	85.1% MeOH	0.088
90% EtOH	−0.727	81.0% MeOH	0.361
80% EtOH	0.000	74.7% MeOH	0.757
70% EtOH	0.644	69.5% MeOH	1.023
60% EtOH	1.139	5% Acetone	3.449
50% EtOH	1.604	Water	3.56[b]
40% EtOH	2.151	HCO₂H	2.08
100% MeOH	−1.052	HOAc, 0.025M KOAc	−1.633
96.8% MeOH	−0.722	97.5% Ac₂O–2.5% HOAc, 0.017 M KOAc	−3.287
91.4% MeOH	−0.329	50.6% Dioxane	1.292
88.3% MeOH	−0.112		

[a] By "$x\%$ ROH" we mean a mixture of x volumes of ROH and $100 - x$ volumes of water.

[b] Extrapolated from 5 per cent acetone.

In Fig. 6-1 values of $\log k$ for the solvolysis of several compounds in various solvents are plotted against the corresponding values of Y for the solvents. The data for 3,3-dimethyl-2-butyl p-bromobenzenesulfonate lie near a straight line and in this respect are typical of the data found for a number of compounds believed to hydrolyze by the S_N1 mechanism. A linear relationship has also been found for several compounds, such as $trans$-2-bromocyclohexyl p-bromobenzenesulfonate, whose solvolysis is thought to involve neighboring-group participation. On the other hand, for compounds like ethyl p-toluenesulfonate, which are believed to react by the S_N2 mechanism, the data for solvolysis in aqueous alcoholic solvents may lie near a straight line, but the solvolysis rate in formic acid or acetic acid is found to be much lower than would be expected from such a linear relationship.   These data were originally explained by stating that Y is a measure of ionizing power only, and therefore substances which were only ionizing in the transition state would give a linear relationship.   Compounds reacting by the S_N2 mechanism, however, are undergoing nucleophilic attack as well as ion

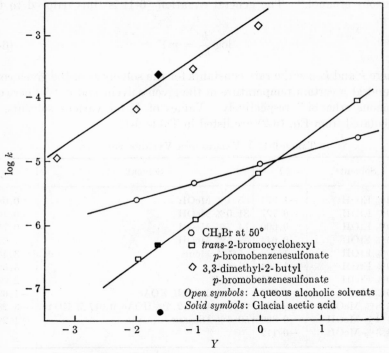

FIG. 6-1. Plots of ionizing power of solvent (Y) vs. log k.

formation, and therefore their reactivity is also a function of the nucleophilicity of the solvent, a characteristic of which Y is no measure.   However, the deviation originally reported for aqueous acetone solutions[1] and more extensive ones reported more recently[2] may necessitate a modification of this explanation.

A second equation has been proposed by Swain for correlating the rate of *all* nucleophilic displacements on carbon, including solvolyses.[3]

[2] S. Winstein, presented orally during discussion at 13th National Organic Chemistry Symposium of the American Chemical Society, June 17, 1953, Ann Arbor, Mich.

[3] (a) C. G. Swain and C. B. Scott. *J. Am. Chem. Soc.*, **75**, 141 (1953); (b) C. G. Swain and R. B. Mosely, *J. Am. Chem. Soc.*, **77**, 3727 (1955); C. G. Swain, R. B. Mosely, and D. E. Bown. *J. Am. Chem. Soc.*, **77**, 3731 (1955).

This equation is of particular interest because it does not depend on whether the reaction mechanism is S_N1 or S_N2. The equation is based on the assumption that all nucleophilic displacements (on electrically neutral species, at least) involve both nucleophilic and electrophilic attack, and has the form

$$\log \frac{k}{k_0} = sn + s'e \tag{6-4}$$

where n is a measure of the nucleophilicity of the nucleophilic reagent, e the electrophilicity of the electrophilic reagent, s the sensitivity of the reactant to changes in nucleophilicity, s' the sensitivity toward changes in electrophilicity, k the rate constant for reaction with a given nucleophilic and a given electrophilic reagent, and k_0 the rate constant for reaction with the standard nucleophilic and electrophilic reagents, whose values of n and e, respectively, are zero. In all cases the electrophilic attack is on the displaced anion and ordinarily involves solvation, but it may involve covalent-bond formation in the case of attack by such electrophilic reagents as silver and mercuric ions. The nucleophilic attack is on carbon (except in a few cases involving neighboring-group participation, where the cationic solvating attack may be on some other atom) and involves covalent-bond formation in S_N2 reactions and cationic solvation in S_N1 reactions. In so far as Eq. (6-4) holds, we may say that solvating power for cations (carbonium ions, at least) is proportional to nucleophilicity and that the transformation from the S_N1 to the S_N2 mechanism is, indeed, smooth and continuous. The application of Eq. (6-4) to solvolyses has given useful information about various solvents and about certain alkyl halides and sulfonates.[3b] When 152 data involving 25 compounds and 17 solvents were fitted to the equation by the method of least squares, the optimum values of n, e, s, and s' obtained were found capable of predicting the solvolysis-rate data used with an average deviation of 33 per cent, although the various rates often deviated from each other by factors of thousands. The resultant values of n and e are listed in Table 6-2 and those of s and s' in Table 6-3. Eighty per cent ethanol was defined as the standard solvent by setting both n and e equal to zero for this medium. The sensitivity values were arbitrarily normalized by setting $s = s' = 1.00$ for $(CH_3)_3CCl$, s/s' for $CH_3Br = s'/s$ for $(C_6H_5)_3CF = 3.00$. Thus, while the absolute values have no meaning, the relative values of n or of e for various solvents and of s, s', or s/s' for various compounds are significant. From the values of n and e a general but by no means rigorous correlation of n with basicity and of e with acidity is seen. The values of s and s' show compounds reacting by the S_N1 mechanism to be relatively more susceptible to electrophilic attack and compounds reacting by the S_N2 mechanism to be more susceptible to nucleophilic attack. The observation that Eq. (6-4) gives much greater deviations when applied to certain new data than when applied to those from which the values of the parameters n, e, s, and s' were obtained[2] is relevant to any mechanistic interpretation.

TABLE 6-2. NUCLEOPHILICITIES, n, AND ELECTROPHILICITIES, e, FOR VARIOUS SOLVENTS[3b]

Solvent	n	e
Formic acid	−4.40	+6.53
97.5% Ac_2O–2.5% HOAc	−8.77	+5.34
HOAc	−4.82	+3.12
H_2O	−0.44	+4.01
50% Acetone–50% H_2O	−0.25	+0.97
80% EtOH–20% H O	0.00	0.00
100% EtOH	−0.53	−1.03
MeOH	−0.05	−0.73
90% Acetone–10% H_2O	−0.53	−1.52

TABLE 6-3. SENSITIVITY OF COMPOUNDS TO NUCLEOPHILIC, s, AND ELECTROPHILIC, s', ATTACK[3b]

Compound	s	s'
$(C_6H_5)_3CF$	0.37	1.11
$(C_6H_5)_2CHF$	0.32	1.17
$(C_6H_5)_2CHCl$	1.24	1.25
$C_6H_5CH_2OSO_2C_6H_4CH_3$-$p$	0.69	0.39
$(CH_3)_3CCl$	1.00	1.00
$(CH_3)_2CHBr$	0.90	0.58
n-C_4H_9Br	0.77	0.34
C_2H_5Br	0.80	0.36
CH_3Br	0.80	0.27
C_6H_5COF	1.36	0.66
p-$O_2NC_6H_4COF$	1.67	0.49

Swain and Dittmer have also suggested another equation for correlating solvolysis rates.[4]

6-2. Effect of the Nucleophilic Reagent on the Rates of Nucleophilic Displacements. It has long been recognized that for a given nucleophilic atom nucleophilicity is fairly well correlated with the basicity of the nucleophilic reagent. For example, Smith has pointed out that in the reaction of the chloroacetate ion with 32 nucleophilic anions whose nucleophilic atom is oxygen the variation in the logarithm of the rate constants (statistically corrected by dividing by the number of equivalent

[4] C. G. Swain and D. C. Dittmer, *J. Am. Chem. Soc.*, **75**, 4627 (1953); **77**, 3737 (1955).

oxygen atoms) is nearly proportional to the differences in the logarithms of their basicity constants.[5]   The sulfite and thiosulfate anions, which form carbon-sulfur bonds rather than carbon-oxygen bonds, were much more nucleophilic than would be expected from their basicity.   By restricting the variation in structure to meta and para substituents on the aromatic ring, a still better correlation may be obtained, at least partially because of the elimination of steric effects, which can also destroy the correlation, since nucleophilic attack on carbon is usually more subject to steric hindrance than is coordination with a proton. Reaction constants, ρ, have been calculated for several series of reactions involving aniline derivatives and substituted phenolate anions as nucleophilic reagents[6] (see Table 6-4).   The negative values of ρ show the nucleophilicity to be increased by electron-donating groups in all cases. Similar results are found in the nucleophilic attack of anilines on halonitro aromatic compounds and on acid halides.[6]

TABLE 6-4. REACTION CONSTANTS, ρ, FOR REACTIONS OF PHENOXIDE IONS AND ANILINE DERIVATIVES AS NUCLEOPHILIC REAGENTS[6]

Reaction	$k_0{}^a$	ρ
Phenolate ions with ethylene oxide in 98% ethanol at 70.4°[b]...	-4.254	-0.946
Phenolate ions with propylene oxide in 98% ethanol at 70.4°[b]..	-4.698	-0.771
Phenolate ions with ethyl iodide in ethanol at 42.5°[c].........	-3.955	-0.991
Phenolate ions with $CH_3OSO_3{}^-$ in H_2O at 100°[d].............	-5.912	-0.797
Dimethylanilines with methyl iodide in aqueous acetone at 35°[e].	-3.336	-2.743
Dimethylanilines with methyl picrate in acetone at 35°[f].......	-4.500	-2.382
Dimethylanilines with trinitrocresol methyl ether in acetone at 25°[f]..	-5.328	-2.903
Phenyldiethylphosphines with ethyl iodide in acetone at 35°[e]...	-3.286	-1.088

[a] All k's in liters mole^{-1} sec^{-1}.
[b] D. R. Boyd and E. R. Marle, *J. Chem. Soc.*, **105**, 2117 (1914).
[c] L. J. Goldsworthy, *J. Chem. Soc.*, 1254 (1926).
[d] G. H. Green and J. Kenyon, *J. Chem. Soc.*, 1589 (1950).
[e] W. C. Davies and W. P. G. Lewis, *J. Chem. Soc.*, 1599 (1934).
[f] E. Hertel and J. Dressel, *Z. physik. Chem.*, **29B**, 178 (1935); **23B**, 281 (1933).

Another generalization is that nucleophilicity increases, within a given group of the periodic table, with the atomic number of the atom forming the new bond to carbon.   That is, $I^- > Br^- > Cl^- > F^-$; $RS^- > RO^-$; $R_2S > R_2O$, etc.   It is noted that this variation, which is the one usually but not invariably observed, is in the direction opposite to that which would be expected from the basicities of the various nucleophilic reagents.

[5] G. F. Smith, *J. Chem. Soc.*, 521 (1943).
[6] L. P. Hammett, "Physical Organic Chemistry," pp. 189–190, McGraw-Hill Book Company, Inc., New York, 1940.

The increased nucleophilicity is most commonly attributed to the increase in polarizability which accompanies the increase in the distance of the outer electronic shell from the nucleus. The greater ease of distortion of the outer shell permits an easier adjustment to the requirements of a stable transition state.

The relative strength of various nucleophilic reagents has been discussed more quantitatively by Swain and Scott.[3a] These workers have applied their equation (6-4) to nonsolvolytic nucleophilic displacements. For this particular purpose they have used a different standard solvent, water, for which $n = e = 0$. Since all of the data used referred to aqueous solutions, in which the electrophilic reagent is water, the term $s'e$ vanishes and Eq. (6-4) assumes the form

$$\log \frac{k}{k_0} = sn \tag{6-5}$$

where k is the second-order rate constant for a nucleophilic displacement by a reagent whose nucleophilicity is n on a compound whose sensitivity to change in nucleophilicity is s, and k_0 is the second-order rate constant for nucleophilic attack by water. Ideally, to get constant values of s and n all of the data should refer to the same solvent and the same temperature. Because of insufficient data in any one solvent, however, values were determined from data in aqueous acetone and aqueous dioxane mixtures ranging from pure water to 39 per cent water–61 per cent dioxane and at temperatures from 0 to 50°. Values of k were

TABLE 6-5. NUCLEOPHILIC CONSTANTS, n, OF VARIOUS NUCLEOPHILIC REAGENTS[a]

Reagent	n	Reagent	n
ClO_3^-, ClO_4^-, BrO_3^-, IO_3^-	$<0^b$	Br^-	3.89
H_2O	0.00	N_3^-	4.00
p-$CH_3C_6H_4SO_3^-$	<1.0	$(NH_2)_2CS$	4.1
NO_3^-	1.03^b	OH^-	4.20
Picrate anion	1.9	$C_6H_5NH_2$	4.49
F^-	2.0	SCN^-	4.77
SO_4^-	2.5	I^-	5.04
$CH_3CO_2^-$	2.72	CN^-	5.1^c
Cl^-	3.04	SH^-	5.1
C_5H_5N	3.6	SO_3^-	5.1
HCO_3^-	3.8	$S_2O_3^-$	6.36
HPO_4^-	3.8	$HPSO_3^-$	6.6

[a] From C. G. Swain and C. B. Scott, *J. Am. Chem. Soc.*, **75**, 141 (1953), unless otherwise stated.

[b] W. L. Petty and P. L. Nichols, Jr., *J. Am. Chem. Soc.*, **76**, 4385 (1954).

[c] M. F. Hawthorne, G. S. Hammond, and B. M. Graybill, *J. Am. Chem. Soc.*, **77**, 486 (1955).

compared only with k_0 values in the same solvent at the same temperature, of course. The sensitivity values are quoted relative to a standard, methyl bromide, for which s was set equal to 1.0. From 47 values of k/k_0 optimum values of a number of n's and s's were determined (see Tables 6-5 and 6-6). The values shown can be used to predict the k/k_0 values with an average deviation of about 60 per cent. A somewhat smaller deviation might have resulted if the data had all referred to exactly the same solvent and temperature, but many large deviations would not be materially diminished by such a modification. It may be

TABLE 6-6. RELATIVE SUSCEPTIBILITIES, s, OF VARIOUS REACTANTS TO
CHANGES IN NUCLEOPHILICITY OF ATTACKING REAGENT[3a]

Reactant	s
$C_2H_5OSO_2C_6H_4CH_3$-p	0.66
$C_6H_5CH_2Cl$	0.87
β-propiolactone[a]	0.77
CH_2—CH—CH_2Cl[b] (epoxide O)	0.93
CH_2—CH—CH_2OH[b] (epoxide O)	1.00
CH_2 ⊕ SCH_2CH_2Cl[b] CH_2	0.95
CH_3Br	1.00
$C_6H_5SO_2Cl$	1.25
C_6H_5COCl	1.43

[a] Refers to a nucleophilic attack on the β-carbon atom.
[b] Refers to a ring-opening attack.

noted that Eq. (6-4) and its special case (6-5) require that the relative order of nucleophilicities of nucleophilic reagents be invariable in a given solvent. That is, that since the iodide ion is almost 10 times as reactive as the hydroxide ion toward 2,3-epoxypropanol in aqueous solution,[3] it should be more reactive than hydroxide ion in all nucleophilic displacements on carbon taking place in aqueous solution. It has been found, however, that toward the ethylene-β-chloroethylsulfonium ion the hydroxide ion is about 12 times as reactive as the iodide ion.[3,7] There is thus a change in the relative reactivities of the two ions of more than 100-fold. Similarly, triethylamine is 26 times as reactive as pyridine toward methyl iodide, while toward isopropyl iodide pyridine is 6 times as reactive as triethylamine. This 150-fold reversal in the relative reactivity of the two amines is reasonably explained on the basis

[7] A. G. Ogston, E. R. Holiday, J. St. L. Philpot, and L. A. Stocken, *Trans. Faraday Soc.*, **44**, 45 (1948).

of steric hindrance.[8] Despite its greater steric requirements, the more basic triethylamine is more reactive than pyridine toward methyl iodide. Since any attack on isopropyl iodide is much more hindered, the steric effects are too large to overcome in this case, and pyridine is the more reactive. A similar explanation may be applied to the 100-*billion-fold* reversal said to exist in the relative nucleophilicities of pyridine and methanol toward triphenylmethyl chloride and methyl bromide in benzene solution (containing methanol for anion solvation),[9a] although it is also stated that this effect may be thermodynamic rather than kinetic.[9b] Some other explanation must be given for the increased reactivity of the hydroxide ion toward the ethylene-β-chloroethyl-sulfonium ion, however.[3] There are also reasons for believing that the rates of nucleophilic attacks on carbonyl carbon atoms may not follow Eq. (6-5).[3]

Edwards has suggested the following four-parameter equation for correlating the rates of substitution reactions:[10]

$$\log \frac{k}{k_0} = \alpha E_n + \beta H$$

Two of the parameters are defined in terms of data independent of those to which the equation is applied.

$$E_n = E^o + 2.6$$

where E^o is the oxidation potential of the nucleophilic reagent, and

$$H = pK_a + 1.74$$

where pK_a is the ionization constant of the conjugate acid of the nucleophilic reagent. k and k_0 are the rate constants for reaction with the nucleophilic reagent and with water, respectively, and α and β are constants for a given reactant, chosen to give the best agreement with the observed data. Unfortunately, many pertinent values of E^o and pK_a are not available, and so the corresponding E_n's and H's were also chosen to agree with the data. In addition to correlating data on nucleophilic displacement on carbon quite well, Edwards's equations give good correlations for displacements on oxygen, hydrogen, and sulfur, and for equilibrium constants for complex-ion formation.

6-3. Effect of Structure of R on the Rates of Nucleophilic Displacements of RY. In most cases reaction rate is discussed in terms of the

[8] H. C. Brown and N. R. Eldred, *J. Am. Chem. Soc.*, **71**, 445 (1949).

[9] (a) C. G. Swain and R. W. Eddy, *J. Am. Chem. Soc.*, **70**, 2989 (1948); (b) C. K. Ingold, "Structure and Mechanism in Organic Chemistry," p. 357, Cornell University Press, Ithaca, N.Y., 1953.

[10] J. O. Edwards, *J. Am. Chem. Soc.*, **76**, 1540 (1954).

increase in free energy required to reach the transition state, and in all cases the rate is governed by the free-energy contents of the intermediate configurations through which the reactants must pass in their transformation to products. Since a reaction mechanism is a description of these intermediate configurations, the rate must be discussed in terms of the reaction mechanism. In fact, it is often possible to state that a given type of structural change increases (or decreases) reactivity in nucleophilic displacements by a certain mechanism in cases where no statement could be made about the effect of this structural change on the rate of nucleophilic displacements in general.

6-3a. *Reactivity in S_N1 Reactions.* In most of the S_N1 reactions which have been studied kinetically the carbonium ion is a very reactive intermediate which is rapidly transformed into the final product, only small amounts usually reverting to reactant. Therefore we should discuss S_N1 reactivity in terms of the energy required to transform the reactant into the transition state leading to the intermediate carbonium ion. However, since this transition state usually differs from the reactant only in its greater similarity to the carbonium ion, the same structural changes which will stabilize a carbonium ion will usually decrease the free-energy content of a transition state leading to a carbonium ion. For this reason and for the sake of the resultant simplification in discussion, we shall follow the common practice of often discussing S_N1 reactivity in terms of the stability of the intermediate carbonium ion. However, it will be well to keep in mind the fact that it is the transition-state stability which is of fundamental importance.

The S_N1 transition state (and the intermediate carbonium ion) differs from the reactant in several important ways. First, there is a much larger partial positive charge on the carbon atom at which displacement occurs. Second, the three groups attached to this carbon atom, but not directly involved in the displacement, become much more nearly coplanar with it. Other differences include the fact that the bond to the group being replaced is considerably extended.

In many studies of S_N1 reactivity the rate of reaction of a halide with silver (or occasionally mercuric) ions is measured. This reaction is used because the metal ion, by coordinating with the halide ion, greatly facilitates its removal from carbon without simultaneously strengthening the nucleophilic attack on carbon. This greatly increases the probability that the reaction mechanism will be S_N1 but does not make it certain. The reaction with silver ion is complicated by catalysis by the precipitated silver halide, and the reaction with mercuric ion, by the existence of several mercury-halide complex ions.

In a discussion of electronic effects it is useful to consider cases in which steric factors are held constant. An example of this type appears in the solvolysis of a series of substituted benzhydryl chlorides. We have described excellent evidence that benzhydryl chloride and its p,p'-dimethyl derivative react by the S_N1 mechanism in aqueous acetone (Sec. 5-2b) and it seems very likely that the ethanolysis, studied by Norris and coworkers,[11] also proceeds by this mechanism. In Fig. 6-2

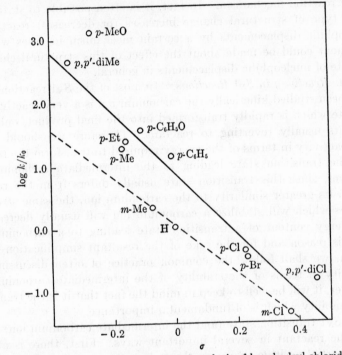

FIG. 6-2. Plot of σ vs. log k/k_0 for the ethanolysis of benzhydryl chlorides.

the relative reactivities of the compounds studied are plotted logarithmically against the σ constants for the substituents present (for p,p'-dimethyl and p,p'-dichloro the appropriate values were doubled). The linearity of the data is not as good as that usually found in Hammett-equation plots. The deviations from linearity appear clearly attributable to too great an interaction between the positively charged carbon atom and the substituents, since the unsubstituted and meta-substituted compounds fall near a line and all of the other groups, falling above this line, are para groups, which can supply electrons to the reaction center by a resonance effect. The distance these para groups lie above the line is in reasonable agreement with what might be expected from an

[11] J. F. Norris and A. A. Morton, *J. Am. Chem. Soc.*, **50**, 1795 (1928); J. F. Norris and C. Banta, *J. Am. Chem. Soc.*, **50**, 1804 (1928); J. F. Norris and J. T. Blake, *J. Am. Chem. Soc.*, **50**, 1808 (1928).

estimate of their relative abilities to supply electrons thus. The reaction is seen to be strongly accelerated by electron-donating groups, ρ being found to be -4.82 from the best line through the data or -3.74 from the dotted line. Somewhat similar deviations from linearity in Hammett-equation plots, particularly for p-methoxy compounds, have been found in the methanolysis and isopropanolysis of benzhydryl halides,[12] the solvolysis of benzyl chlorides in 50 per cent aqueous acetone[13] and 50 per cent aqueous ethanol[14] and of benzyl p-toluenesulfonates in 23.4 per cent aqueous acetone,[15] and the ethanolysis of triarylmethyl chlorides.[16]

The effect of one ortho substituent in most of the reactions which have been studied kinetically may be rationalized by the assumption of a resonance effect like that in the para position but with an inductive effect that is much stronger since the substituent is now much nearer the center of reaction.

The replacement of the α-hydrogen atoms of an alkyl halide by saturated alkyl groups causes a large increase in reactivity by the S_N1 mechanism, since the alkyl groups are much more effective than the hydrogen atoms at supplying electrons to the electron-deficient carbon atom. For this reason, tertiary alkyl halides solvolyze 10^3 to 10^4 times as rapidly as secondary halides in most solvents. The secondary halides are not always more reactive than primary halides in solvolyses, however, because of the incursion of the S_N2 mechanism in the latter case. The nature of the three α-alkyl groups in a tertiary halide usually does not have a large effect on the S_N1 reactivity except when these groups are particularly bulky. Brown and coworkers have pointed out that interference between such large alkyl groups may be relieved upon transformation to a carbonium ion, since an increase, (from about 109.5 to about 120°) in the size of the angle between the bonds attaching the three alkyl groups to the α-carbon accompanies this transformation.[17] Hughes and coworkers have also reported evidence for this type of *steric acceleration* in the solvolysis of tertiary halides.[18]

The S_N1 reactivities of halogen atoms attached to alicyclic rings vary in an interesting manner, depending on the ring size to a considerable

[12] S. Altscher, R. Baltzly, and S. W. Blackman, *J. Am. Chem. Soc.*, **74**, 3649 (1952).

[13] G. M. Bennett and B. Jones, *J. Chem. Soc.*, 1815 (1935).

[14] S. C. J. Olivier, *Rec. trav. chim.*, **41**, 646 (1922).

[15] J. K. Kochi and G. S. Hammond, *J. Am. Chem. Soc.*, **75**, 3445 (1953).

[16] A. C. Nixon and G. E. K. Branch, *J. Am. Chem. Soc.*, **58**, 492 (1936).

[17] H. C. Brown and R. S. Fletcher, *J. Am. Chem. Soc.*, **71**, 1845 (1949); H. C. Brown and A. Stern, *J. Am. Chem. Soc.*, **72**, 5068 (1950); H. C. Brown and H. L. Berneis, *J. Am. Chem. Soc.*, **75**, 10 (1953).

[18] F. Brown, T. D. Davies, I. Dostrovsky, O. J. Evans, and E. D. Hughes, *Nature*, **167**, 987 (1951).

extent. Cyclopropyl chloride is very unreactive, and cyclopropyl p-toluenesulfonate has been found to undergo acetolysis at only one-fifty-thousandth the rate for cyclohexyl p-toluenesulfonate and to yield the rearranged product allyl acetate.[19] Roberts and Chambers have pointed out that the unreactivity of these compounds is probably related to that of vinyl and phenyl halides. Like carbon atoms joined by a double bond (a two-membered ring) but to a somewhat smaller extent, the carbon atoms in cyclopropane (and probably also cyclobutane) rings appear somewhat more electronegative than ordinary saturated aliphatic carbon atoms. Also, the carbon-halogen bonds in cyclopropyl halides, like those in vinyl halides, may have partial double-bond character. Brown and coworkers have explained the unreactivity of cyclopropyl halides in terms of another factor which they call I strain (internal strain).[20] The internal angles of a cyclopropyl compound, being about 60°, are strained by 49.5° from the optimum value (109.5°) for tetrahedral carbon. The formation of a carbonium ion with optimum bond angles of 120° would increase this strain and is hence more difficult. Similar arguments would lead to the prediction of successively smaller diminutions in the S_N1 reactivities of cyclobutyl and cyclopentyl halides. As shown in Table 6-7, the decrease in reactivity of a cyclobutyl type of

TABLE 6-7. RATES OF SOLVOLYSIS OF 1-METHYL-1-CHLOROCYCLOALKANES IN "80 PER CENT ETHANOL"[a] AT 25°[19]

Cycloalkane	$10^6 k$, sec⁻¹	Cycloalkane	$10^6 k$, sec⁻¹
Cyclobutane	0.62	Cyclotridecane	8.4
Cyclopentane	367	Cyclopentadecane	5.3
Cyclohexane	2.94	Cycloheptadecane	5.6
Cycloheptane	320		
Cyclooctane	842	Analogous aliphatic chlorides:	
Cyclononane	129	t-Butyl	8.9
Cyclodecane	52.3	3-Methylpentyl	23.9
Cyclohendecane	35.3	6-Methylhendecyl	13.3

[a] 80 per cent ethanol–20 per cent water by volume.

halide has been observed in the case of 1-chloro-1-methylcyclobutane, which undergoes solvolysis in 80 per cent ethanol at less than one-tenth the rate for t-butyl chloride. The solvolysis of cyclobutyl chloride in 50 per cent ethanol, however, is about 15 times as rapid as that of sec-butyl chloride,[21] probably because of the unusual carbonium ion (see

[19] J. D. Roberts and V. C. Chambers, J. Am. Chem. Soc., 73, 5034 (1951).

[20] H. C. Brown, R. S. Fletcher, and R. B. Johannesen, J. Am. Chem. Soc., 73, 212 (1951); H. C. Brown and M. Borkowski, J. Am. Chem. Soc., 74, 1894 (1952).

[21] J. D. Roberts, J. Am. Chem. Soc., 71, 1880 (1949).

Sec. 14-1d) formed from the cyclobutyl compound.[19] On the other hand, evidently I strain is not the most important factor with cyclopentyl halides, since these compounds are more reactive than their aliphatic analogs.[19-21] Roberts and Chambers have suggested that this is probably because carbonium-ion formation involves a partial relief of the strain caused by opposed valences which gives the cyclopentane ring a nonplanar configuration (see Sec. 1-5). Brown and coworkers give a similar explanation and add that the slightly decreased S_N1 reactivity of cyclohexyl halides (see Table 6-7) results from the fact that the valences in the cyclohexyl transition state do not have the stable, perfectly staggered configuration of the unreacted molecule. Halogen atoms attached to rings with from seven to about ten members are said to be S_N1 reactive because more strain is required to stagger the valences in the reacting molecule than in the transition state.[20] The reactivity of the larger ring halides is seen to approach that of typical aliphatic compounds.

A group of alicyclic halides whose reactivity is of particular theoretical interest is composed of those bicyclic compounds having a halogen atom at a bridgehead. Bartlett and Knox reported the first study on a compound of this type, apocamphyl chloride.[22] This halide gave no reaction upon being refluxed with alcoholic silver nitrate for 48 hr or with 30 per

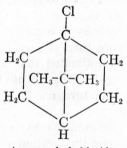

Apocamphyl chloride

cent potassium hydroxide in aqueous ethanol for 21 hr; it is thus seen to be remarkably unreactive, since, for example, typical tertiary chlorides give almost immediate precipitates with ethanolic silver nitrate at room temperature. The low S_N1 reactivity of this compound is attributed to the fact that if a carbonium ion were formed at the bridgehead, the bicyclic ring system would prevent its assuming a planar configuration. Since the electron-deficient carbon atom of a carbonium ion should form bonds by sp^2 hybridization, the most stable configuration for these bonds would be a coplanar one (the carbon-boron bonds in trialkylboron

[22] P. D. Bartlett and L. H. Knox, *J. Am. Chem. Soc.*, **61**, 3184 (1939).

compounds are known to be coplanar), and therefore apocamphyl chloride could form only a very highly strained carbonium ion.   Reaction by the S_N2 mechanism is prevented by the impossibility of rearward attack and of inversion without enormous distortion of bond angles and distances.   Using more vigorous reaction conditions, Doering and coworkers found 1-bromobicyclo[2,2,1]heptane (I) to yield the corresponding alcohol upon treatment with aqueous silver nitrate at 150° for 2 days.[23] The corresponding bicyclo[2,2,2]octane derivative (II) reacted analo-

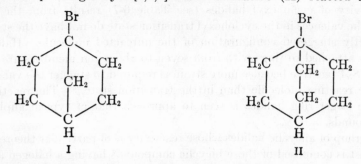

gously at room temperature in 4 hr.   Although II is still far less reactive than a typical tertiary alkyl bromide, it is much more reactive than I, a fact which is attributed to the possibility of spreading over a larger number of bonds the strain required to approach planarity.

Because of resonance stabilization of the intermediate carbonium ion, the replacement of α-hydrogen atoms by phenyl radicals increases the S_N1 reactivity even more than replacement by alkyl groups does. Thus it may be reasonably estimated that in "80 per cent acetone" triphenylmethyl chloride hydrolyzes about 10^6 times as rapidly as benzhydryl chloride, which in turn reacts about 10^3 times as rapidly as α-phenylethyl chloride.[24]

Unsaturation can have profound effects on S_N1 reactivity, the nature of these effects depending upon the location of the multiple bond.   Several reasons may be suggested for the familiar inertness of vinyl and phenyl halides (except for some negatively substituted derivatives whose reactions are discussed in Sec. 17-2).   The multiply bound carbon atoms have a greater electronegativity (see Sec. 2-4b) and hence decrease the ease with which a halide ion may be removed with its bonding electron pair.   Furthermore, the resonance stabilization resulting from the considerable contribution of structures like III is lost upon carbonium-

[23] W. von E. Doering, M. Levitz, A. Sayigh, M. Sprecher, and W. P. Whelan, Jr., *J. Am. Chem. Soc.*, **75**, 1008 (1953).

[24] E. D. Hughes, C. K. Ingold, and A. D. Scott, *J. Chem. Soc.*, 1201 (1937); M. G. Church, E. D. Hughes, and C. K. Ingold, *J. Chem. Soc.*, 966 (1940); C. G. Swain, C. B. Scott, and K. H. Lohmann, *J. Am. Chem. Soc.*, **75**, 136 (1953).

ion formation.   On the other hand, allyl halides, like benzyl halides,

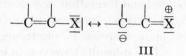

III

display considerably increased S_N1 reactivity, due to resonance stabilization of the intermediate carbonium ions.   More distantly located double bonds usually have little effect except in cases where neighboring-group participation (Sec. 14-1c) may occur.

An α-halogen substituent may withdraw electrons by the inductive effect to decrease S_N1 reactivity.   On the other hand, it may supply electrons to a deficient carbon atom by a resonance effect

$$-\overset{\underset{\oplus}{|}}{C}-\overline{\overline{X}}| \leftrightarrow -\overset{|}{C}=\overset{\oplus}{\overline{\overline{X}}}$$

to increase S_N1 reactivity.   Olivier and Weber found that in the rates of hydrolysis in 50 per cent aqueous acetone, $C_6H_5CCl_3 > C_6H_5CHCl_2 > C_6H_5CH_2Cl$.[25]   The hydrolysis rate was found to be increased by the addition of hydroxide ion in the last case but not in the first two.   For this reason and because α-chlorine increases the reactivity although it is known to decrease reactivity in certain proved S_N2 reactions, it seems likely that the hydrolysis mechanism is S_N1 for $C_6H_5CCl_3$ and C_6H_5-$CHCl_2$.   Hughes has laid this increase in reactivity to resonance stabilization, as shown above, implying that this effect is larger than the inductive effect.[26]   The effect of α-bromine has been compared with that of α-chlorine by a study of the hydrolysis rates of $C_6H_5CCl_2Br$, C_6H_5-$CClBr_2$, and $C_6H_5CBr_3$.[27]   The generally observed greater reactivity of bromides compared to chlorides and the fact that the replacement of the first halogen atom must be the rate-controlling step of the reaction make it very likely that the relative reactivities depend on the stabilities of $C_6H_5CCl_2^+$, $C_6H_5CClBr^+$, and $C_6H_5CBr_2^+$.   The relative solvolysis rates in 50 per cent aqueous acetone at 30° were 1.88:1.59:1.00, or, with a statistical correction, the relative reactivities per bromine were 5.64:2.39:1.00.   The apparently greater ability of α-chlorine to stabilize carbonium ions (compared to α-bromine), may be rationalized in terms of the greater ease of double-bond formation generally found for an element in an earlier period of the periodic table.   A comparison of the hydrolysis rates of $C_6H_5CCl_3$ and $C_6H_5CF_2Cl$ gave a relative reactivity per chlorine of 880:1, showing α-fluorine to be much less capable of

[25] S. C. J. Olivier and A. P. Weber, *Rec. trav. chim.*, **53**, 869 (1934).
[26] E. D. Hughes, *Trans. Faraday Soc.*, **37**, 603 (1941).
[27] J. Hine and D. E. Lee, *J. Am. Chem. Soc.*, **73**, 22 (1951).

stabilizing carbonium ions.[28] It may be suggested that while the increase in ease of double-bond formation may overrule the small difference in electronegativity between bromine (2.8) and chlorine (3.0), it cannot outweigh the large increase in electronegativity found upon going to fluorine (4.0). It is difficult, however, to extend this argument to a rationalization of the values of the sigma constants for fluorine, chlorine, and bromine.

The great solvolytic reactivity of α-halo ethers[29] shows that α-alkoxyl groups increase S_N1 reactivity enormously because of the particular facility with which the oxygen atom can supply electrons by a resonance effect.

The RS— group also appears to increase S_N1 reactivity by a large factor[29,30] although not so large as that found for the RO— group, presumably because oxygen forms double bonds more readily than sulfur.

As β substituents, where the electron-withdrawing inductive effect may operate but the electron-donating resonance effect may not, such groups as halogen, —OH, —OR, —OAc, —SR, —NR$_2$, etc., all decrease the ease of carbonium-ion formation, although the unimolecular reactivity may increase because of neighboring-group participation. The magnitude of both these effects is discussed in Sec. 6-3c (see Table 6-11).

Carbonyl groups appear to diminish S_N1 reactivity because of the partial positive charge placed on carbon by the contribution of resonance structures of the type of IV.

$$-\overset{\displaystyle |}{C}=\overline{O}| \leftrightarrow -\overset{\displaystyle |}{\underset{\oplus}{C}}-\overline{\underset{.}{O}}|^{\ominus}$$

IV

When a halogen atom is attached directly to a carbonyl group, this type of effect may be opposed by the stabilizing contribution of resonance structures like V.

$$-\overset{\oplus}{C}=\overline{O}| \leftrightarrow -C\equiv\overset{\oplus}{O}|$$

V

The effect of —CO$_2$R, —CN, —SO$_2$R, —NO$_2$, and related groups is similar to that of carbonyl groups.

6-3b. *Reactivity in S_N2 Reactions.* In this section we shall usually make the common assumption that in the S_N2 transition state the three atoms covalently bound to the α-carbon atom are essentially coplanar with it and that the entering nucleophilic group (X) and the group being

[28] J. Hine and D. E. Lee, *J. Am. Chem. Soc.*, **74**, 3182 (1952).
[29] H. Böhme, *Ber.*, **74B**, 248 (1941).
[30] H. Böhme, H. Fischer, and R. Frank, *Ann.*, **563**, 54 (1949).

displaced (Y) are attached to the α-carbon atom to a nearly equal extent and are approximately collinear with it, as shown below (if X = Y, the α-carbon atom is exactly coplanar with R, R', and R'' and exactly equally attached to X and Y; if R = R' = R'', X, Y, and C_α are exactly collinear).

This assumption implies that the plot of free energy vs. extent of reaction contains but a single maximum, like that shown in Fig. 6-3a.   By

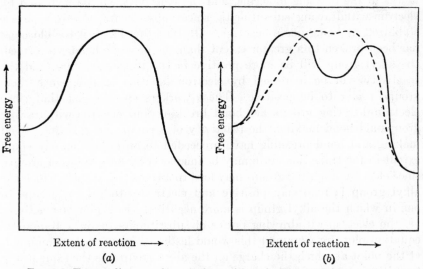

Fig. 6-3. Energy diagrams for reactions with and without an intermediate.

contrast, the proof of the existence of an intermediate in the S_N1 reaction shows that there is an intermediate minimum and hence two maxima in this energy curve.   Between the limits of such a curve, shown by the solid line in Fig. 6-3b, and the single maximum curve of Fig. 6-3a, it is possible to construct any number of intermediate curves, such as that shown by dashed lines in Fig. 6-3b.   Although we know that there is no very stable intermediate in the S_N2 mechanism, it is possible that the energy diagram does contain a small minimum.

In any event, in the transition state of a nucleophilic displacement on carbon, the nature of the C—X and C—Y bonds may vary considerably. They may be relatively long and ionic, as in the S_N1 transition state. Here X need not even be the nucleophilic reagent to which the α-carbon atom later forms a covalent bond but may instead be a molecule of solvent. In this case the alkyl group (R_3C) will be positively charged. On the other hand, if the bonds are shorter and fairly covalent, as they appear to be in the S_N2 transition state, then the alkyl group may be negatively charged, or at least less positive than it was in the reacting molecule. This idea has been expressed in a somewhat different manner by Baker and Nathan,[31] and more recently by Swain and Langsdorf,[32] who point out that as an over-all result of reaction a new bond must be formed and the old bond broken and that the relative extent to which each process has occurred in the transition state may vary. If, in the transition state, the new bond has been formed to a greater extent than the old one has been broken, the alkyl group will be more negative than it was in the reacting molecule, and the reactivity will be increased by electron-withdrawing substituents, since substituents of this type are stabilized by being made negative. On the other hand, if the old bond has been broken to a greater extent than the new one has been formed, the alkyl group will be more positive in the transition state, and the reactivity will be increased by electron-donating groups, since these groups prefer to be positive. These workers also suggest that since electron-donating groups aid bond breaking and electron-withdrawing groups aid bond making, the reactivity of a compound for which bond making and bond breaking have proceeded to an approximately equal extent in the transition state may be increased by both types of groups, since electron-donating groups may lead to a transition state in which the alkyl group is relatively positive and electron-withdrawing groups to one in which the alkyl group is more negative. In a plot of reactivity vs. the electron-withdrawing power of substituents (as in a Hammett-equation plot, for example) this would lead to a curve with a minimum at the point at which the charge on the alkyl group was the same in the transition state as in the reacting molecule, and indeed such minima have been reported.[31,32]

While bond breaking is always vastly more extensive than bond making in the S_N1 transition state, either may predominate in the S_N2 transition state, so that S_N2 reactions are sometimes aided by electron withdrawal and sometimes by electron supply. Furthermore, electronic effects are usually smaller for S_N2 displacements at a saturated carbon atom than for S_N1 reactions (although with acyl, vinyl, and phenyl halides, where the new bond may be very largely formed before the old one is broken, electron-withdrawing groups may have very large effects). However, since the α-carbon atom is bound to X and Y by relatively

[31] J. W. Baker and W. S. Nathan, *J. Chem. Soc.*, 1840 (1935); cf. E. D. Hughes, C. K. Ingold, and U. G. Shapiro, *J. Chem. Soc.*, 228 (1936).

[32] C. G. Swain and W. P. Langsdorf, Jr., *J. Am. Chem. Soc.*, **73**, 2813 (1951).

short partial covalent bonds in the S_N2 transition state, the reaction rate is quite sensitive to steric hindrance.

In discussing electronic effects alone, it is useful to consider the S_N2 reactions of some meta- and para-substituted benzyl halides and related compounds.   In a study of the exchange of radioactive bromide ions with benzyl bromides in ethylene diacetate solution, Sugden and Willis found relative rates of 6.2, 1.0, 10.0, and 11.2 for the p-methoxy, unsubstituted, p-cyano, and p-nitro compounds, respectively.[33]   If the reaction was really second-order for the p-methoxy compound (this was not tested, although it was for the p-nitro), it would appear to be an S_N2 reaction whose rate minimum occurs approximately at the unsubstituted benzyl bromide.   Hence, in this reaction the unsubstituted benzyl group bears about the same charge in the transition state as it does in the reactant molecule, while with the p-methoxy derivative it is more positive in the transition state and with p-cyano and p-nitro compounds more negative.   In somewhat similar cases, the second-order rate constants for reaction of benzyl chlorides with sodium ethoxide are increased both by m- and p-methyl groups and by m- and p-halogen atoms (by factors of less than 2.0 in all cases, however),[34a] and the rate of reaction of benzyl bromides with nitrate ion is increased by both p-methyl and p-nitro groups.[34b]   Any rate minimum in the reaction of benzyl fluorides with sodium ethoxide must occur with a somewhat stronger electron-donating group, since a p-methyl substituent increases the reactivity only very slightly and the m-methyl group produces a small decrease, while all electron-withdrawing groups increase the reactivity.[35]   In the reaction of iodide ion in acetone with benzyl chlorides, Bennett and Jones tested only electron-withdrawing substituents and found all to increase the reactivity,[36] a value of ρ of $+0.785$ having been calculated for the reaction.[6]   In this relation it is of interest that p-methyl and p-t-butyl groups have been reported to increase the reactivity of benzyl bromides toward iodide in acetate (as well as ethoxide ion in ethanol and t-butoxide ion in t-butyl alcohol).[37]   The reactivity of β-phenylethyl chlorides toward potassium iodide in acetone is increased (about 50 per cent) by the electron-donating p-methoxy group as well as by electron-withdrawing p-halogens (about 100 per cent) and the p-nitro group (400 per cent).[38]

[33] S. Sugden and J. B. Willis, *J. Chem. Soc.*, 1360 (1951).

[34] (a) H. Franzen, *J. prakt. Chem.*, **97**, 82 (1918); H. Franzen and I. Rosenberg, *J. prakt. Chem.*, **101**, 333 (1921); (b) J. W. Baker and W. S. Nathan, *J. Chem. Soc.*, 236 (1936).

[35] W. T. Miller, Jr. and J. Bernstein, *J. Am. Chem. Soc.*, **70**, 3600 (1948).

[36] G. M. Bennett and B. Jones, *J. Chem. Soc.*, 1815 (1935).

[37] Work of C. W. L. Bevan and E. D. Hughes, quoted in Ingold, *op. cit.*, p. 327.

[38] G. Baddeley and G. M. Bennett, *J. Chem. Soc.*, 1819 (1935).

Since tertiary amines react with benzyl halides to form quaternary ammonium salts in which the benzyl group is relatively positive-charged due to the inductive effect of the attached nitrogen atom, it seems possible that the charge on the benzyl group in the transition state would be considerably greater than in S_N2 reactions involving attack by anions. Since in cases of the latter type the charge in the transition state appears to be in the vicinity of that in the halide molecule for the *unsubstituted* benzyl halides, the unsubstituted benzyl group should be more positive in the transition state of an S_N2 attack by a tertiary amine, so that the reactivity would be increased by electron-donating groups and decreased by electron-withdrawing groups (until the electron withdrawal becomes strong enough to produce a rate minimum). This is indeed found to be the case. Baker and Nathan found the reactivities of benzyl bromides toward pyridine in acetone to be increased by electron-donating and decreased by electron-withdrawing groups until a rate minimum is reached in the vicinity of the p-nitro compound.[31] The data seem to be approaching a minimum in this vicinity in the reactions of trimethylamine with benzyl halides.[32] Since electron withdrawal, after having reached a certain magnitude, should increase the rate of quaternization, it is not surprising that the reactivity of phenacyl halides, in which the electron-withdrawing power of the carbonyl group has been added to that of every substituent, toward tertiary amines is increased by electron withdrawal and decreased by electron donation.[39]

The effect of ortho substituents on the reactivity of benzyl halides is fairly predictable qualitatively when steric hindrance (usually not large for one ortho substituent) is added to electronic effects of the type described.

Because of the complications produced by the possibility of steric interference with the attack of the nucleophilic reagent, of steric acceleration of the departure of the group displaced, and of entropy effects due to interference with rotation around single bonds and changes in the extent of solvation, it is very difficult to learn what influences electronic effects have on the S_N2 reactivity of alkyl halides and even more difficult to predict the reactivity which will result from the addition of an electronic effect to the other effects described. Nevertheless, some arguments will be presented leading to some generalizations which are in agreement with many of the known data and which permit predictions in untested cases.

In view of the fact that the S_N2 reactivity (in the cases studied) of methyl halides is decreased by the introduction of either an α-methyl group (electron donating) or an α-halogen atom (electron withdrawing),

[39] J. W. Baker, *J. Chem. Soc.*, 1148 (1932); 445 (1938).

it seems likely that the decrease is at least partially due to steric hindrance. Since it appears that steric effects are often the dominant factor in determining S_N2 reactivity, the discussion of this subject by Dostrovsky, Hughes, and Ingold[40] is of particular interest. This discussion is in terms of an S_N2 transition state of the type shown in Fig. 6-4. Either Fig. 6-4a or b may be considered as a model for the transition state of an S_N2 reaction of a methyl halide, where Cα represents the carbon atom, a, b, and c the hydrogen atoms, and X and Y the entering and departing nucleophilic groups. We shall use this model as a basis for comparison.

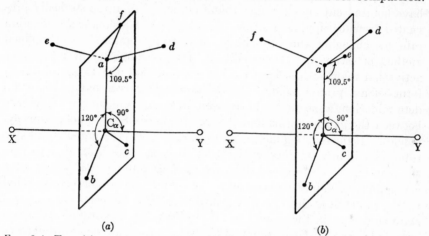

(a)   (b)

Fig. 6-4. Transition states for reaction by the S_N2 mechanism. [*Reproduced with permission from Dostrovsky, Hughes, and Ingold, J. Chem. Soc., 173 (1946).*]

In the transition state for ethyl halides a represents the β-carbon atom, d, e, and f being β-hydrogens. Fig. 6-4a very probably represents a more stable ethyl transition state than Fig. 6-4b, in which one hydrogen is placed as closely as possible to the entering nucleophilic group. Nevertheless, from calculations based on certain reasonable assumptions, it seems that the interaction of the β-hydrogen atoms with X and Y, as shown in Fig. 6-4a, will produce steric strains.[41] This agrees with the previous suggestion that the greater reactivity of methyl compared to ethyl halides, which has been observed in all of the nucleophilic displacements proved to be S_N2 in character, is at least partly due to steric hindrance. As would be expected, continued replacement of α-hydrogen atoms by methyl groups produces continued deactivation due to steric

[40] I. Dostrovsky, E. D. Hughes, and C. K. Ingold, *J. Chem. Soc.*, 173 (1946).

[41] For calculations of steric hindrance in S_N2 reactions other than those of Ref. 40, see E. C. Baughan and M. Polanyi, *Trans. Faraday Soc.*, **37**, 648 (1941); A. G. Evans and M. Polanyi, *Nature*, **149**, 608 (1942); A. G. Evans, *Trans. Faraday Soc.*, **42**, 719 (1946).

hindrance. For example, the following relative reactivities of alkyl bromides toward iodide ions in acetone have been reported: Me, 10,000; Et, 65; i-Pr, 0.50; t-Bu, 0.039.[42]

The introduction of a β-methyl group into an ethyl halide to get the n-propyl compound need not produce added steric hindrance, since the carbon of the β-methyl group may be at f in Fig. 6-4a, too distant from X and Y to cause interference. However, as Hammett and coworkers have found, the decreased reactivity of n-propyl halides (compared to ethyl) is an entropy effect.[43] In explanation, Magat and coworkers have pointed out that the fact that the methyl group is sterically prevented from occupying positions d and e should decrease the reaction rate by changing the probability or entropy factor.[44] A simplified method of estimating the magnitude of this change in the entropy of activation may be based on the assumption that the three rotational forms of a n-propyl halide have the same energy content (actually no determination appears to have been made of the energy difference between the gauche forms and the trans form [see Sec. 1-5] of a n-propyl halide). If the reacting molecule can then exist in three equally probable rotational isomeric forms, while the transition state is limited to one, the reaction should proceed only one-third as rapidly as it would for a compound which has the same activation energy but which, like an ethyl halide, can exist in three equally probable configurations in the transition state as well as in the reactant. The decrease in entropy of activation expected from the above argument (2.18 e.u.) is not far from the difference between ethyl and n-propyl halides which has been observed in several cases (2.3 e.u. for reaction with sodium thiophenolate in methanol,[45] 3.0 e.u. for reaction with sodium thiosulfate in 50 per cent ethanol[43]). When two β-methyl groups are present, however, as in an isobutyl halide, there will be increased steric repulsions even in the more favorable transition state shown in Fig. 6-4b (methyl groups at d and e), and indeed isobutyl halides show a decrease in reactivity in which increased activation energy is an important factor.[40,43] The presence of three β-methyl groups, as in a neopentyl halide, produces greatly increased strain in the transition state (Fig. 6-4a).

In accord with these generalizations, in S_N2 reactions methyl halides are usually found to be from 4 to 150 times as reactive as the corresponding ethyl halides, which in turn are usually from 1.5 to 5 times as reactive

---

[42] Data of P. B. D. de la Mare and E. D. Hughes, reported in Ingold, op. cit., p. 323.

[43] T. I. Crowell and L. P. Hammett, J. Am. Chem. Soc., 70, 3444 (1948); P. M. Dunbar and L. P. Hammett, J. Am. Chem. Soc., 72, 109 (1950).

[44] N. Ivanoff and M. Magat, J. chim. phys., 47, 914 (1950); E. Bauer and M. Magat, J. chim. phys., 47, 922 (1950).

[45] J. Hine and W. H. Brader, Jr., J. Am. Chem. Soc.. 75, 3964 (1953).

as the n-propyl halides. The reactivity of higher straight-chain primary halides, including n-propyl, does not usually differ from the average value by more than 50 per cent. If there is branching on the β-carbon (or considerable branching on the γ-carbon), the reactivity will be less; e.g., toward sodium ethoxide in ethanol at 95° the relative reactivities of ethyl, isobutyl, and neopentyl bromides are 1, 0.04, and 10^{-5}, respectively.[46]

While no completely successful general theory of electronic effects on the S_N2 reactivity of aliphatic compounds appears to have been suggested, we shall discuss this point in a manner similar to that used for benzyl halides and related compounds earlier in this section. While there are few reactions for which the rate minimum may be said to have been located, it appears that reactivity is usually increased both by strongly electron-withdrawing groups and strongly electron-donating groups, although in the latter case the S_N1 reactivity may be so high that the study of the S_N2 mechanism becomes very difficult. Weakly electron-withdrawing groups appear most commonly to decrease the S_N2 reactivity somewhat. Conant, Kirner, and Hussey have determined the reactivities of a number of alkyl chlorides toward potassium iodide in acetone,[47] a particularly good reaction for the study of the S_N2 mechanism because of the nucleophilicity of the iodide ion and the poor ionizing power of acetone (see Table 6-8). Many of these data may be rationalized on the basis of electronic and steric effects of the type described. It is seen that the replacement of an α-alkyl group by a —COR group increases the reactivity in all cases, presumably at least in part because of the considerable positive charge which is present on the carbon atom of any carbonyl group. The activating influence of —COR is seen to increase with the decreasing power of R to furnish electrons to the positively charged carbon atom. It seems likely that part of the increase in S_N2 reactivity observed with α-halocarbonyl compounds is due to diminished steric hindrance, since an examination of the S_N2 transition state in Fig. 6-4 shows that all three valences of the carbonyl carbon atom may lie in the plane perpendicular to X---C---Y, so that an α-COR group may present less steric hindrance to reaction than an α-alkyl group. The same type of argument could be used to support a steric explanation for part of the increased reactivity of allyl and benzyl halides.

Groups which can feed electrons strongly to an adjacent atom that is

[46] I. Dostrovsky and E. D. Hughes, *J. Chem. Soc.*, 157 (1946).

[47] J. B. Conant and W. R. Kirner, *J. Am. Chem. Soc.*, **46**, 233 (1924); J. B. Conant and R. E. Hussey, *J. Am. Chem. Soc.*, **47**, 476 (1925); J. B. Conant, W. R. Kirner, and R. E. Hussey, *J. Am. Chem. Soc.*, **47**, 488 (1925); W. R. Kirner, *J. Am. Chem. Soc.*, **48**, 2745 (1926); **50**, 2446 (1928).

deficient, e.g., α-methoxy and α-acetoxy, have also been found to increase the S_N2 reactivity (compared to α-alkyl groups), although here too the effect is probably partly steric.

On the other hand, the replacement of α-alkyl groups by halogen atoms decreases the S_N2 reactivity.[48] The fact that this is not always true for fluorine (coupled with other data) suggests that steric effects are important here.

TABLE 6-8. RELATIVE REACTIVITIES OF ALKYL CHLORIDES TOWARD POTASSIUM IODIDE IN ACETONE AT 50°[47]

Alkyl group	k^a	Alkyl group	k^a
C_2H_5	2.52	$NCCH_2{}^b$	3,070
$n\text{-}C_3H_7$	1.08	$C_6H_5COCH_2{}^b$	105,000
$n\text{-}C_4H_9$	1.00	$CH_3COCH_2{}^b$	35,700
$n\text{-}C_5H_{11}$	1.35	$EtO_2CCH_2{}^b$	1,720
$n\text{-}C_6H_{13}$	1.30	$EtO_2CCH_2CH_2$	1.6
$n\text{-}C_{12}H_{25}$	1.17	$EtO_2CCH_2CH_2CH_2$	1.6
$n\text{-}C_{30}H_{61}$	0.92	H_2NCOCH_2	99
$i\text{-}C_3H_7{}^b$	0.015	$CH_3CO_2CH_2{}^b$	270
$sec\text{-}C_4H_9{}^b$	0.022	$CH_3OCH_2{}^b$	918
$CH_2{=}CHCH_2{}^b$	79	$C_6H_5OCH_2CH_2$	0.3
$C_6H_5CH_2{}^b$	197	$CH_3SCH_2CH_2$	1.5
$C_6H_5CH_2CH_2$	1.16	$ClCH_2{}^c$	0.19[d]
Cyclohexyl	$<10^{-3}$	$ICH_2{}^c$	0.14
C_6H_5	$<10^{-3}$		

[a] Relative to $n\text{-}C_4H_9$.

[b] Extrapolated from data at other temperatures.

[c] J. Hine, C. H. Thomas, and S. J. Ehrenson, *J. Am. Chem. Soc.*, **77**, 3886 (1955).

[d] A statistical factor of two has been applied in this case to obtain the reactivity per chlorine.

The relative effects of various alkyl groups on the rate of S_N2 attack by iodide ion in acetone (see Table 6-8) are considerably like those found in other S_N2 reactions. In fact, a linear free-energy approximation could be devised with the form

$$\log \frac{k}{k_0} = r\alpha$$

where k is the S_N2 rate constant for the given compound, k_0 is that for a standard compound (e.g., the n-butyl compound), α is a structure constant describing the effect of the alkyl group on S_N2 reactivity, and r is a reaction constant dependent upon the nature of the nucleophilic reagent, solvent, etc., and describing the sensitivity of the rate to changes in α. Such a linear free-energy approximation would probably give a

[48] J. Hine, C. H. Thomas, and S. J. Ehrenson, *J. Am. Chem. Soc.*, **77**, 3886 (1955).

somewhat poorer agreement (but not very much poorer) with the observed data than the linear free-energy relationships we have described previously. While no such equation appears to have been suggested yet, it might be useful if only as an ideal relationship, the significant departures from which require explanation.

As shown in Table 6-9, the replacement of β-hydrogen atoms by fluorine, chlorine, or bromine atoms has been found to decrease the reactivity toward sodium thiophenolate in methanol.[45] The decrease in entropy of activation which is observed to accompany the increasing size of the

TABLE 6-9. REACTIVITIES OF ALKYL BROMIDES TOWARD SODIUM THIOPHENOLATE IN METHANOL AT 20°[45]

Alkyl group	k, liters mole^{-1} sec^{-1}, $\times 10^4$	$\Delta H,^{\ddagger a}$ kcal/mole	$\Delta S^{\ddagger b}$, e.u./mole
HCH$_2$CH$_2$	39.1	18.1	-7.7
CH$_3$CH$_2$CH$_2$	25.6	17.7	-10.0
C$_2$H$_5$CH$_2$CH$_2$	26.9	17.7	-10.0
FCH$_2$CH$_2$	4.95	19.4	-7.3
ClCH$_2$CH$_2$	5.61	19.1	-8.3
BrCH$_2$CH$_2$	4.99^c	18.7	-9.7

^{a} ± 0.3 kcal.
^{b} ± 0.7 e.u.
^{c} Rate constant *per* bromine (one-half the total rate constant for ethylene bromide).

β substituent may be due to increasing interference in rotation around the C$_\alpha$—C$_\beta$ bond in the transition state. The increase in heat of activation which accompanies the increased electron-withdrawing power of the β substituent may be an electronic effect. The introduction of a halogen atom on the γ- or a more distant carbon atom of an alkyl chain usually has little effect on the S_N2 reactivity.[49]

The apparently electronic deactivating influence of β-halogens and alkoxy radicals is anomalous, however, since the fact that a p-nitro group increases the reactivity of β-phenylethyl chloride toward iodide ions in acetone by 400 per cent[38] would, from the theory of electronic effects we have been using, lead to the prediction that S_N2 reactivity should be increased by all electron-withdrawing groups equal or superior to the p-nitrophenyl group (a category in which the halogens would be expected to belong).

As previously stated, the increased reactivity of benzyl and allyl halides compared to ordinary saturated primary halides may have a steric basis, since a phenyl or vinyl radical is probably thinner than an alkyl radical. However, these compounds are often equally or more

[49] W. H. Brader, Jr., Ph.D. thesis, Georgia Institute of Technology, 1954.

reactive than methyl halides, as in the reaction with iodide in acetone, where methyl and benzyl bromides are about equally reactive.[50] Steric effects should make the benzyl compound considerably less reactive, and yet its reactivity cannot be explained in terms of an inductive effect, since α-fluorine, a smaller and more strongly electron-withdrawing group, caused decreased reactivity (compared to α-hydrogen) toward iodide in acetone.[48] Indeed an electronic explanation for the reactivity of benzyl (compared to methyl) halides does not appear to be forth-coming from the general theory in terms of which we have been discussing S_N2 reactivity, since in reaction with iodide in acetone the unsubstituted benzyl compound appears from the data given previously[36,37] to lie at about the rate minimum. However, in none of the anomalous cases which we have mentioned do any of the rate constants differ by more than a factor of 10 from values in reasonable agreement with the general theory.

The decreased S_N2 reactivities of cyclopropyl and cyclobutyl halides (see Table 6-10) have been attributed to the same factors which explained their S_N1 inertness, since a more electronegative carbon atom should be less susceptible to nucleophilic attack, a carbon-halogen bond with double-bond character should be more difficult to break, and I strain should still be present, the S_N2 transition state, too, having optimum bond angles of $120°$.[19,20,51] Cyclohexyl bromide is also seen to be rather unreactive. Since the bromine atom in this molecule probably occupies an equatorial position (see Sec. 1-6), it is understandable that nucleo-

TABLE 6-10. REACTIVITY OF CYCLOALKYL BROMIDES TOWARD IODIDE ION IN ACETONE[51]

Alkyl group	$10^7 k$ at $70°$, liters mole^{-1} sec^{-1}
Cyclopropyl	<0.01^a
Cyclobutyl	0.98
Cyclopentyl	208
Cyclohexyl	1.29
Cycloheptyl	127
Isopropyl	130

^{a} Based on the report of "no reaction" at $100°$ in J. D. Roberts and V. C. Chambers, *J. Am. Chem. Soc.*, **73**, 5034 (1951).

philic attack from the rear should be sterically hindered. In addition, the perfectly staggered configuration of the valences in a cyclohexane derivative would be destroyed in the S_N2 transition state. Cyclopentyl and cycloheptyl bromides are found to be about as reactive as the isopropyl compounds, probably because of a compensation of effects.

[50] A. G. Evans and S. D. Hamann, *Trans. Faraday Soc.*, **47**, 25 (1951).
[51] P. J. C. Fierens and P. Verschelden, *Bull. soc. chim. Belges*, **61**, 427 (1952).

6-3c. *Reactivity in Neighboring-group Displacements.* Winstein, Grunwald, and coworkers have given an excellent discussion of the effect of structure on the rate of reactions involving neighboring groups.[52] Using solvolysis data for reactions in which S_N2 attack by solvent seems very unlikely, these workers point out that the reaction of a compound containing the β neighboring group —SA may have as its rate-controlling step either a carbonium-ion formation

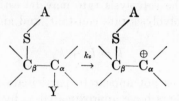

or a nucleophilic displacement by the neighboring group.

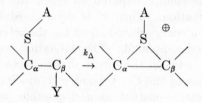

Before considering the effect of the nature of —SA on the reactivity, it is useful to discuss the effect of the nature of C_α and C_β. As previously stated, methyl groups on C_α increase k_c, the rate constant for carbonium-ion formation, by a factor of about 10^4. Methyl groups on C_β have little effect unless the large number required for considerable B strain are present. The initial product of neighboring-group participation will be a resonance hybrid of the structures

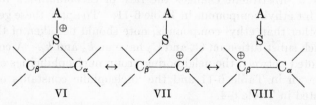

to which VII and VIII will contribute equally if C_α and C_β are identically substituted. In the transition state leading to this intermediate, however, a structure similar to VII should contribute more than one analogous to VIII. Therefore it is reasonable that the rate should be increased by methylation of either carbon atom but more so by methylation of C_α.

[52] S. Winstein, E. Grunwald, et al., *J. Am. Chem. Soc.*, **70**, 812, 816, 821, 828 (1948)

Winstein and Grunwald state that a methyl group on C_α increases k_Δ, the rate constant for neighboring-group displacement, by about 200-fold and on C_β by about 20-fold. This stabilizing effect of both α- and β-methyl groups on the three-membered ring of the transition state may be related to their stabilization of double bonds, or two-membered rings (see Sec. 1-1d).

The nucleophilic driving force which the participation of the neighboring group adds to the solvolysis rate may be estimated from a determination of k, the solvolysis rate constant, and an estimate of k_c, since

$$k = k_c + k_\Delta$$

Since β-hydrogen does not appear to participate in the cases studied, Winstein and coworkers have approximated k_c by estimating the effect which the transformation of β-hydrogen to the substituent in question would have on the energy required to reach the transition state for carbonium-ion formation. Then k_c is determined by the amount by which this change in energy would affect k_H, the solvolysis rate constant for the unsubstituted compound. The estimation involved a calculation on the interaction between the dipole due to —SA and the one being formed by ionization of the C—Y bond. It was improved by treating the effective dielectric constant as a disposable parameter given the value necessary to make k equal k_c for the substituent β-chlorine, for which there is good evidence for nonparticipation in the cases studied. The nucleophilic driving force of the β substituent may be expressed either in terms of k_Δ/k_c, the ratio of the rate of the neighboring-group displacement to that of the carbonium-ion formation, or in terms of k/k_H, the factor by which the presence of the β substituent changes the solvolysis rate. Estimates of these factors and of k_c/k_H, the factor by which the β substituent changes the rate of carbonium-ion formation, are given for ethyl compounds in Table 6-11. To apply these generalizations to other than ethyl compounds, note should be taken of the differences which substitution on C_α and C_β have on k_Δ and k_c. A correlation may be noted between the neighboring-group nucleophilicities of various groups shown in Table 6-11 and the nucleophilic constants of related groups listed in Table 6-4.

A factor of considerable importance in determining the reactivity of a neighboring group is its distance from the carbon atom it attacks. While nearness of a neighboring group should in itself facilitate reaction, the closer neighboring group will produce small, and hence strained, rings. To avoid strain a ring of five members or more should be formed. In all of the cases which have been investigated there have been other factors operating in addition to ring size. Freundlich, Salomon, and coworkers have studied the cyclization of compounds of the type $H_2N(CH_2)_nBr$ when n was varied from two to six with the results shown in Table 6-12.[53] Here it seems that an increase in ring size from three to four does not offset the effect of separating the two reactive centers, but the almost total removal of ring strain in the five-membered case does. Thereafter, with no further large change in ring strain the distance factor controls. In addition to these factors, however, it might also be noted

TABLE 6-11. EFFECTS OF β SUBSTITUENTS ON RATES OF NEIGHBORING-GROUP DISPLACEMENTS AND CARBONIUM-ION FORMATION OF ETHYL COMPOUNDS[52]

β-Group	k/k_H	k_Δ/k_c	k_c/k_H
O^{-a}	10^{10}	10^4	10^6
SCH_2CH_2OH	10^7	10^9	10^{-2}
NH_2	10^4	10^5	10^{-1}
I	1.6×10^3	2×10^6	7×10^{-4}
Br	0.4	2×10^3	2×10^{-4}
OH, OCH_3	0.1	10	10^{-2}

^{a} The values for this substituent were obtained from data on base-catalyzed transformations of halohydrins to epoxides and involve estimates of the acidities of the halohydrins.

TABLE 6-12. RATES OF CYCLIZATION OF ω-AMINOALKYL BROMIDES IN WATER AT $25°$[53]

Compound	$10^4 k, sec^{-1}$
$H_2N(CH_2)_2Br$	6
$H_2N(CH_2)_3Br$	0.08
$H_2N(CH_2)_4Br$	$5,000^a$
$H_2N(CH_2)_5Br$	80
$H_2N(CH_2)_6Br$	0.1

^{a} Estimated from k for the chloride ($80 \times 10^{-4} sec^{-1}$).

that the amino group in aminoethyl bromide is probably the least basic of those listed, so that its nucleophilicity (toward external carbon atoms anyway) should be the least. Similarly the ease of replacement of the bromine in this molecule will be affected by the presence, on the β-carbon atom, of an amino group (becoming an ammonium group as the reaction proceeds). The substitution of alkyl groups alpha to the bromine atom in the series above could change the order of reactivities considerably since, as mentioned earlier, this would increase the ease of formation of the three-membered ring, but, as Freundlich and Salomon have found, it decreases the rate of reaction to give a five-membered ring (just as it decreases intermolecular S_N2 reactivity).

[53] This work is summarized and discussed by G. Salomon, *Helv. Chim. Acta*, **16**, 1361 (1933); **17**, 851 (1934).

The first-order decomposition of the anions of a number of bromo acids, believed to involve the intermediate formation of lactones in all cases except those noted, has been studied by Lane, Heine, and coworkers.[54] The data (Table 6-13) show that in this case the four-membered ring is formed faster than the three. Two double bonds on the same carbon atom, as in allenes and ketenes, usually produce some instability. By the analogy of small rings to double bonds, it seems possible that the attachment of a double-bonded oxygen atom to small lactone rings might increase the ring-stability factor to the point where it is controlling. However, as in the case of the bromoamines, there are certainly other factors present too.

TABLE 6-13. RATES OF LACTONIZATION OF THE ANIONS OF BROMO ACIDS IN WATER AT $25°$[54]

Acid	$10^6 k$, sec^{-1}
α-Bromopropionic	0.42
α-Bromohexanoic	0.55
β-Bromopropionic	3.5
β-Bromohexanoic	35
γ-Bromopentanoic	5,500
ϵ-Bromohexanoic	1.7
ζ-Bromoheptanoic	0.43^a

^{a} This reaction may just be hydrolysis, and if so, the k is a maximum for lactonization.

6-4. Effect of the Nature of Y on the Reactivity of RY. Since the group Y, in being displaced, is acquiring sole possession of an electron pair which it previously merely shared, it is reasonable that its reactivity should increase as the basicity of Y| decreases. This correlation is only very approximate unless one restricts the comparison to Y groups in which the nature of the atom forming the bond to carbon is the same, and even in this case it is not at all perfect. Fairly good Hammett-equation relationships have been obtained in two reactions of ethyl esters of various benzenesulfonic acids. For the solvolysis in 30 per cent ethanol at $25°$, log k_0 (sec^{-1}) $= -5.262$, and $\rho = 1.190$,[55] while for reaction with sodium ethoxide in ethanol at $35°$,[56] log k_0 (liters mole^{-1} sec^{-1}) $= -2.89$ and $\rho = 1.38$. A considerably broader linear free-energy relationship has been found by Hammett and Pfluger to exist for the reaction of trimethylamine with methyl esters.[57] These workers

$$RCO_2CH_3 + (CH_3)_3N \rightarrow RCO_2^{\ominus} + (CH_3)_4N^{\oplus}$$

[54] J. F. Lane and H. W. Heine, *J. Am. Chem. Soc.*, **73**, 1348 (1951); H. W. Heine, E. Becker and J. F. Lane, *J. Am. Chem. Soc.*, **75**, 4514 (1953).

[55] Hammett, *op. cit.*, p. 190.

[56] M. S. Morgan and L. H. Cretcher, *J. Am. Chem. Soc.*, **70**, 375 (1948).

[57] L. P. Hammett and H. L. Pfluger, *J. Am. Chem. Soc.*, **55**, 4079 (1933).

found that a logarithmic plot of the rate constants for these reactions against the ionization constants of the corresponding acids, RCO_2H, approximates a straight line even when data on aliphatic acids and ortho- as well as meta- and para-substituted benzoic acids are used. They state that the relation does not extend to the reaction of trimethylamine with the methyl "esters" of phenols, however.

Since the coordination of a proton with $Y|$ will always decrease its basicity, the group YH will always be more readily displaced than Y itself. This fact probably finds its greatest utility in the reactions of alcohols and ethers, since there are very few instances of nucleophilic displacements of OH and OR groups attached to saturated carbon atoms. These groups are, however, sufficiently basic to exist to a considerable extent as OH_2^+ and OHR^+ under acidic conditions, and it is almost always in these forms that they react. The solvolysis of fluorides has also been shown to be acid-catalyzed.[35,58] While the solvolysis of chlorides has been found to be insensitive to acid catalysis in aqueous solution,[59a] certain reactions of chlorides are subject to acid catalysis in more weakly basic solvents, such as nitrobenzene.[59b] The Friedel-Crafts reaction is an example of a Lewis acid–catalyzed nucleophilic displacement reaction which proceeds with bromides and iodides as well as chlorides and fluorides.

Another factor which may have an enormous effect on reactivity is the release during a nucleophilic displacement of the strain associated with a three- or four-membered ring. While unprotonated OR groups are ordinarily displaced only with the greatest difficulty, ethylene oxide is so reactive that it will render an aqueous solution of potassium chloride basic to phenolphthalein quickly at room temperature due to the reaction[60]

$$Cl^- + \underset{\displaystyle \overset{\textstyle \diagdown \diagup}{O}}{CH_2CH_2} \rightarrow ClCH_2CH_2O^\ominus + H_2O \rightarrow ClCH_2CH_2OH + OH^-$$

Brønsted, Kilpatrick, and Kilpatrick have made a careful kinetic study of the analogous reactions of glycidol (2,3-epoxypropanol) and epichlorohydrin (2,3-epoxypropyl chloride) and have shown that they involve a bimolecular attack by the chloride ion in the rate-controlling (first) step. Similar reactions have been found for a number of other nucleophilic anions, including hydroxide ion, which yield the hydrolysis

[58] N. B. Chapman and J. L. Levy, *J. Chem. Soc.*, 1677 (1952).

[59] (a) S. C. J. Olivier and G. Berger, *Rec. trav. chim.*, **41**, 637 (1922); S. C. J. Olivier and A. P. Weber, *Rec. trav. chim.*, **53**, 869 (1934); (b) H. F. Herbrandson, R. T. Dickerson, Jr., and J. Weinstein, *J. Am. Chem. Soc.*, **76**, 4046 (1954).

[60] J. N. Brønsted, M. Kilpatrick, and M. Kilpatrick, *J. Am. Chem. Soc.*, **51**, 428 (1929).

product, a glycol. In addition, at pH's lower than about 4, acid-catalyzed reactions become noticeable. These include third-order reactions such as one whose rate is

$$v = k[C_2H_4O][H^+][Br^-]$$

and which probably proceeds by the mechanism

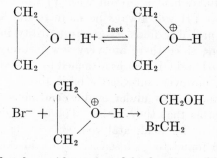

and also a second-order acid-catalyzed hydration, which may be either an S_N2 attack of water on the conjugate acid of the epoxide or the spontaneous formation of a carbonium ion from this conjugate acid followed by combination with water, depending on the structure of the epoxide.[61] There is also a first-order uncatalyzed hydration reaction which, in many cases at least, probably involves an S_N2 attack by solvent molecules. A mechanism involving an S_N2 attack by hydroxide ions on the conjugate acid of the epoxide is in agreement with the kinetics, since the product, $[H^+][OH^-]$, is a constant. But in the cases of ethylene oxide and glycidol it does not seem likely that this mode of reaction comprises a very large fraction of the total in view of the magnitude of the rate constants for reaction of hydroxide ions with the epoxides themselves[7,62] and the extent to which acid is found to catalyze the reactions with other nucleophilic reagents.[60]

Searles has shown that a change in ring size has the expected effect, the reaction of thiosulfate ion with ethylene oxide proceeding more than 15 times as rapidly as the reaction with trimethylene oxide.[63] The acid-catalyzed reaction, however, appears to proceed at about the same rate for both compounds. This is probably due to the fact that the greater basicity of trimethylene oxide increases the equilibrium concentration of its conjugate acid. The difficulty of cleavage of the five-membered ring of tetrahydrofuran is comparable to that of an aliphatic ether.

[61] The mechanisms of this and related reactions are discussed by S. Winstein and R. B. Henderson in R. C. Elderfield, "Heterocyclic Compounds," vol. I, chap. 1, John Wiley & Sons, Inc., New York, 1950.

[62] H. J. Lichtenstein and G. H. Twigg, *Trans. Faraday Soc.*, **44**, 905 (1948).

[63] S. Searles, *J. Am. Chem. Soc.*, **73**, 4515 (1951).

In comparisons of the ease of displacement of various Y groups when there are variations in the nature of the atom whose bond to carbon is broken, there appears to be no over-all theory to correlate the existing data, although the basicity of the group displaced is still important. Some of the more common groups, in the order of their decreasing ease of displacement, are as follows: $-\overset{+}{N} \equiv N > OSO_2R > I \sim Br > NO_3 \sim Cl > OH_2^+ \sim SMe_2^+ > F > OSO_3^- > NR_3^+ > OR > NR_2$. This list is by no means invariable. There will be a large change in the relative reactivities of charged groups compared to uncharged ones as the solvent is changed (the list above was largely estimated from data in aqueous solution). These changes may be predicted qualitatively from the theory of solvent effects of Sec. 3-2a. There will also be changes in the series with variations in the nature of the alkyl group to which Y is attached and with variations in the nucleophilic reagent. Most of the data on variations of Y concern alkyl halides. Glew and Moelwyn-Hughes found the relative rates of solvolysis in water at 100° to be $CH_3F:CH_3Cl:CH_3Br:CH_3I::1:25:300:100$.[64] More often the iodide is found to be the most reactive of the halides, as in the example of Tronov and Krüger, who report the relative reactivities of isoamyl halides toward piperidine to be $RF:RCl:RBr:RI::1:68:17,800:50,500$.[65] The reactivity of fluorides relative to chlorides is often much lower than in the two preceding cases, k_{RCl}/k_{RF} being about 10^6 in the solvolysis of triphenylmethyl halides in 85 per cent acetone.[66]

[64] D. N. Glew and E. A. Moelwyn-Hughes, *Proc. Roy. Soc. (London)* **211A**, 254 (1952).

[65] B. V. Tronov and E. A. Krüger, *Zhur. Russ. Fiz.-Khim. Obshchestva*, **58**, 1270 (1926); *Chem. Abstr.*, **21**, 3887⁹ (1927).

[66] C. G. Swain and C. B. Scott, *J. Am. Chem. Soc.*, **75**, 246 (1953).

CHAPTER 7

ELIMINATION REACTIONS

Elimination reactions are usually considered to be reactions in which two atoms or groups are removed from a molecule without being replaced by other atoms or groups. Most commonly these groups are on adjacent atoms, so that these adjacent atoms are joined by a multiple bond in the product, e.g.,

$$X-\overset{|}{\underset{|}{C_\beta}}-\overset{|}{\underset{|}{C_\alpha}}-Y \xrightarrow{-\text{ X and Y}} \overset{|}{C}=\overset{|}{C}$$

Elimination reactions of this type may be called beta eliminations, and since they are the most common, the "beta" is often omitted. In addition, an alpha-elimination has already been described as the rate-controlling step in the basic hydrolysis of haloforms (Sec. 5-6); such reactions as

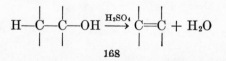

may be called gamma eliminations.

7-1. Beta Eliminations of HY to Form Carbon-Carbon Double and Triple Bonds. In the majority of beta-elimination reactions which have been studied one of the two atoms or groups removed from the molecule is a hydrogen atom. For such reactions, e.g., the dehydrohalogenation of alkyl halides,

$$H-\overset{|}{\underset{|}{C}}-\overset{|}{\underset{|}{C}}-X + KOH \rightarrow \overset{|}{C}=\overset{|}{C} + KX + H_2O$$

the dehydration of alcohols,

$$H-\overset{|}{\underset{|}{C}}-\overset{|}{\underset{|}{C}}-OH \xrightarrow{H_2SO_4} \overset{|}{C}=\overset{|}{C} + H_2O$$

168

and the Hofmann degradation of quaternary ammonium hydroxides

$$H—\overset{|}{\underset{|}{C}}—\overset{|}{\underset{|}{C}}—NR_3{}^+ \xrightarrow{OH^-} \overset{|}{\underset{|}{C}}=\overset{|}{\underset{|}{C}} + R_3N$$

Hughes, Ingold, and coworkers have suggested two mechanisms. One of these, the $E1$ (elimination unimolecular), like the S_N1 mechanism, involves as the first step the formation of a carbonium ion.[1] Instead of combining with a nucleophilic reagent, the carbonium ion in this case donates a proton to a base to become an olefin. In the $E2$ mechanism a base attacks and removes the β-hydrogen atom while simultaneously a double bond is formed between C_α and C_β, and the Y group is displaced.[2]

7-1a. *The E2 Mechanism.* The $E2$ mechanism for removal of HY is kinetically first order in RY and also in base. This shows that both reactants are involved during or before the rate-controlling step of the reaction. Certainly the only reasonable function of the base is the removal of an H^+ ion from the β-carbon atom. One mechanism of this type which would have second-order kinetics might be called the *carbanion mechanism*. It involves the reversible formation of a carbanion, which, as the rate-controlling step, subsequently loses Y.

$$H—\overset{|}{\underset{|}{C}}—\overset{|}{\underset{|}{C}}—Y + B \rightleftharpoons {}^{\ominus}|\overset{|}{\underset{|}{C}}—\overset{|}{\underset{|}{C}}—Y + BH \qquad (7\text{-}1)$$

$${}^{\ominus}|\overset{|}{\underset{|}{C}}—\overset{|}{\underset{|}{C}}—Y \rightarrow \overset{|}{\underset{|}{C}}=\overset{|}{\underset{|}{C}} + Y$$

For ordinary alkyl halides this mechanism seems very improbable, however, since many dehydrohalogenation reactions of alkyl halides proceed readily under conditions which would be utterly inadequate for the formation of a carbanion with no better stabilizing substituents than a β-halogen atom. Skell, Hauser, and coworkers have tested for this mechanism in the reaction of β-phenylethyl bromide with sodium ethoxide and the reaction of several alkyl halides with potassium amide.[3] They ran the reaction in ethanol containing a large fraction of C_2H_5OD, and after the reaction was only about half completed, they isolated the unreacted bromide. If the carbanion mechanism (7-1) had operated, this β-phenylethyl bromide would have contained deuterium due to the

[1] E. D. Hughes, *J. Am. Chem. Soc.*, **57**, 708 (1935); E. D. Hughes, C. K. Ingold, and coworkers, *J. Chem. Soc.*, 1271, 1277, 1280, 1283 (1937).

[2] C. K. Ingold and coworkers, *J. Chem. Soc.*, 997 (1927); 3125, 3127 (1928); 2338, 2342 (1929); 705 (1930); 68, 523, 526, 531, 533, 991, 1571 (1933); 236, 244 (1935); 225 (1936); 1177, 1192 (1937).

[3] P. S. Skell and C. R. Hauser, *J. Am. Chem. Soc.*, **67**, 1661 (1945).

reversible first step. The fact that it contained none shows that the removal of the β-hydrogen makes the loss of bromide ion inevitable. No evidence for the carbanion mechanism was found in the potassium amide dehydrohalogenation of n-octyl bromide and chloride and 2-ethylhexyl bromide.[3] This fact, as well as other data, makes it very likely that in the kinetically second-order base-catalyzed transformation of ordinary alkyl halides to olefins the removal of the β-proton, the formation of the double bond, and the displacement of Y all occur simultaneously thus:

$$\text{HO}^- + \text{H}-\overset{|}{\underset{|}{\text{C}}}-\overset{|}{\underset{|}{\text{C}}}-\text{Y} \rightarrow \text{HO}\cdots\text{H}\cdots\overset{|}{\text{C}}\!=\!\overset{|}{\text{C}}\cdots\text{Y} \rightarrow \text{HOH} + \overset{|}{\text{C}}\!=\!\overset{|}{\text{C}} + \text{Y}$$

This mechanism, the $E2$, has been found to possess a stereospecificity which brings to mind that of the S_N2 reaction, viz., the reaction proceeds most readily if the hydrogen atom removed is trans to the Y group. In the formation of triple bonds this was shown long ago by Michael, who found that chlorofumaric acid undergoes alkaline dehydrohalogenation about 50 times as rapidly as chloromaleic acid.[4] Miller and Noyes have shown that the alkaline dehydrohalogenation of dihaloethylenes occurs more rapidly for the cis compounds, where the elimination must be trans, than for the trans compounds, where it must be cis.[5] The relative reactivities toward sodium methoxide in methanol at 60° were found to be 3.3×10^3 for the chloride, 5.5×10^5 for the bromide, and 1.3×10^5 for the iodide. Hückel, Tappe, and Legutke have shown that the preference for trans elimination holds for the base-catalyzed formation of double bonds as well. These workers studied the formation of 2-menthene (I) and 3-menthene (II) from menthyl (III) and neomenthyl (IV) chlorides and menthyl (V) and neomenthyl (VI) trimethylammonium hydroxides.[6] From their observations shown in the reaction scheme it may be seen that when the group Y has a hydrogen atom trans to it on only one of the adjacent carbon atoms, elimination occurs exclusively in that direction. This is not due to any overwhelmingly greater ease of removal of hydrogen from the methylenic carbon atom, since when the methylenic and methinyl carbons bear trans hydrogens, elimination occurs to a considerable extent in each direction. Therefore the difference in behavior is due to a strong preference for trans rather than cis elimination. Another illustration of the stereospecificity of the $E2$ mechanism is due to Cristol and coworkers, who have

---

[4] A. Michael, *J. prakt. Chem.*, **52**, 308 (1895); see also S. J. Cristol and A. Begoon, *J. Am. Chem. Soc.*, **74**, 5025 (1952).

[5] S. I. Miller and R. M. Noyes, *J. Am. Chem. Soc.*, **74**, 629 (1952); see also G. Chavanne, *Bull. soc. chim. Belges*, **26**, 287 (1912).

[6] W. Hückel, W. Tappe, and G. Legutke, *Ann.*, **543**, 191 (1940).

studied the isomeric benzene hexachlorides (1,2,3,4,5,6-hexachlorocyclo-hexanes),[7] of which there are eight possible stereoisomers, neglecting optical activity. The kinetics of the dehydrochlorination of five of these isomers were studied, and it was found that one isomer reacted

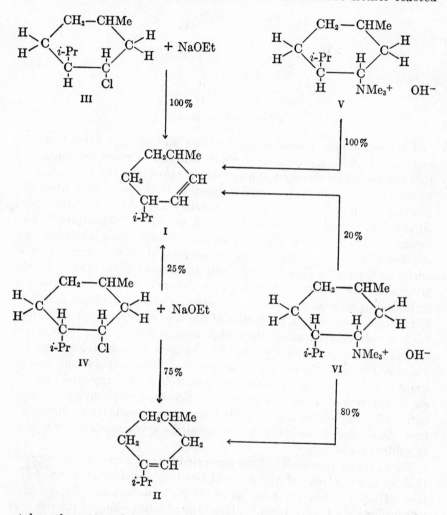

at less than 10^{-4} the rate of any of the others (which differed in rate from each other by considerably smaller factors). This one, the β isomer, had already been shown independently to be the 1,3,5-*cis*-2,4,6-*trans*-hexachlorocyclohexane isomer,

[7] S. J. Cristol, *J. Am. Chem. Soc.*, **69**, 338 (1947); **71**, 1894 (1949); S. J. Cristol, N. L. Hause, and J. S. Meek, *J. Am. Chem. Soc.*, **73**, 674 (1951).

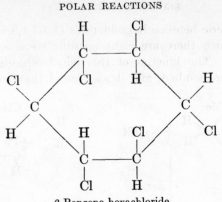

β-Benzene hexachloride

and hence the only isomer which contains no hydrogen atom trans to, and on a carbon adjacent to, a chlorine atom. Cristol has suggested that the occurring cis elimination probably takes place by the carbanion mechanism. In support of this suggestion it is found that when the reaction is run in deuteroethanol, unreacted material isolated after about 50 per cent completion contains a small amount of deuterium.[8] This mechanism has also been suggested for the cis eliminations of the dichloro-ethylenes,[5] and the observation of base-catalyzed deuterium exchange of trichloroethylene[9] shows it may occur in a trans elimination. In the latter case the carbanion mechanism is favored, since the carbanion is stabilized by an α- and two β-chlorine atoms and a double bond and since, in addition, some of the properties of haloacetylenes suggest that these triple bonds may be at a rather high energy level. By effects of the type of the two just described and by changing Y so as to make its displacement more difficult, many instances of the carbanion mechanism could probably be found. Letsinger and Bobko have reported that the cis elimination of methanol from trans-1-methoxy-2-phenylcyclohexane by butyllithium occurs more rapidly than the analogous trans elimination from the cis isomer, and they have suggested a cyclic reaction mechanism to explain these data.[10]

The ordinary prevalence of the concerted trans E2 mechanism suggests that as the electrons of the β-C—H bond are freed by removal of H$^+$, they attack C$_α$ from the rear (as in the S$_N$2 mechanism), displacing Y and forming the double bond.[7] This type of interlocking of the removal of H$^+$, formation of a double bond, and displacement of Y is not possible when the β-hydrogen is cis, and, according to Cristol and Hause, it is possible only when the β-hydrogen is exactly trans, so that Y, C$_α$, C$_β$,

[8] S. J. Cristol and D. D. Fix, J. Am. Chem. Soc., 75, 2647 (1953).

[9] L. C. Leitch and H. J. Bernstein, Can. J. Research, 28B, 35 (1950).

[10] R. L. Letsinger and E. Bobko, J. Am. Chem. Soc., 75, 2649 (1953).

and H_β can be coplanar in the transition state.[11] As evidence for this requirement, it is of interest that the trans isomer (VII) of 11,12-dichloro-9,10-dihydro-9,10-ethanoanthracene undergoes base-catalyzed elimination of hydrogen chloride somewhat faster than does the cis isomer

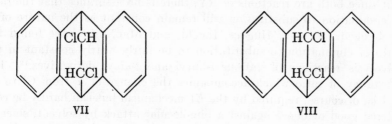

VII   VIII

(VIII).[11] Because of the restraint due to the bicyclic ring system, the valences of the ethano bridge cannot become staggered but must be opposed (or very nearly so). This means that in VIII the β-hydrogen atom cannot become coplanar with C_α, C_β, and Cl without introducing considerable strain into the molecule, so that in this case trans elimination does not have the advantage it does in systems like cyclohexane derivatives, where this coplanar configuration is relatively easily attained.

7-1b. *The E1 Mechanism.* In this mechanism the reactant first loses Y to yield a carbonium ion, which may then donate a β-proton to some base to give an olefin. For this reason the possibility of elimination by this mechanism accompanies any S_N1 reaction whose intermediate carbonium ion bears a β-hydrogen atom.

$$H\!-\!\overset{|}{\underset{|}{C}}\!-\!\overset{|}{\underset{|}{C}}\!-\!Y \rightarrow H\!-\!\overset{|}{\underset{|}{C}}\!-\!\overset{|}{\underset{|}{C}}{}^{\oplus} - \begin{array}{c} \xrightarrow{\;\;X\;\;} H\!-\!\overset{|}{\underset{|}{C}}\!-\!\overset{|}{\underset{|}{C}}\!-\!X \quad (S_N1) \\[1em] \xrightarrow{-\,H^+} \overset{|}{C}\!=\!\overset{|}{C} \qquad\quad (E1) \end{array}$$

While elimination by the $E1$ mechanism will usually be a first-order process (no examples involving mass-law effects having yet been investigated), this kinetic order will not serve to distinguish it from an $E2$ attack by solvent, which would be pseudounimolecular. There is, however, evidence from several sources that at least some elimination reactions do not involve a bimolecular attack by solvent in the rate-controlling step but do proceed through an intermediate carbonium ion. For one thing, it may be seen that to a first approximation the fraction of RY solvolyzing which gives elimination and that which gives sub-

[11] S. J. Cristol and N. L. Hause, *J. Am. Chem. Soc.*, **74,** 2193 (1952).

stitution should be independent of the nature of Y, since these fractions are determined by reactions of the *carbonium ion*. A bimolecular nucleophilic attack should also produce a mixture of substitution and elimination by the simultaneous occurrence of the $S_N 2$ and $E2$ mechanisms. But since both are reactions of RY, there is no assurance that the ratio of elimination to substitution will remain constant as the nature of Y is changed. Cooper, Hughes, Ingold, and MacNulty have found the ratio of elimination to substitution to be fairly nearly constant in the solvolysis reactions of various *t*-butyl and *t*-amyl derivatives.[12] The constancy of ratio which accompanies the change of Y from Cl to Br to I is, of course, required by the $E1$ mechanism but can hardly be considered good evidence against a bimolecular attack by solvent, since in known bimolecular nucleophilic attacks on alkyl halides the change in the ratio of elimination to substitution with a change in Y from Cl to Br to I is not great. It is striking, however, that the solvolysis of *t*-butyl- and *t*-amyldimethylsulfonium ions gives about the same fraction of elimination as that of a halide (Table 7-1), since in the known bimo-

TABLE 7-1. FRACTION OF ELIMINATION OCCURRING IN THE SOLVOLYSIS OF SOME *t*-ALKYL CHLORIDES AND DIMETHYLSULFONIUM IONS IN "80 PER CENT ETHANOL"[12]

Compound	Temperature, °C	Fraction elimination
t-BuCl	65.3	0.363
t-BuSMe$_2{}^+$	65.3	0.357
t-AmCl	50	0.403
t-AmSMe$_2{}^+$	50	0.478

lecular nucleophilic attacks which have been studied the sulfonium ions tend to give a far larger fraction of elimination.[13] To explain the small differences in the fraction of elimination found in solvolyses, it has been suggested that the group displaced may have a small influence if the carbonium ion is so reactive that it reacts before this group is very far away. A *t*-amyl derivative may undergo an elimination reaction to yield two possible olefins, and the reaction of sodium ethoxide with *t*-amyl bromide yields 71 per cent 2-methyl-2-butene and 29 per cent 2-methyl-1-butene,[14] while its reaction with the *t*-amyldimethylsulfonium ion at the same temperature yields 14 per cent 2-methyl-2-butene and 86 per cent 2-methyl-1-butene.[13] In view of this pronounced effect of the change from bromine to the dimethylsulfonium group, we may consider as good evidence for the $E1$ mechanism the fact that the olefin

[12] K. A. Cooper, E. D. Hughes, C. K. Ingold, and B. J. MacNulty, *J. Chem. Soc.*, 2038 (1948).

[13] E. D. Hughes, C. K. Ingold, and L. I. Woolf, *J. Chem. Soc.*, 2084 (1948).

[14] M. L. Dhar, E. D. Hughes and C. K. Ingold, *J. Chem. Soc.*, 2065 (1948).

obtained from the ethanolysis of t-amyl bromide (82 per cent 2-methyl-2-butene) and the one obtained from the t-amyldimethylsulfonium ion (87 per cent 2-methyl-2-butene) have compositions which differ by little more than the experimental error.[12]

There is, no doubt, a continual gradation between the $E1$ and $E2$ mechanisms rather analogous to that between the S_N1 and S_N2 mechanisms (Sec. 5-2e).

7-1c. *Orientation in Elimination Reactions.* Since the formation of two olefins from a given starting material may be considered as the operation of two different elimination reactions, the question of predicting the orientation, i.e., of what relative amounts of the two are formed, is simply one of predicting the relative rates of the two reactions. The nature of the $E2$ mechanism suggests several factors which could reasonably affect the reaction rate. At least two factors concern the ease of removal of the β-hydrogen atom. One is its "acidity" and the other is steric hindrance. Next, the stability of the olefin being formed must be considered. This may be influenced by resonance factors (conjugation and hyperconjugation) and occasionally by steric influences. Also there will be a dependence upon the ease with which Y is removed with its bonding electron pair. All of these factors, of course, are in addition to the stereochemical preference for coplanarity of Y, C_α, C_β, and H_β, discussed in Sec. 7-1a. There is evidence for the operation of all of these factors, but their relative importance varies with the structure of the reactant and the nature of the reaction. This is illustrated best by discussing some specific examples. In the Hofmann degradation of n-propylethyldimethylammonium hydroxide there are two possible paths for elimination, depending upon whether the hydroxide ion attacks a β-hydrogen on the ethyl or the n-propyl group.

$$
\begin{array}{c}
\text{CH}_3 \\
| \oplus \\
\text{CH}_3\text{—CH—CH}_2\text{—N—CH}_2\text{—CH}_2 \qquad \text{OH}^- \\
| \qquad\quad | \qquad\quad | \\
\text{H} \qquad\quad \text{CH}_3 \qquad \text{H}
\end{array}
$$

There is probably not a great deal of difference between the ease of displacement of the two different Y groups (n-$C_3H_7NMe_2$ and C_2H_5-NMe_2), since they differ very little in basicity. The possible olefins differ substantially in stability, the double bond of propylene having received considerable stabilization by hyperconjugation (Sec. 1-1d). Despite this fact, the principal reaction product is ethylene. In explanation, Ingold and coworkers[2,15] have pointed out that the acidity of the

[15] C. K. Ingold, "Structure and Mechanism in Organic Chemistry," sec. 31. Cornell University Press, Ithaca, N.Y., 1953.

β-hydrogen atom resulting from the inductive effect of the strongly electron-withdrawing positively charged nitrogen atom will be reduced by an electron-feeding methyl radical in the n-propyl group but not in the ethyl group. They then state that the resultant greater acidity of the β-hydrogens of the ethyl group is a more important factor than olefin stability in this case. Schramm, however, has suggested that the orientation in cases of this type may be determined by steric factors.[16] The high degree of branching at the nitrogen atom is said so to shield the β-hydrogen atoms that only those which are at the end of an alkyl chain are very readily attacked.

While the underlying cause may not be known definitely, orientation of the type described appears to be rather general in the E2 eliminations of tetraalkylammonium compounds, trialkylsulfonium salts, and dialkyl sulfones; i.e., the hydrogen atom tends to be removed preferentially from the β-carbon which bears the smallest number of alkyl groups (or the largest number of hydrogen atoms), provided all of the alkyl groups are equally substituted on the α-carbon atom. This is the essence of what is known as Hofmann's rule. In agreement with Ingold's explanation, it is seen that in the classes of compounds for which this type of orientation occurs the group displaced is attached to the alkyl group by an atom which has a considerably positive charge, and, in agreement with the steric explanation, it is seen that there is branching at this atom in all cases.

The most common method for dehydrohalogenating alkyl halides, the use of KOH in ethanol, follows a pattern different from that described by Hofmann's rule. Here the elimination usually proceeds in accord with the *Saytzeff rule*, in that hydrogen is removed from the β-carbon atom which bears the largest number of alkyl groups (the least number of hydrogens). According to Ingold and coworkers, this occurs because the halogen atom is much less effective than the positively charged atom of an onium ion at increasing the acidity of β-hydrogen atoms.[2,15] Because of this decreased acidity of the β-hydrogen atom, acidity becomes a factor of smaller importance in the reaction, so that the controlling factor is now the stability of the olefin formed. An alternate explanation is that it is the smaller size of halogen atoms compared to SR_2^+ and NR_3^+ groups which diminishes the steric effect and makes olefin stability more important.[16] Brown and Moritani have shown that this steric explanation is probably correct.[17a] They found that in the dehydrohalogenation of alkyl halides by potassium alkoxides the orientation changes regularly with the size of the alkoxide ion, so that Hofmann-type orientation

[16] C. H. Schramm, *Science*, **112**, 367 (1950).

[17] (a) H. C. Brown and I. Moritani, *J. Am. Chem. Soc.*, **75**, 4112 (1953); (b) H. C. Brown, private communication.

is observed with the relatively bulky tertiary alkoxides[17a] (Table 7-2). The powerful basicity of *t*-alkoxide ions is apparently not an important cause of this change in orientation, since it is also found with highly hindered *t*-amines (but not unhindered ones).[17b] The predominance of Hofmann-type elimination in the ethoxide-catalyzed dehydrobromination of 2-bromo-2,4,4-trimethylpentane need not be attributed entirely

TABLE 7-2. ORIENTATION IN DEHYDROHALOGENATIONS USING VARIOUS POTASSIUM ALKOXIDES[17]

Alkyl halide	1-Olefin, %			
	EtOK	*t*-BuOK	*t*-AmOK	Et$_3$COK
C$_2$H$_5$CHBrCH$_3$	19[a]	53.4		
C$_3$H$_7$CHBrCH$_3$	29[a]	66		
C$_2$H$_5$CBr(CH$_3$)$_2$	29[a]	72	78	89
(CH$_3$)$_2$CHCBr(CH$_3$)$_2$	...	87		
(CH$_3$)$_3$CCH$_2$CBr(CH$_3$)$_2$	85	99		

[a] From C. K. Ingold, "Structure and Mechanism in Organic Chemistry," sec. 31, Cornell University Press, Ithaca, N.Y., 1953.

to interference with the attack of ethoxide ions on the methylene hydrogen atoms, since here the removal of methyl hydrogen may lead to the more stable product. The 1-olefin (IX) is more stable than its 2 isomer (X) in this case, probably because the interference between the *t*-butyl

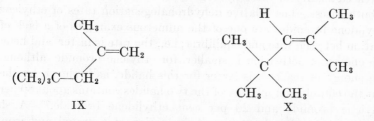

attached to the double bond in X and the methyl group cis to it more than compensates for the fact that there are three alkyl groups attached to the double bond in X but only two attached to the double bond of IX.

While the preceding discussion has concerned only the *E*2 reaction of RY compounds, in which R is an unsubstituted saturated aliphatic radical, the factors which are important with these compounds operate generally, although their relative importance varies. The influence of a phenyl group on the rate of *E*2 reactions is striking, as Hughes, Ingold, and coworkers have pointed out. Since conjugation with the benzene ring considerably stabilizes an olefinic double bond, the presence of a phenyl group on either the α- or β-carbon atom greatly increases the rate of $E2$ reactions. The increase is definitely greater when the phenyl group is on the β-carbon atom, for in this position it may also substantially increase the acidity of the β-hydrogen atoms. The only Hammett-equation data available relate to a case where the phenyl group is in the β position. Cristol and coworkers studied the dehydrochlorination of some 2,2-diaryl-1,1,1-trichloroethanes and some 2,2-diaryl-1,1-dichloro-ethanes.[18] In the reaction with alkali in 92.6 weight per cent ethanol, $\rho = 2.729$, and $\log k_0$ $(\sec^{-1}) = -2.822$ for the trichloroethanes, while for the dichloroethanes, $\rho = 2.456$, and $\log k_0$ $(\sec^{-1}) = -3.430$. This fact shows that electron-withdrawing groups increased the reactivity in both cases, as would be expected from their effect on the acidity of the β-hydrogen atoms. The effect of vinyl groups appears to be similar to that of phenyl groups, although less research has been carried out along this line.

Halogen atoms increase $E2$ reactivity somewhat when attached to the α-carbon atom and considerably more so on the β-carbon. Cristol and coworkers, for example, have found that the substitution of an additional 1-chlorine atom increases the reactivity of 2,2-bis-(p-chlorophenyl)ethyl chloride by a factor of about six and that two such chlorine atoms produce about a twenty-five-fold increase.[18] The larger effect of β-halogens is shown by Olivier and Weber's observation that in the presence of alkali ethylene bromide is transformed to vinyl bromide about 200 times as fast as ethylidene bromide is.[19] This larger effect must be due to the increased acidity of the β-hydrogen, since the olefin stability is identical in both cases. The relative dehydrohalogenation rates of ethylene and ethylidene bromides are one of the numerous examples of a lack of correlation between rate and equilibria; i.e., the rate is faster, and hence the free energy of activation is smaller, for ethylene bromide, although the free energy of reaction is larger for this halide, as is shown by the fact that the equilibrium mixture of the two halides contains about 80 per cent ethylene bromide and 20 per cent ethylidene bromide.[20] A similar situation holds for the dehydrobromination of n-propyl and isopropyl bromides and many other pairs.

The effect of alkoxide radicals is also of interest. While α-alkoxy halides form carbonium ions so easily that the $E2$ mechanism is difficult to isolate, there do appear to be data available on β-alkoxy halides. McElvain, Clarke, and Jones have shown that dehydrobromination of the diethylacetal of α-bromoisovaleraldehyde gives the acetal of an

[18] S. J. Cristol, N. L. Hause, A. J. Quant, H. W. Miller, K. R. Eilar, and J. S. Meek, *J. Am. Chem. Soc.*, **74**, 3333 (1952).

[19] S. C. J. Olivier and A. P. Weber, *Rec. trav. chim.*, **53**, 1087 (1934).

[20] F. R. Mayo and A. A. Dolnick, *J. Am. Chem. Soc.*, **66**, 985 (1944).

unsaturated aldehyde rather than a ketene acetal.[21] No reasonable explanation

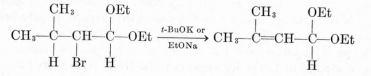

appears to have been advanced for this orientation, but it must be due to a deactivation toward the ketene acetal formation rather than to any great activation of the elimination reaction shown, since its second-order rate constant[21] is considerably smaller than those for similar bromides without the ethoxy group.[15]

As β substituents, such tautomerically electron-withdrawing groups as —COR, —NO$_2$, —SO$_2$R, —CN, etc., enormously increase the rate of $E2$ reactions.   While this may be partly due to stabilization of the double bond by conjugation, the major factor must be the increase in the acidity of the hydrogen atom removed, since the ease of dehydrohalogenating α-halocarbonyl and related compounds does not approach that of the β-halo isomers.

In some cases where both C$_\alpha$ and C$_\beta$ are optically active Cram and Elhafez have pointed out that the diastereomer yielding the more stable of the two cis-trans isomers of the olefin will undergo the $E2$ reaction more rapidly.[22]

While most of the factors which affect reactivity in $E2$ reactions probably still have some effect in $E1$ reactions, it appears that the olefin-stability factor is usually dominant.   As previously explained, the nature of Y need not affect the orientation, since Y is removed *before* the step in which the olefin is formed.

7-1*d*. *Olefin Yield in Elimination Reactions.* Since the attack of a nucleophilic reagent on RY may result in either an $E2$ or an S_N2 reaction, the yield of olefin is determined by the relative rates of the reactions (except in cases where carbonium-ion formation or some other competing reaction occurs).   While the previous discussions of the effect of structure on the rates of $E2$ and S_N2 reactions might make possible a comparison of the relative yields of olefins obtainable from various compounds, they do not tell which reactions are really useful for the preparation of olefins (or substitution products), a purpose for which some numerical "orienting" data on specific compounds are desirable.   Table 7-3 lists some of the data of Hughes, Ingold, and coworkers on the reaction

[21] S. M. McElvain, R. L. Clarke, and G. D. Jones, *J. Am. Chem. Soc.*, **64**, 1966 (1942).

[22] D. J. Cram and F. A. A. Elhafez, *J. Am. Chem. Soc.*, **74**, 5851 (1952).

of alkyl bromides with sodium ethoxide.[14,23] It is seen that olefin is obtained from ethyl bromide rather slowly and in very poor yield. The *rate* of olefin formation is increased by either α- or β-methyl groups, but the *yield* of olefin is increased more by α-methyl groups, largely because the α-methyl group slows the competing S_N2 reaction more.

The yield of olefin does not change greatly with the nature of the halogen atom, but the order appears to be RI > RBr > RCl from the

TABLE 7-3. RATES OF ELIMINATION AND SUBSTITUTION IN THE REACTION OF ALKYL BROMIDES WITH SODIUM ETHOXIDE [14,23]

| Alkyl bromide | Temp.,[a] °C | k_2, liters mole^{-1} sec^{-1}, $\times 10^5$ | | | Olefin, % |
		Total	S_N2	E2	
CH_3CH_2Br	55	174	172	1.6	0.9
$CH_3CH_2CH_2Br$	55	60	54.7	5.3	8.9
$CH_3(CH_2)_3Br$	55	43.9	39.6	4.3	9.8
$CH_3(CH_2)_4Br$	55	39.2	35.7	3.5	8.9
$(CH_3)_2CHCH_2Br$	55	14.3	5.8	8.5	59.5
$C_6H_5CH_2CH_2Br$	55	593	32	561	94.6
$CH_3CHBrCH_3$	25	0.295	0.058	0.237	80.3
$C_2H_5CHBrCH_3$	25	0.422	0.075	0.347	82.2[b]
$n\text{-}C_3H_7CHBrCH_3$	25	0.343	0.067	0.276	80.7[c]
$C_2H_5CHBrC_2H_5$	25	0.455	0.054	0.401	88.1
$CH_3CBr(CH_3)_2{}^d$	25	4.17	<0.1	4.17	>97
$C_2H_5CBr(CH_3)_2{}^d$	25	9.44	<0.2	9.44	>97[e]

[a] Between 25 and 55° the k's should change by factors of from 20 to 40.

[b] Olefin: 81 per cent 2-butene, 19 per cent 1-butene.

[c] Olefin: 71 per cent 2-pentene, 29 per cent 1-pentene.

[d] The data for this compound had to be corrected for a considerable amount of solvolysis.

[e] Olefin: 72 per cent 2-methyl-2-butene, 28 per cent 2-methyl-1-butene.

fact that the reaction of alkali at 80° gives 58 per cent and 61 per cent olefin from *i*-PrCl and *i*-PrBr in "80 per cent ethanol" and 58 per cent and 74 per cent olefin from *i*-PrBr and *i*-PrI in "60 per cent ethanol."[24] When the structure of Y is so changed as to make RY an onium ion, there is a large increase in the relative extent to which attacks on R give elimination rather than substitution. For example, while the reaction of ethyl bromide with alkali in ethanol yields only 0.9 per cent ethylene (Table 7-3) and, judging from solvent effects found with other bromides, probably yields even less olefin in aqueous ethanol, the reaction of the

[23] M. L. Dhar, E. D. Hughes, C. K. Ingold, and S. Masterman, *J. Chem. Soc.*, 2055, 2058 (1948).

[24] E. D. Hughes and U. G. Shapiro, *J. Chem. Soc.*, 1177 (1937).

triethylsulfonium ion with alkali in either 60 or 80 per cent ethanol yields essentially 100 per cent ethylene.[25] Since β-methyl groups increase the $E2$ rates for halides and decrease them for onium ions, it would be of interest to compare the 59.5 per cent of elimination found with isobutyl bromide (Table 7-3) with that for triisobutylsulfonium ion. Unfortunately, the latter data are not available. However, Hughes, Ingold, and Maw found that the isobutyldimethylsulfonium ion reacts with sodium ethoxide to give 2.4 per cent isobutylene and 97.6 per cent substitution.[26] Almost undoubtedly, however, the substitution occurs largely at a methyl rather than isobutyl group. If these attacks on methyl occur from 32 to 6,200 times as fast as on isobutyl, as has been found for some other nucleophilic displacements,[27] we may estimate that the attack on the isobutyl group in this case gives from 61 to 99.7 per cent elimination.

The yield of olefins obtained from a carbonium ion appears to depend mainly on the relative stability of the substitution product and of the olefin. In most cases the larger changes in stability occur with the olefin and may often be attributed to hyperconjugation. Thus in ethanol at 25°, the t-butyl carbonium ion gives 19 per cent olefin, and the t-amyl carbonium ion, which can form the more stable 2-methyl-2-butene, gives 36.3 per cent olefin.[14] However, in 80 per cent ethanol, where the t-butyl and t-amyl carbonium ions yield 16 and 34 per cent olefin, respectively, the solvolyses of dimethyl-t-butylcarbinyl chloride and dimethyl-neopentylcarbinyl chloride yield 61 and 65 per cent olefin.[28] Brown and Fletcher have proposed a steric explanation for this large increase in olefin yield. They point out that the substitution product may contain steric strains not present in the olefin, so that the increased yield need not be due to an increased rate of transformation of carbonium ion to olefin but may be due to a decrease in its rate of transformation to substitution product.

Hughes, Ingold, and coworkers have examined the available data on $E1$ and $E2$ eliminations of alkyl chlorides, bromides, iodides, and sulfonium ions and have pointed out that in all cases the elimination reactions have the higher activation energy, i.e., that the proportion of olefin formed increases with the temperature.[29] A typical example is

[25] J. L. Gleave, E. D. Hughes, and C. K. Ingold, *J. Chem. Soc.*, 236 (1935).

[26] E. D. Hughes, C. K. Ingold, and G. A. Maw, *J. Chem. Soc.*, 2072 (1948).

[27] S. S. Woolf, *J. Chem. Soc.*, 1172 (1937); D. Segaller, *J. Chem. Soc.*, **105**, 106 (1914); I. Dostrovsky and E. D. Hughes, *J. Chem. Soc.*, 157 (1946); S. F. Acree and G. H. Shadinger, *Am. Chem. J.*, **39**, 226 (1908); P. M. Dunbar and L. P. Hammett, *J. Am. Chem. Soc.*, **72**, 109 (1950).

[28] H. C. Brown and R. S. Fletcher, *J. Am. Chem. Soc.*, **72**, 1223 (1950).

[29] K. A. Cooper, E. D. Hughes, C. K. Ingold, G. A. Maw, and B. J. MacNulty, *J. Chem. Soc.*, 2049 (1948).

that of isopropyl bromide, which upon reaction with alkali in "60 per cent ethanol" gives 53.2 per cent olefin at 45° and 63.6 per cent at 100°. According to Chapman and Levy, however, the bimolecular reaction of sodium ethoxide with alkyl fluorides yields less olefin at higher temperatures.[30]

Since the $E2$ attack of an anion on a neutral molecule involves charge dispersal in the transition state,

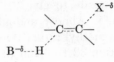

the Hughes-Ingold theory of solvent effects (Sec. 3-2a) would predict an increase in rate with the decreasing ion-solvating power of the medium, just as for the related S_N2 reaction. Hughes, Ingold, and coworkers state that the charge is *more* dispersed in the $E2$ transition state, so that the $E2$ rate changes faster with solvent.[31] Therefore the yield of olefin increases with the alcohol content of aqueous ethanol solvents in the base-catalyzed second-order reaction of alkali with alkyl halides.[31] This is not an entirely satisfactory test of the theory, however, since the nature of the nucleophilic reagent changes (from hydroxide to ethoxide ion) with the composition of the solvent in this case. Elimination reactions of other charge types are also discussed, and in all of the cases for which data are given the olefin yield increases with the alcohol content of the solvent.

7-2. Other Types of Elimination Reactions. *7-2a. Eliminations to Form Multiple Bonds to Nitrogen, Oxygen, and Sulfur.* While elimination reactions to form $C{=}N$, $C{\equiv}N$, $N{=}N$, $C{=}O$, $C{=}S$, etc., bonds share many of the characteristics of the elimination reactions which yield olefins, they also have certain characteristics of their own which warrant discussion. The elimination of HX from compounds of the type

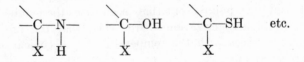

occurs with particular facility, but since these reactions are simply the reverse of carbonyl addition–type reactions, they are considered in Chap. 11.

[30] N. B. Chapman and J. L. Levy, *J. Chem. Soc.*, 1673 (1952).

[31] K. A. Cooper, M. L. Dhar, E. D. Hughes, C. K. Ingold, B. J. MacNulty, and L. I. Woolf, *J. Chem. Soc.*, 2043 (1948).

In comparing the ease of removal of RX from compounds of the type

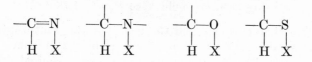

with the ease of analogous eliminations of HX to form olefins, note that X is practically always either a halogen atom or a group containing a relatively electronegative atom, such as oxygen or nitrogen, at its point of attachment.   In the *olefin-forming* eliminations the bond to X derives considerable strength from the difference in electronegativity between carbon and the atom by which X is attached (see Sec. 1-3c).   When X is attached to oxygen, nitrogen, or sulfur much of this extra stability is usually absent.   Furthermore, it may be seen from Table 1-4 that a carbon-carbon double bond is about 60 kcal/mole stronger than the corresponding single bond, while a carbon-oxygen double bond is about 94 kcal stronger than the single bond.   Similarly, a carbon-carbon triple bond is about 113 kcal stronger than a single bond, while a carbon-nitrogen triple bond is about 143 kcal stronger than a single bond.   If the transition state in the elimination reaction has acquired sufficient similarity to the products (as it appears to have in most olefin-forming eliminations) the lowered energy of reaction will be reflected in a lower energy of activation and hence a faster rate.   This provides a probable explanation for the fact that the bimolecular removal of HX from compounds of the type shown above by the action of basic reagents usually proceeds much more rapidly than the analogous olefin-forming eliminations (the simple removal of X with its bonding electron pair more often causes rearrangement [Chap. 15] than elimination by a mechanism of the *E*1 type).   The increase of the acidity of the hydrogen being removed (which is due to the relative electronegativity of the oxygen, nitrogen, or sulfur atom) is probably also a factor in producing this increase in reactivity.

Hauser, LeMaistre, and Rainsford have studied the alkaline dehydrochlorination of some ald-chlorimines of substituted benzaldehydes in 92.5 per cent ethanol at 0°.[32]   The reaction is speeded by electron-

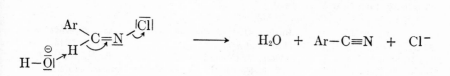

---

[32] C. R. Hauser, J. W. LeMaistre, and A. E. Rainsford, *J. Am. Chem. Soc.*, **57**, 1056 (1935).

withdrawing groups, having $\rho = +2.240$, and

$$\log k_0 \text{ (liters mole}^{-1} \text{ sec}^{-1}) = -1.796^{33}$$

The positive character of ρ and the fact that the p-nitro compound is somewhat more reactive than predicted from the Hammett equation suggest that the benzyl carbon atom may have acquired considerable carbanion character in the transition state, although it does not demand the intermediacy of a free carbanion. An idea of the ease of the corresponding elimination reaction to form a carbon-carbon triple bond is obtained by noting that in the case of carbon the more reactive bromide, β-bromostyrene, is treated with alcoholic alkali at 130° for several hours to produce phenylacetylene.[34] A number of other studies of elimination reactions which form carbon-nitrogen bonds have been reported.[35]

Kornblum and DeLaMare[36] have described the base-catalyzed transformation of α-phenylethyl t-butyl peroxide to acetophenone and t-butyl alcohol and have pointed out that the mechanism is probably of the $E2$ type.

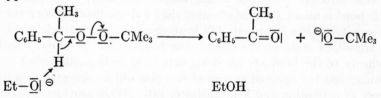

In olefin-forming eliminations alkoxide ions are displaced only under drastic conditions or with particularly favorable compounds.

Baker and Easty have studied in more detail the bimolecular transformation of alkyl nitrates to carbonyl compounds.[37] This reaction

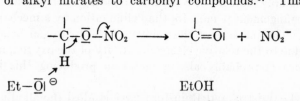

was complicated, although in a fairly predictable manner, by the simul-

[33] L. P. Hammett, "Physical Organic Chemistry," p. 190, McGraw-Hill Book Company, Inc., New York, 1940.

[34] J. U. Nef, *Ann.* **308**, 265 (1899).

[35] Among these are W. E. Jordan, H. E. Dyas, and D. G. Hill, *J. Am. Chem. Soc.*, **63**, 2383 (1941); O. L. Brady et al., *J. Chem. Soc.*, 1221, 1227, 1232, 1234, 1243 (1950); W. R. Bamford and T. S. Stevens, *J. Chem. Soc.*, 4735 (1952); R. H. Wiley, H. L. Davis, D. E. Gensheimer, and N. R. Smith, *J. Am. Chem. Soc.*, **74**, 936 (1952).

[36] N. Kornblum and H. E. DeLaMare, *J. Am. Chem. Soc.*, **73**, 880 (1951).

[37] J. W. Baker and D. M. Easty, *Nature*, **166**, 156 (1950); *J. Chem. Soc.*, 1193, 1208 (1952); cf. G. R. Lucas and L. P. Hammett, *J. Am. Chem. Soc.*, **64**, 1928 (1942).

taneous occurrence of an S_N2 reaction and an olefin-forming $E2$ reaction. The rate of the carbonyl-forming elimination reaction was found to increase on going from methyl to ethyl nitrate but then to decrease on going to isopropyl nitrate. The first increase may be attributable to the stabilizing influence of a methyl radical on a carbonyl group, while the decrease would be rationalized by either of the arguments used to explain Hofmann-type orientation in olefin-forming eliminations.

Teich and Curtin have suggested a similar mechanism for the alkaline cleavage of S-desylthioglycolic acid which yields desoxybenzoin.[38]

7-2b. *Elimination of Groups Other than* HX. In $E2$ reactions the incipient removal of a β-hydrogen atom without its bonding electron pair makes the β-carbon atom so electron-rich that a nucleophilic group attached to the α-carbon atom is displaced to permit the formation of a carbon-carbon double bond. It therefore seems reasonable that any other β-group X which may be removed readily without its bonding electron pair may give an elimination reaction similarly. Examples of this type are numerous and include the reaction of β-haloalkylsilanes with alkali[39]

$$(C_2H_5)_3Si\!-\!CH_2\!-\!CH_2\!-\!Cl \longrightarrow (C_2H_5)_3SiOH + C_2H_4 + Cl^-$$
$$\uparrow$$
$$OH^-$$

and the base-catalyzed decomposition of 3-bromo-2,2-dimethyl-1-propanol.[40] Olefin formation in the reaction of metals with 1,2-dihalides and β-halo ethers, sulfides, amines, etc., probably proceeds by a similar

$$\begin{array}{ccccccc}
CH_2\!-\!Br & & CH_2\!-\!Br & & CH_2 & & \\
| & OH^- & |^k & & \| & & \\
CH_3\!-\!C\!-\!CH_2\!-\!OH & \longrightarrow & CH_3\!-\!C\!-\!CH_2\!-\!\overline{O}| \ominus & \longrightarrow & CH_3\!-\!C & + CH_2O + Br^- \\
| & & | & & | & & \\
CH_3 & & CH_3 & & CH_3 & &
\end{array}$$

mechanism, in which an organometallic compound may be formed, but at the same time as, or after, the metal—C_β bond is formed, the low electronegativity of the metal produces such a high electron density on the β-carbon atom that Y is eliminated and a double bond formed.[41]

$$X\!-\!C\!-\!C\!-\!Y + M \longrightarrow M\!-\!C\!-\!C\!-\!Y \longrightarrow M^+ + {>}C{=}C{<} + Y$$

[38] S. Teich and D. Y. Curtin, *J. Am. Chem. Soc.*, **72**, 2481 (1950).

[39] L. H. Sommer, L. J. Tyler, and F. C. Whitmore, *J. Am. Chem. Soc.*, **70**, 2872 (1948).

[40] S. Searles and M. J. Gortatowski, *J. Am. Chem. Soc.*, **75**, 3030 (1953).

[41] E. D. Amstutz, *J. Org. Chem.*, **9**, 310 (1944).

Winstein, Pressman, and Young have found that the second-order (first-order in each reactant) dehalogenation of the 2,3-dibromobutanes by iodide ion transforms the meso isomer to *trans*-2-butene and the *dl* compound to *cis*-2-butene, showing that the elimination goes trans.[42] They point out that one bromine atom undergoes nucleophilic attack by iodide ion while simultaneously the double bond is formed, and the other bromine is displaced as an anion. It has been suggested that the reaction involves the formation of a vicinal diiodide, which then loses iodine, and it may indeed be seen from the larger rates of dehalogenation

TABLE 7-4. RATES OF DEHALOGENATION OF VICINAL DIBROMIDES BY IODIDE
ION IN 99 PER CENT METHANOL AT $59.72°$[46]

Dibromide	$10^6 k$, *liters* $mole^{-1} sec^{-1}$
$BrCH_2CH_2Br$	83.2
$CH_3CHBrCH_2Br$	3.1
$C_2H_5CHBrCH_2Br$	4.1
meso-$CH_3CHBrCHBrCH_3$	2.5
dl-$CH_3CHBrCHBrCH_3$	1.3

of ethylene iodide and ethylene bromoiodide compared to ethylene bromide[43] that the replacement of bromine by iodine may increase the reactivity. Nevertheless, the nucleophilic displacement of bromide by iodide ions does not appear to be important in the dehalogenation of 2,3-dibromobutane. A mechanism involving a rate-controlling *displacement* followed by rapid elimination of iodine bromide would disagree with the observed stereochemistry. A mechanism involving two consecutive displacements would demand the second to be faster than the first (since the over-all reaction is cleanly second-order) and thus require that a β-iodobromide have much greater S_N2 reactivity than the corresponding β-bromobromide. Studies on the effect of halogen substituents on S_N2 reactivity show that such a situation is very improbable.[44] A reaction mechanism involving rate-controlling nucleophilic displacement on carbon seems very plausible for the iodide-ion dehalogenation of many vicinal dibromides (such as 1,2-dibromides) with more S_N2 reactivity than 2,3-dibromobutane.[45] Such a mechanism seems to offer the only reasonable explanation of why the terminal olefins, ethylene, propylene, and 1-butene, are formed from their dibromides faster than are the more stable 2-butenes[46] (Table 7-4). This mechanism, for which

[42] S. Winstein, D. Pressman, and W. G. Young, *J. Am. Chem. Soc.*, **61**, 1645 (1939).

[43] A. Slator, *J. Chem. Soc.* **85**, 1697 (1904); C. F. van Duin, *Rec. trav. chim.*, **45**, 345 (1926).

[44] J. Hine and W. H. Brader, Jr., *J. Am. Chem. Soc.*, **75**, 3964 (1953); W. H. Brader, Jr., Ph.D. thesis, Georgia Institute of Technology, 1954.

[45] J. Hine and W. H. Brader, Jr., *J. Am. Chem. Soc.*, **77**, 361 (1955).

[46] R. T. Dillon, *J. Am. Chem. Soc.*, **54**, 952 (1932).

the following detailed formulation is suggested,

$$I^- + BrCH_2CH_2Br \rightarrow ICH_2CH_2Br + Br^-$$

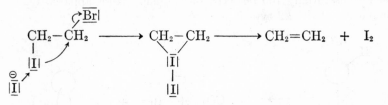

is further supported by the observation that the rate constant for dehalogenation of ethylene bromide under a certain set of conditions is just that which would be expected for the nucleophilic displacement of bromide by iodide ions under these conditions.[45] It is probably the greater ease with which iodine expands its outer octet of electrons that makes iodine more susceptible to nucleophilic attack than bromine. Reasons for suggesting the intermediacy of a species in which one, but only one, halogen atom is bound directly to carbon will be described in Sec. 9-1*a*.

The beta elimination of groups other than H—X may also proceed by a mechanism analogous to the *E*1 mechanism, and of course this carbonium-ion mechanism and the *E*2 type of mechanism are not separated sharply but blend gradually into each other. Thus it is found in general that when a carbonium ion is formed and there is a substituent on the β-carbon which may separate readily without its bonding electron pairs, an olefin may be formed.

Grovenstein and Lee and also Cristol and Norris have studied a reaction of this sort, the first-order transformation of the anion of cinnamic acid dibromide to β-bromostyrene.[47] In aqueous solution the reaction of the dibromide prepared from *trans*-cinnamic acid yields β-bromostyrene containing about 78 per cent of the more stable trans isomer and 22 per cent cis. The investigators have pointed out that this suggests the following mechanism

$$C_6H_5CHBrCHBrCO_2^- \rightarrow Br^- + C_6H_5\overset{\oplus}{C}HCHBrCO_2^-$$
$$\downarrow$$
$$C_6H_5CH{=}CHBr + CO_2$$

since rotation around the C_α—C_β bond of the carbonium ion prior to decarboxylation may account for the lack of stereospecificity. If

[47] E. Grovenstein, Jr., and D. E. Lee, *J. Am. Chem. Soc.*, **75**, 2639 (1953); S. J. Cristol and W. P. Norris, *J. Am. Chem. Soc.*, **75**, 2645 (1953).

carbonium-ion formation is discouraged by decreasing the ion-solvating power of the medium, as by running the reaction in ethanol or acetone, the percentage of cis isomer in the β-bromostyrene produced increases, reaching essentially 100 per cent in acetone. Here, apparently, a trans elimination of the $E2$ type is occurring.

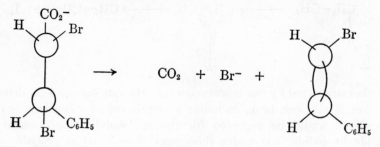

7-2c. Alpha Eliminations. Evidence has already been described (Sec. 5-6) that the rate-controlling steps in the alkaline hydrolysis of certain haloforms consist of an alpha elimination of hydrogen halide.

Hill, Judge, Skell, Kantor, and Hauser have reported that the potassium amide dehydrochlorination of α,α-dideutero-n-octyl chloride containing an average of 1.98 deuterium atoms per molecule yielded 1-octene containing only 1.84 deuterium atoms per molecule.[48] The observed

$$n\text{-}C_6H_{13}CH_2CD_2Cl \xrightarrow{\text{KNH}_2} n\text{-}C_6H_{13}CH=CD_2$$
$$\text{1.98 D per molecule} \qquad \text{1.84 D per molecule}$$

decrease in deuterium concentration was not due to exchange of the chloride before reaction, since this was tested for and found not to occur. Although there appears to be a possibility that some of the olefin may have lost deuterium by exchange after it was formed, this possibility cannot explain the data found with β,β-dideutero-n-octyl bromide. This halide, containing 1.99 deuterium atoms per molecule, yields an olefin containing 1.07 deuteriums per molecule, although a purely beta elimination could yield an olefin with no more than 1.00 deuterium per molecule if all of the deuterium in the halide was in the β position, as claimed (it was not checked for this particular compound although it was for some closely related ones). Hauser and coworkers explain these data in terms of an alpha elimination and simultaneous shift of a β-hydrogen to an α position accompanying the ordinary beta elimination.

This type of alpha-elimination mechanism with rearrangement is more strongly demanded in the case of β,β-diphenylvinyl halide derivatives, which upon treatment with potassium amide yield diphenyl-

[48] D. G. Hill, W. A. Judge, P. S. Skell, S. W. Kantor, and C. R. Hauser, *J. Am. Chem. Soc.*, **74**, 5599 (1952).

acetylene derivatives.[49] It is not known whether the carbanion shown

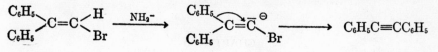

is actually formed, perhaps reversibly, as a true intermediate, or whether the entire reaction is concerted. Deuterium-exchange data show that no carbanion is formed reversibly in the case of the *n*-octyl halides.[48]

[49] G. H. Coleman and R. D. Maxwell, *J. Am. Chem. Soc.*, **56**, 132 (1934); G. H. Coleman, W. H. Holst, and R. D. Maxwell, *J. Am. Chem. Soc.*, **58**, 2310 (1936); C. R. Hauser, *J. Am. Chem. Soc.*, **62**, 933 (1940).

CHAPTER 8

GENERAL AND SPECIFIC ACID-BASE CATALYSIS

8-1. Definitions and Examples. Brønsted and coworkers have shown that it is possible to divide acid- (and base-) catalyzed reactions into two categories according to whether the catalysis is kinetically attributable to all of the acids (or bases) present in the solution or merely to the conjugate acid (or base) of the solvent. The first type is called a *general* acid- (or base-) catalyzed reaction, and the second, a *specific* acid- (or base-) catalyzed reaction. That is, a reaction in aqueous solution whose rate is merely proportional to the hydronium-ion concentration (and the concentration of reactant, of course) is said to be specific acid-catalyzed (or specific hydronium-ion-catalyzed), whereas in a general acid-catalyzed reaction there will be a term proportional to the concentration of each of the acids in solution.

8-1a. *Hydrolysis of Ethyl Orthoacetate.* An example of a reaction which has been found to be subject to general acid catalysis is the hydrolysis of ethyl orthoacetate

$$CH_3C(OC_2H_5)_3 + H_2O \rightarrow CH_3CO_2C_2H_5 + 2C_2H_5OH$$

which was studied by Brønsted and Wynne-Jones.[1] It is possible to study the reaction under such conditions that the further hydrolysis of the ethyl acetate formed is negligible and the concentrations of the acids and bases present remain essentially constant. Under these conditions it is found the reaction is always of the first order, being pseudounimolecular.

$$v = k \text{ [ethyl orthoacetate]}$$

The extent of acid and/or base catalysis may then be determined by measuring k (dilatometrically) in the presence of varying concentrations of acids and/or bases. Catalysis by bases was shown to be absent by the fact that k had the same value (5.8×10^{-6} sec^{-1}) in 0.1 N and 0.5 N aqueous sodium hydroxide solutions at 20°. The rate was then measured in the presence of m-nitrophenol–sodium m-nitrophenolate buffers of various concentrations (enough sodium chloride being present to keep the ionic strength at 0.05 in all cases since the ionization constant of an

---

[1] J. N. Brønsted and W. F. K. Wynne-Jones, *Trans. Faraday Soc.*, **25**, 59 (1929).

acid varies with ionic strength). The results obtained are shown in Table 8-1. The rate constants are seen to increase with increasing m-nitrophenol concentration even though the hydronium-ion concentration is kept constant by increasing the sodium m-nitrophenolate concentration to keep the buffer ratio constant. This fact demonstrates that some of the observed acid catalysis is due to undissociated m-nitrophenol. Plots of k vs. [$HOC_6H_4NO_2$-m] for given hydronium-ion concentrations give reasonably straight lines, showing that the part of the reaction

TABLE 8-1. HYDROLYSIS OF ETHYL ORTHOACETATE IN THE PRESENCE OF A m-NITROPHENOLATE BUFFER

[$NaOC_6H_4NO_2$]	[$HOC_6H_4NO_2$]	10^9[H_3O^+]	$10^4 k$
0.00242	0.00242	4.8	1.21
0.00566	0.00566	4.8	1.20
0.0160	0.0160	4.8	1.35
0.0202	0.02021	4.8	1.44
0.00284	0.00384	6.5	1.54
0.00756	0.01025	6.5	1.61
0.0135	0.0183	6.5	1.77
0.00145	0.0031	10.2	2.37
0.00483	0.0103	10.2	2.47
0.0145	0.0309	10.2	2.84

due to m-nitrophenol is first-order therein. For hydronium-ion concentrations of 4.8, 6.5, and 10.2×10^{-9} these lines have intercepts of k equal to 1.1, 1.45, and 2.3×10^{-4} sec^{-1} respectively. A plot of these values of k vs. the hydronium-ion concentration (including the point $k = 0.058 \times 10^{-4}$, where [H_3O^+] $\sim 10^{-13}$, already mentioned) gives another straight line, showing the hydronium-ion-catalyzed portion of the reaction to be first-order in hydronium ion. The rate constant may thus be expressed as the sum of a term for m-nitrophenol, one for hydronium ion, and one for the "uncatalyzed" reaction, probably due to the action of the acid, water.

$$k = k_w[H_2O] + k_h[H_3O^+] + k_n[HOC_6H_4NO_2\text{-}m]$$

At 20°, $k_w = 1 \times 10^{-7}$, $k_h = 2.1 \times 10^4$, and $k_n = 1.7 \times 10^{-3}$ liters mole^{-1} sec^{-1}. The constant k_h is the *catalytic constant* for hydronium ion; k_n, that for m-nitrophenol; and k_w, that for water. In general, for reactions which are subject to general acid catalysis the rate constant is equal to the concentration of every acid present multiplied by its catalytic constant.

$$k = \sum^i k_i[A_i] \tag{8-1}$$

8-1*b*. *Other General and Specific Acid- and Base-catalyzed Reactions.*
While a specific hydronium-ion-catalyzed reaction is one whose rate
constant is simply proportional to the hydronium-ion concentration,
this classification depends upon the accuracy of the data used, since for
many reactions now classified as specific acid-catalyzed it might be
possible to find catalysis by other acids by increasing the accuracy of
the kinetic measurements. Brønsted and Wynne-Jones reported that
the hydrolysis of ethyl orthopropionate and ethyl orthocarbonate was
also general acid-catalyzed, but that the hydrolysis of ethyl orthoformate
and of diethylacetal was specific hydronium-ion-catalyzed. In the
latter two cases the rate constant showed no tendency to increase with
the increasing concentration of the weak acid component of the buffer,
provided the hydronium-ion concentration was held constant.

Quite analogous to general and specific acid catalysis are general base
catalysis, for which

$$k = \sum^i k_i[\mathrm{B}_i] \qquad (8\text{-}2)$$

and specific base catalysis, for which

$$k = k_{\mathrm{OH}}[\mathrm{OH}^-]$$

in aqueous solution. An example of a general base-catalyzed reaction
is the decomposition of nitramide.[2] The decomposition of nitroso-
triacetonamine appears to be a specific hydroxide-ion-catalyzed reaction.[3]

Many reactions are, of course, catalyzed by both acids and bases.
Familiar examples are the hydrolyses of esters, amides, and nitriles.
For reactions of this sort either the acidic or the basic catalysis may be
general, or both may be. For example, the mutarotation of glucose[4]
and the enolization of acetone[5] have been found to be general acid- and
general base-catalyzed, while oxygen exchange between H_2O^{18} and
acetone is reported to be general acid-catalyzed but specific base- (hydroxide-ion) catalyzed.[6]

8-1*c*. *The Brønsted Catalysis Law.* Since an acid is acting as a proton
donor when catalyzing a reaction just as it is when ionizing, it might
reasonably be expected that those acids whose ionization constants
show them to be the best proton donors should also be the most effective
catalysts. This statement is a qualitative description of what is probably
the oldest linear free-energy relationship (Sec. 2-4*e*) widely used in

[2] J. N. Brønsted and K. Pedersen, *Z. physik. Chem.*, **108**, 185 (1924).

[3] R. P. Bell, "Acid-Base Catalysis," p. 77, Oxford University Press, London, 1941.

[4] J. N. Brønsted and E. A. Guggenheim, *J. Am. Chem. Soc.*, **49**, 2554 (1927).

[5] H. M. Dawson et al., *J. Chem. Soc.*, 2282 (1926); 2844 (1928); 1884 (1929).

[6] M. Cohn and H. C. Urey, *J. Am. Chem. Soc.*, **60**, 679 (1938).

organic chemistry, the Brønsted catalysis law.[2] According to this generalization a plot of the logarithms of the catalytic constants for a number of acids (or bases) in a given reaction against the logarithms of their ionization constants will yield a straight line. That is, if k_c is the

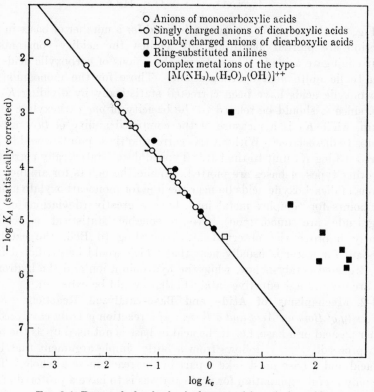

FIG. 8-1. Brønsted plot for basic decomposition of nitramide.

catalytic constant and K_a the acidity constant, then

$$\log k_c = x \log K_a + C \qquad (8\text{-}3)$$

where the constants x and C are the slope and intercept of the line respectively. The equation may be expressed exponentially as

$$k_c = GK_a{}^x \qquad (8\text{-}4)$$

The relationship usually holds rather well when the acids (or bases) studied are of the same general type, i.e., when all are carboxylic acids, or all are phenols or primary amines, etc. When less closely related acids (or bases) are compared, the relationship holds less well but is still quite useful. Relationships can often be improved by the application of certain statistical corrections, an example of which is given below.

The operation of the Brønsted catalysis law is probably best illustrated by discussion of the reaction to which it was first applied, the base-catalyzed decomposition of nitramide.[2]

$$H_2NNO_2 \xrightarrow{base} N_2O + H_2O$$

In Fig. 8-1 the catalytic constants obtained for a number of bases in this reaction are plotted logarithmically against the acidity constants of their conjugate acids.[7] The data for the anions of carboxylic acids are seen to lie quite near a straight line. Those for the monoanions of dicarboxylic acids have been corrected statistically by dividing K_A by two, since k_c should be related to the basicity of *one* carboxylate anion group, while K_A is a measure of the combined ability of *two* carboxy groups to dissociate.[8] Without this correction these points would be displaced 0.3 log K_A unit to the left. Typical data (statistically corrected) for other types of bases are plotted. While the points for anilines and anions of dicarboxylic acids lie near the line for monocarboxylate anions, the points for complex metal ions deviate greatly (deviations of this magnitude are uncommon). No reasonable statistical corrections greatly improve the observed fit. According to Bell, the catalytic constant for water is usually near that which would be predicted from the Brønsted catalysis law, while the hydronium ion and the hydroxide ion are usually less effective catalysts than would be expected.[7]

8-2. Mechanisms of Acid- and Base-catalyzed Reactions. *8-2a. Necessity of Both an Acid and a Base.* If a reaction is truly catalyzed by either an acid or a base, i.e., if the acid or base is not used up as the reaction proceeds, then it follows from a fairly simple argument that both an acid and a base must take a part in the reaction as a whole. Thus the only useful explanation for acid catalysis is to have a proton donated or partially donated to the reactant or some reaction intermediate. However, if the reaction as a whole is not to use up acid, then a proton must also be removed, and this removal is the action of a base. Since any reaction mixture which contains an acid capable of donating a proton to the reactant will also contain a base (if only the one resulting from the proton donation) and since a hydroxylic solvent contains a weak acid and base in every solvent molecule, there will always be both an acid and a base present to perform these necessary functions (with the rate depending on their strength).

8-2b. Mechanisms of Reactions Catalyzed by Acids or by Bases. Although a reactant may thus require both an acid and a base to assist in its trans-

---

[7] Data collected in Bell, *op. cit.*, chap. V.

[8] For a more detailed discussion of statistical factors in general acid-base catalysis see *ibid.*

formation to the product, it does not necessarily follow that both must enter the reaction at or before the rate-controlling step. It seems possible that under a given set of conditions one could take part in the rate-controlling step and the other enter only into a subsequent rapid step.[9] It is useful to refer to such reactions as being catalyzed by acid *or* base, depending upon which reacts during the rate-controlling portion of the reaction. We shall discuss possible reaction mechanisms for cases of this sort in terms of the transformation of a very weakly basic reactant S to the product P. If the reaction involves the transformation of S to its conjugate acid as its rate-controlling step

$$S + HA \underset{k_{-1}}{\overset{k_1}{\rightleftharpoons}} A^- + SH^+$$

$$SH^+ + A^- \overset{k_2}{\to} P + HA \qquad k_2 \gg k_{-1} \tag{8-5}$$

then the rate equation for the reaction

$$v = k_1[S][HA]$$

will predict general acid catalysis regardless of the nature of the rapid second step of the reaction. Arguments concerning the plausibility of such mechanisms have been raised for the cases in which the rate-controlling proton transfer is between two such atoms as nitrogen, oxygen, sulfur, or a halogen. These arguments point out that (at that time) no such proton-transfer reaction had been found to occur at a rate slow enough to measure. No one has directly measured the rate of ionization of a phenol or carboxylic acid in a hydroxylic solvent, nor has anyone succeeded in measuring the rate of deuterium exchange between hydroxy and/or amino groups.[10] However, the observation of Brodskii and Sulima that the rate of deuterium exchange of ammonium ions in acidic aqueous solution is quite slow enough to measure conveniently at 0°, coupled with the often-demonstrated fact that hydrogen atoms bound to carbon may undergo deuterium exchange slowly, suggests that the rapid deuterium exchange occurs with hydrogen atoms attached to atoms with unshared electron pairs.[11] Therefore the rapid deuterium

[9] It might be possible, of course, by changing the conditions to slow the "subsequent rapid step" sufficiently to make it rate controlling.

[10] J. Hine and C. H. Thomas, *J. Am. Chem. Soc.*, **75**, 739 (1953); **76**, 612 (1954); R. P. Bell and R. G. Pearson, *J. Chem. Soc.*, 3443 (1953).

[11] A. I. Brodskii and L. V. Sulima, *Doklady Akad. Nauk S.S.S.R.*, **74**, 513 (1950); *Chem. Abstr.*, **45**, 424a (1951); cf. L. Kaplan and K. E. Wilzbach, *J. Am. Chem. Soc.*, **76**, 2593 (1954); C. G. Swain, J. T. McKnight, M. M. Labes, and V. P. Kreiter, *J. Am. Chem. Soc.*, **76**, 4243 (1954).

exchanges may be only *exchanges*, perhaps involving merely a small shift of protons within a cyclic hydrogen-bonded complex[10-12]

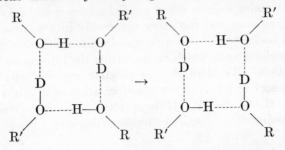

without the occurrence of any net proton donations to give ROH_2^+ or RO^-. Since many reactants are considerably weaker bases than the solvents in which they are studied, it would appear that mechanisms of the type of (8-5) are possible for certain general acid- or base-catalyzed reactions. A mechanism in which the rate-controlling reaction is of a reversibly formed hydrogen-bonded complex of reactant and catalyzing acid

$$S + HA \underset{k_{-1}}{\overset{k_1}{\rightleftharpoons}} S\text{---}HA$$
$$S\text{---}HA \underset{k_{-2}}{\overset{k_2}{\rightleftharpoons}} SH^+ + A^- \tag{8-6}$$
$$SH^+ + A^- \overset{k_3}{\rightarrow} P + HA \qquad k_3 \gg k_{-2}$$

might be regarded simply as a more detailed description of a manner in which mechanism (8-5) could occur.

Another possible mechanism involves the rapid reversible transformation of the reactant into its conjugate acid, which then undergoes the first-order rate-controlling step of the reaction. This step cannot yield the product directly, since a base must enter into the reaction somewhere and it has not yet done so. The rate-controlling step may yield a product (PH^+) which is transformed rapidly and inevitably to the final product (by A^- or any other base).

$$S + HA \underset{k_{-1}}{\overset{k_1}{\rightleftharpoons}} SH^+ + A^-$$
$$SH^+ \underset{k_{-2}}{\overset{k_2}{\rightleftharpoons}} PH^+ \tag{8-7}$$
$$PH^+ + A^- \overset{k_3}{\rightarrow} P + HA \qquad k_{-1} \gg k_2; \; k_3 \gg k_{-2}$$

For this mechanism the rate equation has the form

$$v = k_2[SH^+] = \frac{k_1 k_2}{k_{-1}} \frac{[S][HA]}{[A^-]}$$

[12] H. Kwart, L. P. Kuhn, and E. L. Bannister. *J. Am. Chem. Soc.*, **76**, 5998 (1954).

But if the ionization of HA is rapid compared to the reaction in hand, then from the ionization-equilibrium expression it follows that

$$\frac{[HA]}{[A^-]} = \frac{[H_3O^+]}{K_A}$$

By substitution, the rate expression becomes

$$v = \frac{k_1 k_2}{k_{-1} K_A} [S][H_3O^+]$$

showing that the rate depends only on the hydrogen-ion concentration and is not increased by increasing [HA] at constant $[H_3O^+]$. Therefore a mechanism of the type of (8-7) is possible for a specific but not for a general acid-catalyzed reaction.

8-2c. *Mechanisms of Reactions Catalyzed by Acids and Bases.* If both acids and bases take part in the rate-controlling portion of the reaction, certain other mechanistic possibilities appear. For example, the rate-controlling step may be a reaction between the conjugate acid of the reactant and the conjugate base of the acid catalyst.

$$S + HA \underset{k_{-1}}{\overset{k_1}{\rightleftharpoons}} SH^+ + A^-$$
$$SH^+ + A^- \overset{k_2}{\to} P + HA \qquad k_{-1} \gg k_2 \qquad\qquad (8\text{-}8)$$

Here the rate equation is

$$v = k_2[SH^+][A^-] = \frac{k_1 k_2}{k_{-1}} [S][HA]$$

showing that the mechanism may account for general acid catalysis.

Lowry has suggested that the acid and base interact with the reactant simultaneously rather than in two separate steps as shown in (8-8).[13] This does not necessarily require a three-body collision but can instead be accomplished by having one of the catalysts react with a hydrogen-bonded complex of the other and the reactant, e.g.,

$$S + HA \underset{k_{-1}}{\overset{k_1}{\rightleftharpoons}} S\text{-}\text{-}\text{-}HA$$
$$B + S\text{-}\text{-}\text{-}HA \overset{k_2}{\to} P + BH^+ + A^- \qquad k_{-1} \gg k_2 \qquad\quad (8\text{-}9)$$

The kinetic equation would be

$$v = \frac{k_1 k_2}{k_{-1}} [S][HA][B] \qquad\qquad\qquad (8\text{-}10)$$

Now we have seen that the general equation for the pseudo first-order rate constant for general acid-catalyzed reactions (8-1) involves no

[13] T. M. Lowry, *J. Chem. Soc.*, 2554 (1927).

dependence on base concentration, while that for general base-catalyzed reactions (8-2) is independent of acid concentrations. Similarly the pseudo first-order rate constants for reactions which are catalyzed by both acids and bases have almost always been found to give a satisfactory fit to the equation

$$k = \sum_{}^{i} k_i[A_i] + \sum_{}^{i} k_i[B_i] \tag{8-11}$$

where again no terms involve *both* acid and base. The absence of any termolecular terms in the observed kinetic equations, however, cannot be regarded as compelling evidence that reaction by mechanisms of the type of (8-9) does not occur. These reactions were carried out in the solvent water, which can act as either an acid or a base. Therefore it can be postulated that in all the kinetic-equation terms involving acids water is acting as a base, its constant concentration being absorbed by the catalytic constant and that in all the terms involving bases water is similarly acting as an acid.

While this argument defends the possibility of mechanism (8-9), the observation of a termolecular term in the kinetic equation of one reaction subject to general acid and base catalysis permits an argument for its probability. Therefore this reaction, the so-called enolization of acetone, will be discussed in some detail.

8-2d. *Enolization of Acetone.* Lapworth first showed that the bromination of acetone in aqueous solution is a first-order reaction whose rate is proportional to the concentration of acetone but independent of that of bromine.[14] A reasonable interpretation of this fact is the suggestion that the rate-controlling step of the reaction is the transformation of the acetone into its enol form, which is then brominated almost instantaneously.

$$CH_3-\overset{\overset{O}{\|}}{C}-CH_3 \rightarrow CH_3-\overset{\overset{OH}{|}}{C}=CH_2 \xrightarrow[Br_2]{fast} CH_3-\overset{\overset{O}{\|}}{C}-CH_2Br + H^+ + Br^-$$

Lapworth also found the reaction to be accelerated by both acids and bases to an extent proportional to the concentration of the acid and/or base used. The reaction rate, however, remained independent of the bromine concentration so long as any bromine was present. From these facts it would appear reasonable that the formation of the enol is catalyzed by both acids and bases. This idea of a rate-controlling enolization has been substantiated by a number of other experimental findings. It has been found that the rate of iodination of acetone not only is similarly independent of the halogen concentration but also proceeds at exactly the

[14] A. Lapworth, *J. Chem. Soc.*, **85**, 30 (1904).

same rate as the bromination reaction.[14,15]   In Sec. 10-1a it will be seen
that for several ketones the rate of the acid-catalyzed or base-catalyzed
deuterium exchange is the same as the rate of bromination and also that a
similar identity exists between the rates of racemization of optically
active ketones of the type RCOCHR'R'' and rates of halogenation.

Let us then consider in more detail the mechanism of the enolization
of acetone, as most commonly measured by its halogenation.   Dawson
and coworkers have shown that both the acid and the base catalysis are
general,[5] and that in an aqueous acetic acid–sodium acetate buffer the
pseudo first-order rate constant may be expressed[16]

$$k = 6 \times 10^{-9} + 5.6 \times 10^{-4}[\text{H}_3\text{O}^+] + 1.3 \times 10^{-6}[\text{HOAc}] + 7[\text{OH}^-]$$
$$+ 3.3 \times 10^{-6}[\text{AcO}^-] + 3.5 \times 10^{-6}[\text{HOAc}][\text{AcO}^-] \quad (8\text{-}12)$$

The last term, involving both an acid and a base, is of particular interest,
of course, in relation to Lowry's hypothesis that the reaction involves
the simultaneous action of an acid and a base.   It has been argued that
this term is much smaller than would be expected from the magnitude
of the other terms,[17] but Swain has very neatly found the fallacy in this
argument.[18]   He points out that the Lowry termolecular mechanism
does not require the part of the reaction rate found proportional to the
acetic acid concentration to be due to the action of acetic acid as an
acid and water as a base.   It may just as well be due to the action
of hydronium ion as an acid and acetate ion as a base, since anything
found proportional to [HOAc] must also be proportional to the product
[H₃O⁺][AcO⁻].   This follows from the ionization equation for acetic
acid.

$$K_a = \frac{[\text{H}_3\text{O}^+][\text{AcO}^-]}{[\text{HOAc}]}$$

therefore $$K_a[\text{HOAc}] = [\text{H}_3\text{O}^+][\text{AcO}^-]$$

Similarly the acetate-ion term must contain that part of the rate due
to the acid HOAc and the base OH⁻ as well as that due to the acid H₂O
and the base AcO⁻, while the first term must be the sum of the [H₂O][H₂O]
and the [H₃O⁺][OH⁻] terms.   It seems very likely that the part of the
reaction due to the [HOAc][AcO⁻] term of Eq. (8-12) proceeds by a
Lowry-type termolecular mechanism.   Bell and Jones have presented a
strong argument, however, that most of the enolization of acetone (and
the majority of other acid-base-catalyzed reactions, as well) does not
proceed by the termolecular mechanism.[19]

[15] P. D. Bartlett, J. Am. Chem. Soc., **56,** 967 (1934).
[16] H. M. Dawson and E. Spivey, J. Chem. Soc., 2180 (1930).
[17] K. J. Pedersen, J. Phys. Chem., **38,** 590 (1934).
[18] C. G. Swain, J. Am. Chem. Soc., **72,** 4578 (1950).
[19] R. P. Bell and P. Jones, J. Chem. Soc., 88 (1953).

8-2e. Correlation of Reaction Rates with Acidity Functions. A number of the reactions which have been studied kinetically in strongly acidic solutions have been shown by Hammett[20] and others to have rates which vary in a simple manner with an acidity function such as H_0 or J_0 (Sec. 2-3d) for the acid solution in which they are studied. Since such variations may often shed useful light on the mechanisms of the reactions involved, they will be discussed in terms of some of the possible mechanisms.

For a mechanism of the type of (8-7), in which the rate-controlling step is a first-order reaction of the conjugate acid of the reactant, we have seen that

$$v = k_2[\text{SH}^+] \tag{8-13}$$

in dilute aqueous solution. In order for (8-13) to hold in more concentrated solutions it is necessary to introduce the activity coefficient of SH^+ and of the transition state $(\gamma_\ddagger)$.

$$v = k_2 [\text{SH}^+] \frac{\gamma_{\text{SH}^+}}{\gamma_\ddagger} \tag{8-14}$$

From the equilibrium expression

$$K_a = \frac{[\text{SH}^+]a_{\text{H}_2\text{O}}}{[\text{S}][\text{H}_3\text{O}^+]} \frac{\gamma_{\text{SH}^+}}{\gamma_\text{S}\gamma_{\text{H}_2\text{O}^+}}$$

a substitution may be made for $[\text{SH}^+]$ in (8-14) to give

$$v = k_2 K_a \frac{[\text{S}][\text{H}_3\text{O}^+]}{a_{\text{H}_2\text{O}}} \frac{\gamma_\text{S}\gamma_{\text{H}_2\text{O}^+}}{\gamma_\ddagger}$$

if the fraction of S present as SH^+ is negligible. Therefore the observed first-order rate constant for the reaction of S in a given solvent may be expressed as

$$k = k_2 K_a \frac{[\text{H}_3\text{O}^+]}{a_{\text{H}_2\text{O}}} \frac{\gamma_\text{S}\gamma_{\text{H}_2\text{O}^+}}{\gamma_\ddagger} = k_2 K_a \frac{a_{\text{H}^+}\gamma_\text{S}}{\gamma_\ddagger}$$

and since h_0 (Sec. 2-3d) is defined as

$$h_0 = \frac{a_{\text{H}^+}\gamma_\text{A}}{\gamma_{\text{AH}^+}}$$

it can be seen that h_0 will be proportional to k (i.e., that H_0 will be proportional to $\log k$) provided that $\gamma_\text{S}/\gamma_\ddagger$ changes with the medium in the same way as does $\gamma_\text{A}/\gamma_{\text{AH}^+}$, where A is any uncharged base. It is entirely

[20] L. P. Hammett, "Physical Organic Chemistry," pp. 273–277, McGraw-Hill Book Company, Inc., New York, 1940.

reasonable that this should occur, since $\gamma_{\ddagger}$ is the activity coefficient of a transition state made up of the base S and a proton.

In view of the fact that this derivation was based on mechanism (8-7), which is applicable only to specific acid-catalyzed reactions, it is of interest that log k for the inversion of sucrose, a specific acid-catalyzed reaction, has been shown by Hammett and Paul to yield a straight line of slope 1.0 when plotted against H_0.[21]

[21] M. A. Paul and L. P. Hammett, *J. Am. Chem. Soc.*, **58**, 2182 (1936).

CHAPTER 9

ADDITION TO CARBON-CARBON MULTIPLE BONDS

While carbon-carbon double and triple bonds may react with either nucleophilic or electrophilic reagents, and the relative tendencies to do so depend on the exact structure of the unsaturated compound, the most common reactions are those with electrophilic reagents. These will be discussed first.

9-1. Addition of Halogens.[1] *9-1a. Mechanism of Halogen Additions.* The addition of halogen to olefins often occurs by a free-radical mechanism (Sec. 20-2a), indeed, always for light-catalyzed and/or vapor-phase reactions. However, there is also a polar mechanism for addition, whose operation is encouraged by ion-solvating media and the absence of light and peroxides. To explain the fact that electron-donating substituents on olefins increase the reactivity in the polar addition of halogens,[2] we must assume that the halogen is behaving as an electrophilic reagent, while the olefin is nucleophilic (in the rate-controlling step, at least). Since it has also been found that the addition of halogen in the presence of nucleophilic reagents often yields products in which the nucleophilic reagent and a bromine atom have added, it was reasonable to suggest that the reaction consists of the addition of a bromine *cation* in the rate-controlling step to yield an intermediate carbonium ion, which may then rapidly react with any available nucleophilic reagent. For instance, this explains the observations of Francis, who found that the reaction of ethylene with bromine in aqueous solution yields, in addition to ethylene bromide, some β-bromoethyl chloride in the presence of sodium chloride and β-bromoethyl nitrate in the presence of sodium nitrate.[3]

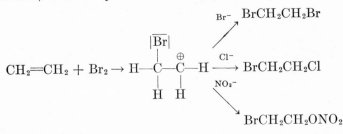

---

[1] This subject has been reviewed through 1949 in P. B. D. de la Mare, *Quart. Revs. (London)*, **3**, 126 (1949).

[2] C. K. Ingold and E. H. Ingold, *J. Chem. Soc.*, 2354 (1931); S. V. Anantakrishnan and C. K. Ingold, *J. Chem. Soc.*, 984, 1396 (1935).

[3] A. W. Francis, *J. Am. Chem. Soc.*, **47**, 2340 (1925).

Combination of such a carbonium ion with solvent could explain the formation of halohydrins in aqueous solution and their ethers in alcoholic solvents. Roberts and Kimball have pointed out that the electron-deficient carbon atom in such an intermediate might very well satisfy its deficiency by coordination with the unshared pairs of the halogen atom to yield an intermediate with a three-membered ring, called a "bromonium ion."[4] Since the opening of this ring by the attack of a nucleophilic reagent would result in a Walden inversion at the carbon atom attacked, this mechanism also has the great advantage of requiring that the addition go trans. Thus, maleic acid yields the racemic dibromide, while fumaric acid gives the meso compound.[5]

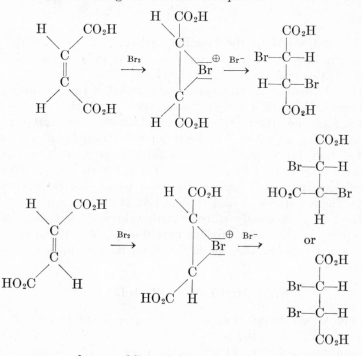

The occurrence of trans addition has been established in a large number of other cases, the only known exception appearing to be in the case of the addition to maleate and fumarate ions in polar solvents.[6] Here both ions yield the same product, meso-dibromosuccinate ion, presumably because in the bromonium ion formed from maleate ion the electrostatic

[4] I. Roberts and G. E. Kimball, J. Am. Chem. Soc., **59**, 947 (1937).

[5] A. McKenzie, Proc. Chem. Soc., **27**, 150 (1911); J. Chem. Soc., **101**, 1196 (1912); B. Holmberg, Chem. Abstr., **6**, 2072 (1912); P. F. Frankland, J. Chem. Soc., **101**, 673 (1912).

[6] R. Kuhn and T. Wagner-Jauregg, Ber., **61**, 519 (1928).

repulsion between the carboxylate groups is so large that it ruptures the three-membered ring with isomerism to the trans intermediate.[5] It has more recently become possible to obtain much support for the bromonium ion from investigations of neighboring-group participation (Secs. 5-4*e* and 6-3*c*). An intermediate of the type of I would also explain trans

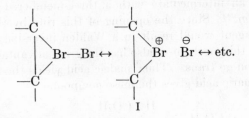

addition and would be the bromine analog of an intermediate which seems from studies of deiodination (Sec. 7-2*b*) to be a very likely one in the addition of iodine to double bonds.

Although these observations, particularly that of trans addition, show the improbability of a simple "broadside" mechanism in which the halogen molecule attacks the olefin to add both halogen atoms simultaneously, the argument has been further strengthened by demonstrating that bromochlorides, bromonitrates, bromohydrins, etc., are not necessarily formed from BrCl, $BrONO_2$, BrOH, etc. Bartlett and Tarbell have presented some of the most convincing evidence of this sort.[7] These workers studied the reaction of stilbene with bromine in methanol to yield mostly stilbene methoxybromide but some stilbene dibromide. If the major product were due to the reaction of stilbene with methyl hypobromite, the latter would have to have been formed by the reaction

$$Br_2 + MeOH \rightleftharpoons MeOBr + H^+ + Br^- \qquad (9\text{-}1)$$

Although it was found that within the experimental error all of the bromine remained in the molecular form in methanolic solution even at concentrations as low as 0.004 M, this does not rule out the possibility of the presence of a very small concentration of MeOBr through which the entire reaction might proceed. The formation of MeOBr could not be rate-controlling, because this would render the rate independent of the concentration of stilbene, when actually the reaction is found to be first-order in stilbene. It is obvious from Eq. (9-1) that the addition of acid will decrease the concentration of hypobromite present at equilibrium. The fact, then, that the reaction rate is not slowed by acid shows that the reaction cannot be simply the addition of MeOBr to stilbene.

[7] P. D. Bartlett and D. S. Tarbell, *J. Am. Chem. Soc.*, **58**, 466 (1936).

The reaction rate was observed to be slowed by bromide ions. One cause of this, no doubt, is the establishment of the equilibrium

$$Br_2 + Br^- \rightleftharpoons Br_3^-$$

which transforms some of the bromine to a less reactive species. Because of this, the liberation of bromide ions during the reaction makes the rate describable only in terms of a rather complicated kinetic equation. When there was added to the original reaction solution a concentration of bromide ions large compared to the concentration of bromine used in the reaction, the reaction followed a simple second-order rate equation

$$v = k[S]x \tag{9-2}$$

where S = stilbene and x = the total amount of material titratable as bromine, i.e., $x = [Br_2] + [Br_3^-]$. The value of k, the second-order rate constant, decreased as the concentration of bromide ion added to the solution in various runs increased. It has been found very useful to compare the exact nature of this decrease with that which would be predicted from various reaction mechanisms. In all cases the concentration of bromine present in the elemental form may be represented

$$[Br_2] = \frac{x}{1 + ([Br^-]/K)} = \frac{Kx}{K + [Br^-]} \tag{9-3}$$

where K is the dissociation constant of the tribromide ion, whose concentration is

$$[Br_3^-] = \frac{x([Br^-]/K)}{1 + ([Br^-]/K)} = \frac{[Br^-]x}{K + [Br^-]} \tag{9-4}$$

Bartlett and Tarbell have pointed out that a satisfactory mechanism may consist of a rate-controlling attack of bromine or (more slowly) tribromide ion on stilbene to yield an intermediate we shall call SB, which then reacts rapidly either with bromide ion to yield stilbene dibromide or with methanol to yield the methoxybromide. It now seems most probable that the reactive intermediate SB is either a bromonium ion or of the type of intermediate I.

$$C_6H_5CH{=}CHC_6H_5 + Br_3^- \xrightarrow{k_1} SB$$

$$C_6H_5CH{=}CHC_6H_5 + Br_2 \xrightarrow{k_2} SB$$

$$SB + Br^- \xrightarrow{k_3} C_6H_5CHBrCHBrC_6H_5 \tag{9-5}$$

$$SB + MeOH \xrightarrow{k_4} C_6H_5CHOMeCHBrC_6H_5$$

where k_3 and $k_4 \gg k_1$ and k_2

This mechanism gives the rate expression

$$-\frac{dx}{dt} = [S](k_1[Br_3^-] + k_2[Br_2])$$

or, from (9-3) and (9-4)

$$-\frac{dx}{dt} = [S]\left(k_1\frac{[Br^-]x}{K + [Br^-]} + k_2\frac{Kx}{K + [Br^-]}\right)$$

so that the experimentally determined second-order rate constant from Eq. (9-2) is represented

$$k = \frac{k_1[Br^-] + k_2K}{K + [Br^-]} \tag{9-6}$$

From the value of $K(0.0024)$ determined in separate direct experiments and values of k_1 and k_2 of 2.02 and 200, respectively, it was found possible to predict k at four different bromide-ion concentrations with an average deviation of 2.8 per cent, showing mechanism (9-5) to be in excellent agreement with experiment. Satisfactory agreement cannot be obtained by postulating the rate-controlling attack of either bromine or the tribromide ion alone.

Bartlett and Tarbell also considered the possibility that the attacking reagent is $MeOBrH^+$ or Br^+ present in equilibrium with methyl hypobromite.

$$
\begin{array}{c}
H \ \oplus \\
| \\
MeOBr + H^+ \rightleftharpoons MeO{-}Br \\
MeOBr + H^+ \rightleftharpoons MeOH + Br^+
\end{array}
$$

The insensitivity of the reaction rate to acidity gives no information about this possibility, since an increase in the hydrogen-ion concentration increases the fraction of methyl hypobromite present as its conjugate acid or as Br^+ by an amount which exactly offsets the decrease in the total concentration due to the reversal of equilibrium (9-1). However, a mechanism involving these intermediates cannot be made to fit the manner in which k decreases with increasing bromide-ion concentration. There is evidence, though, in other cases where $MeOBr$, $MeOBrH^+$, and Br^+ are present in greater concentrations relative to Br_2, that they too may be effective brominating agents.

Let us consider the alternate mechanism

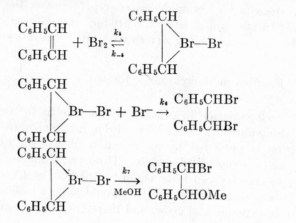

$$(9\text{-}7)$$

where $k_{-5} \gg k_6$ and k_7

If we call the reactive intermediate SB,

$$- \frac{dx}{dt} = [SB](k_6[Br^-] + k_7)$$

From the steady-state assumption

$$[SB] = \frac{k_5}{k_{-5}} [S][Br_2]$$

Therefore

$$- \frac{dx}{dt} = \frac{k_5}{k_{-5}} (k_6[Br^-] + k_7)[S][Br_2]$$

Substituting from Eq. (9-3),

$$- \frac{dx}{dt} = \frac{k_5}{k_{-5}} (k_6[Br^-] + k_7) \frac{K[S]x}{K + [Br^-]}$$

so that the second-order rate constant is represented

$$k = \frac{(k_5 k_6 K/k_{-5})[Br^-] + (k_5 k_7 K/k_{-5})}{K + [Br^-]}$$

$$(9\text{-}8)$$

Comparison with Eq. (9-6), which has already been found to describe the variation of k with $[Br^-]$ satisfactorily, shows that (9-8) will do this also if

$$\frac{k_5 k_6 K}{k_{-5}} = k_1 \quad \text{and} \quad \frac{k_5 k_7}{k_{-5}} = k_2$$

i.e., if

$$\frac{k_5 k_6}{k_{-5}} = \frac{2.02}{0.0024} = 840 \quad \text{and} \quad \frac{k_5 k_7}{k_{-5}} = 200$$

$$(9\text{-}9)$$

Since mechanisms (9-5) and (9-7) thus fit the observed kinetics, we shall consider the effect of bromide-ion concentration on the product composition. In mechanism (9-5) the product composition is unrelated to the reaction kinetics, being determined after the rate-controlling step thus:

$$\text{Fraction methoxybromide formed} = \frac{1}{1 + (k_3/k_4)[Br^-]} \qquad (9\text{-}10)$$

The observed variation in product composition is in reasonable agreement with a value of k_3/k_4 of 1.21. From mechanism (9-7) the product composition is predicted by an equation like (9-10) except that the fraction k_3/k_4 is replaced by k_6/k_7. However, from the values in Eqs. (9-9), k_6/k_7 may be seen to be equal to 840/200, or 4.2. The disagreement between this number and 1.21 would appear to be rather large to attribute to experimental error, and therefore mechanism (9-7) must be regarded as improbable.

There are a number of other mechanisms which could be considered, some of which do not predict the correct relationship between k and $[Br^-]$, some of which incorrectly predict the product composition, and others which do not differ significantly from those described.

Further evidence that the reaction does not consist of the direct one-step addition of halogen or a hypohalite comes from the observation of Tarbell and Bartlett that the addition of chlorine to the dimethylmaleate and dimethylfumarate ions yields β-lactones, presumably by the mechanism

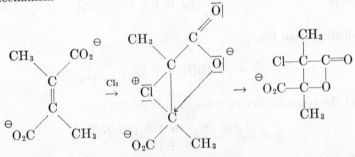

since neither of the β-lactones can be made from either the one dichloro acid or the one chlorohydrin known under the conditions used.[8]

While there appear to be no other studies of the kinetics and product composition of the addition of halogen to an olefinic double bond in aqueous or alcoholic solutions comparable in thoroughness to the work of Bartlett and Tarbell on stilbene,[6] the data which have been obtained in these solvents are of the same type as theirs. Thus, the additions of

[8] D. S. Tarbell and P. D. Bartlett, *J. Am. Chem. Soc.*, **59**, 407 (1937).

bromine to maleic and fumaric acids and of iodine to allyl alcohol are all first-order in halogen and first-order in olefin,[9] as are the additions of bromine to *cis*-cinnamic and acrylic acid in aqueous acetic acid and water.[10]

Many studies have been carried out in acetic acid solution, particularly by Robertson and coworkers. The reaction kinetics are often more complicated in this solvent, with third-order terms (first-order in olefin and second-order in halogen) appearing and overshadowing the second-order reaction even in fairly dilute solutions in the reactions of bromine, bromine chloride, iodine, and iodine chloride with a variety of olefins.[10,11] White and Robertson have suggested that this may indicate that the olefin and halogen form a complex which then reacts with another molecule of halogen, as in a scheme of the following type:

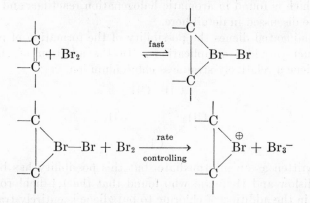

This sort of mechanism appears reasonable for bromonium ion formation in acetic acid solution, where a "bare" bromide ion might be difficult to displace unless it were being coordinated with a bromine molecule in the process. The fact that chlorine addition to olefins in acetic acid solution is *first-order* in chlorine may be correlated with the lack of stability of the trichloride anion. Nevertheless, the investigations of these third-order halogenations which have been carried out to date do not seem to have yielded enough information to distinguish between this mechanism and several other possibilities.

In nonpolar solvents, such as carbon tetrachloride and hydrocarbons, halogen addition is much slower and is complicated by catalysis by the surface of the reaction vessel and traces of water and other ion-solvating molecules.[10]

[9] A. Berthoud and M. Mosset, *J. chim. phys.*, **33,** 272 (1936).

[10] P. W. Robertson, N. T. Clare, K. J. McNaught, and G. W. Paul, *J. Chem. Soc.*, 335 (1937).

[11] E. P. White and P. W. Robertson, *J. Chem. Soc.*, 1509 (1939).

Some unsaturated compounds, particularly vinyl and allyl halides, when undergoing halogen addition in the presence of halide ions follow a kinetic equation with a third-order term containing the concentrations of olefin, halogen, and halide ion.[12] This may indicate a nucleophilic attack by the halide ion on a reversibly formed olefin-halogen complex, but other interpretations are also available.

For many compounds like α,β-unsaturated carbonyl compounds, nitriles, etc., the situation is further complicated by acid catalysis.[13] This probably involves the formation of the conjugate acid of the unsaturated compound, toward which the halogen acts as a nucleophilic reagent.

In the absence of the free halogens it is usually possible to study reactions of olefins with hypohalous acids and some derivatives, such as their conjugate acids, H_2OX^+. The situation here is rather analogous to that which is found in aromatic halogenation reactions and therefore will not be discussed in detail here.

With conjugated dienes the possibility of the formation of more than one product provides complications. In the addition of chlorine to 1,3-butadiene a relatively strainless chloronium ion

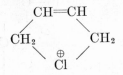

may be written as an intermediate, but this possibility has been ruled out by Mislow and Hellman, who found that the 1,4-dichloro-2-butene produced in the addition of chlorine to butadiene is entirely trans rather than cis as would be predicted from the intermediate above.[14] It therefore appears that in the reactive intermediate, chlorine interacts with only one of the double bonds, giving an intermediate which may be a chloronium ion

$$CH_2\underset{\underset{\oplus}{Cl}}{\diagdown\diagup}CH-CH=CH_2$$

or which may have the carbonium-ion structure

$$Cl-CH_2-\overset{\oplus}{CH}-CH=CH_2 \leftrightarrow Cl-CH_2-CH=CH-\overset{\oplus}{CH_2}$$

since chlorine is not a very effective neighboring group and since this carbonium ion is resonance-stabilized. The intermediate may combine

12 K. Nozaki and R. A. Ogg, Jr., *J. Am. Chem. Soc.*, **64**, 697, 704, 709 (1942).
13 P. B. D. de la Mare and P. W. Robertson, *J. Chem. Soc.*, 888 (1945).
14 K. Mislow and H. M. Hellman, *J. Am. Chem. Soc.*, **73**, 244 (1951).

with a chloride ion at either of two carbon atoms regardless of whether it is a chloronium or carbonium ion (in the former case Cl^- may attack by either the S_N2 or S_N2' mechanism). In general, in cases of this sort the product isolated need not be the one formed more rapidly from the reactive intermediate, since in all cases the products are allyl halides and may ionize to the reactive intermediate cation with some degree of ease. If the two possible products are interconvertible under the reaction conditions, then the more stable, or *thermodynamically controlled*, product will be formed preferentially. If, on the other hand, the possible products are not interconvertible under the reaction conditions, the more rapidly formed, or *kinetically controlled*, product will be isolated in larger yield. The fact then that Muskat and Northrup obtained about twice as much 1,2-dichloro-3-butene as 1,4-dichloro-2-butene under conditions where the two compounds are not interconvertible[15] shows that the former is the kinetically controlled product, while the observation of Pudovik that zinc chloride will isomerize either dichloride to a mixture containing about 70 per cent of the 1,4 isomer[16] shows that the latter is the thermodynamically controlled product. These facts are in agreement with the useful, but not entirely general, rule of Catchpole, Hughes, and Ingold that cations of this sort which may combine with anions in two different ways usually do so to give the less stable isomer more rapidly.[17] That is, the kinetically controlled and thermodynamically controlled products are usually different. Any correlation between the free energies of reaction and of activation is thus a negative one for reactions of this type.

9-1b. *Reactivity in Halogen Additions.* Since the double bond behaves as a nucleophilic reagent in the addition of halogens, hypohalous acids, etc., it is reasonable to expect electron-donating groups to increase the reactivity of olefins toward such reagents. In the addition of chlorine to compounds of the type $RC_6H_4CH{=}CHCOC_6H_5$ in acetic acid solution, for example, ρ appears to have a value of about -4.5.[18] Relative reactivities toward bromine in acetic acid are listed in Table 9-1 for a number of olefins. The results are approximately in line with what would be expected of the electron-feeding abilities of the substituent groups. The greater reactivity of either *cis-* or *trans-*cinnamic acid compared to phenylpropiolic acid seems to be fairly general for olefins compared to their corresponding acetylenes. While the free energy of reaction is undoubtedly more favorable for the acetylenes, the rate is

---

[15] I. E. Muskat and H. E. Northrup, *J. Am. Chem. Soc.*, **52**, 4043 (1930).

[16] A. N. Pudovik, *Zhur. Obshchei Khim.*, **19**, 1179 (1949); *Chem. Abstr.*, **44**, 1005 (1950).

[17] A. G. Catchpole, E. D. Hughes, and C. K. Ingold, *J. Chem. Soc.*, 8 (1948).

[18] From data of P. W. Robertson quoted by de la Mare in Ref. 1.

slower, probably because of the instability of either a vinyl carbonium ion or an unsaturated three-membered ring.

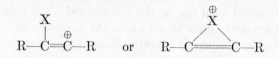

The difference in reactivity between allyl chloride and bromide, though not large, is not in the direction which would be expected.

Another type of reactivity problem arises when the addition of such unsymmetrical reagents as ICl, HOCl, etc., to unsymmetrical olefins

TABLE 9-1. RELATIVE REACTIVITIES TOWARD BROMINE IN ACETIC ACID
AT 24°[18]

Compound	Relative reactivity
$C_6H_5CH=CH_2$	Very fast
$C_6H_5CH=CHC_6H_5$	18
$CH_2=CHCH_2Cl$	1.6
$CH_2=CHCH_2Br$	1.0
$C_6H_5CH=CHCOC_6H_5$	0.33
$C_6H_5CH=CHBr$	0.11
$cis\text{-}C_6H_5CH=CHCO_2H$	0.063
$trans\text{-}C_6H_5CH=CHCO_2H$	0.017
$C_6H_5C\equiv CCO_2H$	0.0053
$CH_2=CHBr$	0.0011

is considered. Here the observed product of the reaction is the one which would be expected if the adding reagent donated its less electro-negative half as a cation to the olefin, forming the more stable of the two possible carbonium ions, e.g.,

$$CH_3\text{—}CH=CH_2 \xrightarrow[H^+]{HOCl} CH_3\text{—}\overset{\oplus}{C}HCH_2Cl \xrightarrow{H_2O} CH_3\text{—}\underset{\underset{OH}{|}}{C}HCH_2Cl + H^+$$

This does not necessarily mean that cyclic halonium ions do not form, or even that their rings are opened by the S_N1 mechanism, but it does mean that if halonium ions are formed and undergo S_N2 attack, then ease of bond breaking is the most important factor in determining at which carbon atom this S_N2 attack will occur.

$$C_6H_5CH=CH_2 + ICl \rightarrow C_6H_5CH\underset{\underset{\oplus}{I}}{\text{—}}CH_2 + Cl^- \rightarrow C_6H_5\underset{\underset{I}{|}}{\overset{\overset{Cl}{|}}{C}}HCH_2$$

This type of orientation is found even with α,β-unsaturated carbonyl compounds,[19] although the S_N2 reactivity might be expected to be large

$$CH_3CH{=}CHCO_2H + ICl \rightarrow CH_3CH{-}CHCO_2H$$
$$\overset{|}{Cl} \quad \overset{|}{I}$$

at the α-carbon atom.

The reactivity may be affected as strongly by the nature of the attacking halogen or halogen derivative as by that of the olefin. The reactivity of X—Y (where at least X is halogen) is increased by increasing the electron-withdrawing power of either X or Y. From data on third-order halogenation in acetic acid solution, White and Robertson have estimated the following relative reactivities:[11]

I_2	IBr	ICl	Br_2	BrCl
1	3×10^3	10^5	10^4	4×10^6

If it is X which is forming the bond to carbon in the rate-controlling step, then an increase in its electronegativity will increase the strength of this bond. An increase in the electron-withdrawing power of Y will make X even more electrophilic toward the nucleophilic olefin. That is, in these nucleophilic displacements on X, bond making is always a more important factor than bond breaking. This might be expected since X, not being a first-row element, may easily expand its octet to form the new bond before the old bond is broken.

9-2. Additions of Strong Acids. *9-2a. Mechanism of Additions of Acids.* As nucleophilic reagents olefins would be expected to react with acids, and it is reasonable that the reaction should be initiated by the donation of a proton to the carbon-carbon multiple bond. While this may indeed happen, it is also possible for some acids to add by a free-radical mechanism. This is true for hydrogen bromide, the acid whose addition to olefins has been studied most often. For this reason, studies of the addition of hydrogen bromide must be viewed with caution if they were carried out before 1933, when Kharasch and Mayo showed that minute amounts of peroxides formed by the exposure of olefins to air may almost entirely reverse the direction of addition.[20] The mechanism of this free-radical reaction and the explanation of the resulting orientation of addition will be discussed in Sec. 20-2b, but here it will suffice to say that the radical reaction may be excluded by working with highly purified reactants in the dark or, more easily, by the use of suitable inhibitors.

[19] C. K. Ingold and H. G. Smith, *J. Chem. Soc.*, 2742 (1931).

[20] M. S. Kharasch and F. R. Mayo, *J. Am. Chem. Soc.*, **55**, 2468 (1933); F. R. Mayo and C. Walling, *Chem. Rev.*, **27**, 351 (1940).

Mayo and coworkers have found the addition of hydrogen bromide to propylene and of hydrogen chloride to isobutylene in a hydrocarbon solvent to be rather complicated reactions, about third-order in hydrogen halide and first-order in olefin, strongly catalyzed by traces of water and certain other possible impurities and therefore not highly reproducible.[21] This kinetic behavior is probably due to the action of "extra" molecules of hydrogen halide in solvating a highly polar transition state. This complication may be avoided by the use of a better ion-solvating reaction medium.

Taft has discussed the mechanism of the acid-catalyzed hydration of isobutene in aqueous solution.[22] Since no acid is used up during this reaction, first-order rate constants are obtained when the olefin is hydrated in any given aqueous solution. It had previously been shown that these rate constants increase with the acidity of the solution more rapidly than does the hydronium-ion concentration, being more than 15 times as large in 1 M nitric acid as in 0.1 M nitric acid.[23] Taft made measurements in solutions up to 5 M in acid and found that the logarithms of the rate constants obtained gave a linear plot (slope 1.07) against the acidity function H_0. This was true only when the directly obtained rate constants, which were in terms of pressure of the gaseous olefin, were changed to rate constants in terms of concentration of dissolved olefin by a rather dependable estimation of the distribution coefficient of the olefin between the gaseous and aqueous phases. Possible reaction mechanisms were then examined in terms of this observed correlation with the acidity function. It could be suggested that the reaction consists of a rate-controlling transfer of a proton from hydronium ion to olefin followed by a rapid reaction of the carbonium ion formed with water. This mechanism leads to the following equation for the pseudo first-order rate constant

$$k = [\mathrm{H_3O^+}] \frac{\gamma_{\mathrm{H_3O^+}}\gamma_\mathrm{S}}{\gamma_\ddagger} = a_{\mathrm{H_2O}} \frac{a_{\mathrm{H^+}}\gamma_\mathrm{S}}{\gamma_\ddagger} \qquad (9\text{-}11)$$

where γ_S is the activity coefficient of the olefin and $\gamma_\ddagger$ that of the activated complex. Yet, as described in Sec. 8-2e, this rate constant must be proportional only to $a_{\mathrm{H^+}}\gamma_\mathrm{S}/\gamma_\ddagger$ if it is to be proportional to h_0. Since the activity of water certainly changes between pure water and 5 M acid, the mechanism does not fit the observed kinetics. It might also be suggested that a carbonium ion present in rapid equilibrium with the reacting olefin combines with water in the rate-controlling step.

[21] F. R. Mayo and J. J. Katz, *J. Am. Chem. Soc.*, **69**, 1339 (1947); F. R. Mayo and M. G. Savoy, *J. Am. Chem. Soc.*, **69**, 1348 (1947).

[22] R. W. Taft, Jr., *J. Am. Chem. Soc.* **74**, 5372 (1952).

[23] H. J. Lucas and W. F. Eberz, *J. Am. Chem. Soc.*, **56**, 460 (1934); J. B. Levy, R. W. Taft, Jr., D. Aaron, and L. P. Hammett, *J. Am. Chem. Soc.*, **73**, 3792 (1951).

$$-\overset{|}{\underset{|}{C}}=\overset{|}{\underset{|}{C}}- + H_3O^+ \rightleftharpoons -\overset{|}{\underset{|}{C}}-\underset{\oplus}{\overset{|}{C}}- + H_2O$$

$$\overset{|}{\underset{H}{}}$$

$$-\overset{|}{\underset{|}{C}}-\underset{\oplus}{\overset{|}{C}}- + H_2O \rightarrow -\overset{|}{\underset{|}{C}}-\overset{|}{\underset{|}{C}}- \xrightarrow[H_2O]{\text{fast}} -\overset{|}{\underset{|}{C}}-\overset{|}{\underset{|}{C}}- + H_3O^+$$

$$\overset{|}{\underset{H}{}} \qquad \overset{|}{\underset{H}{}} \underset{\oplus}{\overset{|}{OH_2}} \qquad \overset{|}{\underset{H}{}} \overset{|}{OH}$$

(9-12)

However, this mechanism not only predicts the same inadmissible kinetics as the one previously considered, but it also predicts that two olefins like 2-methyl-2-butene and 2-methyl-1-butene which would yield the same carbonium ion (both yield t-amyl alcohol on hydration) would be equilibrated with each other much faster than they would be hydrated. In contradiction, Levy, Taft, and Hammett have found no observable isomerization of either olefin even after the hydration reaction was 50 per cent completed.[24] Making the proton donation and combination with water simultaneous will not give suitable kinetics either. In fact, no mechanism involving a water molecule covalently bonded (this does not include a solvation bond) will fit the observed kinetics. A suitable mechanism should, like (8-7), involve a rate-controlling unimolecular reaction of a protonated form of the reactant. Taft has suggested such a mechanism.

$$-\overset{|}{\underset{|}{C}}=\overset{|}{\underset{|}{C}}- + H_3O^+ \underset{k_{-1}}{\overset{k_1}{\rightleftharpoons}} \left[-\overset{|}{\underset{\downarrow}{C}}=\overset{|}{\underset{|}{C}}- \right]^+ + H_2O$$

$$\overset{}{\underset{H}{}}$$

$$\text{II}$$

$$\left[-\overset{|}{\underset{\downarrow}{C}}=\overset{|}{\underset{|}{C}}- \right]^+ \underset{k_{-2}}{\overset{k_2}{\rightleftharpoons}} -\overset{|}{\underset{|}{C}}-\overset{|}{\underset{|}{C}}-$$

$$\overset{}{\underset{H}{}} \qquad \overset{|}{\underset{H}{}} \overset{}{\underset{\oplus}{}}$$

$$\text{II}$$

(9-13)

$$-\overset{|}{\underset{|}{C}}-\overset{|}{\underset{|}{C}}- \xrightarrow[H_2O]{k_3} -\overset{|}{\underset{|}{C}}-\overset{|}{\underset{|}{C}}- \xrightarrow[H_2O]{k_4} -\overset{|}{\underset{|}{C}}-\overset{|}{\underset{|}{C}}- + H_3O^+$$

$$\overset{|}{\underset{H}{}} \overset{}{\underset{\oplus}{}} \qquad \overset{|}{\underset{H}{}} \underset{\oplus}{\overset{|}{OH_2}} \qquad \overset{|}{\underset{H}{}} \overset{|}{OH}$$

$$k_{-1} \gg k_2; \ k_3 > k_{-2}$$

The rate-controlling step involves the isomerization of a protonated form of the olefin (II) to a carbonium ion of the type more commonly written. This mechanism would result in a kinetic equation of the form

$$k = \frac{k_1 k_2}{k_{-1}} \frac{a_{H_3O^+}}{a_{H_2O}} \frac{\gamma_S}{\gamma_{\ddagger}} = \frac{k_1 k_2}{k_{-1}} \frac{a_{H^+} \gamma_S}{\gamma_{\ddagger}}$$

[24] J. B. Levy, R. W. Taft, Jr., and L. P. Hammett, *J. Am. Chem. Soc.*, **75**, 1253 (1953).

so that log k would be expected to give a straight line of unit slope when plotted against H_0, as it is observed to do. The intermediate II, in which a proton has coordinated with the electrons of the pi bond (Sec. 1-2)

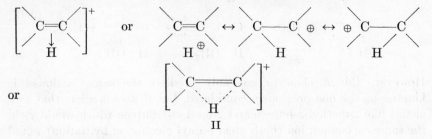

is closely related to carbonium ions of the type described in Sec. 5-4i and, like these, has been called a *pi complex* by Dewar[25] and a *protonated double bond* by Price.[26] Since the hydration of isobutene is reversible under the conditions used, the principle of microscopic reversibility requires that the dehydration of t-butyl alcohol by aqueous acid involve as its rate-controlling step the formation of the pi complex II.

Taft has also discussed the acid-catalyzed hydration of crotonaldehyde and of β,β-dimethylacrolein studied under similar conditions by Lucas and coworkers.[27] The rates of these reactions have been studied in solutions up to 1.9 M in acid and found to be very nearly proportional to the hydronium-ion concentration but *not* to h_0. A mechanism of the type of (9-13) can therefore be ruled out for these reactions. The most probable mechanism appears to be

$$CH_3CH{=}CHCHO + H_3O^+ \underset{k_{-1}}{\overset{k_1}{\rightleftharpoons}} [CH_3CH{=}CH{-}CHOH]^+ + H_2O$$

$$[CH_3CH{=}CH{-}CHOH]^+ + H_2O \underset{k_{-2}}{\overset{k_2}{\rightleftharpoons}} \underset{\overset{|}{OH_2}}{CH_3CH{-}CH{=}CHOH} \qquad (9\text{-}14)$$

$$\underset{\overset{|}{OH_2}}{CH_3CH{-}CH{=}CHOH} \xrightarrow[H_2O]{k_3} \underset{\overset{|}{OH}}{CH_3CHCH_2CHO} + H_3O^+$$

$$k_3 \text{ and } k_{-1} \gg k_2$$

yielding the expression

$$k = \frac{k_1 k_2}{k_{-1}} [H_3O^+] \frac{\gamma_{H_3O^+}\gamma_S}{\gamma_{\ddagger}}$$

[25] M. J. S. Dewar, "The Electronic Theory of Organic Chemistry," pp. 18, 144, 169, 211, Oxford University Press, London, 1949.

[26] C. C. Price, "Mechanisms of Reactions at the Carbon-Carbon Double Bond," p. 40, Interscience Publishers, Inc., New York, 1946.

[27] S. Winstein and H. J. Lucas, *J. Am. Chem. Soc.*, **59**, 1461 (1937); H. J. Lucas, W. T. Stewart, and D. P. Pressman, *J. Am. Chem. Soc.*, **66**, 1818 (1944).

in reasonable agreement with the observed kinetics. Kinetically the initial rapid reversible proton donation could just as well have been to the carbon-carbon double bond, but there are chemical reasons why the reaction at oxygen, an atom of considerable basicity, seems more likely. For example, the electron-withdrawing —CHO group would be expected to decrease the ability of the double bond to coordinate with a proton, and yet crotonaldehyde is found to be hydrated under conditions too mild to detect any hydration of 2-butene or crotyl alcohol.

According to Taft, mechanism (9-13) would not be expected to give stereospecific addition. However, the fact that the cis-trans isomers tiglic and angelic acids add hydrogen iodide to give different products shows that there is a stereospecific mechanism for the addition of HX. As Grovenstein and Lee have pointed out,[28] there is good evidence that this addition is trans, since the hydroiodide from tiglic acid (III) gives *trans*-2-butene, while the angelic acid derivative gives the cis isomer upon treatment with sodium carbonate[29] (see Sec. 7-2b).

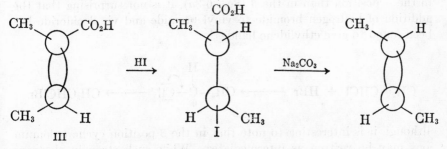

While mechanism (9-13) might *permit* such specific trans addition, trans addition would be *required* by a mechanism in which the pi complex was directly attacked by an iodide ion. In any case, while mechanism (9-13) seems reasonable for the hydration in largely aqueous solutions of unsaturated hydrocarbons which may form tertiary alcohols, larger changes in the structure of the reactants or in the reaction conditions may lead to a modification or change in the mechanism of addition of HX, just as has been found in the case of α,β-unsaturated aldehydes.

9-2b. *Reactivity in Additions of Acids.* A discussion of the effect of the structure of the olefin on reactivity in additions by acids may be divided into two parts. One aspect to be considered is the relative reactivity of various olefins, and the other is the reactivity of the two carbon atoms joined by a given multiple bond. We shall consider first the latter problem, the orientation of addition of acids to unsymmetri-

[28] E. Grovenstein, Jr. and D. E. Lee, *J. Am. Chem. Soc.*, **75**, 2639 (1953).

[29] W. G. Young, R. T. Dillon, and H. J. Lucas, *J. Am. Chem. Soc.*, **51**, 2528 (1929).

cally substituted multiple bonds, which has been studied more and is probably more important to the synthetic organic chemist.

Markownikoff was the first to formulate a generalization applicable to this problem. His rule for the addition of hydrogen halides to olefins states that the addition occurs so as to place the halogen atom on the carbon bearing the least number of hydrogen atoms.[30] This rule, given for additions to hydrocarbons only, appears to be entirely general for monoolefins of this type when the addition proceeds by the polar mechanism. It is also applicable to a majority of olefins in general, but it is the nature of the numerous exceptions which has probably contributed the most to the development of current theory. According to this view, the reaction is initiated by a proton donation to the olefin (this may involve the formation of a pi complex [see mechanism (9-13)]) to yield largely the most stable possible carbonium ion, which may then combine with a nucleophilic reagent to give the observed final product. Since a halogen substituent appears to yield a more stable carbonium ion when in the α position than in the β (Sec. 6-3a), it is not surprising that the addition of hydrogen bromide to vinyl bromide and vinyl chloride has been found to give ethylidene halides,

$$CH_2{=}CHCl + HBr \longrightarrow CH_3{-}\overset{H}{\underset{\oplus}{C}}{-}\overset{\frown}{\underline{Cl}} \longrightarrow CH_3CHClBr$$

although it is interesting to note that in the β position cyclic halonium ions may be written as intermediates. While such strongly electron-withdrawing groups as CN, COR, CO_2H, NO_2, SO_2R, etc., when attached directly to one of the two carbon atoms of the double bond, cause the halogen atom of HX being added to become attached to the other carbon atom, this may be due to addition by a 1,4 mechanism followed by tautomerism of the resultant enol, as shown in mechanism (9-14). This explanation, however, cannot be applied to the similar orientation in additions to the vinyltrimethylammonium ion[31]

$$(CH_3)_3\overset{\oplus}{N}CH{=}CH_2 + HI \rightarrow (CH_3)_3\overset{\oplus}{N}CH_2CH_2I$$

or to 1,1,1-trifluoro-2-propene.[32]

$$CH_2{=}CHCF_3 + HBr \xrightarrow{\text{AlBr}_3} BrCH_2CH_2CF_3$$

[30] W. Markownikoff, *Ann.*, **153**, 256 (1870).
[31] E. Schmidt, *Ann.*, **267**, 300 (1892).
[32] A. L. Henne and S. Kaye, *J. Am. Chem. Soc.*, **72**, 3369 (1950).

In these cases the strongly electron-withdrawing character of the substituent would cause the secondary carbonium ion, in which there is a positive charge on the adjacent carbon atom, to be less stable than the primary carbonium ion, in which the charge is one atom further removed (if indeed the reaction involves a carbonium-ion intermediate).

Perhaps the best generalization which can be made about the relative ease with which various olefins add strong acids is that the ease of additions increases with the stability of the intermediate carbonium ion, e.g.,

$$(CH_3)_2C{=}CH_2 \sim (CH_3)_2C{=}CHCH_3 > CH_3CH{=}CH_2 > CH_2{=}CH_2$$

This generalization fails in some cases where the double bond of the olefin is particularly stabilized by resonance, as in certain stilbene derivatives.

The reactivity of the halogen acids toward olefins increases with their acidity in the order HF < HCl < HBr < HI. It may be seen that HI should not only be best at donating a proton to a multiple bond but also at furnishing the most nucleophilic anion to combine with the carbonium ion formed. The reactivity increases with the ion-solvating power of the medium, and it is often useful to employ Friedel-Crafts catalysts, such as $AlBr_3$, BF_3, $SnCl_4$, etc., which are specifically active in coordinating with halide ions or solvating them. Often opposing this ion-solvating effect is a decrease in reactivity with increasing basicity of the solvent. The enormous reactivity of sulfuric acid toward olefins would be expected in view of its high acidity and ion-solvating power and its low basicity.

9-3. Additions of Other Electrophilic Reagents. *9-3a. Additions of Carbonium Ions.* Whitmore was one of the first to use the carbonium-ion concept widely in explaining the mechanisms of organic reactions and was apparently the first to suggest that the acid-catalyzed polymerization of olefins may involve the formation of a carbonium ion and its combination with a molecule of olefin to yield a new carbonium ion.[33]

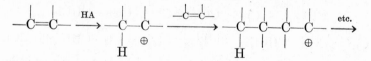

The polymerization may be terminated by the combination of the carbonium ion with some nucleophilic reagent other than an olefin or by loss of a β-proton to give an olefin. The structure of polymers thus formed may be predicted by the same rules used in predicting the direction of addition of other unsymmetrical reagents to unsymmetrical olefins, as shown in the following mechanism for the dimerization of isobutylene.

[33] F. C. Whitmore, *Ind. Eng. Chem.*, **26**, 94 (1934).

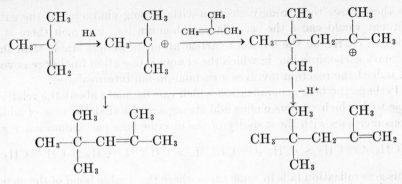

Thus a proton adds to isobutylene to give the tertiary rather than a primary carbonium ion, and the intermediate tertiary butyl cation combines with another isobutylene molecule so as to give a new tertiary carbonium ion, which may (among other possible fates) lose a β-proton to become an olefin in either of two possible ways.

In many polymerizations catalyzed by Friedel-Crafts catalysts, especially in hydrocarbon solvents, the presence of small amounts of certain "promoters" (especially water) seems to be required. The function of the promoter may be to solvate ions and/or furnish protons for donation to olefin molecules, but this subject does not appear to have been studied in detail.

A number of studies have been made of the relative reactivity of various olefins in Friedel-Crafts polymerizations, and especially copolymerizations, by several methods, including the determination of monomer reactivity ratios[34] (see Sec. 20-1c).

The familiar addition of alkyl halides to olefins probably proceeds by an analogous mechanism, e.g.,

$$CHCl_3 + AlCl_3 \rightleftharpoons \overset{\oplus}{C}HCl_2 + AlCl_4^-$$

$$\overset{\oplus}{C}HCl_2 + Cl_2C{=}CCl_2 \rightleftharpoons Cl_2\overset{\oplus}{C}{-}CCl_2{-}CHCl_2$$

$$Cl_2\overset{\oplus}{C}{-}CCl_2{-}CHCl_2 + AlCl_4^- \rightleftharpoons Cl_3C{-}CCl_2{-}CHCl_2 + AlCl_3$$

It is often possible to add such saturated hydrocarbons as isobutane to such olefins as isobutylene. The unmodified Whitmore mechanism gives no hint as to how the isobutane becomes involved in the reaction, but this has been provided by a brilliant experiment of Bartlett, Condon, and Schneider. These workers mixed two rapidly flowing isopentane

[34] R. E. Florin, *J. Am. Chem. Soc.*, **71**, 1867 (1949); **73**, 4468 (1951); C. G. Overberger, L. H. Arond, and J. J. Taylor, *J. Am. Chem. Soc.*, **73**, 5541 (1951); C. G. Overberger, L. H. Arond, D. Tanner, J. J. Taylor, and T. Alfrey, Jr., *J. Am. Chem. Soc.*, **74**, 4848 (1952); C. G. Overberger and G. F. Endres, *J. Am. Chem. Soc.*, **75**, 6349 (1953).

streams, one containing dissolved aluminum bromide and the other t-butyl chloride, in a nozzle from which the mixture was forced into a vigorously stirred water bath.[35]   Only about 0.001 sec was thus allowed for reaction before the reaction was quenched by combination of the aluminum bromide with water.   Nevertheless, during this time the reaction of t-butyl chloride was essentially complete, and t-amyl bromide was formed in about 60 per cent yield.   The most reasonable mechanism for this reaction involves the abstraction of a hydride anion from isopentane by the t-butyl carbonium ion to yield a t-amyl carbonium ion.

$$(CH_3)_3CCl + AlBr_3 \rightarrow (CH_3)_3\overset{\oplus}{C} + ClAlBr_3^-$$

$$(CH_3)_3\overset{\oplus}{C} + C_2H_5CH(CH_3)_2 \rightarrow (CH_3)_3CH + C_2H_5\overset{\oplus}{C}(CH_3)_2$$

$$C_2H_5\overset{\oplus}{C}(CH_3)_2 + ClAlBr_3^- \rightarrow \underset{\underset{Br}{|}}{C_2H_5C(CH_3)_2} + ClAlBr_2$$

The possibility of hydride-ion transfers to carbonium ions has since found wide application in many reaction mechanisms and, as Bartlett, Condon, and Schneider point out, permits a suitable mechanism for the addition of isobutane to isobutene, the isobutane being changed to a t-butyl carbonium ion by reaction with an "isooctyl" carbonium ion.

9-3b. *Additions of Metal Cations.*   The ability of certain metallic cations to coordinate with carbon-carbon double and triple bonds has long been recognized.   In many cases solid addition compounds are formed.   By measuring the effect of silver nitrate on increasing the solubility of olefins in water, Winstein and Lucas have determined equilibrium constants for the coordination of silver ions with several olefins.[36]   They have suggested the structure

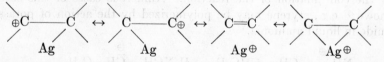

for the complex, and the particular aptness of this formulation for metal ion–olefin complexes makes the formulation appear more plausible for related but less stable species such as the proton-olefin pi complex (II).

9-4. Additions of Nucleophilic Reagents.   9-4a. *Additions to α,β-Unsaturated Carbonyl Compounds, Nitriles, etc.*   Just as the addition of electrophilic reagents has been found to occur more readily when a relatively stable intermediate carbonium ion may be formed, so might it

[35] P. D. Bartlett, F. E. Condon, and A. Schneider, *J. Am. Chem. Soc.* **66,** 1531 (1944).

[36] S. Winstein and H. J. Lucas, *J. Am. Chem. Soc.,* **60,** 836 (1938); H. J. Lucas, R. S. Moore, and D. Pressman, *J. Am. Chem. Soc.,* **65,** 227 (1943).

be expected that nucleophilic reagents would add to carbon-carbon multiple bonds if a sufficiently stable intermediate carbanion may be formed. Thus, as one of a large number of possible examples, alcohols may be added to α,β-unsaturated carbonyl compounds in the presence of a sodium alkoxide catalyst.

$$CH_3O^- + CH_2{=}CHCHO \rightarrow \left[\begin{array}{c} \overset{H}{\underset{}{\underset{\ominus}{C}}}\overset{H}{\underset{}{C}}{=}\overline{O}| \\ CH_3OCH_2{-}\underset{\ominus}{C}{-}C{=}\overline{O}| \\ \updownarrow \\ CH_3OCH_2{-}\overset{H}{C}{=}\overset{H}{C}{-}\underset{}{\overline{O}}|^{\ominus} \end{array} \right]$$

$$CH_3OCH_2CH_2CHO \leftarrow$$

In the Michael reaction the nucleophilic reagent is a carbanion

$$C_6H_5CH{=}CHCOC_6H_5 + \overset{\ominus}{C}H(CO_2Et)_2 \rightarrow$$

$$\left[\begin{array}{c} \overset{\ominus}{} \quad |\overset{|O}{\underset{\|}{}} \\ C_6H_5{-}CH{-}\overline{C}H{-}C{-}C_6H_5 \\ CH(CO_2Et)_2 \\ \updownarrow \\ |\overset{\overline{O}|}{\underset{}{}}{}^{\ominus} \\ C_6H_5{-}CH{-}CH{=}C{-}C_6H_5 \\ CH(CO_2Et)_2 \end{array} \right]$$

$$C_6H_5{-}\underset{\underset{CH(CO_2Et)_2}{|}}{CH}{-}CH_2COC_6H_5 \leftarrow$$

9-4b. Carbanion-catalyzed Polymerizations. When a carbanion adds to an olefin to form a new carbanion capable of addition to another molecule of olefin, it may become possible to form quite long chains by the continuation of the reaction. Numerous cases of this sort are known;[37] e.g., styrene may be polymerized by the action of potassium amide in liquid ammonia.[38]

$$\overset{\ominus}{N}H_2 + CH_2{=}CHC_6H_5 \rightarrow H_2NCH_2{-}\overset{\ominus}{C}H{-}C_6H_5$$

$$\downarrow C_6H_5CH{=}CH_2$$

$$\overset{etc.}{\longleftarrow} H_2NCH_2CHCH_2{-}\overset{\ominus}{C}H{-}C_6H_5$$

$$\underset{C_6H_5}{|}$$

Studies of copolymerizations have also been made.[37,39]

[37] F. R. Mayo and C. Walling, Chem. Rev., **46,** 191 (1950); C. Walling, E. R. Briggs, W. Cummings, and F. R. Mayo, J. Am. Chem. Soc., **72,** 48 (1950).

[38] W. C. E. Higginson and N. S. Wooding, J. Chem. Soc., 760, 1178 (1952).

[39] F. C. Foster, J. Am. Chem. Soc., **74,** 2299 (1952).

9-4c. *Additions of Nucleophilic Reagents to Fluoroolefins.* Although fluorine atoms and fluorinated alkyl groups do not have the ability to stabilize carbanions comparable to that of carbonyl, cyano, nitro, etc., groups, they are able to make possible the addition of nucleophilic reagents to carbon-carbon multiple bonds. The addition of ethanol in the presence of sodium ethoxide occurs readily with tetrafluoroethylene, trifluorochloroethylene, 1,1-difluoro-2,2-dichloroethylene, and 1,1-difluoro-2-chloroethylene, where the intermediate carbanion may be stabilized by both α- and β-halogen atoms.[40]

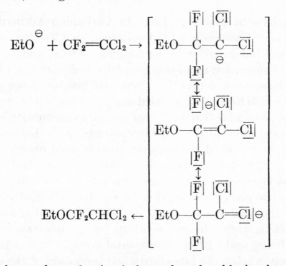

In the case above, the carbanion is formed at the chlorine-bearing carbon atom. This is probably because in the β position the carbanion stabilization is solely due to electronegativity, while in the α position the ease of expanding the outer shell of electrons to accommodate 10 may also be important (Sec. 13-1a). Thus fluorine is best as a β substituent, and chlorine is better in the α position. Addition may also occur when the intermediate contains only β-halogen substituents, but this apparently occurs somewhat less readily. Ethanol may be added to $CH_2{=}CH{-}CF_3$ and $CH{\equiv}C{-}CF_3$ in the presence of sodium ethoxide.[41]

[40] W. E. Hanford and G. W. Rigby, U.S. Patent 2,409,274, Oct. 15, 1946; *Chem. Abstr.*, **41**, 982b (1947); W. T. Miller, Jr., E. W. Fager, and P. H. Griswold, *J. Am. Chem. Soc.*, **70**, 431 (1948).

[41] A. L. Henne, M. A. Smook, and R. L. Pelley, *J. Am. Chem. Soc.*, **72**, 4756 (1950); A. L. Henne and M. Nager, *J. Am. Chem. Soc.*, **74**, 650 (1952).

CHAPTER 10

CARBANIONS AND ENOLIZATION

10-1. Mechanism and Reactivity in Carbanion Formation. 10-1a.
Enolization and Halogenation, Racemization, and Deuterium Exchange.
The kinetics of halogenation of one ketone, acetone, and the identity of
the rates of bromination and iodination have been described in Sec. 8-2d,
along with the statement that these processes involve as the rate-controlling step the reaction with an acid and/or base. The reaction with
acid yields an enol and that with base probably an enolate anion, either
of which may react almost instantaneously with halogen. Further
evidence for such a mechanism comes from several observations of the
identity of rates of halogenation, deuterium exchange, and racemization
of suitable compounds.[1] The largest amount of work appears to have
been done with phenyl *sec*-butyl ketone. Bartlett and Stauffer have
found that the rate constant for acid-catalyzed iodination is 0.0298
under conditions where the rate constant for racemization is 0.0296, the
two figures being well within experimental error.[2] It is reasonable that
both reactions involve the rate-controlling formation of the enol, which,
having a plane of symmetry, is as likely upon reketonization to give the
d isomer as the *l*.

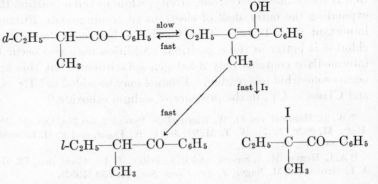

[1] L. Ramberg and A. Mellander, *Arkiv Kemi, Mineral. Geol.*, **11B**(31) (1934);
L. Ramberg and I. Hedlund, *Arkiv Kemi, Mineral. Geol.*, **11B**(41) (1934); C. K. Ingold
and C. L. Wilson, *J. Chem. Soc.*, 773 (1934).

[2] P. D. Bartlett and C. H. Stauffer, *J. Am. Chem. Soc.*, **57**, 2580 (1935).

Using the same ketone, Hsü and Wilson have found the rate of the base-catalyzed bromination (acetate ion was the base) to be equal to the rate of racemization under the same conditions.[3] Furthermore it has been demonstrated that the rates of the deuteroxide-catalyzed racemization and deuterium exchange are identical.[4] In the base-catalyzed reactions it is probable that it is the planar enolate anion which is being formed in the rate-controlling step.

These enol and enolate-anion formations can be formulated according to the termolecular mechanism, whose existence seems proved, as described in Sec. 8-2*d*, but whose exclusive operation is doubtful.

10-1*b*. *Stereochemistry of Carbanions.* In order for there to be any considerable contribution of structures like that shown on the right

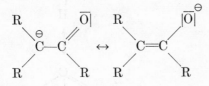

to the total structure of an enolate anion, it is necessary that the $\overset{\backslash}{\underset{/}{C}}=C-\overline{O}|^{\ominus}$ system and the three atoms attached directly thereto lie at least very nearly in the same plane. The fact that proton removal from an asymmetric carbon atom to form a carbanion results in racemization, mentioned in the previous section, does not demonstrate this point unambiguously, since another explanation of this fact is possible. That is, since carbanions are isoelectronic with amines, it is possible that their normal structure is pyrimidal and that, like amines, their optical inactivity is due to a rapid equilibrium between two enantiomorphic structures.

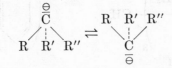

This possibility in the case of carbanions derived from carbonyl compounds has been disposed of by the very interesting observation of Bartlett and Woods on bicyclo[2,2,2]octanedione-2,6 (I).[5] In the first place, unlike typical β-diketones (including cyclic ones), this compound

[3] S. K. Hsü and C. L. Wilson, *J. Chem. Soc.*, 623 (1936).
[4] S. K. Hsü, C. K. Ingold, and C. L. Wilson, *J. Chem. Soc.*, 78 (1938).
[5] P. D. Bartlett and G. F. Woods, *J. Am. Chem. Soc.*, **62**, 2933 (1940).

shows very little tendency to form an enol, giving no interaction with $FeCl_3$ or Cu^{++}. Furthermore, the fact that it is no more soluble in aqueous alkali than in pure water shows that its ability to form a carbanion is abnormally small for a β-diketone, most β-diketones being acids with pK's around 9. The logical explanation is that resonance contributions of structures like that shown on the right are made negli-

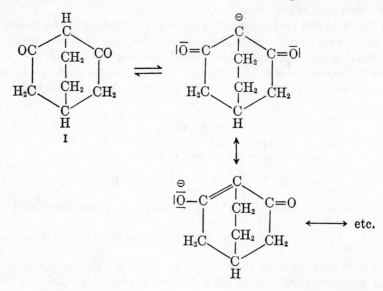

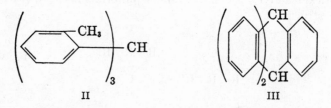

gible by the fact that the bicyclic ring system prevents the coplanarity of the four atoms attached to the double bond (cf. Bredt's rule). For similar reasons, tri-*o*-tolylmethane (II) and triptycene (III) are much weaker acids than triphenylmethane.[6]

II　　　　　　III

In all of these cases there is interference with resonance involving structures with double bonds at the anionic carbon atom. No carbanions without contributing structures of this type have been studied stereochemically, and indeed it is not certain that any are known. It is of interest in this connection, however, that Letsinger has reported that

[6] P. D. Bartlett and J. E. Jones, *J. Am. Chem. Soc.*, **64**, 1837 (1942); P. D. Bartlett, M. J. Ryan, and S. G. Cohen, *J. Am. Chem. Soc.*, **64**, 2649 (1942).

2-octyllithium is capable of maintaining its optical activity.[7] While the bond to lithium in this case is certainly partially covalent, the carbon atom attached must have considerable anionic character. The alkyl group of an alkyl sodium or potassium compound should have more (but not complete) carbanion character, and no evidence has been found for any of these compounds' maintaining their configuration at the atom to which the metal is attached.

Curtin and Harris have prepared the cis and trans isomers of 1,2-diphenylvinyllithium.[8]

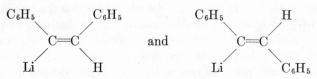

It is noted that the nitrogen analogs of vinyl anions (oximes, azo compounds, etc.) may display stereochemical stability sufficient to result in cis-trans isomers.

10-1c. *Relative Ease of Carbanion Formation.* Pearson and Dillon have tabulated many of the existing data on the rate constants and equilibrium constants for the reaction

$$HA + H_2O \overset{k_1}{\rightleftharpoons} H_3O^+ + A^-$$

where the hydrogen atom removed from HA was attached to carbon.[9] Some of their data are listed in Table 10-1. Many of the generalizations

TABLE 10-1. RATE AND EQUILIBRIUM CONSTANTS FOR THE IONIZATION OF CARBON-BOUND HYDROGEN ATOMS IN WATER AT 25°[9]

Compound	K_a	k_1
CH_3NO_2	6.1×10^{-11}	2.6×10^{-6}
$CH_3CH_2NO_2$	2.5×10^{-9}	2.2×10^{-6}
$CH_2(NO_2)_2$	2.7×10^{-4}	~ 50
CH_3COCH_3	$\sim 10^{-20}$	2.8×10^{-8}
$CH_2(COCH_3)_2$	1.0×10^{-9}	1.0
$CH(COCH_3)_3$	1.4×10^{-6}	
$CH_2(SO_2CH_3)_2$	1×10^{-14}	
$CH(SO_2CH_3)_3$	Strong	
$CH_2(CN)_2$	6.5×10^{-12}	9.0×10^{-1}
$CH_2(CO_2Et)_2$	5×10^{-14}	1.5×10^{-3}

which may be made about such data imply the existence of a linear free-

[7] R. L. Letsinger, *J. Am. Chem. Soc.*, **72**, 4842 (1950).

[8] D. Y. Curtin and E. E. Harris, *J. Am. Chem. Soc.*, **73**, 4519 (1951).

[9] R. G. Pearson and R. L. Dillon, *J. Am. Chem. Soc.*, **75**, 2439 (1953).

energy relationship of some sort, and while some such generalizations are useful, none are very precise in the present case. For example, it is seen that while nitroethane is a considerably stronger acid than nitromethane, its rate of ionization is smaller. Again, $CH_2(COCH_3)_2$ is a stronger acid than $CH_2(SO_2CH_3)_2$, but $CH(COCH_3)_3$ is much weaker than $CH(SO_2CH_3)_3$. Pearson and Dillon have discussed the very important problem of why these deviations from linear free-energy relationship occur and have referred to other discussions, but the problem is still worth additional study.

Bonhoeffer, Geib, and Reitz have tabulated data on the rate of removal of carbon-bound hydrogen by deuteroxide ions in deuterium oxide solution.[10] In addition to groups such as $-NO_2$, $-COR$, etc., it might be mentioned that α-halogen atoms also increase the ease of carbanion formation, chloroform undergoing base-catalyzed deuterium exchange about as readily as acetone.[11]

10-2. Carbanions and Tautomerism. *10-2a. The Stepwise Mechanism for Tautomerism.* Isomerization reactions having the form

$$H—X—Y=Z \rightleftharpoons X=Y—Z—H$$

have been found to occur very commonly with organic compounds. Such an isomerism is an example of tautomerism, and the atomic system shown is called a triad system. Two types of mechanisms, concerted and stepwise, may be suggested for these reactions, depending on whether the removal of a hydrogen from X is depicted as occurring simultaneously with, or in a separate step from, the addition of hydrogen to Z. We shall deal here only with prototropic tautomerism (overwhelmingly the most common kind), in which the hydrogen atoms are added and removed as protons. There appear to be well-established examples of the occurrence of both concerted and stepwise mechanisms in reactions of this type.

Tautomerism occurs most rapidly when both X and Z are oxygen or nitrogen atoms. In fact, these react so fast that none appear to have been studied kinetically. In many cases of this sort the evidence for the stepwise mechanism, originally suggested by Ingold, Shoppee, and Thorpe[12], appears clear, since the (usually) ionic intermediate may be stable enough to study independently without having to rely on indirect arguments for its formation. In the tautomerism of an unsymmetrical amidine, for example,

[10] K. F. Bonhoeffer, K. H. Geib, and O. Reitz, *J. Chem. Phys.*, **7**, 664 (1939).
[11] J. Hine, R. C. Peek, Jr., and B. D. Oakes, *J. Am. Chem. Soc.*, **76**, 827 (1954).
[12] C. K. Ingold, C. W. Shoppee, and J. F. Thorpe, *J. Chem. Soc.*, 1477 (1926).

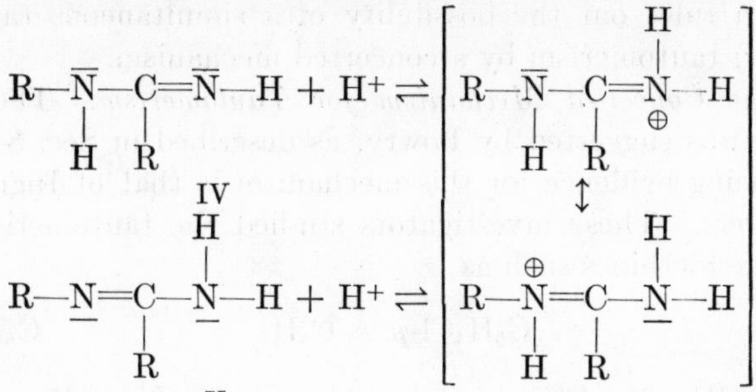

$$R-\overline{N}-C=\overline{N}-H + H^+ \rightleftharpoons \left[R-\overline{N}-\underset{R}{\overset{H}{\underset{|}{C}}}=\overset{H}{\underset{\oplus}{N}}-H \right.$$

$$\begin{matrix} | & | \\ H & R \end{matrix}$$
$$\text{IV}$$

$$\updownarrow$$

$$R-N=\underset{R}{\overset{H}{\underset{|}{C}}}-N-H + H^+ \rightleftharpoons \left. R-\overset{\oplus}{N}=C-\overset{H}{\underset{|}{N}}-H \right]$$

$$\text{V}$$

there is certainly every reason to believe that the amidine is a mixture of the two tautomers shown and that either may react reversibly with acids to yield the same cation with the resonance hybrid structure shown. Thus there *is* a stepwise mechanism for the tautomerism. It may be useful to point out a similarity between this and a concerted mechanism by noting that the solvation of a cation is a type of basic function and that the hydrogen atom attached to the alkylated nitrogen atom, partly because of such solvation, has become less tightly bound in the cation than it was in IV. The fact that the donation of a proton to Z is accompanied by a "partial loss" of a proton from X does not make the mechanism concerted (by the definition given above, at least), because there is formed a stable species (the cation) that is quite distinct from the species (V) which results from the "complete loss" of a proton from X. Nor is the distinction in the present case blurred by the possibility that mechanisms for tautomerism of various compounds under various conditions may vary continuously from stepwise to concerted, with some cases not being clearly assignable to either category (cf. Sec. 5-2e).

Just as a stepwise mechanism may involve acid catalysis by having a proton added to Z before one is lost from X, so may we have a base-catalyzed mechanism in which a proton is lost from X before one is gained at Z, as in the tautomerism of a thio acid.

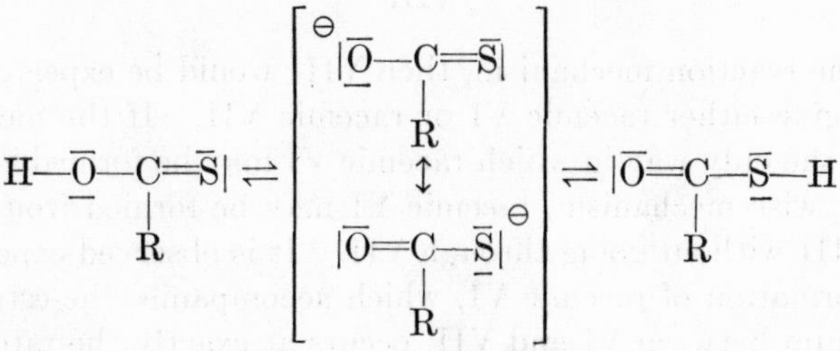

$$H-\overline{O}-C=\overline{S}| \rightleftharpoons \left[\begin{matrix} \overset{\ominus}{|\overline{O}}-C=\overline{S}| \\ | \\ R \\ \updownarrow \\ |\overline{O}=C-\overset{\ominus}{\overline{S}|} \\ | \\ R \end{matrix} \right] \rightleftharpoons |\overline{O}=C-\overline{S}-H$$

None of these arguments demonstrating the occurrence of a stepwise tautomerism rules out the possibility of a simultaneous (and possibly much faster) tautomerism by a concerted mechanism.

10-2b. *The Concerted Mechanism for Tautomerism.* The concerted mechanism was suggested by Lowry, as described in Sec. 8-2c, but the first convincing evidence for this mechanism is that of Ingold, Wilson, and coworkers. These investigators studied the tautomerism of some methyleneazomethines such as

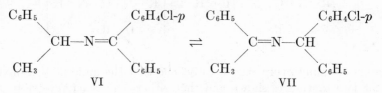

This reaction was studied in ethanol, where it is catalyzed by sodium ethoxide. When optically active VI is isomerized, the VII formed might be expected to be somewhat racemized due to the possibility that a new proton may be added to the right-hand carbon in two sterically different ways, but due to the influence of the original asymmetric carbon atom one way might be preferred, giving the VII obtained some optical activity. In practice, however, any such preference is apparently quite small, since the VII was found to be completely racemic (within the experimental error) not only in this case but in that of all of the methyleneazomethines studied.[13] It was further shown that the inactivity of VII was not due to any racemization of VI prior to reaction. These circumstances make it convenient to learn whether the base-catalyzed tautomerism proceeds by a stepwise or by a concerted mechanism. The stepwise mechanism would have the form

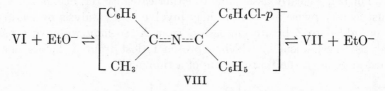

If this is the reaction mechanism, then VIII would be expected to add a proton to give either racemic VI or racemic VII. If the mechanism is concerted, the only way in which racemic VI may be formed is from VII. By the stepwise mechanism, racemic VI may be formed from the intermediate VIII without going through VII. It is observed experimentally that the formation of racemic VI, which accompanies the establishment of equilibrium between VI and VII, occurs at exactly the rate predicted

[13] C. K. Ingold and C. L. Wilson, *J. Chem. Soc.*, 1493 (1933); 93 (1934); S. K. Hsü, C. K. Ingold, and C. L. Wilson, *J. Chem. Soc.*, 1778 (1935).

(from the equilibrium constant and the forward rate constant) for the re-formation of VI from VII. This shows that essentially all of the racemization of VI occurs through VII as an intermediate, as is predicted by the concerted mechanism. This may be explained by a stepwise mechanism only by assuming that the intermediate VIII adds a proton almost invariably to form VII, as might result from a strong preference for the proton to become attached to a carbon atom bearing two aryl radicals. This explanation, however, was shown to be untenable by the observation that IX, in which such a preference would regenerate starting

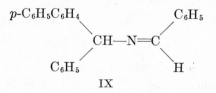

IX

material, displays just the same type of behavior as VI. This was also found to be the case for two other methyleneazomethines.

Perez Ossorio and Hughes have obtained further evidence in support of the concerted mechanism for this reaction in a comparison of the rate of tautomerism of IX, in a NaOEt-EtOD solution, with the rate at which IX and its tautomer acquire deuterium under the same conditions.[14] The initial rates for these two reactions were found to be identical, as predicted by the concerted mechanism. The stepwise mechanism would predict that deuterium could be acquired (by the combination of the intermediate anion with a deuteron to give deuterated IX) without the formation of the tautomer and therefore that the rate of deuterium exchange would exceed that of tautomerism.

The concerted, or termolecular, mechanism thus appears to have been demonstrated for the tautomerism of the methyleneazomethines. Some of the evidence for and against its occurrence in the enolization of acetone has been described in Sec. 8-2d. As Hsü, Ingold, and Wilson have pointed out, the stepwise mechanism for tautomerism involving an ionic intermediate appears to be favored when this ion is relatively stable, while the concerted mechanism may operate in other cases.

10-2c. *Tautomerism of α,β- and β,γ-Unsaturated Carbonyl and Related Compounds.* The isomerization of X to XI in alkaline "deuterated" ethanol solution has been studied by Ingold, de Salas, and Wilson, who found that X underwent a deuterium exchange to equilibrate two of its hydrogen atoms with the solvent at a rate vastly in excess of the rate at which it isomerized to XI or the rate at which XI exchanges.[15] The estab-

[14] R. Perez Ossorio and E. D. Hughes, *J. Chem. Soc.*, 426 (1952).
[15] C. K. Ingold, E. de Salas, and C. L. Wilson, *J. Chem. Soc.*, 1328 (1936).

lishment of the equilibrium is catalyzed by alkali and lies almost entirely to the right. These results are explained by a mechanism in which the basic catalyst transforms X into a resonance-stabilized anion which may combine with a hydrogen ion to yield either X or XI. It is of particular interest to note, though, that the rapidity of deuterium exchange requires that the intermediate anion accept a proton more rapidly to form X than

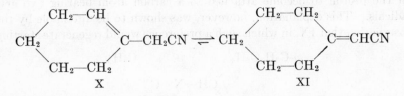

the much more stable XI. This is in agreement with the general rule of Ingold that "when a proton is supplied by acids to the mesomeric anion of weakly ionizing tautomers of markedly unequal stability, then the tautomer which is most quickly formed is the thermodynamically least stable. . . . "[16] It is not clear how "weakly ionizing" (weakly acidic) tautomers must be or how unequal their stability to fall within the dominion of the rule. Since the transition states leading to the two tautomers have considerable resemblance to the common anion, it might be expected that they should resemble each other more than do the two tautomers. Therefore the less stable isomer should comprise a higher percentage of the kinetically controlled product than of the thermo-dynamically controlled one. While this statement includes Ingold's general rule and is found to be in excellent agreement with the experi-mental data, the rationalization upon which it was based gives no explanation for the Ingold rule. According to Ingold, since the ionized form of the molecule is the least stable, it resembles the less stable isomer more and requires less electronic reorganization to be transformed to it.[16] Since some facts which are quoted in support of the rule (such as the preferential combination of the anions of aliphatic nitro compounds and β-diketones with protons to give acinitro compounds and enols) may be explained by assuming that proton transfers tend to occur more rapidly at oxygen than at carbon, it will be interesting to see how the scope of the rule is delineated by further experimental data.

Ives and Rydon have obtained data analogous to that found for cyclo-hexenylacetonitrile in studying the tautomerism of vinylacetic acid to crotonic acid.[17] In strongly basic solution at 100° the vinylacetate

[16] C. K. Ingold, "Structure and Mechanism in Organic Chemistry," p. 565, Cornell University Press, Ithaca, N.Y., 1953; cf. A. G. Catchpole, E. D. Hughes, and C. K. Ingold, *J. Chem. Soc.*, 11 (1948).

[17] D. J. G. Ives and H. N. Rydon, *J. Chem. Soc.*, 1735 (1935).

anion undergoes deuterium exchange much faster than it is isomerized to crotonate ion, whose exchange rate is quite slow.

10-2d. *Equilibrium in Tautomerism.* The percentages of enol found in a number of compounds capable of keto-enol tautomerism are listed in Table 10-2. Acetone is seen to be almost negligibly enolized. Replace-

TABLE 10-2. PERCENTAGE OF ENOL IN KETO-ENOL TAUTOMERS AT EQUILIBRIUM

Compound	Enol, %	
	Pure	In water
CH_3COCH_3	0.00025^a	
$CH_3COCH_2COCH_3$	80^b	15^c
$CH_3COCH_2CO_2Et$	7.5^b	
$CH_3COCHMeCO_2Et$	4.1^b	
$CH_3COCH(C_6H_5)CO_2Et$	30^b	
Cyclopentanone	0.0048^a	
Cyclohexanone	0.020^a	
$CH_3COCOCH_3$	0.0056^a	
1,2-Cyclohexanedione	$\sim100^a$	40^a
5,5-Dimethyl-1,3-cyclohexanedione	....	95^c

[a] G. Schwarzenbach and C. Wittwer, *Helv. Chim. Acta,* **30,** 656, 659, 663, 669 (1947).
[b] J. B. Conant and A. F. Thompson, Jr., *J. Am. Chem. Soc.,* **54,** 4039 (1932).
[c] G. Schwarzenbach and E. Felder, *Helv. Chim. Acta,* **27,** 1044 (1944).

ment of a hydrogen atom by an acetyl group gives a compound (acetyl-acetone), however, which is 80 per cent enolized at equilibrium. This result is no doubt due to the stabilizing influence of the unenolized carbonyl group conjugated with the double bond of the enol and of the internal hydrogen bond. The effect of the internal hydrogen bond is shown by the fact that in water, where the keto form may also be hydrogen-bonded (by the solvent), only 15 per cent enol is present at equilibrium, whereas in hexane or in the vapor phase about 92 per cent enol is present at equilibrium.[18] The carbethoxy group is considerably less effective than the acetyl group at promoting enolization, while the replacement of an active hydrogen atom of acetoacetic ester by a methyl group is interestingly seen to have a small but negative influence. The phenyl group shows its expected favorable effect, and there appears to be a preference of double bonds for six- rather than five-membered rings.[19] Aliphatic α-diketones are but little enolized and probably exist in a trans configuration

[18] J. B. Conant and A. F. Thompson, Jr., *J. Am. Chem. Soc.,* **54,** 4039 (1932).
[19] Cf. H. C. Brown, J. H. Brewster, and H. Shechter, *J. Am. Chem. Soc.,* **76,** 467 (1954).

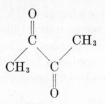

because of the large repulsion between the dipoles of the carbonyl groups. In cyclic α-diketones, where such stabilization of the keto form is not possible, extensive enolization occurs. In these cases a hydrogen-bonded ring would contain only four atoms other than hydrogen and would thus probably not be very stable. It is probably for this reason and because of hydrate formation of the keto form that the enol is relatively less stable in water. Part of the stabilizing influence of the six-membered ring on the enol form is probably unrelated to its being an α-diketone, since 5,5-dimethyl-1,3-cyclohexanedione is also largely enolic.

Kon, Linstead, and coworkers have studied the effect of structure on the equilibrium between α,β- and β,γ-unsaturated acids, esters, nitriles, etc.[20] Most of their results may be explained qualitatively on the basis

$$-\underset{|}{\overset{|}{C}}-\underset{}{\overset{|}{C}}=\underset{}{\overset{|}{C}}-CO_2^- \rightleftharpoons -\underset{}{\overset{|}{C}}=\underset{}{\overset{|}{C}}-\underset{|}{\overset{|}{C}}-CO_2^-$$

of the effect of alkyl groups on stabilizing the double bonds by hyperconjugation and the more powerful effect of $-CO_2^-$, $-CO_2H$, $-CO_2R$, $-COR$, $-CN$, phenyl, etc., groups in stabilizing them by resonance.

The fact that 2,5-dihydrofuran rearranges to 2,3-dihydrofuran in the presence of alkali-metal alkoxides[21] shows that carbon-carbon double bonds may be stabilized by groups strongly supplying electrons by resonance as well as by strongly electron-withdrawing groups.

10-3. Carbanions in Displacement Reactions. *10-3a. Alkylation of β-Diketones and Related Compounds.* The alkylation of malonic ester, acetoacetic ester, β-diketones, etc., carried out most commonly by the reaction of a sodium salt with an alkyl halide, is best interpreted as a nucleophilic substitution of a carbanion for a halide anion. The reaction usually proceeds satisfactorily with halides with sufficient S_N2 reactivity, but with tertiary halides the basicity of the carbanion usually causes elimination reactions to predominate greatly over substitution processes. Evidence for the S_N2 character of the reaction has been obtained in

[20] For summaries of this work see J. W. Baker, "Tautomerism," chap. 9, Routledge and Kegan Paul, Ltd., London, 1934; R. P. Linstead in H. Gilman "Organic Chemistry," p. 819, John Wiley & Sons, Inc., New York, 1938.

[21] R. Paul, M. Fluchaire, and G. Collardeau, *Bull. soc. chim. France,* 668 (1950).

several cases, as in the demonstration that the anion from malonic ester causes a Walden inversion in its reaction with cyclopentene oxide[22a] and the observation that the reaction of this anion with ethyl bromide is kinetically first-order in each reactant.[22b]

Kornblum, Smiley, Blackwood, and Iffland have pointed out that in the alkylation of such resonance-stabilized anions as

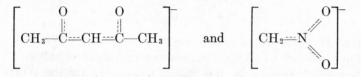

which may react at either of several atoms, the tendency for alkylation at the most electronegative atom usually increases with the S_N1 character of the reaction.[23] In the alkylation of the anion of diphenylacetophenone, Rinderknecht has suggested steric causes for the variation of the extent of oxygen alkylation and carbon alkylation with the nature of the alkyl halide.[24]

10-3b. *The Wurtz Reaction.* Two plausible mechanisms have been suggested for the Wurtz reaction. In one, the alkyl halide molecules react with sodium to give free radicals, which may then couple or disproportionate. In the second, one molecule of alkyl halide is changed to an alkylsodium molecule, which then reacts with the other molecule of alkyl halide. While a radical mechanism seems probable for the reaction of alkyl halides with sodium in the vapor phase at elevated temperatures (see Sec. 19-2b), the reaction as ordinarily carried out in solution may be satisfactorily explained on the basis of an alkylsodium intermediate. By vigorously stirring the reaction mixture so that the formation of alkylsodium could successfully compete with its subsequent reaction with alkyl halide, Morton and coworkers have been able to transform alkyl halides to alkylsodium compounds in high yield, showing that although the sodium surface may intermediately transform the alkyl halide into a free radical, this free radical is probably then transformed to an alkylsodium compound before it can escape.[25] Whitmore and Zook pointed out that the disproportionation products (alkane and alkene of the same carbon content as the alkyl halide used) whose presence had been cited as evidence for a free-radical mechanism could

[22] (a) W. E. Grigsby, J. Hind, J. Chanley, and F. H. Westheimer, *J. Am. Chem. Soc.*, **64**, 2606 (1942); (b) R. G. Pearson, *J. Am. Chem. Soc.*, **71**, 2212 (1949).

[23] N. Kornblum, R. A. Smiley, R. K. Blackwood, and D. C. Iffland, Abstracts of Papers, ACS meeting, Sept. 11–16, 1955, p. 39-*o*.

[24] H. Rinderknecht, *J. Am. Chem. Soc.*, **73**, 5770 (1951).

[25] A. A. Morton, J. B. Davidson, and H. A. Newey, *J. Am. Chem. Soc.*, **64**, 2240 (1942).

be explained as well by the simultaneous occurrence of elimination and substitution in the reaction of alkylsodium with alkyl halide, e.g.,

$$n\text{-}C_4H_9Cl + 2Na \rightarrow NaCl + n\text{-}C_4H_9Na$$

$$n\text{-}C_4H_9Na + n\text{-}C_4H_9Cl \begin{array}{c} \nearrow \ C_2H_5CH{=}CH_2 + n\text{-}C_4H_{10} + NaCl \\ \\ \searrow \ n\text{-}C_8H_{18} + NaCl \end{array}$$

and that these disproportionation-type products were obtained in the reaction of preformed alkylsodium compound with alkyl halide.[26] Additional evidence against the free-radical mechanism for the Wurtz reaction as ordinarily carried out is that optically active α-phenylethyl chloride[27] and 2-chlorooctane and 2-chlorobutane[28] react with sodium to give optically active hydrocarbons as Wurtz coupling products.[29] Benzhydrylsodium reacts with active α-phenylethyl chloride to give optically active 1,1,2-triphenylpropane.[30] The S_N2-like character of the reaction is attested by the observation of Letsinger and coworkers that the optically active 2-benzylbutane obtained from the reaction of benzylsodium with active sec-butyl chloride or bromide is probably of the inverted configuration.[31] In this connection it is of interest that ethylsodium reacts with 2-chlorooctane to give 3-methylnonane with but 20 per cent racemization,[32] while with 2-bromooctane 97 per cent racemization occurs.[33] This racemization is probably due to the formation by metal-halogen interchange of the 2-octylsodium compound,

$$C_2H_5Na + n\text{-}C_6H_{13}\underset{\underset{Br}{|}}{C}HCH_3 \rightarrow C_2H_5Br + n\text{-}C_6H_{13}\underset{\underset{Na}{|}}{C}HCH_3$$

which has too much carbanion character to maintain its configuration. Since this metal-halogen interchange is essentially a nucleophilic displacement on halogen, it occurs much more rapidly on bromine, which can more easily expand its outer valence shell.   In fact, in the Wurtz

[26] F. C. Whitmore and H. D. Zook, J. Am. Chem. Soc., 64, 1783 (1942); cf. A. A. Morton, J. B. Davidson, and B. L. Hakan, J. Am. Chem. Soc., 64, 2242 (1942).

[27] E. Ott, A. Behr, and R. Schröter, Ber., 61, 2124 (1928).

[28] J. F. Lane and S. E. Ulrich, J. Am. Chem. Soc., 72, 5132 (1950).

[29] For evidence that an intermediate free radical would have been expected to racemize, see Sec. 23-1.

[30] E. Bergmann, Helv. Chim. Acta, 20, 590 (1937).

[31] R. L. Letsinger, J. Am. Chem. Soc., 70, 406 (1948); R. L. Letsinger, L. G. Maury, and R. L. Burwell, Jr., J. Am. Chem. Soc., 73, 2373 (1951).

[32] S. E. Ulrich, F. H. Gentes, J. F. Lane, and E. S. Wallis, J. Am. Chem. Soc., 72, 5127 (1950).

[33] N. G. Brink, J. F. Lane, and E. S. Wallis, J. Am. Chem. Soc., 65, 943 (1943).

reaction with active *sec*-butyl bromide, where no bromide as S_N2-reactive as ethyl bromide is present to compete with reversible metal-halogen interchange, racemic 3,4-dimethylhexane is formed,[34] with analogous results being obtained with 1,2-diphenylethyl bromide[34] and 2-bromo-octane.[28] Lack of racemization in the reaction of benzylsodium with 2-bromobutane may be attributed to inhibition of metal-halogen interchange, in this case by the much greater acidity of toluene than butane. This explanation for the racemization of the bromides seems more probable than the suggestion that they (but not the chlorides) react by the S_N1 mechanism.[28,32]

10-3c. The Favorskii Rearrangement. The Favorskii rearrangement is a reaction of α-halo ketones with hydroxide (or alkoxide) ions to give salts (or esters) of acids with a somewhat rearranged carbon skeleton but the same number of carbon atoms. Loftfield has given an excellent discussion of the mechanisms of these reactions in addition to contributing to the solution of the problems involved.[35] He describes the evidence that when the α-halo ketone has available an α'-hydrogen atom, the reaction proceeds through an intermediate containing a cyclopropanone ring. This mechanism predicts that α-chlorocyclohexanone labeled with C^{14} at the chlorine-bearing carbon atom when treated with alkoxide ions will yield an ester of cyclopentanecarboxylic acid containing half of the C^{14} at the α-carbon atom and half at the β-carbon.

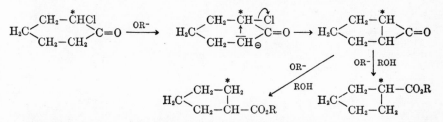

Loftfield has shown that this product is in agreement with the experimental facts, an important observation since the other reasonable mechanisms differing significantly from that given above all predict that the C^{14} should be entirely in the α position. Nevertheless, in those cases where the absence of α'-hydrogen atoms makes the cyclopropanone mechanism impossible (and perhaps in some other cases also), one of these alternate mechanisms must be operating. In the rearrangement of α-chlorocyclohexyl phenyl ketone, the mechanism is very probably closely related to that of the benzilic acid rearrangement[36] (cf. Sec.

[34] E. S. Wallis and F. H. Adams, *J. Am. Chem. Soc.*, **55**, 3838 (1933).

[35] R. B. Loftfield, *J. Am. Chem. Soc.*, **72**, 632 (1950); **73**, 4707 (1951); **76**, 35 (1954).

[36] B. Tchoubar and O. Sackur, *Compt. rend.*, **208**, 1020 (1939); C. L. Stevens and E. Farkas, *J. Am. Chem. Soc.*, **74**, 5352 (1952).

14-2). With an α, α'-dibromo ketone, the opening of the cyclopropanone ring may be accompanied by a loss of halide ion to yield an α,β-unsaturated acid, e.g.,[37]

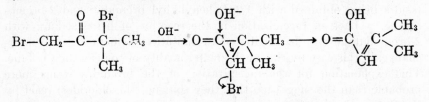

The Stevens rearrangement and related reactions are examples of rearrangements involving displacements by carbanions, which we have discussed under S_Ni reactions (Sec. 5-3).

[37] A. E. Favorskii, *J. prakt. Chem.*, [2], **88**, 658 (1913).

CHAPTER 11

ADDITION TO ALDEHYDES AND KETONES

Because of the considerable contribution of structures of the type of II to the total structure of carbonyl compounds,

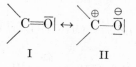

I   II

the carbon atom has marked electrophilic character. Therefore, addition reactions to carbonyl compounds almost invariably involve the attack of a nucleophilic reagent on the carbonyl carbon atom. Under acidic conditions the carbonyl compound may be transformed partially into its conjugate acid, in which the carbon atom is much more strongly electrophilic.

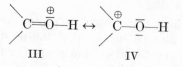

III   IV

That is, IV contributes more to the total structure of the conjugate acid than II (in which there is charge separation) does to the structure of the carbonyl compound itself. Thus carbonyl addition reactions may be catalyzed by acids, since the acids convert the carbonyl compound to a form which is more reactive toward nucleophilic reagents. Even the partial donation of a proton to the carbonyl group, as in a hydrogen-bonded complex with an acid, would be expected to increase its electrophilicity.

11-1. Addition of Water and Alcohols. **11-1a.** *Hydrates of Aldehydes and Ketones.* Any electron-feeding group attached to a carbonyl group will decrease its electrophilicity and stabilize it by distributing the positive charge. This stabilizing influence and the converse destabilizing influence of electron-withdrawing groups is reflected in the extent to which aldehydes and ketones form hydrates. In dilute aqueous solution

239

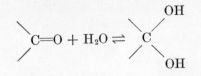

at 20° formaldehyde exists about 99.99 per cent in the hydrated form,[1] acetaldehyde is about 58 per cent hydrated,[2] and acetone is almost negligibly so (all at equilibrium).   Chloral and a number of compounds with the —COCOCO— grouping form stable crystalline hydrates.

11-1b. *Mechanism of the Hydration of Acetaldehyde.*   Bell and coworkers have studied the kinetics of the hydration of acetaldehyde.[3]   The reaction was found to be subject to both general acid and general base catalysis.   For the acid-catalyzed reaction the following mechanism was suggested:

$$CH_3CHO + HA \underset{}{\overset{fast}{\rightleftharpoons}} CH_3CHO\text{----}HA$$

$$CH_3\text{---}\overset{\overset{\displaystyle H}{|}}{C}\text{=}O\text{---}HA + H_2O \xrightarrow{slow} CH_3\text{---}\overset{\overset{\displaystyle H}{|}}{\underset{\underset{\displaystyle \oplus}{\underset{\displaystyle H\text{---}O\text{---}H}{|}}}{C}}\text{---}OH + A^- \qquad (11\text{-}1)$$

$$CH_3\text{---}\overset{\overset{\displaystyle H}{|}}{\underset{\underset{\displaystyle \oplus}{\underset{\displaystyle H\text{---}O\text{---}H}{|}}}{C}}\text{---}OH + A^- \xrightarrow{fast} CH_3CH(OH)_2 + HA$$

A mechanism involving a rate-controlling proton donation to the carbonyl oxygen atom could also be suggested if the possibility were admitted that such a reaction could occur slowly enough to measure.   For the base-catalyzed reaction the mechanism

$$HOH + B \underset{}{\overset{fast}{\rightleftharpoons}} HOH\text{---}B$$

$$CH_3\text{---}\overset{\overset{\displaystyle H}{|}}{C}\text{=}O + HOH\text{---}B \xrightarrow{slow} CH_3\text{---}\overset{\overset{\displaystyle H}{|}}{\underset{\underset{\displaystyle H\text{---}O}{|}}{C}}\text{---}O^\ominus + HB^+ \qquad (11\text{-}2)$$

$$CH_3\text{---}\overset{\overset{\displaystyle H}{|}}{\underset{\underset{\displaystyle H\text{---}O}{|}}{C}}\text{---}O^\ominus + HB^+ \xrightarrow{fast} CH_3CH(OH)_2$$

[1] R. Bieber and G. Trümpler, *Helv. Chim. Acta,* **30,** 1860 (1947).

[2] R. P. Bell and J. C. Clunie, *Trans. Faraday Soc.,* **48,** 439 (1952).

[3] R. P. Bell and B. deB. Darwent, *Trans. Faraday Soc.,* **46,** 34 (1950); R. P. Bell and J. C. Clunie, *Proc. Roy. Soc. (London),* **212A,** 33 (1952).

was proposed. The possibility that the reaction proceeds by a Lowry-type termolecular mechanism (see Sec. 8-2c) was considered. From the rate of the spontaneous (water-catalyzed) reaction and the catalytic constants for hydronium, hydroxide, and acetate ions and for acetic acid, the method of Swain[4] was used to estimate the magnitude of the termolecular rate term in which acetic acid acted as the acid and acetate ion as the base. Although the predicted magnitude of the termolecular term was far too large for it to have been overlooked, none was observed experimentally, and it was concluded that the termolecular mechanism is probably unimportant in this instance. It might be argued that this is one reaction for which the method of estimation would not work. The hydroxide ion, like any other base, can remove a proton from a water molecule as the water molecule attacks the carbonyl carbon atom [mechanism (11-2)], and in addition, being itself a fragment of water, hydroxide ion is unique among bases in being able to initiate hydrate formation by direct attack on the carbonyl carbon atom. However, this objection is not relevant in the present case, since it so happens that the value of the catalytic constant for hydroxide ion used in this estimation can be reduced as much as desired without significantly changing the magnitude of the termolecular term predicted.

11-1c. O^{18} *Exchange of Acetone.* To study the rate of formation of a hydrate so unstable that its equilibrium concentration is too small to measure, it is necessary to use a method which tells not how much hydrate *is present* but how much *has been formed.* Exchange with water containing excess O^{18} provides a method of this type, because the hydrate, when formed, will lose H_2O^{16} and H_2O^{18} with almost equal likelihood.

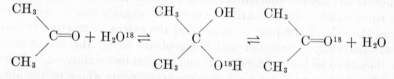

The O^{18} exchange of acetone was studied by Cohn and Urey, who found the reaction in the absence of catalysts to proceed very slowly even at 100°, but in the presence of 10^{-4} N hydrochloric acid or 10^{-3} N sodium hydroxide to occur too rapidly to measure conveniently even at 25°.[5] The acid catalysis was shown to be general, and although *general* base catalysis was not detected (in the hydration of acetaldehyde, catalysis by bases other than hydroxide ion is quite small), the reaction mechanism is very probably the same as that of the hydration of acetaldehyde.

11-1d. *Mutarotation of Glucose.* Alcohols add to carbonyl groups with a facility comparable to that of water. There have been a number of

[4] C. G. Swain, *J. Am. Chem. Soc.,* **72,** 4578 (1950); see also Sec. 8-2d.

[5] M. Cohn and H. C. Urey, *J. Am. Chem. Soc.,* **60,** 679 (1938).

studies of the equilibria in such reactions,[6] but only a few studies of the reaction kinetics have been made.[7] The mutarotation of sugars, particularly glucose, has received a great deal of attention, and since these reactions involve the establishment of equilibrium between diastereomeric cyclic hemiacetals through the open-chain hydroxyaldehyde (or ketone) as a reactive intermediate, their rate-controlling step is the reverse of the addition of an alcohol to an aldehyde (or ketone). Thus in the case of glucose the reaction path is

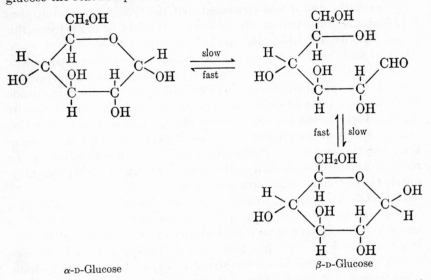

α-ᴅ-Glucose   β-ᴅ-Glucose

ignoring the smaller concentrations of furanose and other forms present at equilibrium. As ordinarily studied, the equilibrium is approached from the side of the pure α isomer and the extent of reaction followed polarimetrically. Brønsted and Guggenheim found the mutarotation of glucose to be both general acid- and general base-catalyzed.[8] Lowry and Faulkner carried out some striking experiments whose results are in support of the termolecular mechanism.[9] Using 2,3,4,6-tetramethylglucose (the nonparticipating hydroxyl groups were methylated to make the compound soluble in organic solvents), these workers found mutarotation to proceed very slowly in dry pyridine, a definitely basic but almost negligibly acidic solvent. Similar results were obtained in the

[6] See for example K. L. Wolf and K. Merkel, *Z. physik. Chem.*, **187A,** 61 (1940); I. L. Gauditz, *Z. physik. Chem.*, **48B,** 228 (1941); F. E. McKenna, H. V. Tartar, and E. C. Lingafelter, *J. Am. Chem. Soc.*, **75,** 604 (1953).

[7] See however (a) I. Lauder, *Trans. Faraday Soc.*, **44,** 734 (1948); (b) G. W. Meadows and B. deB. Darwent, *Trans. Faraday Soc.*, **48,** 1015 (1952).

[8] J. N. Brønsted and E. A. Guggenheim, *J. Am. Chem. Soc.*, **49,** 2554 (1927).

[9] T. M. Lowry and I. J. Faulkner, *J. Chem. Soc.*, **127,** 2883 (1925).

acidic but very weakly basic solvent cresol.   In a mixture of cresol and pyridine, however, the mutarotation proceeded quite rapidly.   In water, which is both basic and acidic, the reaction proceeds fairly rapidly. These facts are interpreted as indicating that the mechanism involves the simultaneous removal of a proton from the hydroxy group and donation of one to the ethereal oxygen atom of the hemiacetal group.[10]   Swain and Brown have studied the kinetics of the amine- and phenol-catalyzed mutarotation of tetramethylglucose in benzene solution and observed third-order kinetics, first-order in amine, phenol, and tetramethylglucose.[11]   In further striking agreement with the termolecular mechanism, these workers have found that 2-hydroxypyridine, which may donate a proton to, and accept one from, the hemiacetal group, is a powerful specific catalyst for the mutarotation.   At a concentration of 0.001 M this compound is 7,000 times as effective a catalyst as a mixture of 0.001 M pyridine and 0.001 M phenol, although it is only one ten-thousandth as strong a base as pyridine and only one-hundredth as strong an acid as phenol.   Also, in its presence the reaction becomes second-order, first-order in 2-hydroxypyridine and first-order in tetramethylglucose.   Other evidence showed that this catalyst forms a complex with the reactant, and so there is excellent evidence for a mechanism of the type

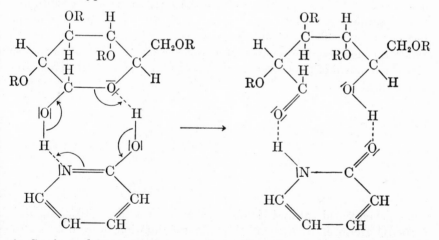

As Swain and Brown point out, the action of enzymes may be due to polyfunctional catalysis of this sort.   The termolecular mechanism might be favored over a stepwise mechanism in an organic solvent as compared to water, since the stepwise mechanism involves the intermediate formation of ions.   Indeed the termolecular mechanism has

[10] T. M. Lowry, *J. Chem. Soc.*, 2554 (1927).

[11] C. G. Swain and J. F. Brown, Jr., *J. Am. Chem. Soc.*, **74**, 2534, 2538 (1952).

not been proved (or disproved) for the reaction in aqueous solution. While no third-order term is required to explain the reaction kinetics, the predicted size of the termolecular term is so small that it could not have been detected if present.[4]

11-1e. *Acetal Formation and Hydrolysis.* The formation of dimethyl and diethyl acetal has been found to be specific acid-catalyzed.[7b,12] From the principle of microscopic reversibility (Chap. 5, Ref. 69) the formation of a number of other acetals must be specific acid-catalyzed also, since their hydrolyses have been found to be, including the inversion of sucrose[13] and the hydrolysis of diethyl acetal.[14] These reactions probably proceed through intermediate carbonium ions, e.g.,

$$
\underset{\text{fast}}{\overset{\text{H}^+}{\rightleftharpoons}}
$$

$$
CH_3CH(OEt)_2 \underset{\text{fast}}{\overset{\text{H}^+}{\rightleftharpoons}} CH_3\overset{\overset{\text{H}}{|}\oplus}{\underset{\underset{OEt}{|}}{CHOEt}} \overset{\text{slow}}{\longrightarrow} CH_3\overset{\oplus}{\underset{\underset{OEt}{|}}{CH}} + EtOH
$$

$$
\text{fast} \downarrow H_2O
$$

$$
CH_3CHO + EtOH + H^+ \overset{\text{fast}}{\longleftarrow} CH_3\overset{\oplus}{\underset{\underset{OEt}{|}}{CHOH_2}}
$$

The acid catalysis is specific, probably because the ethoxy group must have a proton completely donated to it before it can split off from the rest of the molecule. In a hemiacetal decomposition, such as the mutarotation of glucose, the removal of a proton from the hydroxy group so aids the removal of the OR group that it can be done by a proton hydrogen-bonded to it.

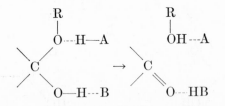

Thus general acid catalysis is observed in such a case. In so far as a carbonyl group may be regarded as a carbonium ion (due to resonance contributions of the polar structure), we may say that the removal of OR was made easy because a particularly stable carbonium ion was thereby formed. In this connection it is of interest (Sec. 8-1b) that while the

[12] A. J. Deyrup, *J. Am. Chem. Soc.*, **56**, 60 (1934); R. P. Bell and A. D. Norris, *J. Chem. Soc.*, 118 (1941).

[13] R. P. Bell, "Acid-Base Catalysis," p. 78, Oxford University Press, London, 1941.

[14] J. N. Brønsted and W. F. K. Wynne-Jones, *Trans. Faraday Soc.*, **25**, 59 (1929).

hydrolysis of ethyl orthoformate is specific acid-catalyzed, that of ethyl orthoacetate, ethyl orthopropionate, and ethyl orthocarbonate is general. In these latter cases the ethoxy groups may be removed by a proton hydrogen-bonded to them, as might be expected from the nature of the particularly stable carbonium ions being formed.

11-2. Addition of Nucleophilic Reagents Containing Sulfur and Nitrogen. 11-2a. *Additions of Hydrogen Sulfide and Mercaptans.* Hydrogen sulfide and mercaptans have a considerably greater tendency to add to carbonyl groups than do water and alcohols. The basicity of sulfur compounds toward carbon compared to their basicity toward hydrogen is usually greater than that of the analogous oxygen compounds. This fact is, no doubt, related to the considerable nucleophilicity of certain sulfur compounds (Sec. 6-2) and might be predicted from the bond energies given in Table 1-4. For example, the reaction of hydrogen sulfide with aldehydes and ketones to yield 1,1-dithiols

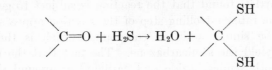

appears to be rather general.[15] In addition to forming thioacetals more easily than alcohols form acetals, mercaptans form thioketals quite generally, while ketal formation from alcohols is, at least, very uncommon.

11-2b. *Addition of Sodium Bisulfite.* Sodium bisulfite adds to many aldehydes and ketones. The products have been shown to be the salts of α-hydroxysulfonic acids.[16]

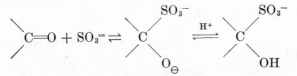

Gubareva[17] has measured the equilibrium constants for the formation of the bisulfite addition compounds from a number of aldehydes and ketones and found them to decrease in the order $CH_3CHO > C_2H_5CHO > C_6H_5CHO > CH_3COCH_3 > C_2H_5COCH_3 > (CH_3)_3CCOCH_3$. This order is probably a result of both steric and electronic factors.

The addition of bisulfite to the keto forms of naphthols and the imino

[15] T. L. Cairns, G. L. Evans, A. W. Larchar, and B. C. McKusick, *J. Am. Chem. Soc.*, **74**, 3982 (1952).

[16] F. Raschig and W. Prahl, *Ann.* **448**, 265 (1926).

[17] M. A. Gubareva, *Zhur. Obshchei Khim.*, **17**, 2259 (1947); *Chem. Abstr.*, **42**, 4820a (1948).

forms of naphthyl amines appears to be important in the Bucherer reaction.[18]

11-2c. *Mechanism of Semicarbazone Formation.* Simple imines in which the carbon-nitrogen double bond has no particular stabilization tend to polymerize or react in some other way to give compounds with carbon-nitrogen single bonds. This tendency is decreased when the double bond is conjugated with an aromatic ring, as in anils and benzalimines. Conjugation with two aromatic rings (benzalaniline derivatives) or with the unshared pairs of oxygen or nitrogen atoms gives quite stable carbon-nitrogen double bonds. For the latter reason it is nitrogen compounds like hydroxylamine, phenylhydrazine, semicarbazide, etc., which are useful in preparing derivatives of aldehydes and ketones. The rate and equilibrium constants in reactions of this sort have been studied considerably.

One of the most carefully studied reactions is semicarbazone formation. Conant and Bartlett found that the reaction is subject to general acid catalysis.[19] The rate-controlling step of the reaction appears to be the formation of the simple addition compound, which is then rapidly dehydrated to yield the semicarbazone. The fact that the reaction is first-order in both semicarbazide and carbonyl compound shows that both take part in or before the rate-controlling step. One mechanism which explains these facts is

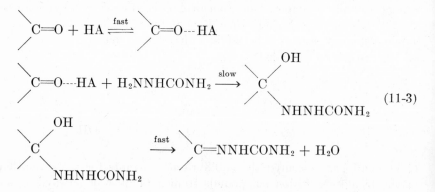

$$\text{(11-3)}$$

An alternate possibility involves the rapid reversible association of semicarbazide and carbonyl compound to give a complex which reacts with acid in the rate-controlling step. From mechanism (11-3) it can be seen that the rate *may* increase with the acidity of the reaction solution due to the increased fraction of the carbonyl compound present in the

[18] W. A. Cowdrey and C. N. Hinshelwood, *J. Chem. Soc.*, 1036 (1946); W. A. Cowdrey, *J. Chem. Soc.*, 1041, 1044, 1046 (1946).

[19] J. B. Conant and P. D. Bartlett, *J. Am. Chem. Soc.*, **54**, 2881 (1932).

form of the more reactive complex with acid. However, due to the equilibrium

$$H_3O^+ + H_2NNHCONH_2 \rightleftharpoons H_3\overset{+}{N}NHCONH_2 \qquad (11\text{-}4)$$

increasing acidity may transform the nucleophilic reagent, semicarbazide, into its unreactive salt. Therefore, it will be necessary to examine the situation in somewhat greater detail to learn the effect of acidity on the reaction rate.[20] A general treatment is quite complicated, so we shall consider first that part of the reaction catalyzed by the hydronium ion and then that part due to catalysis by any *one* weak acid. The first part of the reaction should follow the kinetic equation

$$v = k_{H^+} \left[\begin{array}{c} \diagdown \\ \diagup \end{array} C{=}O \right] [CON_3H_5][H_3O^+] \qquad (11\text{-}5)$$

The rate constant (k') in any given run (at a given pH) is determined from the equation

$$v = k' \left[\begin{array}{c} \diagdown \\ \diagup \end{array} C{=}O \right] (CON_3H_5) \qquad (11\text{-}6)$$

where (CON_3H_5) is the stoichiometric concentration of semicarbazide; i.e.,

$$(CON_3H_5) = [CON_3H_5] + [CON_3H_6^+] \qquad (11\text{-}7)$$

From (11-7) and the equilibrium constant (K_s) for reaction (11-4)

$$[CON_3H_5] = \frac{(CON_3H_5)}{1 + K_s[H_3O^+]} \qquad (11\text{-}8)$$

Substitution of (11-8) into (11-5) gives

$$v = k \frac{\left[\begin{array}{c} \diagdown \\ \diagup \end{array} C{=}O \right] (CON_3H_5)[H_3O^+]}{1 + K_s[H_3O^+]}$$

showing that

$$k' = k_{H^+} \frac{[H_3O^+]}{1 + K_s[H_3O^+]}$$

From this expression and the fact that $K_s = 4.5 \times 10^3$ it may be seen that the rate of this part of the reaction should at first increase rapidly with the acidity and then at pH's below 4 begin to approach asymptotically the value for which $k' = k_{H^+}/K_s$.

[20] L. P. Hammett, "Physical Organic Chemistry," p. 331, McGraw-Hill Book Company, Inc., New York, 1940.

An analogous treatment for that part of the reaction catalyzed by the weak acid, HA, gives the expression

$$k' = k_{HA} \frac{[HA]}{1 + K_s[H_3O^+]} = k_{HA} \frac{[H_3O^+](HA)}{(K_A + [H_3O^+])(1 + K_s[H_3O^+])} \quad (11\text{-}9)$$

where (HA), the total buffer concentration, is equal to $[HA] + [A^-]$, and K_A is the ionization constant of HA. At constant total buffer concentration, (HA), it may be seen, by setting the derivative of (11-9) with respect to $[H_3O^+]$ equal to zero, that the optimum hydronium-ion concentration for the reaction is

$$[H_3O^+] = \sqrt{K_A K_s}$$

Because of the contribution of that part of the reaction due to hydronium ion, the optimum rate for the reaction as a whole should occur at an acidity somewhat greater than $\sqrt{K_A K_s}$.

Conant and Bartlett found several instances in which there was a maximum in the plot of pH vs. k' for semicarbazone formation in aqueous solution,[19] and Westheimer obtained several from data on the reaction in aqueous methyl cellosolve.[21]

11-2d. *Reactivity in Semicarbazone Formation.* Conant and Bartlett and other workers have measured the reactivity of a number of aldehydes and ketones toward semicarbazide and have discussed the possible causes of the differences noted. A particularly careful discussion has been given by Price and Hammett, who point out that no explanation based

TABLE 11-1. REACTION RATES AND HEATS AND ENTROPIES OF ACTIVATION FOR SEMICARBAZONE FORMATION[22]

Compound	$10^3 k$, at 0.03°	$\Delta H,^{\ddagger}$ kcal	$\Delta S^{\ddagger} - \Delta S^{\ddagger}_{acetone}$, e.u.
Acetone................	63.5	2.0	0.0
Diethyl ketone..........	6.88	1.4	−6.5
Pinacolone..............	0.771	1.8	−9.7
Cyclopentanone.........	8.26	4.0	3.3
Cyclohexanone..........	437	1.1	0.4
Furfural................	6.56	4.1	3.2
Acetophenone...........	0.204	4.6	−1.9

solely on potential-energy effects, such as electronic displacements and dipole-dipole interactions, can hope to explain the data on this reaction (or most others, for that matter), since the observed differences in rates are due to large changes in the entropy as well as heat of activation[22] (cf. Secs. 2-4e and 3-3). Some of the relevant data are listed in Table 11-1. As Price and Hammett note, the eightyfold difference in rate

[21] F. H. Westheimer, *J. Am. Chem. Soc.*, **56**, 1962 (1934).

[22] F. P. Price, Jr. and L. P. Hammett. *J. Am. Chem. Soc.* **63**, 2387 (1941).

between acetone and pinacolone (methyl *t*-butyl ketone) is almost entirely due to entropy factors, suggesting that the *t*-butyl group has a number of modes of internal motion in pinacolone which are not possible in the more crowded transition state.   On the other hand, the increased reactivity of cyclohexanone (compared to acetone) is almost entirely due to a lower heat of activation.   Brown, Fletcher, and Johannesen have pointed out that a cyclohexane ring in which all of the carbon atoms are tetragonal may exist in the particularly stable chair form, in which all of the valences are staggered (see Sec. 1-6), but that when one of the carbon atoms is trigonal, as in cyclohexanone, this stable configuration is impossible.[23] Since the rate-controlling step in the semicarbazone formation involves the transformation of a trigonal carbon atom to a tetragonal configuration, the reaction occurs particularly easily with cyclohexanone.   In the case of cyclopentanone the valences are more easily staggered in the ketone than in the reactive intermediate, and a decrease in reactivity is observed.   The differences in reactivity on this basis would be expected to be, and indeed are found to be, unrelated to the stabilities of the semicarbazones as measured by the equilibrium constants for their formation.   The constant for the formation of the derivative from cyclopentanone is about twice that from acetone, and cyclohexanone has an intermediate value.[22]

In addition to steric effects of the ordinary type and of the more unusual variety described above, there appear to be two important types of electronic effects useful in rationalizing the effect of structure on rate and equilibrium in semicarbazone formation (and many other carbonyl reactions as well).   These rationalizations will be made in terms of the reactant V, intermediate VI, and product VII.

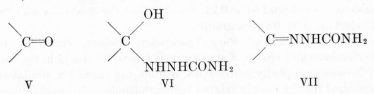

$$\begin{array}{ccc}
& \text{OH} & \\
\diagup \qquad \diagdown & & \\
\text{C}{=}\text{O} \qquad \text{C} & & \text{C}{=}\text{NNHCONH}_2 \\
& \diagdown & \\
& \text{NHNHCONH}_2 & \\
\text{V} \qquad\qquad \text{VI} & & \text{VII}
\end{array}$$

The equilibrium constant depends on the relative stability of V and VII, and the rate will be discussed in terms of V and VI (assuming that the transition state differs from V by looking more like VI, so that it will be relatively stabilized by the same structural features that stabilize VI). Because of the double bonds present, both V and VII will be more strongly electron-withdrawing groups than VI, and since oxygen is more electronegative than nitrogen, V will be more strongly electron-withdrawing than VII.   Therefore electron donor groups will stabilize V most and VI least.   In addition, however, regardless of their polar

[23] H. C. Brown, R. S. Fletcher, and R. B. Johannesen, *J. Am. Chem. Soc.*, **73**, 212 (1951).

character, unsaturated groups will stabilize V and VII by conjugation with their double bonds. Thus the replacement of the methyl group of acetaldehyde by a phenyl group, to yield benzaldehyde, stabilizes both V and VII relative to VI, since the effect of conjugation is greater than that of the increased negativity of the phenyl group, which does, however, make the stabilization of V less than that of VII. This rationalization is in agreement with the observation of Conant and Bartlett that acetaldehyde reacts more than 100 times as fast as benzaldehyde under their conditions although the equilibrium constant for the formation of benzaldehyde semicarbazone is about 7 times as favorable as that for the acetaldehyde derivative.

Besides the nonquantitative nature of the electronic effects and the difficulties in estimating the presence, magnitude, and nature of steric effects, there are a number of factors which complicate any prediction of the effect of structure on reactivity in carbonyl addition reactions of this type. These include varying susceptibilities to acid catalysis. Thus, as Westheimer has noted, acetone forms its semicarbazone more than three times as rapidly as furfural in an acetate buffer, while in the more acidic chloroacetate buffer the reaction of furfural is more than twice as fast as that of acetone.[21] A number of such variations in relative reactivities with the nature of the buffer have been found. Another complication arises from the fact, noted in Sec. 11-1a, that many aldehydes and ketones are partially hydrated at equilibrium in aqueous solution, so that only a fraction is present in the reactive carbonyl form.

It is of interest that in a study of the kinetics of semicarbazone formation by substituted acetophenones Cross and Fugassi have found large differences in the entropy as well as in the heat of activation.[24] The value of ρ was found to be 0.91, showing that the reactivity was increased by electron-withdrawing groups.

11-2e. *Formation of Phenylhydrazones, Oximes, etc.* The reaction mechanisms and effects of structure on reactivity found in the formation of hydrazones, phenylhydrazones, oximes, etc., are very similar to those described for the closely related semicarbazones. General acid catalysis has been demonstrated for phenylhydrazone and oxime formation.[25] The presence of an optimum acidity at which the reaction rate is a maximum was first discovered by Barrett and Lapworth in the case of oxime formation.[26] These workers also found that oxime formation is catalyzed not only by acids but by hydroxide ion. This catalysis must be due to the transformation of hydroxylamine to its more reactive conjugate base. Because of the much greater acidity of hydrogen atoms attached

[24] R. P. Cross and P. Fugassi, *J. Am. Chem. Soc.*, **71**, 223 (1949).

[25] G. H. Stempel, Jr. and G. S. Schaffel, *J. Am. Chem. Soc.*, **66**, 1158 (1944).

[26] E. Barrett and A. Lapworth, *J. Chem. Soc.*, **93**, 85 (1908).

to oxygen, the reaction is probably due to the H_2NO anion, for although the HNOH anion should be much more nucleophilic, its concentration would probably be too small for it to be effective.

11-3. Carbon-Carbon Condensations. *11-3a. Cyanohydrin Formation.* Lapworth demonstrated that the addition of HCN to aldehydes and ketones is a base-catalyzed reaction; he therefore concluded that the rate-controlling step of the reaction is the combination of the carbonyl compound with a cyanide ion.[27] Svirbely and Roth have found the additions of cyanide ion to acetone, acetaldehyde, and propionaldehyde to be slightly subject to general acid catalysis, the effect being beyond the experimental error only for the latter compound.[28] This shows that cyanohydrin formation may occur by a mechanism similar to that described for other carbonyl addition reactions.

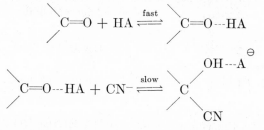

The equilibrium constants for cyanohydrin formation have been determined for a number of substituted benzaldehydes.[29] The cyanohydrins are found to be stabilized by electron-withdrawing groups and destabilized by electron-donating groups, as would be expected. The fact that pinacolone forms as stable a cyanohydrin as acetone and that the cyanohydrin of phenyl *t*-butyl ketone is more stable than that of acetophenone[30] suggests that the increased ability of the methyl group to stabilize the carbonyl group by hyperconjugative electron donation may equal or surpass the destabilization of the cyanohydrin by steric interactions with the *t*-butyl group.

Prelog and Kobelt have measured the dissociation constants for the cyanohydrins of a number of cyclic ketones with the result shown in Table 11-2.[31] These workers have discussed the theoretical basis for these results, as have Brown, Fletcher, and Johannesen.[23]

[27] A. Lapworth, *J. Chem. Soc.*, **83**, 995 (1903); **85**, 1206 (1904).
[28] W. J. Svirbely and J. F. Roth, *J. Am. Chem. Soc.*, **75**, 3106 (1953).
[29] A. Lapworth and R. H. F. Manske, *J. Chem. Soc.*, 2533 (1928); J. W. Baker and M. L. Hemming, *J. Chem. Soc.*, 191 (1942); J. W. Baker and H. B. Hopkins, *J. Chem. Soc.*, 1089 (1949); J. W. Baker, G. F. C. Barrett, and W. T. Tweed, *J. Chem. Soc.*, 2831 (1952).
[30] A. Lapworth and R. H. F. Manske, *J. Chem. Soc.*, 1976 (1930).
[31] V. Prelog and M. Kobelt, *Helv. Chim. Acta*, **32**, 1187 (1949).

TABLE 11-2. DISSOCIATION CONSTANTS OF CYANOHYDRINS OF UNSUBSTITUTED
CYCLIC KETONES[31]

Ring size	$100K$	Ring size	$100K$	Ring size	$100K$
5	2.1	11	112	16	9
6	0.1	12	31	17	12
7	13	13	26	18	10
8	86	14	6	19	10
9	170	15	11	20	7

11-3b. Aldol Condensation of Acetaldehyde. It is well known that aldol condensations may be base-catalyzed. The most likely function to attribute to the base is the formation of a carbanion, which may then add to a carbonyl group; e.g., in the case of acetaldehyde

$$CH_3CHO + OH^- \underset{k_{-1}}{\overset{k_1}{\rightleftharpoons}} \overset{\ominus}{C}H_2CHO + H_2O$$

$$CH_3CHO + \overset{\ominus}{C}H_2CHO \underset{k_{-2}}{\overset{k_2}{\rightleftharpoons}} CH_3\underset{|}{C}HCH_2CHO \qquad (11\text{-}10)$$
$$O\ominus$$

$$CH_3\underset{|}{C}HCH_2CHO + H_2O \underset{k_{-3}}{\overset{k_3}{\rightleftharpoons}} CH_3\underset{|}{C}HCH_2CHO + OH^-$$
$$O\ominus \qquad\qquad OH$$

Bonhoeffer and Walters found that when this reaction is carried out in heavy water solution and the aldol isolated as soon as an appreciable amount has been formed, it contains no carbon-bound deuterium.[32] This shows that k_2 is much larger than k_{-1}, or that essentially every carbanion formed adds to another molecule of acetaldehyde, since if a significant fraction reacted with water the acetaldehyde would acquire deuterium in its methyl group and hence yield deuterated aldol. This is in agreement with the earlier observation of Bell that the reaction is first-order in acetaldehyde, for if k_{-1} were much larger than k_2, the reaction would be second-order in aldehyde. With comparable values of k_{-1} and k_2 the kinetics would be somewhat complicated.[33] The reaction was not reported to be purely first-order in hydroxide ion, however, the rate equation having the form

$$v = (2.7 \times 10^{-4} + 0.112[OH^-])[CH_3CHO]$$

The explanation for this equation is not clear. It is not likely that the first term is due to basic catalysis by water, since the coefficient of the

[32] K. F. Bonhoeffer and W. D. Walters, Z. physik. Chem., **181A**, 441 (1938).
[33] R. P. Bell, J. Chem. Soc., 1637 (1937).

hydroxide-ion term is only 415 times as large, whereas inspection of a number of catalytic constants for water and hydroxide ion[34] shows that the latter is usually between 10^7 and 10^{11} times as large as the former. Neither can the rate be controlled by the speed with which equilibrium is established between the acetaldehyde and its hydrate, since Bell and coworkers have shown that the dehydration reaction is much faster than the carbanion formation.[2,3,35]

11-3c. *Aldol Condensation of Acetone.* Because of the stabilizing influence of the extra methyl radical on the carbonyl group of acetone, the equilibrium constant for the aldol condensation of this compound is much less favorable than that for acetaldehyde. Although the condensation does not proceed to a sufficient extent to make kinetic study convenient, the reverse reaction, the dealdolization of diacetone alcohol, has received considerable study. This reaction is base-catalyzed, as expected, and the basic catalysis is specific,[36] the rate equation being[37]

$$v = k[\text{diacetone alcohol}][\text{OH}^-]$$

From this rate equation and the equilibrium expression for the reaction

$$K = \frac{[\text{acetone}]^2}{[\text{diacetone alcohol}]}$$

the rate equation for the aldol condensation reaction may be obtained by the principle of microscopic reversibility. It is found to be

$$v = kK[\text{acetone}]^2[\text{OH}^-] \tag{11-11}$$

Since the reaction mechanism is almost undoubtedly

$$CH_3COCH_3 + OH^- \underset{k_{-1}}{\overset{k_1}{\rightleftharpoons}} \overset{\ominus}{C}H_2COCH_3 + H_2O$$

$$CH_3COCH_3 + \overset{\ominus}{C}H_2COCH_3 \underset{k_{-2}}{\overset{k_2}{\rightleftharpoons}} (CH_3)_2\underset{\underset{O}{|\ominus}}{C}-CH_2COCH_3 \tag{11-12}$$

$$(CH_3)_2\underset{\underset{O}{|\ominus}}{C}-CH_2COCH_3 + H_2O \underset{k_{-3}}{\overset{k_3}{\rightleftharpoons}} (CH_3)_2\underset{\underset{OH}{|}}{C}-CH_2COCH_3 + OH^-$$

the rate equation, (11-11), shows that k_{-1} is much larger than k_2. Walters and Bonhoeffer, in fact, have calculated that it is more than 1,000 times

[34] Bell, "Acid-Base Catalysis," p. 92.
[35] R. P. Bell, *Trans. Faraday Soc.*, **37**, 716 (1941).
[36] F. H. Westheimer and H. Cohen, *J. Am. Chem. Soc.*, **60**, 90 (1938).
[37] K. Koelichen, *Z. physik. Chem.*, **33**, 129 (1900); V. K. La Mer and M. L. Miller, *J. Am. Chem. Soc.*, **57**, 2674 (1935).

as large.[38] The striking difference in the ratio k_{-1}/k_2 between the two mechanisms (11-10) and (11-12) is in the direction which might have been predicted, since the much more reactive carbonyl group of acetaldehyde should coordinate with a carbanion much more rapidly than that of acetone.

Although the reaction is catalyzed by certain amines,[39] Westheimer and Cohen have shown that this is a specific effect of primary and secondary (but not tertiary) amines rather than a general base catalysis.[36] It therefore appears that this specific effect is due to the reaction of the amine with the carbonyl group to give the intermediate[40]

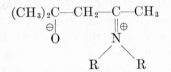

which should cleave much more rapidly than the conjugate base of diacetone alcohol since the positively charged nitrogen atom is a much more strongly electron-withdrawing group than neutral oxygen.

11-3d. Other Additions of Carbanions to Aldehydes and Ketones. There are a number of other base-catalyzed carbon-carbon condensations which have been found to be kinetically first-order in base, active hydrogen compound, and carbonyl compound, i.e., third-order over-all. Coombs and Evans have found the condensation of benzaldehyde with acetophenone in ethanol to give benzalacetophenone to obey the rate equation[41]

$$v = k[C_6H_5CHO][C_6H_5COCH_3][OEt^-]$$

The reaction of *p*-methoxybenzaldehyde is only about one-seventh as fast as that of benzaldehyde, since the methoxy group decreases the electrophilic character of the carbonyl carbon atom. The substitution of a *p*-methoxy group on the acetophenone would be expected to make the carbanion more difficult to form, but once it is formed, it should be more nucleophilic. Evidently the former factor is the more important, since *p*-methoxyacetophenone reacts only about one-fourth as fast as acetophenone. Other examples include the addition of ethyl malonate to formaldehyde[42] and the reaction of benzaldehyde with phenacyl chloride, in which the condensation is followed by a rapid epoxide formation.[43]

[38] W. D. Walters and K. F. Bonhoeffer, *Z. physik. Chem.*, **182A**, 265 (1938).
[39] J. G. Miller and M. Kilpatrick, *J. Am. Chem. Soc.*, **53**, 3217 (1931).
[40] Hammett, *op. cit.*, p. 345.
[41] E. Coombs and D. P. Evans, *J. Chem. Soc.*, 1295 (1940).
[42] K. N. Welch, *J. Chem. Soc.*, 653 (1931).
[43] M. Ballester and P. D. Bartlett, *J. Am. Chem. Soc.*, **75**, 2042 (1953).

$$C_6H_5COCH_2Cl + OH^- \overset{fast}{\rightleftharpoons} C_6H_5CO\overset{\ominus}{C}HCl + H_2O$$

$$C_6H_5CHO + C_6H_5CO\overset{\ominus}{C}HCl \overset{slow}{\longrightarrow} C_6H_5CH\underset{\underset{O}{\overset{\ominus}{|}}}{}\underset{\underset{Cl}{|}}{CHCOC_6H_5}$$

$$C_6H_5CH\underset{\underset{O}{\overset{\ominus}{|}}}{}\underset{\underset{Cl}{|}}{CHCOC_6H_5} \overset{fast}{\longrightarrow} C_6H_5CH\underset{\diagdownO\diagup}{}CHCOC_6H_5$$

Earlier in the history of organic chemistry there was considerable debate as to which component of the Perkin reaction mixture was the reactant and which the catalyst. However, as Breslow and Hauser have noted, from the standpoint of current theory it may be seen that the α-hydrogen atoms of acetic anhydride must be vastly easier to remove by base than those of sodium acetate, and therefore it seems most likely that acetic anhydride is the active hydrogen compound and that the sodium acetate acts as a basic catalyst.[44] This view is supported by Kalnin's observation[45] that sodium acetate may be replaced by other bases, such as sodium carbonate, sodium phosphate, quinoline, pyridine, and triethylamine, whose effectiveness appears to increase with their basicity; it also agrees with the kinetic study of Buckles and Bremer.[46]

Gettler and Hammett have encountered an interesting but unexplained complication in a study of the base-catalyzed condensation of benzaldehyde with methyl ethyl ketone in aqueous dioxane solution.[47]

The reaction

$$CH_2O \rightarrow HOCH_2CHO \rightarrow HOCH_2(CHOH)_nCHO$$

occurs in the presence of thallium hydroxide, calcium hydroxide, or certain other bases and bears a superficial resemblance to an ordinary aldol condensation. It does not appear to be of the ordinary aldol type, however, because formaldehyde would not be expected to form a very stable carbanion, and the reaction is much less effectively catalyzed by sodium, lithium, or barium hydroxide (a Cannizzaro reaction takes place instead). Nevertheless, despite a number of investigations, including a careful study by Pfeil and Schroth,[48] the exact nature of the reaction is not clear.

[44] D. S. Breslow and C. R. Hauser, *J. Am. Chem. Soc.*, **61**, 786, 793 (1939).
[45] P. Kalnin, *Helv. Chim. Acta*, **11**, 977 (1928).
[46] R. E. Buckles and K. G. Bremer, *J. Am. Chem. Soc.*, **75**, 1487 (1953).
[47] J. D. Gettler and L. P. Hammett, *J. Am. Chem. Soc.*, **65**, 1824 (1943).
[48] E. Pfeil and G. Schroth, *Chem. Ber.*, **85**, 293 (1952).

11-3e. *The Mannich Reaction.* In the Mannich reaction an active hydrogen compound, formaldehyde, and ammonia (or a primary or secondary amine) react as shown below.

$$—\overset{|}{\underset{|}{C}}—H + CH_2O + HNR_2 \rightarrow —\overset{|}{\underset{|}{C}}—CH_2NR_2 + H_2O$$

Alexander and Underhill have found the Mannich reaction involving ethylmalonic acid and dimethylamine to be a third-order reaction, first order in each reactant.[49] They have obtained good evidence that the reaction involves an initial addition of dimethylamine to formaldehyde to give dimethylaminomethanol. It therefore seems reasonable that the rate-controlling step of the reaction is of the following type:[50]

$$(CH_3)_2\overset{\oplus}{N}{=}CH_2 + \overset{\ominus}{\underset{\underset{C_2H_5}{|}}{C}}(CO_2H)_2 \rightarrow (CH_3)_2N{-}CH_2{-}\underset{\underset{C_2H_5}{|}}{C}(CO_2H)_2 \quad (11\text{-}13)$$

The reaction was found to have a maximum rate at a pH of about 3.8. Application of a discussion of the type given for semicarbazone formation (Sec. 11-2c) to the present case might be thought to lead to the prediction that only a *general* acid-catalyzed reaction could show such a rate maximum. Further consideration shows that such an analogy is overdrawn, however, since the concentration of the intermediate, $C_2H_5\overset{\ominus}{C}(CO_2H)_2$ must be directly proportional to that of the monoanion of ethylmalonic acid. This anion will be changed largely to the acid in strongly acidic solutions, to the dibasic anion in basic solutions, and will have a maximum concentration in solutions of intermediate pH. Therefore, a mechanism having reaction (11-13) as the rate-controlling step could be specific acid-catalyzed and still predict a maximum in the plot of rate vs. pH. The existence of such a maximum would not, of course, prove this mechanism. One of the several ways in which a mechanism based on (11-13) could be modified to agree with the possibility of general acid catalysis is described by Alexander and Underhill.[49]

The possibility of the following type of mechanism in certain cases, such as those involving a compound with two active hydrogen atoms on the same carbon, does not appear to have been investigated.

$$R{-}COCH_3 + CH_2O \rightleftharpoons R{-}COCH_2CH_2OH$$
$$R{-}COCH_2CH_2OH \rightleftharpoons R{-}COCH{=}CH_2 + H_2O$$
$$R{-}COCH{=}CH_2 + Me_2NH \rightleftharpoons R{-}CO\overset{\ominus}{C}HCH_2\overset{\oplus}{N}HMe_2$$
$$R{-}CO\overset{\ominus}{C}HCH_2\overset{\oplus}{N}HMe_2 \rightleftharpoons R{-}COCH_2CH_2NMe_2$$

[49] E. R. Alexander and E. J. Underhill, *J. Am. Chem. Soc.*, **71**, 4014 (1949).
[50] S. V. Lieberman and E. C. Wagner, *J. Org. Chem.*, **14**, 1001 (1949).

There are a few reports which are anomalous in view of the mechanisms described for the Mannich reaction.[51]

11-3f. *The Benzoin Condensation.* The benzoin condensation has the over-all appearance of a simple addition of an active hydrogen compound to an aldehyde. However, it would not be expected that the hydrogen atom attached to the carbonyl group would be active enough to be removed easily in aqueous solution. This fact—together with the fact that the reaction is not catalyzed by hydroxide ion or by bases in general but is specifically catalyzed by cyanide—makes a mechanism of the type outlined by Lapworth[52] plausible. In this mechanism the addition of the cyanide ion to the carbonyl group places the attached hydrogen atom in the alpha position of a nitrile and hence makes it active.

$$C_6H_5\text{—CHO} + CN^- \rightleftharpoons C_6H_5\text{—}\underset{\underset{O}{|\ominus}}{CH}\text{—CN} \rightleftharpoons C_6H_5\text{—}\overset{\ominus}{\underset{\underset{OH}{|}}{C}}\text{—CN}$$

$$C_6H_5\text{—}\overset{\ominus}{\underset{\underset{OH}{|}}{C}}\text{—CN} + C_6H_5\text{—CHO} \rightleftharpoons C_6H_5\text{—}\underset{\underset{O}{\ominus|}}{CH}\text{—}\overset{CN}{\underset{\underset{OH}{|}}{C}}\text{—}C_6H_5$$

$$C_6H_5\text{—}\underset{\underset{O}{\ominus|}}{CH}\text{—}\overset{CN}{\underset{\underset{OH}{|}}{C}}\text{—}C_6H_5 \rightleftharpoons C_6H_5\text{—}\underset{\underset{OH}{|}}{CH}\text{—}\underset{\underset{O}{\|}}{C}\text{—}C_6H_5 + CN^-$$

This mechanism, with either the last or the next to the last step rate-controlling and all previous steps rapid and reversible, agrees with the report that the reaction is first-order in cyanide ion and second-order in benzaldehyde[53] but does not agree with Wiberg's observation that the deuterium exchange of benzaldehyde which accompanies the benzoin condensation run in a deuterated solvent occurs at a rate comparable to that of the condensation reaction.[54] A more thorough investigation is promised.

11-3g. *Acid-catalyzed Aldol Condensations.* The combination of several reactions of types already discussed will show that aldol condensation might be expected to be catalyzed by acids as well as by bases. This is in agreement with experimental fact and may be illustrated for the case of acetone. Being a weak base, acetone will be in equilibrium with a certain amount of its conjugate acid in an acidic solution. While this

[51] K. Bodendorf and G. Koralewski, *Arch. Pharm.*, **271**, 101 (1933); G. F. Grillot and R. I. Bashford, Jr., *J. Am. Chem. Soc.*, **73**, 5598 (1951).

[52] A. Lapworth, *J. Chem. Soc.*, **83**, 995 (1903); **85**, 1206 (1904).

[53] G. Bredig and E. Stern, *Z. Elektrochem.*, **10**, 582 (1904); E. Stern, *Z. physik. Chem.*, **50**, 513 (1905).

[54] K. B. Wiberg, *J. Am. Chem. Soc.*, **76**, 5371 (1954).

conjugate acid should more commonly lose a proton from its oxygen atom to revert to acetone, it may occasionally lose one from carbon to form the enol.

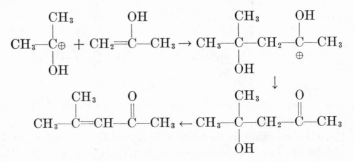

Since the enol is an olefin in which the very strongly electron-donating hydroxyl group is attached to the carbon-carbon double bond, it might be expected to be very reactive toward acidic reagents, such as the conjugate acid of the ketone, which adds to form the conjugate acid of diacetone alcohol.

The observed product, mesityl oxide, would be expected, since the tertiary alcohol diacetone alcohol is known to be very easily dehydrated by acidic reagents.

Few reactions of this sort appear to have received careful mechanistic study.

11-3h. *Addition of Organometallic Compounds to Aldehydes and Ketones.* Because of the rapidity of the additions of many organometallic compounds to aldehydes and ketones, kinetic studies are often not feasible. For this and other reasons there have been few thorough studies of the reaction mechanisms involved. One of the most important characteristics of organometallic compounds is the polar nature of the carbon-metal bond. While this does give the alkyl group considerable carbanion character, the bond also has definite covalent character. This fact and the low ion-solvating power of the typical reaction media make the reactions much more complicated than a simple combination of carbanions with a carbonyl group. The action of the metal as a Lewis acid by coordinating with the carbonyl oxygen atom is usually an important factor in the reaction.

Swain and Kent have given evidence that in the reaction of organolithium compounds with ketones a reversibly formed complex decomposes to give the final product.[55]

$$R''-\underset{\underset{R'}{|}}{C}=O \ + \ Li-R \ \rightleftharpoons \ R''-\underset{\underset{R'}{|}}{\overset{\oplus}{C}}-\bar{O}-Li^{\ominus} \longrightarrow R''-\underset{\underset{R'}{|}}{\overset{\overset{R}{|}}{C}}-\bar{O}-Li$$

In the addition of Grignard reagents to ketones it appears that one molecule of Grignard reagent coordinates with the ketone, while a second donates the alkyl group to the carbonyl carbon atom.[56]

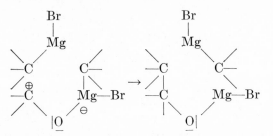

The common competing reaction, reduction, involves only one molecule of Grignard reagent.

As evidence for this interpretation, Swain and Boyles have shown that the addition of magnesium bromide (which should aid the addition reaction since it should coordinate with a carbonyl group better than a Grignard reagent) approximately doubles the yield of addition product in the reaction of the n-propyl Grignard reagent with diisopropyl ketone.[56]

11-4. Hydride-transfer Reactions. 11-4a. *The Cannizzaro Reaction.* The transformation of an aldehyde into an equimolar mixture of the corresponding alcohol and acid (or its salt) is usually known as the Cannizzaro reaction. The reaction may be carried out in several ways:

[55] C. G. Swain and L. Kent, *J. Am. Chem. Soc.*, **72**, 518 (1950).
[56] C. G. Swain and H. B. Boyles, *J. Am. Chem. Soc.*, **73**, 870 (1951).

enzymatically; by the use of metal catalysts, such as nickel and platinum; in a two-phase system (an organic phase and a strongly alkaline aqueous phase); and in homogeneous alkaline solution. We shall discuss only the reaction carried out homogeneously.

When benzaldehyde or formaldehyde undergoes the Cannizzaro reaction in heavy water solution, the alcohol produced contains no carbon-bound deuterium, showing that the hydrogen is transferred directly from one molecule of aldehyde to the other.[57] The Cannizzaro reactions of furfural,[58] formaldehyde,[59] and sodium benzaldehyde-*m*-sulfonate,[60] under certain conditions, have been found to be fourth-order reactions, second-order in aldehyde and second-order in alkali. From data of this sort Hammett suggested the following reaction mechanism,[61]

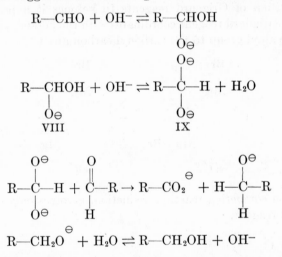

in which the rate-controlling step consists of the donation of a hydride ion from the reactive intermediate IX to the carbonyl carbon atom of an aldehyde molecule. It appears that the α-hydrogens on all alkoxide ions may be easily removed as hydride ions, due to the tendency of the negatively charged oxygen atom to form a double bond with carbon. The intermediate IX has a particularly strong tendency to donate hydride ions because of the presence of two negatively charged oxygen atoms on the same carbon (the product being a resonance stabilized carboxylate anion). The intermediate VIII should also be capable of acting as a hydride ion donor, and since it should be only very weakly acidic, it must

[57] H. Fredenhagen and K. F. Bonhoeffer, *Z. physik. Chem.*, **181A,** 379 (1938).

[58] K. H. Geib, *Z. physik. Chem.*, **169A,** 41 (1934).

[59] H. v. Euler and T. Lövgren, *Z. anorg. Chem.*, **147,** 123 (1925).

[60] E. A. Shilov and G. I. Kudryavtsev, *Doklady Akad. Nauk S.S.S.R.*, **63,** 681 (1948).

[61] Hammett, *op. cit.*, pp. 350–352.

be present in a much higher concentration than IX at equilibrium. It must be the greater reactivity of IX, then, which makes it the principal reacting species in those cases for which the Cannizzaro reaction follows fourth-order kinetics. The Cannizzaro reaction of benzaldehyde and several derivatives has been found to be third-order (second-order in aldehyde and first-order in base),[62] and under some conditions, at least, this is true for formaldehyde and furfural.[63] Evidently it is the intermediate VIII which is the principal hydride-ion donor in these cases.

It is reported that electron-withdrawing substituents increase the reactivity of aldehydes in the Cannizzaro reaction.[62]

The Cannizzaro reaction may occur intramolecularly not only with dialdehydes[64] but also with α-ketoaldehydes. The base-catalyzed rearrangement of phenylglyoxal to the salt of mandelic acid has been studied carefully. Alexander found the reaction to be second-order, first-order in hydroxide ion and first-order in phenylglyoxal, and suggested the following mechanism by analogy with the intermolecular Cannizzaro reaction.[65]

$$C_6H_5COCHO + OH^- \overset{\text{fast}}{\rightleftharpoons} C_6H_5COCHOH$$
$$\underset{O^\ominus}{|}$$

Further support for this mechanism may be found in the following: when the reaction is run in deuterium oxide solution, the product contains no carbon-bound deuterium;[66] it is the hydrogen atom and not the phenyl group which migrates;[66,67] and 2,4,6-trimethylphenylglyoxal undergoes the rearrangement readily.[68]

11-4b. *The Tishchenko Reaction.* The hydride-ion transfer characteristic of the Cannizzaro reaction has a more than formal resemblance

[62] E. L. Molt, *Rec. trav. chim.*, **56**, 233 (1937); A. Eitel and G. Lock, *Monatsh.*, **72**, 392 (1939); E. Tommila, *Ann. Acad. Sci. Fennicae*, **59A**(8) (1942).

[63] I. I. Paul, *Zhur. Obshchei Khim.*, **11**, 1121 (1941); V. Pajunen, *Suomen Kemistilehti*, **21B**, 21 (1948); *Ann. Acad. Sci. Fennicae*, ser. A, II, **37**, 7 (1950); A. Eitel, *Monatsh.*, **74**, 124 (1942).

[64] J. Thiele and O. Günther, *Ann.*, **347**, 106 (1906); E. M. Fry, E. J. Wilson, Jr., and C. S. Hudson, *J. Am. Chem. Soc.*, **64**, 872 (1942).

[65] E. R. Alexander, *J. Am. Chem. Soc.*, **69**, 289 (1947).

[66] W. von E. Doering, T. I. Taylor, and E. F. Schoenewaldt, *J. Am. Chem. Soc.*, **70**, 455 (1948).

[67] O. K. Neville, *J. Am. Chem. Soc.*, **70**, 3499 (1948).

[68] A. R. Gray and R. C. Fuson, *J. Am. Chem. Soc.*, **56**, 739 (1934).

to the transfer of a hydride ion from a hydrocarbon to a carbonium ion described in Sec. 9-3*a*, since in so far as the polar resonance structure contributes to the total structure of an aldehyde, the aldehyde may be thought of as a carbonium ion. While the aldehyde is not nearly so electrophilic as a carbonium ion, the intermediate VIII (or IX) must be a vastly better hydride-ion donor than is a hydrocarbon. Viewed in these terms, the Tishchenko reaction, in which the aluminum alkoxide–catalyzed transformation of an aldehyde into the ester of the corresponding acid and alcohol,[69] is explained readily by a mechanism analogous to that first written for the Meerwein-Ponndorf-Oppenauer equilibration by Woodward, Wendler, and Brutschy.[70]

$$C_6H_5—CHO + Al(OCH_2C_6H_5)_3 \rightleftharpoons C_6H_5—CHOAl(OCH_2C_6H_5)_2$$
$$\overset{|}{O}CH_2C_6H_5$$

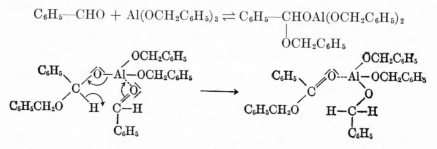

Although the oxygen atom attached to aluminum is not so negative as in a dissociated anion and therefore the α-hydrogen atom is not so easily lost as an anion, the coordination of aluminum with the oxygen atom of the aldehyde considerably increases the electrophilicity of the carbonyl carbon atom, so that it is a much better hydride-ion abstractor. A similar mechanism explains Pfeil's observations that in aqueous solution barium, calcium, and thallium hydroxide are more effective bases for the Cannizzaro reaction than are sodium, potassium, and tetramethylammonium hydroxide.[71] The sodium alkoxide–catalyzed transformation of aldehydes into esters[72] probably has a mechanism like that of the Cannizzaro reaction, proceeding through intermediate VIII (but not IX), except that the function of the hydroxide ion is assumed by the alkoxide ion.

Kharasch and Snyder have shown that in the case of the Cannizzaro reaction carried out with an organic phase and an aqueous phase, most of the reaction takes place in the organic phase if the aqueous phase is sufficiently strongly alkaline.[73] They further showed that this reaction

[69] W. Tishchenko, *Zhur. Fiz. Khim.*, **38**, 355 (1906).

[70] R. B. Woodward, N. L. Wendler, and F. J. Brutschy, *J. Am. Chem. Soc.*, **67**, 1425 (1945).

[71] E. Pfeil, *Chem. Ber.*, **84**, 229 (1951).

[72] L. Claisen, *Ber.*, **20**, 649 (1887); O. Kamm and W. F. Kamm, "Organic Syntheses," 2d ed., Collective vol. I, p. 104, John Wiley & Sons, Inc., New York, 1941.

[73] M. S. Kharasch and R. H. Snyder, *J. Org. Chem.*, **14**, 819 (1949).

in the organic phase is powerfully catalyzed by the benzyl alcohol initially produced by the slower reaction in the aqueous layer.   Evidently the sodium or potassium benzylate formed from the alcohol and alkali dissolves in the organic phase to catalyze a Tishchenko reaction to yield benzyl benzoate, which may be hydrolyzed by the alkali.   Indeed Lachman has isolated benzyl benzoate from the reaction by avoiding overheating and excess alkali.[74]   There is evidence that in at least some cases, however, the heterogeneous Cannizzaro reaction may proceed by a free-radical mechanism.[75]

Just as the reaction has been found to be catalyzed by the strongly basic alkali-metal alkoxides and the amphoteric aluminum alkoxides, it may also be catalyzed by strong acids.   Nemtsov and Trenke have studied such a case in the aqueous sulfuric acid–catalyzed transformation of formaldehyde to methanol, formic acid, and products of their further reaction.[76]   The mechanism is probably of the form

$$H_2C(OH)_2 \underset{H_2SO_4}{\rightleftharpoons} HOCH_2OH_2^{\oplus} \rightleftharpoons HOCH_2^{\oplus}$$

$$HOCH_2^{\oplus} + H_2C(OH)_2 \rightarrow HOCH_3 + HC(OH)_2^{\oplus}$$

$$HC(OH)_2^{\oplus} \rightleftharpoons H^{\oplus} + HCO_2H$$

11-4c. The Meerwein-Ponndorf-Oppenauer Equilibrium.   The Meerwein-Ponndorf reduction and the Oppenauer oxidation are two applications of the fact that aluminum and other alkoxides catalyze the establishment of equilibrium between primary or secondary alcohols and the corresponding aldehydes or ketones.

$$RCHOHR' + R''COR''' \underset{Al(OR)_3}{\rightleftharpoons} RCOR' + R''CHOHR'''$$

The aluminum alkoxide–catalyzed reaction probably proceeds by a mechanism of the type written for the Tishchenko reaction and suggested by Woodward, Wendler, and Brutschy.[70]

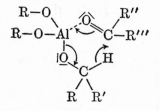

A mechanism for the alkali-metal alkoxide–catalyzed reaction can easily be written by analogy with the Cannizzaro reaction.

[74] A. Lachman, *J. Am. Chem. Soc.*, **45**, 2356 (1923).

[75] M. S. Kharasch and M. Foy, *J. Am. Chem. Soc.*, **57**, 1510 (1935).

[76] M. S. Nemtsov and K. M. Trenke, *Zhur. Obshchei Khim.*, **22**, 415 (1952); *Chem. Abstr.*, **46**, 8485i (1952).

The Lobry de Bruyn–Alberda van Ekenstein rearrangement, in which glucose, fructose, and mannose are interconverted by use of an alkaline catalyst,[77] is an interesting reaction whose over-all result is the intramolecular oxidation-reduction characteristic of the Meerwein-Ponndorf-Oppenauer equilibrium.

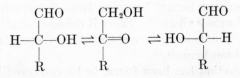

Two reasonable mechanisms may be suggested for this reaction. One is an internal oxidation-reduction involving a hydride-ion shift

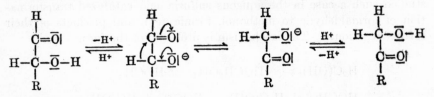

while the other is a base-catalyzed enolization to give an enediol that may either revert to starting aldose or be converted to the corresponding ketose or the epimeric aldose.

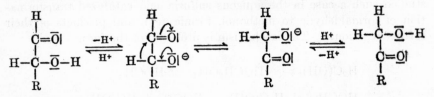

[77] C. A. Lobry de Bruyn and W. Alberda van Ekenstein, *Rec. trav. chim.*, **14**, 203 (1895); **19**, 5 (1900).

It seems that these mechanisms could be distinguished by running the reaction in heavy water solution. The enediol mechanism would give products containing carbon-bound deuterium, while the hydride-shift mechanism would not. Fredenhagen and Bonhoeffer have reported that the products are free of such deuterium, and Goto has also made this observation.[78] However, Topper and Stetten and also Sowden and Schaffer state that carbon-bound deuterium is acquired.[79]

11-4d. *The Leuckart Reaction.* The reductive amination of an aldehyde or a ketone by the use of formamide, ammonium formate, or an amine formate is called the Leuckart reaction. The fact that the reaction may be carried out with ammonium formate under conditions at which formamide will not work suggests that the action of the latter may be due to its hydrolysis to ammonium formate.[80] The suggestion that the reaction involves a hydride transfer from a formate ion to an imonium ion seems plausible.[81]

$$\left[\begin{array}{c} \backslash \oplus \diagup \\ C = N \\ \diagup \backslash \\ \updownarrow \\ \backslash \oplus \bar{} \\ C - N \\ \diagup \backslash \end{array} \right] + HCO_2^- \rightarrow CO_2 + \begin{array}{c} | \\ -C-\bar{N}- \\ | \\ H \end{array}$$

The formate ion would not be expected to be a very strong hydride donor, since it is considerably stabilized by resonance and since its oxygen atoms bear only a fractional negative charge. However, the Leuckart reaction is aided by the following facts: it is usually run at temperatures of 150° and above, the hydride donor is present in high concentration, and the imonium ion is a better hydride-ion acceptor than is an aldehyde or ketone. Other mechanisms have been suggested for the reaction.[82]

[78] H. Fredenhagen and K. F. Bonhoeffer, *Z. physik. Chem.*, **181A**, 392 (1938); K. Goto, *J. Chem. Soc. Japan*, **63**, 217 (1942).

[79] Y. J. Topper and D. Stetten, Jr., *J. Biol. Chem.*, **189**, 191 (1951); J. C. Sowden and R. Schaffer, *J. Am. Chem. Soc.*, **74**, 505 (1952).

[80] E. R. Alexander and R. B. Wildman, *J. Am. Chem. Soc.*, **70**, 1187 (1948).

[81] F. S. Crossley and M. L. Moore, *J. Org. Chem.*, **9**, 529 (1944); E. Staple and E. C. Wagner, *J. Org. Chem.*, **14**, 559 (1949); D. S. Noyce and F. W. Bachelor, *J. Am. Chem. Soc.*, **74**, 4577 (1952)

[82] V. J. Webers and W. F. Bruce, *J. Am. Chem. Soc.*, **70**, 1422 (1948); C. B. Pollard and D. C. Young, Jr., *J. Org. Chem.*, **16**, 661 (1951).

CHAPTER 12

ESTERIFICATION AND ESTER HYDROLYSIS

Since esterification and hydrolysis may be part of the same equilibrium, information about the mechanism of both may be obtained from a study of one. The majority of the studies that have been made in this case have been on ester hydrolysis. A considerable number of mechanisms may be visualized for ester hydrolysis. Of these, only a few are common, and some are hardly more than mechanistic curiosities. These mechanisms may be subdivided on three different bases depending upon (1) whether the cleavage takes place between the ethereal oxygen and the acyl carbon atom or the alkyl carbon atom, (2) whether or not the reaction is acid- or base-catalyzed, and (3) whether certain parts of the reaction occur by a concerted or a stepwise mechanism. Since most of the ester hydrolysis reactions carried out synthetically probably occur by acyl-oxygen fission mechanisms, these will be discussed first.

12-1. Acyl-Oxygen Fission Mechanisms for Esterification and Hydrolysis. *12-1a. Evidence for Acyl-Oxygen Fission.* Holmberg showed that either the acid or alkaline hydrolysis of acetoxysuccinic acid gave malic acid with retention of configuration at the asymmetric carbon atom.[1]

$$HO_2C-CH_2\overset{*}{C}H-CO_2H \xrightarrow[H_2O]{H^+ \text{ or } OH^-} HO_2C-CH_2\overset{*}{C}H-CO_2H$$
$$\underset{OAc}{|} \qquad\qquad\qquad \underset{OH}{|}$$

Polanyi and Szabo found that when the alkaline hydrolysis of *n*-amyl acetate is carried out in water containing an excess of O^{18}, it is the acetate ion formed which contains the O^{18}. They point out that this proves the ester must have undergone acyl-oxygen fission.[2] Datta, Day, and Ingold have made

$$n\text{-}C_5H_{11}O\overset{O}{\overset{\|}{C}}CH_3 + H_2O^{18} \xrightarrow{OH^-} n\text{-}C_5H_{11}OH + CH_3\overset{O^{18}}{\overset{\|}{C}}-\overline{O}|^{\ominus}$$

the analogous observation in the acid hydrolysis of methyl hydrogen succinate,[3] as have Long and Friedman in both the basic and acid

[1] B. Holmberg, *Ber.*, **45**, 2997 (1912).

[2] M. Polanyi and A. L. Szabo, *Trans. Faraday Soc.*, **30**, 508 (1934).

[3] S. C. Datta, J. N. E. Day, and C. K. Ingold, *J. Chem. Soc.*, 838 (1939).

hydrolysis of γ-butyrolactone.[4] By similar means, Roberts and Urey showed that the water produced in the esterification of methanol with benzoic acid derives its oxygen from the benzoic acid.[5] Prevost and Ingold and Ingold showed that both the alkaline and acid hydrolysis of crotyl acetate and of α-methylallyl acetate yielded the corresponding alcohol.[6] If the reaction had proceeded by a carbonium-ion mechanism, both reactants should have yielded the same product, since the carbonium ions formed should be identical.

In addition to the rather direct evidence described above, it might be mentioned that ester hydrolysis often occurs at a rate unreasonably fast for an alternate mechanism, such as an S_N2 reaction at the alkyl carbon atom. For these reasons it seems likely that most common esterification and hydrolysis reactions involve acyl-oxygen fission.

12-1b. *Evidence for the Carbonyl Addition Mechanism of Esterification and Hydrolysis.* The alkaline hydrolysis of most esters is a kinetically second-order reaction, first-order in ester and first-order in hydroxide ion. To agree with this and the fact of acyl-oxygen fission, two reaction mechanisms have been suggested. One of these mechanisms consists of the base-catalyzed addition of water to the carbonyl group to give the monoester of an orthoacid, II—a reactive intermediate that may lose water to revert to ester or lose alcohol to form the acid, which rapidly yields the anion in alkaline solution. This mechanism is shown below for the case of an ester labeled in the carbonyl group with O^{18} to distinguish two of the oxygen atoms of II (for reasons which will become apparent shortly).

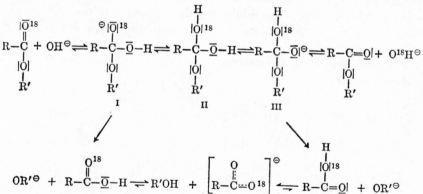

In the alternate mechanism the hydroxide ion simply displaces the alkoxide ion by an S_N2-type reaction.

[4] F. A. Long and L. Friedman, *J. Am. Chem. Soc.*, **72**, 3692 (1950).

[5] I. Roberts and H. C. Urey, *J. Am. Chem. Soc.*, **60**, 2391 (1938).

[6] C. Prevost, *Ann. chim. (Paris)*, **10**, 147 (1928); E. H. Ingold and C. K. Ingold, *J. Chem. Soc.*, 756 (1932).

$$OH^- + \underset{\underset{R}{|}}{\overset{\overset{O}{\|}}{C}}-OR \rightleftharpoons \left[HO\cdots\underset{\underset{R}{|}}{\overset{\overset{O}{\|}}{C}}\cdots OR\right]^{\ominus} \rightleftharpoons HO-\underset{\underset{R}{|}}{\overset{\overset{O}{\|}}{C}} + OR'^{\ominus}$$

$$\rightarrow RCO_2^- + R'OH$$

IV

Bender has solved the problem of deciding between these two mechanisms very neatly.[7]   The mechanisms differ in their description of the ester–hydroxide-ion adduct.   In the S_N2 mechanism this (IV) is a transition state, lying at the top of a potential-energy curve, while in the carbonyl addition mechanism it (I) is an intermediate, lying at an energy minimum.   Since the intermediate I is an alkoxide anion, the equilibrium between it and its conjugate acid, II, would be expected to be very rapidly established.   Upon reionization the intermediate II would be as likely to form III as I.   Since hydroxide ions and alkoxide ions are of comparable basicity, the intermediates I and III would be expected to lose these two ions at comparable rates (although the greater size of the alkoxide anions might somewhat favor their loss).   Therefore it may be seen that the carbonyl addition mechanism leads to the prediction that if the hydrolysis of ester, labeled with O^{18} in the carbonyl oxygen atom, is interrupted before completion, the unreacted ester will be found to have lost O^{18} (due to having been re-formed through the intermediate III).   Bender found this decrease in O^{18} content to occur during the alkaline hydrolysis of three different esters, ethyl, isopropyl, and t-butyl benzoate.   This establishes the carbonyl addition mechanism since the S_N2-type mechanism gives no explanation for how this loss of O^{18} could occur.[7]

For acid hydrolysis the carbonyl addition mechanism has the form outlined below.

$$R-\underset{}{\overset{\overset{O}{\|}}{C}}-OR' \underset{}{\overset{H^+}{\rightleftharpoons}} \left[R-\underset{}{\overset{\overset{OH}{|}}{C}}\cdots OR'\right]^{\oplus} \overset{H_2O}{\rightleftharpoons} R-\underset{\underset{OH_2}{\overset{|}{\oplus}}}{\overset{\overset{OH}{|}}{C}}-OR' \rightleftharpoons R-\underset{\underset{OH}{|}}{\overset{\overset{OH}{|}}{C}}-OR'$$

$$H^+ \updownarrow$$

$$RCO_2H \rightleftharpoons RC(OH)_2{}^+ + ROH \rightleftharpoons R-\underset{\underset{OH}{|}}{\overset{\overset{OH}{|}}{C}}-\overset{\oplus}{OH}R'$$

[7] M. L. Bender, *J. Am. Chem. Soc.*, **73**, 1626 (1951).

The S_N2-type mechanism may be written

$$RCO_2R \xrightleftharpoons{H^+} R\overset{\overset{\displaystyle O}{\|}}{C}\overset{\oplus}{-}OHR \xrightleftharpoons{H_2O} \left[H_2O\cdots\overset{\overset{\displaystyle O}{\|}}{\underset{\underset{\displaystyle R}{|}}{C}}\cdots OHR \right]^+$$

$$\rightleftharpoons R\overset{\overset{\displaystyle O}{\|}}{C}\overset{\oplus}{-}OH_2 + ROH$$

$$\text{⥮}$$

$$RCO_2H + H^+$$

Here too the carbonyl addition mechanism may be distinguished by the loss of O^{18} during reaction, and again Bender has observed such a loss (in the acid hydrolysis of ethyl benzoate).[7]

Swarts has given evidence for the formation of an addition compound between ethyl trifluoroacetate and sodium ethoxide.[8] Bender has confirmed and extended this observation by infrared measurements and

$$CF_3CO_2Et + NaOEt \rightleftharpoons CF_3\overset{\overset{\displaystyle OEt}{|}}{\underset{\underset{\displaystyle OEt}{|}}{C}}\overset{\ominus}{-}O \quad \overset{\oplus}{Na}$$

pointed out its support for the carbonyl addition mechanism.[9]

12-1c. *The Oxocarbonium-ion Mechanism for Esterification and Hydrolysis.* Another method by which esters can be formed and hydrolyzed with acyl-oxygen fission involves the intermediate formation of an oxocarbonium ion (RCO^+), also called an acylium ion. Treffers and Hammett have obtained good evidence for the existence of such an ion by observing that 2,4,6-trimethylbenzoic acid dissolves in sulfuric acid to form four particles.[10]

$$RCO_2H + 2H_2SO_4 \rightarrow RCO^+ + H_3O^+ + 2HSO_4^-$$

This interpretation is further supported by the following facts: the methyl ester of the acid may be hydrolyzed easily by dissolving it in concentrated sulfuric acid and pouring the solution into ice water;[10] the methyl ester may be easily prepared by pouring a sulfuric acid solution of the acid into cold methanol.[11] These facts are significant because analogous treatment fails to hydrolyze methyl benzoate or to esterify benzoic acid. Furthermore, with dilute acid catalysts, 2,4,6-

[8] F. Swarts, *Bull. soc. chim. Belges*, **35**, 414 (1926).

[9] M. L. Bender, *J. Am. Chem. Soc.*, **75**, 5986 (1953).

[10] H. P. Treffers and L. P. Hammett, *J. Am. Chem. Soc.*, **59**, 1708 (1937).

[11] M. S. Newman, *J. Am. Chem. Soc.*, **63**, 2431 (1941).

trimethylbenzoic acid is tremendously more difficult to esterify than benzoic acid, and its esters are more difficult to hydrolyze than benzoates. The behavior of the trimethylbenzoic acid does not appear to be due to steric factors alone, since it is not shared by 2,4,6-tribromobenzoic acid, nor is it entirely electronic, since 2,6-dimethylbenzoic acid yields about three and one-half particles in sulfuric acid, while 2,4-dimethylbenzoic acid yields only two. As Newman has pointed out, both factors appear to be important. It is probable that the carbonyl oxygen atom of benzoic acid is more basic than the hydroxylic oxygen because the donation of a proton to the former gives a resonance-stabilized cation (V). However, for the maximum contribution of structures of the type

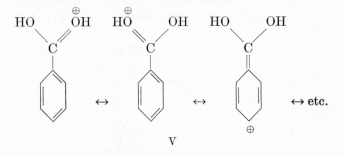

V

shown on the right the oxygen atoms must lie in the same plane as the ring. Two o-methyl groups must make this very difficult. On the other hand, o- and p-methyl groups may stabilize the oxocarbonium ion (VI) by the contribution of resonance structures of the type shown.

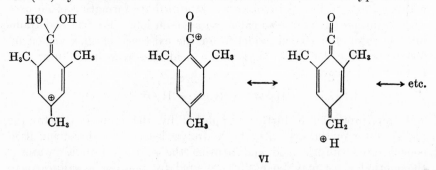

VI

12-2. Alkyl-Oxygen Fission Mechanisms for Esterification and Hydrolysis. *12-2a. Alkyl Carbonium Ions in Esterification and Hydrolysis.* From a knowledge of reactivity in nucleophilic displacements at saturated carbon one might expect the conjugate acid of an ester to cleave to form the acid and a carbonium ion, if the carbonium ion to be formed is sufficiently stable. Cohen and Schneider have presented a convincing argument that a mechanism of this sort occurs in the acid hydrolysis of t-butyl benzoate and probably most other esters of tertiary alcohols.[12]

$$R-\overset{\overset{\displaystyle O}{\|}}{C}-OR' \underset{H^+}{\rightleftharpoons} R-\overset{\overset{\displaystyle \oplus\ OH}{\|}}{C}-OR' \rightleftharpoons RCO_2H + \overset{\oplus}{R'}$$

$$\overset{\oplus}{R'} + H_2O \rightleftharpoons R'\overset{\oplus}{OH_2} \rightleftharpoons R'OH + \overset{\oplus}{H}$$

While the chemical nature of the products of ester *hydrolysis* does not tell which bond to oxygen has been broken, this is not true of *alcoholysis*, where acyl-oxygen fission gives ester interchange and alkyl-oxygen fission produces ether and acid.

$$R-\overset{\overset{\displaystyle O}{\|}}{C}\!\mid\!-O-R' + R''OH \rightarrow R-\overset{\overset{\displaystyle O}{\|}}{C}-O-R'' + R'OH$$

$$R-\overset{\overset{\displaystyle O}{\|}}{C}-O\!\mid\!-R' + R''OH \rightarrow R-\overset{\overset{\displaystyle O}{\|}}{C}-O-H + R'OR''$$

It is therefore noteworthy that the methanolysis of both t-butyl benzoate and t-butyl 2,4,6-trimethylbenzoate gives methyl t-butyl ether and the acid in good yield in acid solution.   With methanolic sodium methoxide t-butyl benzoate gives methyl benzoate and t-butyl alcohol by ester interchange involving nucleophilic attack of the methoxide ion on the carbonyl group.   Under the same conditions t-butyl 2,4,6-trimethyl-benzoate gives no reaction, presumably because of hindrance at the carbonyl group.   Cohen and Schneider also showed that while t-butyl 2,4,6-trimethylbenzoate is easily cleaved by hydrochloric acid, the methyl ester is unaffected.   From their data it appears that the esters of most tertiary alcohols may be cleaved to carbonium ions if they are first protonated.   In order for this cleavage to occur without acid catalysis, the carbonium ion to be formed should be more stable or the anion to be formed should be less basic, or both.   Hammond and Rudesill have found an example of such an uncatalyzed ionization of an ester to a carbonium ion and a carboxylate anion in the solvolysis of triphenyl-methyl benzoate.[13]   They found that the ethanolysis of this ester yields benzoic acid and ethyl triphenylmethyl ether and the addition of sodium ethoxide had only a "salt effect" on the reaction rate.   Here then the reaction involves only a simple ionization of the ester.

$$C_6H_5CO_2C(C_6H_5)_3 \rightarrow C_6H_5CO_2^- + (C_6H_5)_3\overset{\oplus}{C} \xrightarrow{EtOH} (C_6H_5)_3COEt + H^+$$

Kenyon and coworkers have described stereochemical evidence for

[12] S. G. Cohen and A. Schneider, *J. Am. Chem. Soc.*, **63**, 3382 (1941).

[13] G. S. Hammond and J. T. Rudesill, *J. Am. Chem. Soc.*, **72**, 2769 (1950).

the intermediacy of carbonium ions in a number of ester-hydrolysis reactions, some of which were acid-catalyzed and some not.[14]

12-2b. *The S_N2 Mechanism for Ester Hydrolysis.* The alkaline hydrolysis of esters ordinarily occurs by the acyl-oxygen fission mechanism, because the carbonyl carbon atom is so much more susceptible to nucleophilic attack. There are several methods by which nucleophilic attack at the alkyl carbon atom may be observed.

The first method was not designed for the purpose described but was discovered accidentally. Hughes, Ingold, and coworkers have pointed out that the hydrolysis of malolactone in neutral solution gives inversion at the asymmetric carbon atom,[15] and Olson and Miller have made the same observation for β-butyrolactone.[16] These facts seem rational in consideration of the strain present in the four-membered rings of these compounds. According to the *I*-strain concept of Brown,[17] the trigonal carbon atom of a carbonyl group, having optimum bond angles of 120°, would be strained about 30°. The hydration of this carbonyl group (the first step of ordinary ester hydrolysis) would make this carbon atom tetrahedral and thus reduce the strain to about 19.5°. This 10.5° decrease in bond strain at this atom is said to be responsible for the observed high reactivity of carbonyl groups in four-membered rings.[17] The S_N2 attack of a solvent molecule in the alkyl carbon atom, however, is accompanied by the release of 10 to 30° of strain at each of four different atoms. Thus it might have been expected that a β-lactone would show much more increased reactivity (compared to an open-chain ester) at its alkyl carbon atom than at the acyl carbon atom. That this larger increase would have been sufficient to cause the mechanism of hydrolysis in neutral solution to involve an S_N2 attack by water molecules could not have been predicted, however. In fact, the nucleophilic attack of hydroxide ions on β-lactones does occur at the acyl carbon atom, the hydrolysis reactions in basic solution giving retention of configuration.[16] The explanation for this is the same, no doubt, as for the fact that hydroxide ions are about 10^4 times as reactive as water molecules in most substitution reactions at a tetrahedral carbon atom but more than 10^{10} times as reactive toward the carbonyl group of an ester.[18] Long

[14] L. Ellison and J. Kenyon, *J. Chem. Soc.*, 779 (1954), and earlier references given therein.
[15] W. A. Cowdrey, E. D. Hughes, C. K. Ingold, S. Masterman, and A. D. Scott, *J. Chem. Soc.*, 1264 (1937).
[16] A. R. Olson and R. J. Miller, *J. Am. Chem. Soc.*, **60**, 2687 (1938); cf. F. A. Long and M. Purchase, *J. Am. Chem. Soc.*, **72**, 3267 (1950); P. D. Bartlett and P. N. Rylander, *J. Am. Chem. Soc.*, **73**, 4273 (1951).
[17] H. C. Brown, R. S. Fletcher, and R. B. Johannesen, *J. Am. Chem. Soc.*, **73**, 212 (1951).
[18] C. G. Swain and C. B. Scott, *J. Am. Chem. Soc.*, **75**, 141 (1953).

and Purchase have shown that the acid-catalyzed hydrolysis of β-propiolactone and β-butyrolactone probably occurs by the acyl–carbonium-ion mechanism.[19] These workers observed that the reaction rates were proportional to h_0 (Sec. 2-3d). This shows that the rate-controlling steps of the reactions involve only the conjugate acid of the lactone and do not involve the attack of water (cf. Secs. 8-2e and 9-2a). This mechanism, like that of nucleophilic attack at the alkyl carbon atom, has the advantage of releasing all of the ring strain at once. The acyl–carbonium-ion mechanism for the hydrolysis of β-butyrolactone is confirmed by Olson and Miller's observation that the reaction is accompanied by retention of configuration.[16] The hydrolysis of γ-butyrolactone has the same mechanism (carbonyl addition) as that of openchain esters, as shown by the proportionality of the rate to the concentration of catalyzing acid, rather than to h_0.[20]

Other methods of observing the S_N2 reactivity at the alkyl carbon atom of an ester include using an alkoxide anion whose nucleophilic attack at acyl carbon will merely yield the starting materials. Bunnett, Robison, and Pennington have isolated dimethyl ether in good yield from the reaction of anhydrous methanolic sodium methoxide with methyl benzoate and several of its derivatives.[21] Hammett and Pfluger have studied the reaction of trimethylamine, a reagent not capable of displacing the strongly basic alkoxide ions to a great extent at equilibrium because it offers no way of later supplying a proton to them.[22] Tani and Fudo have studied the similar reagent sodium thiomethylate.[23] Goering, Rubin, and Newman have studied the methyl esters of various 2,6-dimethylbenzoic acids, in which nucleophilic attack at the carbonyl carbon atom is sterically hindered, and have found evidence for S_N2 attack at the alkyl carbon.[24]

12-3. Reactivity in the Hydrolysis and Formation of Esters. Our discussion of reactivity in esterification and hydrolysis will be limited almost entirely to reactions proceeding by the common mechanism, the carbonyl addition mechanism, with acyl-oxygen fission. Ideas on reactivity by carbonium-ion mechanisms and the S_N2 mechanism may be obtained from the discussion in Chap. 6.

[19] F. A. Long and M. Purchase, *J. Am. Chem. Soc.*, **72**, 3267 (1950).

[20] F. A. Long, F. B. Dunkle, and W. F. McDevit, *J. Phys. Chem.*, **55**, 829 (1951); cf. A. A. Frost and R. G. Pearson, "Kinetics and Mechanism," chap. 11c, John Wiley & Sons, Inc., New York, 1953.

[21] J. F. Bunnett, M. M. Robison, and F. C. Pennington, *J. Am. Chem. Soc.*, **72**, 2378 (1950).

[22] L. P. Hammett and H. L. Pfluger, *J. Am. Chem. Soc.*, **55**, 4079 (1933).

[23] H. Tani and K. Fudo, *Chem. Abstr.*, **45**, 10198c (1951).

[24] Harvey L. Goering, T. Rubin, and M. S. Newman, *J. Am. Chem. Soc.*, **76**, 787 (1954).

12-3a. Reactivity in Alkaline Ester Hydrolysis. From the carbonyl addition mechanism described for alkaline ester hydrolysis (Sec. 12-1*b*) there appear to be four factors worth considering in discussing the effect of structure on reactivity.

1. The electrophilicity of the carbonyl carbon atom. The greater the electron deficiency at this carbon atom, the more rapid will be the attack of the nucleophilic hydroxide ion.

2. Steric hindrance. Bulky groups may interfere with the attack of the hydroxide ion.

3. Stabilization of the carbonyl group by conjugation. Benzoates and esters of α,β-unsaturated acids are more slowly hydrolyzed than would be expected from rules 1 and 2. Since the carbonyl group is destroyed in the rate-controlling step of hydrolysis, it is reasonable that double bonds conjugated with the carbonyl group should decrease the reactivity.

4. The basicity of the anion being displaced. That is, in the intermediate anion

the alkoxide and hydroxide ions might be expected to be lost in the order of their stabilities, so that the least basic would be lost preferentially. Actually Bender's comparisons of the relative rates of hydrolysis and O^{18} exchange show that the EtO^-, $i\text{-}PrO^-$, and $t\text{-}BuO^-$ anions are all lost in preference to hydroxide.[7]   Perhaps steric factors are also at work here. In any case, this factor does not appear to be important.

One obvious corollary of the first factor is that the esters of strong acids will be hydrolyzed more rapidly than those of weak acids (steric effects being equal). The reaction constants tabulated by Jaffé for the alkaline hydrolysis of substituted benzoic esters vary from 1.129 to 2.849.[25]

Some typical data on alkaline ester hydrolysis are listed in Table 12-1. Note that the electron-withdrawing chlorine atom and carbomethoxy group increase the reactivity considerably. Contribution of structures of the type

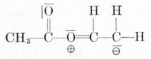

[25] H. H. Jaffé, *Chem. Rev.*, **53**, 191 (1953).

decreases the ability of the ethereal oxygen atom to supply electrons to the carbonyl group. This fact, together with the increased electronegativity of the unsaturated carbon atom, probably contributes to the reactivity of vinyl acetate. The decreased reactivity of the *t*-butyl ester is probably largely due to steric factors.

TABLE 12-1. RELATIVE RATES OF ALKALINE ESTER HYDROLYSIS IN WATER AT 25°[a]

Ester	Rel. rate	Ester	Rel. rate
$CH_3CO_2CH_3$	1.000	$CH_3CO_2CH_2CH_2OH$	1.52
$CH_3CO_2C_2H_5$	0.601	HCO_2CH_3	223
$CH_3CO_2CH(CH_3)_2$	0.146	$ClCH_2CO_2CH_5$	761
$CH_3CO_2C(CH_3)_3$	0.0084		
		$CH_3O\overset{\text{O}}{\overset{\|}{C}}-CO_2CH_3$	170,000
$CH_3CO_2CH_2C_2H_5$	0.549	$^{\ominus}O_2CCO_2CH_3$	8.4
$CH_3CO_2CH{=}CH_2$	57.7		
$CH_3CO_2C_6H_5$	7.63	$CH_3O\overset{\text{O}}{\overset{\|}{C}}-CH_2CO_2CH_3$	13.7
		$HOCH_2CO_2C_2H_5$	11.9

[a] Listed in L. P. Hammett, "Physical Organic Chemistry," p. 211, McGraw-Hill Book Company, Inc., New York, 1940, from A. Skrabal and coworkers, *Monatsh.*, **45**, 148 (1924); **47**, 17, 39 (1926); **48**, 459 (1927); **50**, 369 (1928); M. H. Palomaa, *Ber.*, **71B**, 480 (1938).

12-3b. *Reactivity in the Acid-catalyzed Hydrolysis and Formation of Esters.* In the common carbonyl addition mechanism for ester hydrolysis, the ester is transformed to its conjugate acid, which then coordinates with a water molecule at its electrophilic carbonyl carbon atom to yield the conjugate acid of the monoester of an ortho acid. This ortho acid monoester may either lose alcohol to yield acid, or water to revert to ester, by a mechanism analogous to that of its formation.

$$R-\overset{\text{O}}{\overset{\|}{C}}-OR \underset{}{\overset{H^+}{\rightleftharpoons}} \left[R-\overset{\text{OH}}{\overset{|}{C}}-OR \right]^+ \overset{H_2O}{\rightleftharpoons} R-\overset{\text{OH}}{\overset{|}{\underset{\underset{\ominus OH_2}{|}}{C}}}-OR$$

$$\Big\Updownarrow H^+$$

$$RCO_2H + ROH \rightleftharpoons R-\overset{\text{OH}}{\overset{|}{\underset{\underset{OH}{|}}{C}}}-OR$$

Electron-supplying substituents should increase the ability of the ester to accept protons but should decrease the electrophilicity of the carbonyl carbon atom and hence the tendency to combine with water. Because of these two opposing factors, it would be difficult to predict the nature of the electronic effect in this reaction. In practice it appears that the two effects are rather closely balanced, so that the net electronic effect is small and may be in either direction. Observed values of Hammett's rho constant for acid-catalyzed esterification and hydrolysis reactions vary from -0.229 to 0.555.[25]

Steric factors are probably the most important in determining the reactivity in these reactions. We expect them to be of considerable magnitude, since the trigonal carbonyl carbon atom is, in the transition state, being made tetrahedral. Since the transition state is much more crowded than either the reactant or product, steric hindrance may change the reaction rate enormously without having much influence on the equilibrium constant for the reaction. In fact, the changes in equilibrium constants for esterification which have been observed[26] are very much smaller than changes in the rate constants. This shows that structural changes have very nearly the same effect upon rates of esterification as on rates of hydrolysis.

The reactivity may also be decreased by conjugation of the carbonyl group with aromatic rings or double bonds.

12-3c. *Linear Free-energy Relationships in Esterification and Hydrolysis.* In a major step toward the goal of quantitative correlations of the rates and equilibria for all organic reactions, Taft has been able to fit the existing data on rates of acid- and base-catalyzed ester hydrolysis, formation, and interchange to linear free-energy relationships. These relationships may be applied to aliphatic and to ortho- as well as meta- and para-substituted aromatic compounds. Quantitative measures of electronic and steric factors are obtained. These are found to be useful in correlating rates and equilibria for a variety of other reactions.

Taft first pointed out that for various *series* of esterification and hydrolysis reactions there is good agreement with Eq. (12-1).[27] (Examples of reaction series are (1) acid-catalyzed hydrolysis of ethyl esters of aliphatic acids in 70 per cent acetone at 25°; (2) basic hydrolysis of ethyl ortho-substituted benzoates in 60 per cent acetone at 25°; etc.)

$$\log \frac{k}{k_0} = fA \tag{12-1}$$

where f is a constant dependent only upon the nature of the reaction series; k_0 is the rate constant for the standard member of the series, e.g., in series 1 above the ethyl ester of *acetic* acid; k is the rate constant for the compound in question, e.g., in series 1 the ethyl ester of any

[26] N. Menshutkin, *Ann. chim. et phys.*, [5], **30**, 81(1883).
[27] R. W. Taft, Jr., *J. Am. Chem. Soc.*, **74**, 2729 (1952).

aliphatic acid; and A is a substituent constant, dependent upon the nature of the substituent which makes the compound in question differ from the standard compound of its series and upon the *set of reaction series* to which the series in question belongs.   The various reaction series are divided into six sets on the basis of three criteria: (*a*) whether the reaction is acid- or base-catalyzed; (*b*) whether the structure is varied in the acyl or alkyl component; and, in the cases where the structure is varied in the acyl component, (*c*) whether the compounds are aliphatic acids and their derivatives or ortho-substituted benzoic acids and their derivatives.   Thus one set includes the acid-catalyzed hydrolysis of various series of the aliphatic esters of a given alcohol and the esterification of various series of aliphatic acids with a given alcohol, i.e., structure is varied in the acyl portion of the molecule within a given series.   Series 1 above is a member of the set just described.   Within each set, one reaction series is defined as the standard, and the value of f, the measure of the sensitivity of the rate to changes in structure, defined as unity for this series.

Taft lists values for f for 28 reaction series in the various sets, but the only really large variations are found in the set of base-catalyzed hydrolyses of a series of esters of given acids.   The standard series ($f = 1.00$) in this set is the basic hydrolysis of various benzoates in 60 per cent acetone at 25°.   For formates, $f = 0.394$; for acetates, propionates, butyrates, and isobutyrates, f is between 0.678 and 0.977; and for trimethylacetates, $f = 1.521$.   This shows that the reaction rate is least sensitive to the nature of the alkyl group in the hydrolysis of alkyl formates and most sensitive in the case of alkyl trimethylacetates.

The observed values of A, the substituent constant, vary much more widely and are therefore of greater interest.   Values of A for a number of substituents are listed in Table 12-2.   Since negative values of A are characteristic of substituents which decrease the reactivity, the data on acid-catalyzed reactions show that the decreases in reactivity follow increases in steric hindrance closely, except that benzoates and cinnamates are less reactive than would otherwise be expected.   In base-catalyzed reactions the reactivity may be increased by such electron-withdrawing groups as phenyl.

Ingold has suggested that since steric effects should be about the same for acid- and base-catalyzed reactions, the ratio of rate constants, k_B/k_A, of base- to acid-catalyzed hydrolysis should be a function only of the polarity of a substituent.[28]   Taft has noted the conformity of this suggestion with evidence that both reactions proceed through a common intermediate (Sec. 12-1*b*) and has used it and Eq. (12-1) to separate the factors which influence reactivity in esterification and hydrolysis into

[28] C. K. Ingold, *J. Chem. Soc.*, 1032 (1930).

TABLE 12-2. SUBSTITUENT CONSTANTS, A[27]

Aliphatic series

Substituent	Substituent in acyl component		Substituent in alkyl component	
	Acid-cat.	Base-cat.	Acid-cat.	Base-cat.
H	+1.24	+2.46		
CH_3	0.00	0.00	0.00	0.00
C_2H_5	−0.07	−0.31	−0.09	−0.49
$ClCH_2$	−0.19			
$C_6H_5CH_2$	−0.38	+0.17	−0.25	−0.25
$i\text{-}C_3H_7$	−0.47	−0.94	−0.42	−1.29
$i\text{-}C_4H_9$	−0.93	−1.24	−0.23	−0.81
$t\text{-}C_4H_9$	−1.54	−2.38	......	−2.83
$(C_6H_5)_2CH$	−1.76	−1.09		
$C_6H_5CH{=}CH$	−1.99	−0.75		
Cl_3C	−2.06			
C_6H_5	−2.55	−1.06	−0.30	+0.62
CH_3OCH_2	......	+1.10		

Ortho-substituted benzoates (substituent in acyl component)

Substituent	Acid-cat.	Base-cat.	Substituent	Acid-cat.	Base-cat.
CH_3O	+1.11	+0.53	Br	−0.06	+0.94
C_2H_5O	+1.01	+0.53	I	−0.29	+0.68
CH_3	0.00	0.00	NO_2	−1.07	+1.70
Cl	+0.09	+1.11	C_6H_5	......	−0.87

polar and steric categories.[29] Thus we might assume for a given reaction the operation of a Hammett-type equation with a correction factor to allow for steric effects

$$\log \frac{k}{k_0} = \rho^*\sigma^* + E_s \tag{12-2}$$

where k is the rate constant for the compound in question, k_0 that for the standard member of the series, σ^* the substituent constant, ρ^* the reaction constant, and E_s the steric factor. For a base-catalyzed reaction we may write Eq. (12-2) in the form

$$\left(\log \frac{k}{k_0}\right)_B = \rho_B^*\sigma^* + E_s \tag{12-3}$$

[29] R. W. Taft, Jr., J. Am. Chem. Soc., **74**, 3120 (1952).

Assuming E_s the same for the acid-catalyzed reaction of the same series of compounds, in the same solvent, and at the same temperature, we write

$$\left(\log \frac{k}{k_0}\right)_{\text{A}} = \rho_{\text{A}}^* \sigma^* + E_s \qquad (12\text{-}4)$$

Subtracting (12-4) from (12-3)

$$\left(\log \frac{k}{k_0}\right)_{\text{B}} - \left(\log \frac{k}{k_0}\right)_{\text{A}} = \sigma^*(\rho_{\text{B}}^* - \rho_{\text{A}}^*) \qquad (12\text{-}5)$$

Thus if values of $[\log (k/k_0)]_{\text{B}}$ and $[\log (k/k_0)]_{\text{A}}$ are available for the hydrolysis of a given series of esters in a given solvent at a given temperature, we may calculate values of $\sigma^*(\rho_{\text{B}}^* - \rho_{\text{A}}^*)$. Furthermore, if these data are not available, we may in many cases calculate them from data on another series of esters, or in another solvent, or at another temperature, by use of Eq. (12-1).

In the case of ortho-substituted benzoates values of σ^* are obtained from the values of $\sigma^*(\rho_{\text{B}}^* - \rho_{\text{A}}^*)$ by using as ρ_{B}^* and ρ_{A}^* the values for ρ found in the same reactions of the meta- and para-substituted benzoates. For the aliphatic series $(\rho_{\text{B}}^* - \rho_{\text{A}}^*)$ was defined as 2.48 in order to give values of σ^* which would, in other reactions, lead to values of ρ^* of about the same magnitude as those obtained with ortho-substituted benzene derivatives.[30] The values of σ^* obtained are listed in Table 12-3. By use of these values of σ^* and data on rate and equilibria in many other reactions, several reactions were found which followed a Hammett-type equation

$$\log \frac{k}{k_0} = \rho^* \sigma^*$$

unmodified for steric factors (most reactions do not). From these data additional values of σ^* have been obtained and are also given in Table 12-3. In some reaction series the data on a few compounds deviate from the relationship. There are often quite rational explanations for these specific deviations.

After values of σ^* and ρ^* have been obtained, it is possible to obtain values for the steric parameter E_s.[29] For the ortho-substituted benzoates values of ρ_{B} and ρ_{A} from the Hammett equation were used. Since ρ_{A} was always relatively small, it was assumed to be zero in determining E_s for the aliphatic substituents. Some of the data thus obtained are listed in Table 12-4. The relative magnitudes of these values of E_s are in general qualitative agreement with known data on bond distances, van der Waals radii, etc. In certain reactions where polar effects are

[30] R. W. Taft, Jr., *J. Am. Chem. Soc.*, **75**, 4231 (1953).

small, Taft has found quantitative agreement between reaction rates and these steric parameters.[31]

TABLE 12-3. POLAR SUBSTITUENT CONSTANTS[30]

I. For RY, where R is substituent, Y is functional group

Substituent, R	σ^*	Substituent, R	σ^*
Cl_3C	$+2.65^a$	$C_6H_5CH_2$	$+0.225$
CH_3OOC	$+2.00^a$	$C_6H_5CHCH_3$	$+0.105$
Cl_2CH	$+1.940$	$C_6H_5(CH_2)_2$	$+0.080$
CH_3CO	$+1.65^a$	$C_6H_5CHC_2H_5$	$+0.040$
$CNCH_2$	$+1.300$	$C_6H_5(CH_2)_3$	$+0.020$
$ClCH_2$	$+1.050$	CH_3	0.000
$BrCH_2$	$+1.030$	Cyclohexylcarbinyl	-0.06
$C_6H_5OCH_2$	$+0.850$	C_2H_5	-0.100
C_6H_5CHOH	$+0.765$	$n\text{-}C_3H_7$	-0.115
CH_3COCH_2	$+0.60^a$	$i\text{-}C_4H_9$	-0.125
C_6H_5	$+0.600$	$n\text{-}C_4H_9$	-0.130
$HOCH_2$	$+0.555$	$(CH_3)_3CCH_2CH_2$	-0.140
CH_3OCH_2	$+0.52$	$i\text{-}C_3H_7$	-0.200
H	$+0.49$	$sec\text{-}C_4H_9$	-0.210
$C_6H_5CH{=}CH$	$+0.41$	$(C_2H_5)_2CH$	-0.225
$(C_6H_5)_2CH$	$+0.405$	$(CH_3)_3CCHCH_3$	-0.285
$ClCH_2CH_2$	$+0.385$	$t\text{-}C_4H_9$	-0.320

II. For $o\text{-}XC_6H_4Y$, where X is substituent, Y is functional group

X	σ^*	X	σ^*
CH_3O	-0.41	Br	$+0.21$
C_2H_5O	-0.32	I	$+0.21$
CH_3	-0.17	NO_2	$+0.78^b$
H	0.00	NO_2	$+1.22^c$
Cl	$+0.20$		

[a] Tentative value.
[b] For benzene derivatives other than anilines.
[c] For derivatives of aniline.

12-4. Esters of Sulfonic and Inorganic Acids. *12-4a. Sulfonic Esters.* Since sulfonic acids are much stronger than carboxylic acids, reaction with alkyl-oxygen fission proceeds much more rapidly with alkyl sulfonates than with the corresponding carboxylic acid esters. Furthermore cleavage at the sulfur-oxygen bond occurs quite slowly. Since the sulfur atom already bears a considerable positive charge, formation of the $RSO_2^\oplus$ ion is very difficult. Nucleophilic attack on sulfur is

[31] R. W. Taft, Jr., *J. Am. Chem. Soc.*, **75**, 4538 (1953).

hindered, probably largely sterically but perhaps also by the energy required for the sulfur atom to expand its octet. For these reasons the most common reactions of esters of sulfonic acids are nucleophilic displacements, by the S_N1 and S_N2 mechanisms, at the alkyl carbon atom. Studies on a number of reactions of this type were described in Chap. 5.

TABLE 12-4. STERIC PARAMETERS, E_s

I. Aliphatic series

Substituent	E_s as acid component	E_s as alkyl component	Substituent	E_s as acyl component
H	+1.24		Cyclopentyl	−0.51
CH_3	0.00	0.00	Cyclohexyl	−0.79
C_2H_5	−0.07	−0.09	Cycloheptyl	−1.10
Cyclobutyl	−0.06		t-C_4H_9	−1.54
$ClCH_2$	−0.19		Neopentyl	−1.74
n-C_3H_7	−0.36		$(C_6H_5)_2CH$	−1.76
n-C_8H_{17}	−0.33		$(C_2H_5)_2CH$	−1.98
$C_6H_5CH_2$	−0.38		Cl_3C	−2.06
i-C_3H_7	−0.47	−0.42	Br_3C	−2.43
i-C_4H_9	−0.93	−0.23	$(Neopentyl)_2CH$	−3.18
C_6H_5	......	−0.30	$(C_2H_5)_3C$	−3.8

II. Ortho-substituted benzoates (acyl component)

Substituent	E_s	Substituent	E_s
CH_3O	+0.97	CH_3	0.00
C_2H_5O	+0.86	I	−0.20
Cl	+0.18	NO_2	−0.71
Br	+0.01	C_6H_5	−0.90

It is found, however, that if the reactivity at the alkyl carbon atom is decreased sufficiently, nucleophilic attack at sulfur may be observed. Bunton and Frei have demonstrated this fact with phenyl p-toluenesulfonate.[32] The alkaline hydrolysis of this compound in H_2O^{18} solution introduced O^{18} into the p-toluenesulfonate but not the phenolate.

$$C_7H_7SO_2 \!\mid\! OC_6H_5 + O^{18}H^{\ominus} \rightarrow C_7H_7SO_2O^{18}H + C_6H_5O^{\ominus}$$

$$C_7H_7SO_2O^{18}H^{\ominus} \rightarrow C_7H_7SO_2O^{18}$$

Burwell has found a somewhat different situation in the hydrolysis

[32] C. A. Bunton and Y. F. Frei, *J. Chem. Soc.*, 1872 (1951).

of *sec*-butyl hydrogen sulfate.[33] The sodium salt undergoes a first-order reaction, presumably involving S_N2 attack by water on carbon, to give alcohol with inverted configuration. In acidic solution, however, the alcohol has retained configuration although it is somewhat racemized. Under these conditions, then, the reaction apparently involves mostly sulfur-oxygen bond cleavage.

12-4b. *Esters of Inorganic Acids.* Blumenthal and Herbert have used H_2O^{18} to demonstrate that the hydrolysis of trimethyl phosphate involves phosphorus-oxygen bond fission in alkaline solution and carbon-oxygen bond cleavage in neutral and acidic solution.[34]

Lucas and Hammett have pointed out, in their study of the hydrolysis of *t*-butyl and benzyl nitrates, that the similarity of these reactions to those of the corresponding halides reveals a probability that the reactions involve carbon-oxygen bond fission.[35] This mechanism is further supported by Baker and Easty's study of the $E1$, $E2$, S_N1, and S_N2 mechanisms in the solvolysis of *t*-butyl, isopropyl, ethyl, and methyl nitrates[36] and is confirmed by Cristol, Shadan, and Franzus' observation that the neutral hydrolysis of optically active 2-octyl nitrate gives 2-octanol with inversion of configuration.[37] Although the nucleophilic attack of water occurs largely at carbon in neutral solution, in alkaline solution it appears that hydroxide ion attacks nitrogen to a considerable extent, since 2-octyl nitrate gives 2-octanol with retained configuration though partially racemized.[37] In this respect, then, the nitrate resembles trimethyl phosphate.

By stereochemical studies on 2-octyl nitrite as well as by other means, Allen has shown that the hydrolysis involves nitrogen-oxygen bond cleavage in acidic, basic, and neutral solution.[38]

Anbar, Dostrovsky, Samuel, and Yoffe have used O^{18} to study the hydrolysis of a considerable number of organic esters of inorganic oxyacids.[39]

[33] R. L. Burwell, Jr., and H. E. Holmquist, *J. Am. Chem. Soc.*, **70**, 878 (1948); R. L. Burwell, Jr., *J. Am. Chem. Soc.*, **74**, 1462 (1952).

[34] E. Blumenthal and J. B. M. Herbert, *Trans. Faraday Soc.*, **41**, 611 (1945).

[35] G. R. Lucas and L. P. Hammett, *J. Am. Chem. Soc.*, **64**, 1928 (1942).

[36] J. W. Baker and D. M. Easty, *J. Chem. Soc.*, 1193, 1208 (1952); see also Sec. 7-2a.

[37] S. J. Cristol, B. Franzus, and A. Shadan, *J. Am. Chem. Soc.*, **77**, 2512 (1955).

[38] A. D. Allen, *J. Chem. Soc.*, 1968 (1954); cf. Ref. 37.

[39] M. Anbar, I. Dostrovsky, D. Samuel, and A. D. Yoffe, *J. Chem. Soc.*, 3603 (1954).

CHAPTER 13

SOME REACTIONS OF CARBOXYLIC ACIDS
AND THEIR DERIVATIVES

13-1. Decarboxylation.[1] In order to separate carbon dioxide from a carboxylic acid, RCO_2H, it is necessary to remove both the hydrogen atom and the R group. The removal of hydrogen is usually accomplished by having the reaction proceed through a form containing the carboxylate anion group or at least the carboxyl group hydrogen-bonded to a base. When the hydrogen atom is thus removed *without* its bonding electron pair, it is necessary to remove R *with* its bonding pair. It would therefore be expected that acids with properly situated, strongly electron-withdrawing groups should be decarboxylated with relative ease. The reaction mechanism

$$R-\overset{\overset{\displaystyle |\overline{O}}{\|}}{C}-\overline{O}|^{\ominus} \longrightarrow R|^{\ominus} + CO_2$$

resembles several others which we have discussed, e.g., the reverse aldol condensation (Sec. 11-3c).

13-1a. The Carbanion Mechanism for Decarboxylation. From the generalization above it would be expected that carboxylate anions should lose carbon dioxide easily if they may thereby form relatively stable carbanions. Pedersen has described some of the most convincing evidence for this reaction mechanism in his study of the decarboxylation of nitroacetic acid and α-nitroisobutyric acid.[2] Both these processes are first-order reactions of the anions of the acids. The addition of bromine has no effect on the rate of decomposition of the α-nitroisobutyrate anion, although it completely changes the nature of the product, from 2-nitropropane to 2-bromo-2-nitropropane. This must be due to the reaction of bromine with the anion of the acinitro compound,

$$O_2NC(CH_3)_2CO_2^- \rightarrow [O_2NC(CH_3)_2]^- + CO_2$$
$$[O_2NC(CH_3)_2]^- + Br_2 \rightarrow O_2NC(CH_3)_2Br + Br^-$$

since 2-nitropropane cannot be brominated under the reaction conditions.

---

[1] For a review of polar mechanisms for decarboxylation, see B. R. Brown, *Quart. Revs. (London)*, **5**, 131 (1951).

[2] K. J. Pedersen, *J. Phys. Chem.*, **38**, 559 (1934).

Similarly the rate of decarboxylation of dibromomalonic acid is proportional to the concentration of the singly charged anion, HO_2CCBr_2-CO_2^-, and the product may be changed from dibromo- to tribromoacetic acid by addition of bromine to the reaction mixture.[3] Again, bromine has no effect on the reaction rate and is incapable of brominating dibromoacetic acid under the reaction conditions.

Several other acids capable of yielding fairly stable carbanions have been found to decarboxylate by first-order reactions of their anions. These include phenylpropiolic acid,[4] 2,4,6-trinitrobenzoic acid,[5] tribromoacetic acid,[4] trichloroacetic acid,[4,6] and trifluoroacetic acid.[7] The relative reactivity of the latter three acids (bromo > chloro > fluoro) shows that factors other than the inductive effect are important in the stabilization of these trihalomethyl anions. It may be that there are considerable contributions of structures in which bromine (and chlorine) have expanded their outer shell of electrons.

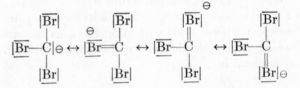

It is perhaps surprising to note the stability of the 2,4,6-trinitrophenyl anion, evidenced by the relative ease of decomposition of the related carboxylate anion,

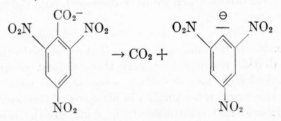

but this is further supported by the observation of deuterium exchange of trinitrobenzene in alkaline ethanol solution.[8]

13-1b. *Decarboxylation of β-Keto Acids.* If the R group of RCO_2^- contains a sufficiently basic functional group, it may accept a proton and greatly increase its electron-withdrawing power, thus facilitating the

[3] J. Muus, *J. Phys. Chem.,* **39,** 343 (1935); **40,** 121 (1936).

[4] R. A. Fairclough, *J. Chem. Soc.,* 1186 (1938).

[5] F. H. Verhoek, *J. Am. Chem. Soc.,* **61,** 186 (1939).

[6] *Ibid.,* **56,** 571 (1934).

[7] I. Auerbach, F. H. Verhoek, and A. L. Henne, *J. Am. Chem. Soc.,* **72,** 299 (1950).

[8] M. S. Kharasch, W. G. Brown, and J. McNab, *J. Org. Chem.,* **2,** 36 (1937); cf., however, J. A. A. Ketelaar, A. Bier, and H. T. Vlaar, *Rec. trav. chim.,* **73,** 37 (1954).

loss of carbon dioxide. This fact appears to be important in the decarboxylation of β-keto acids.

The kinetic equation for the decarboxylation of acetoacetic acid in aqueous solution has the form[9]

$$v = k[CH_3COCH_2CO_2H] + k'[CH_3COCH_2CO_2^-]$$

That part of the reaction due to the acetoacetate anion very probably proceeds by the carbanion mechanism. In a study of the reaction as a whole, Pedersen has used α,α-dimethylacetoacetic acid to avoid the type of keto-enol tautomerism which could complicate the study of acetoacetic acid itself.[10] From the identical form of the observed kinetic equation and the fact that the k's were of the same general order of magnitude, it seems very likely that both reactions involve the same (keto) form of the acid. Subsequently Pedersen suggested that the reaction proceeds through a dipolar-ion tautomer whose concentration is proportional to that of the undissociated acid.[2]

$$CH_3-\overset{\overset{\textstyle |\overline{O}}{\|}}{C}-C(CH_3)_2-CO_2H \rightleftharpoons CH_3-\overset{\overset{\textstyle \oplus|O-H}{\|}}{C}-C(CH_3)_2-CO_2^{\ominus}$$

$$\rightarrow CH_3-\overset{\overset{\textstyle O-H}{|}}{C}=C(CH_3)_2 + CO_2$$

$$CH_3-CO-CH(CH_3)_2$$

Excellent evidence that the enol and not the keto form of methyl isopropyl ketone is the initial product of the reaction is found in the observation that in the presence of iodine or bromine the iodo or bromo ketone is formed, although the iodine (or bromine) has no effect on the reaction rate and is incapable of halogenating the ketone significantly under the reaction conditions.[11] Westheimer and Jones have pointed out that the fraction of the acid present as the dipolar ion should decrease with the dielectric constant of the solvent.[12] Since they find considerable changes in solvent to have little effect on the reaction rate, they state that the dipolar ion is an unlikely intermediate. It would seem, however, that although the relative concentration of the dipolar ion should decrease

[9] E. M. P. Widmark, *Acta med. Scand.*, **53**, 393 (1920); *Chem. Abstr.*, **15**, 2763[f] (1921).

[10] K. J. Pedersen, *J. Am. Chem. Soc.*, **51**, 2098 (1929).

[11] *Ibid.*, **58**, 240 (1936).

[12] F. H. Westheimer and W. A. Jones, *J. Am. Chem. Soc.*, **63**, 3283 (1941).

with the ion-solvating power of the medium, its specific rate constant for reaction should increase, because this reaction involves charge destruction in the transition state. Actually, the coulombic attraction between the unlike charges should give the dipolar ion a cyclic configuration

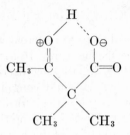

not differing greatly from that of the chelated intermediate suggested by Westheimer and Jones.

The decarboxylation of β-keto acids is not subject to general base catalysis but is specifically catalyzed by primary amines.[13] This strongly suggests an intermediate of the following type[1,11] (cf. Sec. 11-3c).

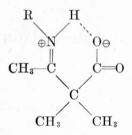

The suggestions that the decarboxylations of β-keto acids yield enols and enolate anions are also supported by the fact that ketopinic acid,

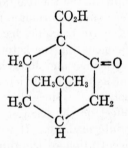

which should be incapable of yielding a stable enol or enolate anion (Bredt's rule, see Sec. 10-1b), is remarkably resistant to decarboxylation.[14]

The decarboxylation of malonic acid probably has a mechanism like

[13] K. J. Pedersen, *J. Am. Chem. Soc.*, **60**, 595 (1938).

[14] Cf. J. Bredt, *Ann. Acad. Sci. Fennicae*, **29A**, no. 2 (1927); *Chem. Abstr.*, **22**, 1152 (1928).

that of acetoacetic acid, since both the acid and the monoanion contribute to the reaction.[4]

Steinberger and Westheimer have made a particularly careful study of the decarboxylation of dimethyloxaloacetic acid.[15] They find that both the monoanion (presumably only one of the two possible forms) and dianion take part in the reaction but find no term in the kinetic equation proportional to the concentration of the acid itself. This may be because the basicity of the carbonyl group is so greatly decreased by the adjacent carboxyl group. They also show that the enol (or enolate anion) is the initial reaction product and that it even has sufficient stability to be detected by spectroscopic methods (as well as by reaction with halogen). It is found that the decarboxylation of the acid is catalyzed by several heavy-metal cations, the most effective of which (and the one actually present in the enzymatic decarboxylation of oxaloacetic acid) is the manganous ion. A plot of the effect of these metal ions vs. pH shows that they coordinate with the dianion. The rate-controlling step of the reaction evidently has the mechanism

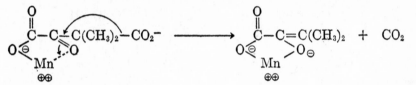

Part of the evidence that it is the carboxylate ion group shown which is involved in chelation with the metal ion is the fact that the decarboxylation of the monoester $C_2H_5O_2C\!-\!CO\!-\!C(CH_3)_2CO_2H$, which was also studied carefully, is not catalyzed by heavy-metal ions, and neither is that of acetoacetic acid.

Pedersen has studied the metal-ion-catalyzed decarboxylation of oxaloacetic acid[16] and Prue that of acetonedicarboxylic acid.[17]

13-1c. *Decarboxylation of α-Imino Acids and Related Compounds.* The decarboxylation reactions we have described have all resembled acid-base reactions except that, instead of the removal of a hydrogen atom without its bonding electron pair, there has been the loss of a carboxylate anion group without its bonding electron pair. From this fact and by analogy with the tautomerism of methyleneazomethines (Sec. 10-2b) it seems logical that acids of the type of I should decarboxylate

[15] R. Steinberger and F. H. Westheimer, *J. Am. Chem. Soc.*, **73**, 429 (1951).
[16] K. J. Pedersen, *Acta Chem. Scand.*, **6**, 285 (1952).
[17] J. E. Prue, *J. Chem. Soc.*, 2331 (1952).

fairly readily and that those of the type of II could also, after tautomerizing to I. Thus, we may explain the observations that aldehydes and ketones catalyze the decarboxylation of α-amino acids, and primary amines that of α-keto acids. For example, the ease with which ninhydrin brings about the decarboxylation of α-amino acids may be explained by the resonance stabilization of the anion (III) formed.

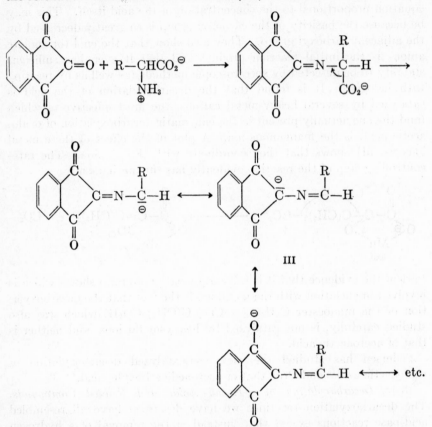

Mechanisms of this kind have been proposed for a number of reactions of the type described,[18] but in no case does there appear to be sufficient experimental evidence to clear up such points as whether the reaction is concerted or stepwise and whether or not the nitrogen atom of the methyleneazomethine group is protonated in the reactive form.

Picolinic acid, quinaldinic acid, and related compounds bear a certain

[18] A. Schönberg, R. Moubasher, and A. Mostafa, *J. Chem. Soc.*, 176 (1948); F. G. Baddar, *J. Chem. Soc.*, S163 (1949); 136 (1950); F. G. Baddar and Z. Iskander, *J. Chem. Soc.*, 203 (1954); D. L. Hammick, A. M. Roe, F. W. Weston, and K. D. E. Whiting, *J. Chem. Soc.*, 3825 (1953).

resemblance to acids I and II. However, they cannot tautomerize in the manner I and II can, and, unlike the anion of I, they cannot lose carbon dioxide to give a carbanion with two essentially equivalent structures; nor can they react by the concerted addition of a proton at one carbon atom and loss of carbon dioxide at another to give a stable product. Nevertheless, acids of this type can be decarboxylated without excessive difficulty. Hammick and coworkers have described good evidence that these reactions involve some type of α-pyridyl (or α-quinolyl) carbanion in their observations that the decarboxylations in the presence of aldehydes and ketones produce α-pyridyl- (and α-quinolyl-) carbinols.[19] By showing that the decarboxylation of quinaldinic acid is first-order, that the rate may be slowed by the addition of either acid or base, and that the dipolar ion, 1-methylquinolinium-2-carboxylate, reacts relatively rapidly, these workers revealed the probability that it is the dipolar-ion tautomer of quinaldinic acid which is the reactive form.[20]

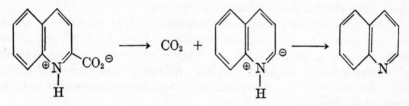

13-1d. *The Carbonium-ion Mechanism for Decarboxylation.* The formation of a carbonium ion at the β-carbon atom of a carboxylic acid (or better still, a carboxylate anion) might well be expected to lead to decarboxylation by a mechanism of the type

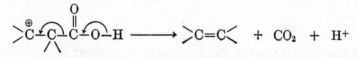

The work of Grovenstein and Lee on certain decarboxylations of this kind[21] has been described under elimination reactions (Sec. 7-2b). These workers pointed out that the reaction may proceed via an intermediate

[19] P. Dyson and D. L. Hammick, *J. Chem. Soc.*, 1724 (1937); M. R. F. Ashworth, R. P. Daffern, and D. L. Hammick, *J. Chem. Soc.*, 809 (1939); cf. B. R. Brown and D. L. Hammick, *J. Chem. Soc.*, 173 (1949).

[20] B. R. Brown and D. L. Hammick, *J. Chem. Soc.*, 659 (1949).

[21] E. Grovenstein, Jr., and D. E. Lee, *J. Am. Chem. Soc.*, **75**, 2639 (1953).

carbonium ion in some cases, while in others the loss of carbon dioxide may be simultaneous with the removal from the β-carbon atom of a group with its bonding electron pair. Johnson and Heinz have suggested a carbonium-ion mechanism for the decarboxylation of cinnamic acids by acidic catalysts.[22]

For β,γ-unsaturated acids a decarboxylation mechanism rather similar to that we have described for β-keto acids has been suggested.[23]

Both these reactions are of the carbonium-ion type in so far as the proton transfer precedes the loss of carbon dioxide and are of the four-center type in so far as the reaction is entirely concerted. There need be no sharp line between the two classes of reactions.

There are a number of aromatic substitution–type reactions in which carboxy groups on an aromatic ring are replaced by hydrogen atoms in the presence of an acid catalyst. They can be regarded as an example of carbonium-ion decarboxylations. Schenkel and Schenkel-Rudin have discussed the decarboxylation of 9-anthracenecarboxylic acid in terms of the mechanism

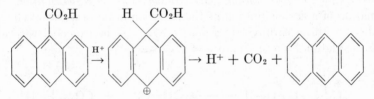

which they refer to as the S_E2 mechanism by analogy to the S_N2 reaction mechanism.[24] It should be noted that this mechanism for the bimolecular electrophilic displacement on an aromatic ring (see Sec. 16-2g) differs from an S_E2 reaction at a saturated carbon atom in the same way that nucleophilic displacements of acyl, vinyl, and aryl halides differ from displacements at a saturated carbon; viz., the reactions at unsaturated carbon can form a stable intermediate (such as the carbonium ion above) for whose existence there is good evidence in some cases, e.g., ester hydrolysis, while the reaction at a saturated carbon is best interpreted as proceeding by a concerted one-step process. Probably

[22] W. S. Johnson and W. E. Heinz, *J. Am. Chem. Soc.*, **71**, 2913 (1949).
[23] R. T. Arnold, O. C. Elmer, and R. M. Dodson, *J. Am. Chem. Soc.* **72**, 4359 (1950).
[24] H. Schenkel and M. Schenkel-Rudin, *Helv. Chim. Acta*, **31**, 514 (1948).

the best evidence for the S_E2 mechanism at a saturated carbon atom is that of Sommer, Barie, and Gould, who found that the reaction

$$(CH_3)_3SiCH_2CH_2CO_2H \xrightarrow{H_2SO_4} HOSO_3\overset{\overset{\displaystyle CH_3}{|}}{\underset{\underset{\displaystyle CH_3}{|}}{Si}}CH_2CH_2CO_2H + CH_4$$

has a rate proportional to the concentration of sulfuric acid and to that of the silane.[25]

Brown, Hammick, Scholefield, and Elliott have studied the acid-catalyzed decarboxylation of some o- and p-hydroxybenzoic acids, and Schubert and Gardner have studied the reaction of mesitoic acid and 2,4,6-trihydroxybenzoic acid.[26]

13-2. Decarbonylation. By decarbonylation we mean the loss of carbon monoxide from a molecule. If the R group in RCHO can form a stable enough anion the compound can be decarbonylated by the base-catalyzed mechanism

$$RCHO + B^{\ominus} \rightarrow BH + RCO^{\ominus} \rightarrow CO + R^{\ominus}$$
$$R^{\ominus} + BH \rightarrow RH + B^{\ominus}$$

while if R in RCO_2H can form a sufficiently stable cation, the acid-catalyzed mechanism

$$RCO_2H + H^+ \rightarrow RCOOH_2^{\oplus} \rightarrow H_2O + RCO^{\oplus}$$
$$RCO^{\oplus} \rightarrow CO + R^{\oplus} \xrightarrow{H_2O} ROH + H^+ \qquad \text{etc.}$$

can occur. Examples of decarbonylations and their reverse, carbonylations, by both mechanisms are known. As an example of the base-catalyzed reaction, it is known that alkali-metal alkoxides catalyze the decomposition of formate esters into carbon monoxide and alcohols (the reverse reaction takes place as well, of course).[27] The acid-catalyzed decarbonylation reaction is general for α-hydroxy acids since the "carbonium ions" formed are simply the conjugate acids of aldehydes and

[25] L. H. Sommer, W. P. Barie, and J. R. Gould, *J. Am. Chem. Soc.*, **75**, 3765 (1953); cf. L. M. Shorr, H. Freiser, and J. L. Speier, *J. Am. Chem. Soc.*, **77**, 547 (1955).

[26] B. R. Brown, D. L. Hammick, and A. J. B. Scholefield, *J. Chem. Soc.*, 778 (1950); B. R. Brown, W. W. Elliott, and D. L. Hammick, *J. Chem. Soc.*, 1384 (1951); W. M. Schubert, *J. Am. Chem. Soc.*, **71**, 2639 (1949); W. M. Schubert and J. D. Gardner, *J. Am. Chem. Soc.*, **75**, 1401 (1953).

[27] F. Adickes and G. Schäfer, *Ber.*, **65B**, 950 (1932); J. A. Christiansen and J. C. Gjaldbaek, *Kgl. Danske Videnskab. Selskab., Mat.-fys. Medd.*, **20**, no. 3 (1942); *Chem. Abstr.*, **38**, 3898⁶ (1944).

ketones. The reaction also occurs with formic acid, benzoylformic acid, and compounds of the type RCO_2H, where R is a tertiary alkyl radical. While the mechanisms of these reactions probably have the general character of that shown above, there are certainly differences in some of the mechanistic details, since the reaction rates are variously affected by changes in the acidity function, H_0.[28]

As one of a large number of examples of acid-catalyzed carbonylations, several polyhalomethanes react with carbon monoxide in the presence of a Lewis acid to give acetyl halide derivatives.[29]

$$CCl_4 + AlCl_3 \rightarrow \overset{\ominus}{AlCl_4} + \overset{\oplus}{CCl_3}$$

$$\overset{\oplus}{CCl_3} + CO \rightarrow Cl_3C\overset{\oplus}{CO} \xrightarrow{\overset{\ominus}{AlCl_4}} Cl_3CCOCl$$

13-3. The Acetoacetic Ester Condensation and Related Reactions.

13-3a. *The Acetoacetic Ester Condensation.* A carbon-carbon bond forming condensation between two molecules of an ester to give a β-keto ester is called an acetoacetic ester, or Claisen, condensation. The latter term is also applied to related reactions. Hauser and Renfrow appear to be the first to have suggested the currently accepted reaction mechanism in terms of modern physical organic chemical concepts.[30] This mechanism, rather similar to that of the aldol condensation, involves the reaction of the basic catalyst with one molecule of ester to yield a carbanion, which adds to the carbonyl group of another ester molecule, displacing an alkoxide ion.

(1) $\overset{\ominus}{EtO} + CH_3CO_2Et \rightleftharpoons EtOH + \overset{\ominus}{CH_2CO_2Et}$

(2) $CH_3\overset{O}{\underset{\|}{C}} + \overset{\ominus}{CH_2CO_2Et} \rightleftharpoons CH_3\overset{\overset{\ominus}{O}}{\underset{|}{C}}CH_2CO_2Et$
$\quad\quad \overset{|}{OEt} \quad\quad\quad\quad\quad\quad\quad\quad\quad \overset{|}{OEt}$

$$\rightleftharpoons CH_3\overset{O}{\underset{\|}{C}}CH_2CO_2Et + \overset{\ominus}{EtO}$$

(3) $CH_3COCH_2CO_2Et + \overset{\ominus}{EtO} \rightleftharpoons CH_3CO\overset{\ominus}{C}HCO_2Et + EtOH$

The last step, in which the β-keto ester is transformed into its conjugate base, is of the greatest importance for the practical success of the reac-

[28] L. P. Hammett, *Chem. Rev.*, **16**, 67 (1935); W. W. Elliott and D. L. Hammick, *J. Chem. Soc.*, 3402 (1951), and references cited therein.

[29] C. W. Theobald, U.S. Patent 2,378,048; *Chem. Abstr.*, **39**, 4085[6] (1945).

[30] C. R. Hauser and W. B. Renfrow. Jr., *J. Am. Chem. Soc.*, **59**, 1823 (1937).

tion. The equilibrium constant for the formation of the β-keto ester itself, as shown in the first two steps of the mechanism, has the form

$$K = \frac{[CH_3COCH_2CO_2Et][EtOH]}{[CH_3CO_2Et]^2}$$

while the equilibrium constant for the whole reaction (all three steps) is

$$K' = \frac{[CH_3CO\overset{\ominus}{C}HCO_2Et][EtOH]^2}{[CH_3CO_2Et]^2[Et\overset{\ominus}{O}]}$$

It may thus be seen that

$$K' = KK_3$$

where
$$K_3 = \frac{[CH_3CO\overset{\ominus}{C}HCO_2Et][EtOH]}{[CH_3COCH_2CO_2Et][Et\overset{\ominus}{O}]}$$

the equilibrium expression for step 3, which must lie well to the right, since acetoacetic ester, whose pK_a is about 10.7 in water,[31] is probably at least 10,000 times as strong an acid as ethanol under these reaction conditions.   That is, the equilibrium constant for the reaction is made much more favorable by the acidity of the β-keto ester, which permits most of the ester to be changed to a form (its conjugate base) incapable of direct cleavage to starting material.   In fact, esters that have only one α-hydrogen atom do not undergo the acetoacetic ester condensation in the presence of sodium alkoxide catalysts, because the β-keto ester formed would not be sufficiently acidic to be transformed to its conjugate base to any significant extent. The equilibrium in such reactions, however, may be forced to the right by the use of more strongly basic catalysts. Sodium triphenylmethyl,[30] mesitylmagnesium bromide,[32] sodium hydride,[33] sodium amide,[34] and diisopropylaminomagnesium bromide[35] are among the other bases which have been found capable of bringing about the formation of β-keto esters that contain no α-hydrogen atoms.

13-3b. *Alkaline Cleavage of β-Diketones and Related Compounds.* In general, compounds of the type RCOX may be easily cleaved by alkali if X$\ominus$ is a fairly stable anion (cf. the alkaline hydrolysis of esters).   It is therefore not unexpected that β-diketones are fairly readily cleaved by

[31] R. G. Pearson and R. L. Dillon, *J. Am. Chem. Soc.*, **75**, 2439 (1953).

[32] M. A. Spielman and M. T. Schmidt, *J. Am. Chem. Soc.*, **59**, 2009 (1937).

[33] F. W. Swamer and C. R. Hauser, *J. Am. Chem. Soc.*, **68**, 2647 (1946).

[34] C. R. Hauser, B. I. Ringler, F. W. Swamer, and D. F. Thompson, *J. Am. Chem. Soc.*, **69**, 2649 (1947).

[35] F. C. Frostick, Jr., and C. R. Hauser, *J. Am. Chem. Soc.*, **71**, 1350 (1949).

bases.   Pearson and Sandy have studied the cleavage of acetylacetone by sodium ethoxide in ethanol.[36]   They made the observation, surprising at first glance, that the reaction is of the first order, its rate being proportional to the concentration of the reactant present in the smaller concentration.   This observation is quite rational, however, in view of the following reaction mechanism.

$$CH_3COCH_2COCH_3 + EtO^{\ominus} \rightleftharpoons CH_3CO\overset{\ominus}{C}HCOCH_3 + EtOH$$

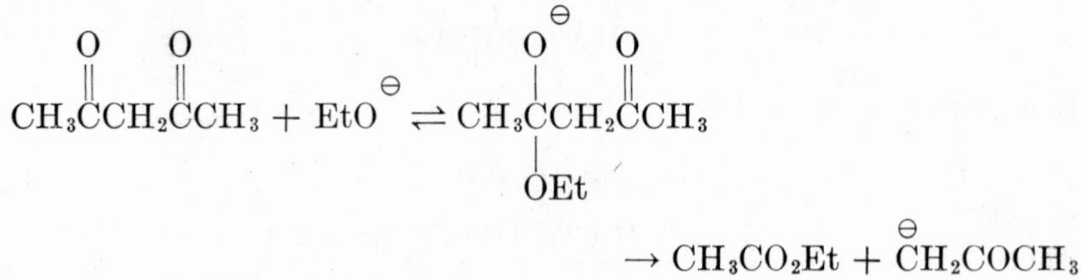

$$\underset{\substack{|| \\ \text{O}}}{CH_3\overset{\text{O}}{\overset{||}{C}}CH_2\overset{\text{O}}{\overset{||}{C}}CH_3} + EtO^{\ominus} \rightleftharpoons CH_3\underset{\substack{| \\ OEt}}{\overset{\overset{\ominus}{}}{\overset{\text{O}}{\overset{|}{C}}}}CH_2\overset{\text{O}}{\overset{||}{C}}CH_3$$

$$\rightarrow CH_3CO_2Et + \overset{\ominus}{C}H_2COCH_3$$

$$\overset{\ominus}{C}H_2COCH_3 + EtOH \rightarrow CH_3COCH_3 + EtO^{\ominus}$$

If we assume that the rate-controlling step is the decomposition of the acetylacetone–ethoxide-ion adduct and that all the other steps are relatively fast, we can derive the kinetic equation:

$$v = k[CH_3COCH_2COCH_3][EtO^-]$$

However, if the acid-base equilibrium of the first equation is established rapidly

$$[CH_3COCH_2COCH_3][EtO^-] = K[CH_3CO\overset{\ominus}{C}HCOCH_3]$$

Therefore $$v = kK[CH_3CO\overset{\ominus}{C}HCOCH_3] \qquad (13\text{-}1)$$

Acetylacetone is an acid of such a strength that the concentration of its anion present in a basic solution will be essentially equal to the concentration of sodium ethoxide or of acetylacetone added, depending on which is the limiting reagent.   The mechanism given, then, explains the observation of first-order kinetics.   The alkaline ethanolysis of phenacylpyridinium ions follows a similar kinetic equation and has the same type of mechanism.[36]

The alkaline hydrolysis of acetylacetone is a more complicated reaction, the kinetic equation having the form of (13-1) with an additional term involving hydroxide ion.[37]

$$v = k[CH_3CO\overset{\ominus}{C}HCOCH_3] + k'[CH_3CO\overset{\ominus}{C}HCOCH_3][OH^-]$$

[36] R. G. Pearson and A. C. Sandy, *J. Am. Chem. Soc.*, **73**, 931 (1951).
[37] R. G. Pearson and E. A. Mayerle, *J. Am. Chem. Soc.*, **73**, 926 (1951).

The first term corresponds to cleavage by a mechanism like that followed in alcoholic solution. As Pearson and Mayerle point out, the second term, involving an additional hydroxide ion, is probably due to cleavage by the mechanism

$$CH_3\overset{\overset{\displaystyle O^{\ominus}}{|}}{\underset{\underset{\displaystyle OH}{|}}{C}}CH_2COCH_3 \underset{OH^-}{\rightleftharpoons} CH_3\overset{\overset{\displaystyle O^{\ominus}}{|}}{\underset{\underset{\displaystyle O^{\ominus}}{|}}{C}}CH_2COCH_3 \rightarrow CH_3CO_2^{\ominus} + \overset{\ominus}{C}H_2COCH_3$$

While the doubly charged intermediate must be present at a much smaller concentration than the singly charged one, its specific rate constant for cleavage is probably much larger. This situation is somewhat similar to that found in the Cannizzaro reaction (Sec. 11-4a).

Dimethylacetylacetone cannot be "protected" by transformation to its conjugate base and is therefore cleaved much more rapidly than the unsubstituted compound or its monomethyl derivative.

$$CH_3\overset{\overset{\displaystyle O}{||}}{C}C(CH_3)_2COCH_3 + OH^- \rightarrow CH_3CO_2^- + (CH_3)_2CHCOCH_3$$

The kinetics in this case are second-order, first-order in hydroxide ion and first-order in ketone.[37]

The study of the basic cleavage of chloral hydrate carried out by Gustafsson and Johanson shows that this part of the haloform reaction probably has a mechanism of the type described for the cleavage of β-diketones.[38] This mechanism should be modified to agree with the observation of general base catalysis,[38] and indeed it is possible that the reactions studied by Pearson and coworkers are also subject to general base catalysis.

13-4. Formation and Hydrolysis of Amides. 13-4a. *Ammonolysis of Esters.* Betts and Hammett have studied the ammonolysis of methyl phenylacetate in methanol and found the reaction to be catalyzed by sodium methoxide and slowed by ammonium chloride.[39] They quite logically suggest that this is due to the attack of amide anions as well as ammonia molecules on the ester.

[38] C. Gustafsson and M. Johanson, *Acta Chem. Scand.*, **2**, 42 (1948).
[39] R. L. Betts and L. P. Hammett, *J. Am. Chem. Soc.*, **59**, 1568 (1937).

$$C_6H_5CH_2CO_2Me + NH_3 \rightarrow C_6H_5CH_2\overset{\overset{\displaystyle \overset{\ominus}{O}}{|}}{\underset{\underset{\displaystyle \overset{\oplus}{NH_3}}{|}}{C}}{-}OMe$$

$$\rightarrow C_6H_5CH_2CONH_2 + MeOH$$

$$C_6H_5CH_2CO_2Me + NH_2^{\ominus} \rightarrow C_6H_5CH_2\overset{\overset{\displaystyle \overset{\ominus}{O}}{|}}{\underset{\underset{\displaystyle NH_2}{|}}{C}}{-}OMe$$

$$\rightarrow C_6H_5CH_2CONH_2 + MeO^{\ominus}$$

The concentration of amide ion present in equilibrium with a given concentration of ammonia is controlled by the basicity of the solution.

$$NH_3 + MeO^- \rightleftharpoons NH_2^- + MeOH$$

This explanation for their data is qualitatively satisfactory, but a quantitative treatment revealed a deviation which they believe to be larger than the experimental error. It may be that this deviation is due to the destruction of sodium methoxide by a small amount of hydrolysis (due to the trace of water almost unavoidably present in their "anhydrous" methanol) occurring simultaneously with the ammonolysis.

Betts and Hammett found methyl p-chlorophenylacetate to react more rapidly than the unsubstituted compound and the p-nitro derivative to be still more reactive. Miller, Day, and coworkers have studied the effect of the structure of the reactants and solvents on reactivity in ester ammonolysis,[40] as have Baltzly, Berger, and Rothstein.[41]

13-4b. *Isomerization of Ammonium Cyanate.* Wöhler's classic study was the first investigation of the transformation of ammonium cyanate to urea.[42] The reaction has since been the object of a number of kinetic studies.[43] Walker and Hambly found that the reaction was second-order, first-order in ammonium ions and first-order in cyanate ions and concluded that the reaction was between the two ions.[44]

$$NH_4^+ + NCO^- \rightarrow (H_2N)_2CO$$

[40] F. H. Wetzel, J. G. Miller, and A. R. Day, *J. Am. Chem. Soc.*, **75**, 1150 (1953) and earlier references cited therein.

[41] R. Baltzly, I. M. Berger, and A. A. Rothstein, *J. Am. Chem. Soc.*, **72**, 4149 (1950).

[42] F. Wöhler, *Pogg. Ann.*, **3**, 177 (1825); **12**, 253 (1828).

[43] A more detailed discussion of the reaction mechanism has been given by A. A. Frost and R. G. Pearson, "Kinetics and Mechanism," chap. 11B, John Wiley & Sons, Inc., New York, 1953.

[44] J. Walker and F. J. Hambly, *J. Chem. Soc.*, **67**, 746 (1895).

Chattaway pointed out that because of the equilibrium

$$NH_4^+ + NCO^- \rightleftharpoons NH_3 + HNCO$$

which lies very largely to the left, the kinetic equation is equally in agreement with a mechanism in which ammonia reacts with cyanic acid (or its tautomer, isocyanic acid)

$$NH_3 + HNCO \xrightarrow{k} (H_2N)_2CO$$

since this mechanism predicts the rate expression

$$v = \frac{kK_W}{K_{NH_3}K_{HNCO}} [NH_4^+][NCO^-] \qquad (13\text{-}2)$$

where K_W is the autoprotolysis constant of water, the solvent, K_{NH_3} is the ionization constant of ammonia, and K_{HNCO} that of cyanic acid.[45]

Inspection of the Brønsted-Bjerrum-Christiansen equation (Eq. [3-7]) shows that the reaction between two oppositely charged ions like the ammonium ion and the cyanate ion should show a large negative ionic strength effect whose size (in dilute solution) is predicted quantitatively. On the other hand, the specific rate constant for reaction between two neutral species like ammonia and isocyanic acid should be relatively little affected by the ionic strength. The isomerization of ammonium cyanate to urea has been found to have a considerable negative ionic-strength effect, whose magnitude is within a factor of two of that predicted theoretically, and the reaction has for this reason been said to occur directly between the ions.[46] However, Weil and Morris have pointed out that although the ionic strength will have little effect on the value of k in Eq. (13-2), it will affect the equilibrium constants in this equation because they are for equilibria between ions and neutral molecules.[47] In fact, these workers show that both mechanisms make the same prediction of the effect of ionic strength on rate.

While it has therefore not been possible to distinguish between the two proposed mechanisms by use of kinetics, there are certainly some very good arguments of other types which make the reaction between ammonia and isocyanic (or cyanic) acid preferable.[48] The carbon atom of cyanic acid (or its tautomer, isocyanic acid) must be relatively electron-deficient and hence susceptible to attack by the unshared electron pair of ammonia.

[45] F. D. Chattaway, *J. Chem. Soc.*, **101**, 170 (1912).
[46] J. C. Warner and F. B. Stitt, *J. Am. Chem. Soc.*, **55**, 4807 (1933).
[47] I. Weil and J. C. Morris, *J. Am. Chem. Soc.*, **71**, 1664 (1949).
[48] Cf. T. M. Lowry, *Trans. Faraday Soc.*, **30**, 375 (1934).

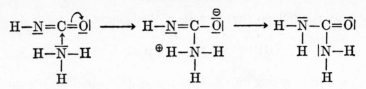

The ease of this reaction is shown by the high reactivity of ammonia and primary and secondary amines (and, to a lesser extent, weaker nucleophilic reagents such as water and alcohols) toward alkyl and aryl isocyanates. The carbon atom of the cyanate anion must be much less electrophilic, and the ammonium ion has *no* unshared electrons. About the only reasonable reaction one could postulate between these two ions is the proton transfer to give ammonia and cyanic (or isocyanic) acid, which we have already mentioned.

13-4c. *Hydrolysis of Amides.* The hydrolysis of amides is speeded by both acids and alkali, and, as Reid has shown, the reaction is in both cases second-order, first-order in amide and first-order in acid or base.[49] A mechanism rather similar to the carbonyl addition mechanism for esterification and hydrolysis (Sec. 12-1b) may be written for each of these reactions. For the alkaline hydrolysis the mechanism

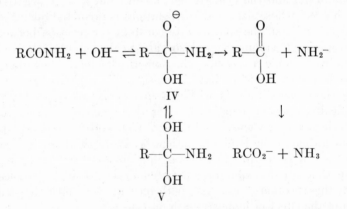

involving the intermediate (V) in which the carbonyl oxygen atom has become identical to the one in the attacking hydroxide ion, has been suggested by Bender, Ginger, and Kemp to explain their observation that the base-catalyzed hydrolysis of benzamide is accompanied by O^{18} exchange (cf. Sec. 12-1b).[50] These workers found no O^{18} exchange during the acid hydrolysis of benzamide. They point out that intermediate V in the mechanism below, because of the greater basicity of

[49] E. E. Reid, *Am. Chem. J.*, **21**, 284 (1899); **24**, 397 (1900).

[50] M. L. Bender, R. D. Ginger, and K. C. Kemp, *J. Am. Chem. Soc.*, **76**, 3350 (1954); M. L. Bender and R. D. Ginger, *J. Am. Chem. Soc.*, **77**, 348 (1955).

NH_2 than OH, may lose NH_3 (rather than H_2O) almost exclusively in acid solution.

$$RCONH_2 + H_2O \xrightarrow{H^+} R-\overset{\overset{\displaystyle OH}{|}}{\underset{\underset{\displaystyle OH}{|}}{C}}-NH_2 + H^+ \rightleftharpoons R-\overset{\overset{\displaystyle OH}{|}}{\underset{\underset{\displaystyle OH}{|}}{C}}-\overset{\oplus}{N}H_3$$

$$RCO_2H + NH_4^+ \leftarrow R\overset{\oplus}{C}(OH)_2 + NH_3$$

Alternately they suggest that the mechanism may be of a considerably different type, involving a direct one-step displacement

$$H_3O^+ + RCONH_2 \rightleftharpoons H_2O + \overset{\overset{\displaystyle O}{\|}}{\underset{\underset{\displaystyle R}{|}}{C}}-\overset{\oplus}{N}H_3 \rightarrow H_2\overset{\oplus}{O}-\overset{\overset{\displaystyle O}{\|}}{\underset{\underset{\displaystyle R}{|}}{C}} + NH_3$$

$$RCO_2H + NH_4^+$$

The first mechanism seems to be preferable, however, since it is more nearly analogous to the basic amide hydrolysis mechanism and the mechanisms of both basic and acid ester hydrolysis.

The rate of hydrolysis of amides in very strongly acidic solutions has been found to reach a maximum for acid of a certain strength (about 6 N in the hydrolysis of formamide in hydrochloric acid[51]) and then to decrease with increasing strength of the acid.[51,52] The approach of the rate to a maximum may be explained qualitatively by the fact that the amides, usually somewhat more basic than water, are transformed essentially completely to their conjugate acids in the strongly acidic solution, so that further acidification serves no useful purpose. Augmenting this effect and tending to reduce the reaction rate is the decrease in the activity of water which accompanies the increasing acidity of the solvent. There may be more complications than these two, however.

The hydrolysis of amides is of great importance in biochemistry as well as in synthetic organic chemistry, and for this reason further studies are needed to confirm or disprove the general picture we have given, to distinguish between some of the alternatives we have described, and to add detail in many places.

13-5. Hydrolysis of Other Acid Derivatives. 13-5a. *Hydrolysis of Nitriles.* Nitriles may be hydrolyzed by either strong acids or strong bases. The hydrolysis of the simplest of the nitriles, hydrogen cyanide,

---

[51] V. K. Krieble and K. A. Holst, *J. Am. Chem. Soc.*, **60**, 2976 (1938).
[52] T. W. J. Taylor, *J. Chem. Soc.*, 2741 (1930).

in strongly acidic solutions has been studied carefully. Krieble and McNally have shown that the reaction rate increases more rapidly than the acid concentration for hydrochloric, hydrobromic, and sulfuric acids and to an extent which varies with the nature of the acid.[53] Thus at a concentration of 5.5 M in sulfuric acid $k = 0.02$, in hydrobromic acid $k = 0.20$, and in hydrochloric acid $k = 1.25$.[54] The rate constants are independent of the concentration of hydrogen cyanide over a wide range. From these results it seems possible that the anion of the catalyzing acid is also involved in the reaction, so that the hydrolysis in hydrochloric acid may involve formimino chloride as an intermediate.

$$\text{HCN} \xrightarrow{\text{HCl}} \overset{\displaystyle \text{Cl}}{\underset{|}{\text{H—C}}}=\text{NH} \xrightarrow{\text{H}_2\text{O}} \text{H—CONH}_2 \rightarrow \text{HCO}_2\text{H} + \text{NH}_4^+$$

From this explanation it might be expected that hydrobromic acid would be a more effective catalyst than hydrochloric, since bromide ions are more nucleophilic than chloride ions. Perhaps the acceleration is due to catalysis by the undissociated acid. Rabinovitch, Winkler, and coworkers have also studied nitrile hydrolysis in strong acids,[55] and Kilpatrick has similarly studied the hydrolysis of cyanamide.[56]

13-5b. Hydrolysis of Acid Halides. Hudson and coworkers have studied the mechanism for the hydrolysis of acyl halides. They find that under certain conditions the reactivity may be increased by either electron-withdrawing or electron-donating groups[57] in a manner rather similar to that described for certain saturated halides in Sec. 6-3b. They further substantiate the proposal that the S_N1 character of the reaction is greatest with the acid halides having strongly electron-donating substituents by showing that it is these halides whose hydrolysis rates are most sensitive to the ion-solvating power of the medium.[58] They also show that although the hydrolysis of acid chlorides is not catalyzed by acids, that of acid fluorides is.[59]

13-5c. Hydrolysis of Acid Anhydrides. As compounds of the type RCOX, acid anhydrides occupy a position between acid halides (in which X has a strong tendency to be lost as the anion) and esters (in which X

[53] V. K. Krieble and J. G. McNally, J. Am. Chem. Soc., **51**, 3368 (1929).

[54] V. K. Krieble and A. L. Peiker, J. Am. Chem. Soc., **55**, 2326 (1933).

[55] B. S. Rabinovitch and C. A. Winkler, Can. J. Research, **20B**, 221 (1942), and earlier references quoted.

[56] M. L. Kilpatrick, J. Am. Chem. Soc., **69**, 40 (1947).

[57] R. F. Hudson and J. E. Wardill, J. Chem. Soc., 1729 (1950); D. A. Brown and R. F. Hudson, J. Chem. Soc., 3352 (1953).

[58] B. L. Archer and R. F. Hudson, J. Chem. Soc., 3259 (1950); D. A. Brown and R. F. Hudson, J. Chem. Soc., 883 (1953).

[59] C. W. L. Bevan and R. F. Hudson, J. Chem. Soc., 2187 (1953).

requires much assistance for displacement). Acids have only a slight tendency to catalyze the hydrolysis of anhydrides in aqueous solution,[60] but in acetic acid solutions, where the existence of much more powerful proton donors is possible, acids are effective catalysts.[61]

Gold and coworkers have studied the hydrolysis of acetic and several other aliphatic anhydrides.[62] Among other effects they studied the catalysis of the reaction by tertiary amines. The catalysis appears to be subject to steric hindrance by bulky groups on the amines and is thus not dependent simply upon the basicity of the amines. This suggests a nucleophilic attack at the carbonyl carbon atom.

$$CH_3\overset{O}{\overset{\|}{C}}O\overset{O}{\overset{\|}{C}}CH_3 + R_3N \rightarrow CH_3\overset{O}{\overset{\|}{C}}NR_3^{\oplus} + CH_3CO_2^-$$
$$\downarrow H_2O$$
$$CH_3CO_2^- + R_3NH^+$$

Berliner and Altschul have studied the hydrolysis of substituted benzoic anhydrides.[63] The reaction rate in 75 per cent dioxane–25 per cent water solution was increased by electron-withdrawing substituents, since these increase the tendency of water molecules to attack the carbonyl carbon atoms. The reaction is of particular interest because the data are in satisfactory agreement with the Hammett equation despite the fact that the entropies of activation vary quite widely for the different compounds studied. This variation is correlated with the σ constants, of course (see Sec. 2-4e).

[60] S. C. J. Olivier and G. Berger, *Rec. trav. chim.*, **46**, 609 (1927).

[61] T. Yvernault, *Compt. rend.*, **233**, 411 (1951); **235**, 167 (1952).

[62] V. Gold and E. G. Jefferson, *J. Chem. Soc.*, 1409, 1416 (1953), and earlier references.

[63] E. Berliner and L. H. Altschul, *J. Am. Chem. Soc.*, **74**, 4110 (1952).

CHAPTER 14

REARRANGEMENTS OF ALKYL GROUPS

Several types of rearrangement reactions have already been described under various other headings. The Stevens rearrangement has been mentioned as an example of an S_Ni reaction (Sec. 5-3); allylic rearrangements by the S_N1 and S_N2' mechanisms were discussed in Sec. 5-5; and the Favorskii rearrangement in Sec. 10-3c. Other carbon-skeleton rearrangements will be discussed here.

14-1. Carbonium-ion Rearrangements. Of the very large number of carbonium-ion rearrangements we shall discuss only a few, most of them chosen because of the care with which they have been studied. It is hoped, nevertheless, that certain generalizations pointed out in this and subsequent sections will lead to an understanding of the nature of most of the rearrangements not mentioned specifically.

14-1a. *Evidence That Carbonium Ions Are Intermediates.* Meerwein and van Emster obtained some of the first strong evidence that carbonium ions may be intermediates in carbon-skeleton rearrangements in their study of the rearrangement of camphene hydrochloride to isobornyl chloride.[1] They observed that the reaction rate increased with the nature of the solvent in roughly the same order which had been found for the ability of solvents to ionize triphenylmethyl chloride. They further established that compounds such as $HgCl_2$, $FeCl_3$, $SnCl_4$, etc., capable of coordinating with a chloride ion, were excellent catalysts for the reaction. It was later shown that the rearrangement of the chloride was slower than that of the bromide or arylsulfonate but faster than that of the trichloroacetate or m-nitrobenzoate.[2] This order of reactivity is understandable, since the ease of ionization should increase with the stability of the anion being formed.

The probability of a carbonium-ion mechanism for rearrangement reactions was emphasized (in somewhat different language) by Whitmore and coworkers in a number of subsequent papers. It was further supported by Dostrovsky and Hughes, who showed that the second-order reaction of neopentyl bromide with sodium ethoxide gave the normal

---

[1] H. Meerwein and K. van Emster, *Ber.*, **55**, 2500 (1922).

[2] H. Meerwein, O. Hammel, A. Serini, and J. Vorster, *Ann.*, **453**, 16 (1927).

product, ethyl neopentyl ether, but that the unimolecular solvolyses and the reaction with silver ion gave rearranged products.[3]

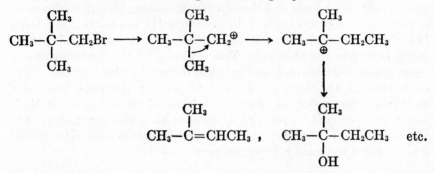

While carbonium-ion rearrangements were originally written as simply involving the shift of an alkyl group or hydrogen atom from an adjacent atom to the electron-deficient carbon atom (as shown in the case of neopentyl above), it was subsequently suggested, first by Nevell, de Salas, and Wilson,[4] that there may be formed a carbonium ion of intermediate structure.

A configuration like this would be expected to be formed at some time as R migrates from one carbon atom to the next. The uniqueness of the present suggestion is that this configuration corresponds to an energy minimum. The formation of such ions may be seen to be an example of neighboring-group participation (Sec. 5-4). We shall therefore discuss the evidence that carbonium ions of the type shown are intermediates in rearrangement reactions in these terms.

14-1b. *Aromatic Radicals as Neighboring Groups.* There is good evidence that neighboring aromatic radicals may participate in displacement reactions in a manner analogous to that described for RS—, R$_2$N—, halogen, etc., groups (Sec. 5-4). Cram's investigations of 3-phenyl-2-butyl and of 3-phenyl-2-pentyl and 2-phenyl-3-pentyl compounds are of interest in this regard.[5] The four stereoisomers of 3-phenyl-2-butanol were separated. These compounds will be called IA and IB (one *dl* pair) and IIA and IIB (the other *dl* pair). Evidence based on the structures of the olefins obtained by the Chugaev decomposition of these alcohols suggests that *dl* pair I has the threo structure shown

[3] I. Dostrovsky and E. D. Hughes, *J. Chem. Soc.*, 157, 164, 166, 169, 171 (1946).
[4] T. P. Nevell, E. de Salas, and C. L. Wilson, *J. Chem. Soc.*, 1188 (1939).
[5] D. J. Cram, *J. Am. Chem. Soc.*, 71, 3863, 3875, 3883 (1949).

and that II is the erythro racemate. Furthermore, the fact that the
p-toluenesulfonate (tosylate) of IA reacts with potassium acetate in
absolute ethanol (conditions thought likely to cause an S_N2 replacement
of tosylate by acetate) to yield the acetate of IIA implies that in IA and
IIA the configuration around the carbon atom to which the phenyl
group is attached is identical. This evidence for the configurations of
these compounds is considerably strengthened by the fact that these
configurations are those which must be used in the most reasonable
mechanism for acetolysis of the tosylates. The acetolysis of these
tosylates was found to proceed as follows: an active threo form (IA)
yields racemic threo acetate, while an active erythro form (IIA) yields
the acetate of the same active erythro alcohol (IIA).

$$\text{IA tosylate} \xrightarrow{\text{HOAc}} \text{IA and IB acetates} \qquad \text{(racemic I acetate)}$$
$$\text{IIA tosylate} \xrightarrow{\text{HOAc}} \text{IIA acetate}$$

As described in the discussion of bromonium ions (Sec. 5-4e), in an S_N2
reaction a IA compound would yield a IIA derivative, while by an S_Ni
mechanism, an active (IA) product would be formed, rather than the
racemic product observed. The results of an ordinary S_N1 reaction
would be the same as the S_N2 or S_Ni noted above, or a combination,
depending on which side of the carbonium ion the entering group is
assumed to attack. The reaction is evidently not an entirely concerted
one like that suggested[6] for the related rearrangement of neopentyl
halides

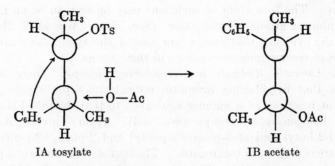

IA tosylate   IB acetate

since this should lead to the formation of only IB acetate. Therefore
the most suitable mechanism appears to be that suggested by Cram,
involving the participation of the neighboring phenyl group. With the
threo IA, the "phenonium ion" formed has a plane of symmetry and
hence can yield only racemic products, since it is equally likely to give the
acetate of IA or IB.

[6] C. G. Swain, *J. Am. Chem. Soc.*, **70**, 1126 (1948).

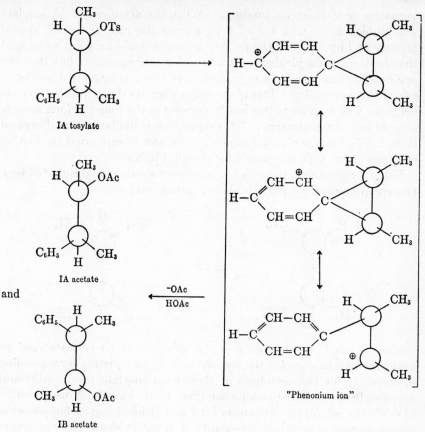

IA tosylate

IA acetate

and

IB acetate

"Phenonium ion"

In the case of the erythro compound, IIA, the intermediate phenonium ion is optically active and gives the acetate of IIA by reaction at either carbon atom.

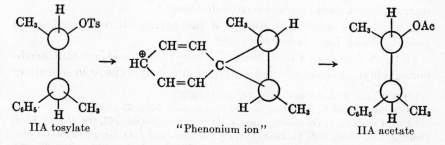

IIA tosylate   "Phenonium ion"   IIA acetate

It is highly unlikely that the acetate of I formed in the acetolysis of IA tosylate is inactive due to racemization after formation. It has also been shown that while the tosylate does racemize somewhat as it reacts, the extent of this racemization is not nearly enough to account for the formation of the racemic product.[7]   When the acetolysis of IA tosylate was studied kinetically both by measuring the rate of loss of optical activity and by titrating the p-toluenesulfonic acid formed, it was found that both methods yielded good first-order rate constants but that the polarimetric rate constants were about five times as large as those determined titrimetrically.[8]   This observation suggests that IA forms racemic ion pairs, which revert to tosylate 80 per cent of the time and form acetate only 20 per cent of the time.   This suggestion is similar to that described in Sec. 5-5c for α,α-dimethylallyl chloride and is supported by further evidence of the type mentioned for the allyl halide.

While a mechanism involving a rapid tautomeric equilibrium between two enantiomorphic 3-phenyl-2-butyl carbonium ions

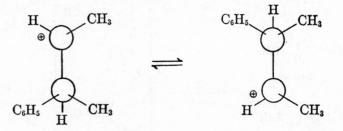

cannot be ruled out absolutely in the solvolysis of IA tosylate (and an analogous mechanism for the solvolysis of IIA tosylate), corresponding mechanisms for the acetolysis of cholesteryl tosylate (Sec. 14-1b) and norbornyl p-bromobenzenesulfonate (Sec. 14-1c) have been disproved.

While the solvolysis mechanism for I and II involving carbon-skeleton rearrangement is certainly reasonable, it is not evident in the structure of the reaction products.   This is not so, however, in the case of the 3-phenyl-2-pentyl tosylates which yield 2-phenyl-3-pentyl acetates as well as unrearranged products.   Studies of the solvolysis of these compounds and the related 2-phenyl-3-pentyl tosylates further support the rearrangement mechanisms we have discussed.[5]

A number of additional studies of the participation of neighboring phenyl radicals have been described.[9]

14-1c. *Neighboring Vinyl Groups.*   There is also evidence that neighboring vinyl (and substituted vinyl) groups may behave in a manner

[7] D. J. Cram, *J. Am. Chem. Soc.*, **74**, 2129 (1952).

[8] S. Winstein and K. Schreiber, *J. Am. Chem. Soc.*, **74**, 2165 (1952).

[9] J. C. Charlton, I. Dostrovsky, and E. D. Hughes, *Nature*, **167**, 986 (1951); D. J. Cram, *J. Am. Chem. Soc.*, **74**, 2159 (1952); D. J. Cram and J. D. Knight, *J. Am. Chem. Soc.*, **74**, 5839 (1952); D. J. Cram and F. A. A. Elhafez, *J. Am. Chem. Soc.*, **75**, 339, 3189 (1953); S. Winstein, B. K. Morse, E. Grunwald, K. C. Schreiber, and J. Corse, *J. Am. Chem. Soc.*, **74**, 1113 (1952); S. Winstein, M. Brown, K. C. Schreiber, and A. H. Schlesinger, *J. Am. Chem. Soc.*, **74**, 1140 (1952); S. Winstein, C. R. Lindegren, H. Marshall, and L. L. Ingraham, *J. Am. Chem. Soc.*, **75**, 147 (1953).

analogous to that described for phenyl groups. Shoppee suggested that the double bond in cholesteryl halides and related compounds may display neighboring-group participation in replacement reactions.[10] Kinetic studies have yielded evidence that a resonance-stabilized carbonium ion of the type (III) shown below is an intermediate in the reactions of certain cholesteryl compounds.[11] A rapid tautomeric equilibrium

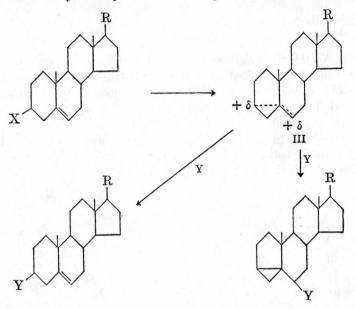

between two isomeric carbonium ions might be suggested to explain this rearrangement, but this would not explain the fact that cholesteryl tosylate solvolyzes about 100 times as rapidly as does cyclohexyl tosylate. The proposed mechanism involving ionization directly to the resonance stabilized III does explain this fact.

Similar participation of a double bond has been used to explain the solvolysis of dehydronorbornyl compounds that yield nortricyclyl derivatives.[12]

[10] C. W. Shoppee, *J. Chem. Soc.*, 1147 (1946).

[11] S. Winstein and R. Adams, *J. Am. Chem. Soc.*, **70**, 838 (1948); R. G. Pearson, L. A. Subluskey, and L. C. King, *J. Am. Chem. Soc.*, **70**, 3479 (1948); R. G. Pearson, L. C. King, and S. H. Langer, *J. Am. Chem. Soc.*, **73**, 4149 (1951); L. C. King and M. J. Bigelow, *J. Am. Chem. Soc.*, **74**, 6238 (1952); C. W. Shoppee and G. H. R. Summers, *J. Chem. Soc.*, 3361 (1952); D. D. Evans and C. W. Shoppee, *J. Chem. Soc.*, 540 (1953).

[12] J. D. Roberts, E. R. Trumbull, Jr., W. Bennett, and R. Armstrong, *J. Am. Chem. Soc.*, **72**, 3116 (1950); J. D. Roberts, W. Bennett, and R. Armstrong, *J. Am. Chem. Soc.*, **72**, 3329 (1950); S. Winstein, H. M. Walborsky, and K. Schreiber, *J. Am. Chem. Soc.*, **72**, 5795 (1950); J. D. Roberts and W. Bennett, *J. Am. Chem. Soc.*, **76**, 4623 (1954); J. D. Roberts, C. C. Lee, and W. H. Saunders, Jr., *J. Am. Chem. Soc.*, **77**, 3034 (1955).

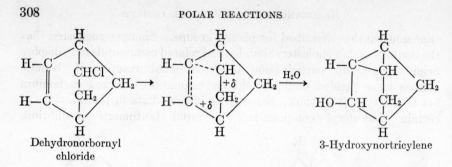

Dehydronorbornyl
chloride

3-Hydroxynortricylene

14-1d. *Neighboring Saturated Alkyl Groups.* The first convincing evidence for the participation of a saturated hydrocarbon radical in a nucleophilic displacement reaction on carbon appears to be due to Winstein and Trifan. These workers showed that optically active *exo*-norbornyl *p*-bromobenzenesulfonate, upon acetolysis, yields racemic *exo*-norbornyl acetate.[13] The racemization was found to proceed more rapidly than the solvolysis, indicating that the initial product of reaction is an ion pair which may recombine or dissociate (see Sec. 5-5c).

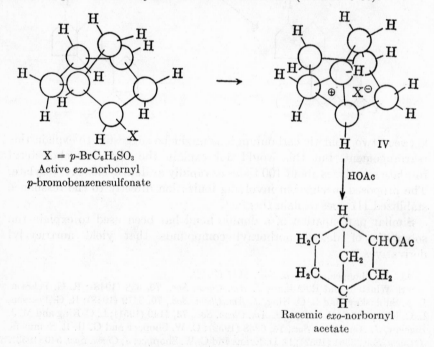

X = p-BrC$_6$H$_4$SO$_3$
Active *exo*-norbornyl
p-bromobenzenesulfonate

Racemic *exo*-norbornyl
acetate

Any explanation postulating a rapid tautomeric equilibrium between two enantiomorphic norbornyl carbonium ions does not explain the

¹³ S. Winstein and D. S. Trifan, *J. Am. Chem. Soc.*, **71**, 2953 (1949); **74**, 1154 (1952).

fact that *exo*-norbornyl *p*-bromobenzenesulfonate solvolyzes about 350 times as rapidly as does the endo isomer. This fact is explained by neighboring-group participation to form a carbonium ion with structure IV, since with the exo compound the neighboring group may attack

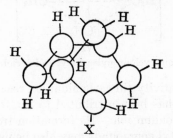

Optically active *endo*-norbornyl *p*-bromobenzenesulfonate

from the rear while the *p*-bromobenzenesulfonate ion is leaving the front. Thus in the case of the exo compound the more stable bridged carbonium ion (IV) is being formed in the transition state, while with the endo compound it appears that an ordinary carbonium ion is formed first and that this rearranges to carbonium ion IV (which does appear to be an intermediate in the solvolysis of the endo compound also, because racemic *exo*-acetate is formed in the acetolysis of optically active *endo-p*-bromobenzenesulfonate). Roberts and Lee have reported studies using C^{14} which show that the carbon-skeleton rearrangement is more drastic than would be expected from the intermediacy of carbonium ion IV alone, and they have suggested that the simultaneous or subsequent formation of carbonium ion V may also be important.[14]

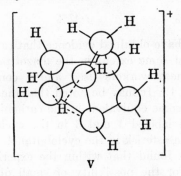

An interesting structure has been proposed for the carbonium-ion intermediate (VI) in the solvolysis of the benzenesulfonate[15] of cyclopropyl-

[14] J. D. Roberts and C. C. Lee, *J. Am. Chem. Soc.*, **73**, 5009 (1951); J. D. Roberts, C. C. Lee, and W. H. Saunders, Jr., *J. Am. Chem. Soc.*, **76**, 4501 (1954).
[15] C. G. Bergstrom and S. Siegel, *J. Am. Chem. Soc.*, **74**, 145 (1952).

carbinol and the reaction of the analogous amine with nitrous acid.[16]

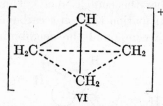

VI

Carbonium ion from cyclopropylcarbinyl and cyclobutyl compounds

The considerable reactivity (in carbonium-ion reactions) of cyclopropyl-carbinyl compounds has been attributed to the formation of this reso-nance-stabilized carbonium ion. Its formation from both cyclopropyl-carbinyl and cyclobutyl compounds may also be used to explain the fact that both of these amines, for example, react to give about the same mixture of cyclopropylcarbinol, cyclobutanol, and allylcarbinol.[17]

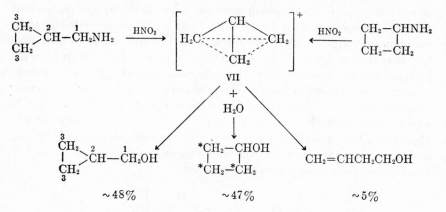

Roberts and Mazur have obtained evidence that carbonium ion VI may be formed to at least some extent in the diazotization of cyclopropyl-carbinylamine.[12] These workers used amine containing C^{14} at the carbon atom labeled 1. It may be noted that the atom labeled 1 and the two labeled 3 become equivalent in the carbonium ion VII. These atoms become those labeled 1 and 3 in the cyclopropylcarbinol and those marked with an asterisk in the cyclobutanol. In agreement with the mechanism, it is found that within the experimental error (when allowance is made for the possibility of small differences due to an "isotope effect"), the C^{14} is distributed equally between the three methylene carbon atoms of cyclobutanol. In the cyclopropylcarbinol 45 per cent of the C^{14} is found at carbon atom 1, and 54 per cent is found in the ring. The mechanism, of course, predicts 33.3 per cent at 1 and

[16] J. D. Roberts and R. H. Mazur, *J. Am. Chem. Soc.*, **73**, 3542 (1951).
[17] *Ibid.*, 2509 (1951).

66.7 per cent in the ring. While not in exact agreement, it does seem that extensive rearrangement has occurred. The most reasonable explanation appears to be that about 81 per cent of the cyclopropyl-carbinol is formed through carbonium ion VII and about 19 per cent through a direct replacement reaction.

14-1e. *Types of Rearrangement Mechanisms.* Even in the simplest example of a rearrangement by the carbonium-ion mechanism we could suggest as many as four steps

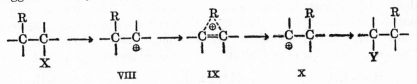

involving an unrearranged carbonium ion (VIII), an intermediate carbonium ion (IX), and a rearranged carbonium ion (X). There are cases, however, in which the experimental evidence suggests that some of the steps have become fused, i.e., in which one or more of the three possible intermediate carbonium ions is no longer a true intermediate. Considering the existence or nonexistence of three different carbonium ions, there will be $2^3 = 8$ different kinds of cases. More work is needed to learn the relation between the structure of the reactants, reaction conditions, etc., and the type of case which will appear. However, it seems that some reactions may be definitely classified as being of a certain type and furthermore that not all are of the same type. Thus in the case of the solvolysis of *exo*-norbornyl *p*-bromobenzenesulfonate the reactant is transformed directly to an ion of type IX (as part of an ion pair), and this ion goes directly to the products, with ions of type VIII and X never appearing as true intermediates. Not all S_N1 reactions, however, involve the initial formation of an ion like IX. With compounds like triphenylmethyl halides such an ion is hardly possible. Even with a compound like α-phenylethyl chloride the considerable racemization which accompanies solvolysis (Sec. 5-2c) makes it unlikely that an ion like IX (which should lead to retention of configuration) was the intermediate in the major portion of the reaction. Nor need an ion like IX be formed directly even in cases where rearrangement occurs. Winstein and Morse have demonstrated this in their observation that optically active α-phenylneopentyl chloride and *p*-toluenesulfonate solvolyze to give completely racemic rearranged products and largely racemic, but partly inverted, unrearranged products.[18] While several types of cases are known, there appears to be no evidence which demands the intermediacy both of ions of the type of IX and of the type of VIII and X in the same reaction. There also appears to be no evidence for the suggested[6] completely concerted mechanism, with no carbonium-ion intermediates.

There is evidently no great energy barrier between the carbonium ions of the type of VIII, IX, and X, since under conditions which would be expected to give VIII, it appears that IX and/or X are formed if more stable (than VIII).

14-1f. *The Pinacol and Related Rearrangements.* Acid-catalyzed transformation to an aldehyde or ketone is a rather general reaction for 1,2-diols. When both hydroxy groups are tertiary, the reaction occurs particularly easily, the intermediate carbonium ion(s) being relatively stable, and is called the pinacol rearrangement. For the simplest such rearrangement, that of pinacol itself, we may write the mechanism

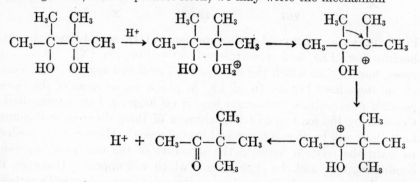

but we really do not know whether the removal of the water molecule actually gives the first carbonium ion shown, an intermediate one, or the last one. In any case, a driving force for the rearrangement may be seen in the fact that the last carbonium ion, the conjugate acid of pinacolone, is the most stable of the three. However, in a related pinacolic deamination, Bernstein and Whitmore showed that the optically active product has undergone an inversion in configuration at its asymmetric carbon atom.[19]

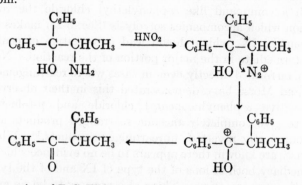

[19] H. I. Bernstein and F. C. Whitmore, *J. Am. Chem. Soc.,* **61,** 1324 (1939).

Therefore any unrearranged carbonium ion, if formed at all, did not have a long enough life to racemize.

Bartlett and Brown have presented evidence which suggests that a phenyl group definitely participates as a neighboring group in the pinacol rearrangement of 7,8-diphenylacenaphthenediol-7,8.[20] These workers showed that the cis compound rearranges about six times as fast as the trans isomer in wet acetic acid with a sulfuric acid catalyst.

The trans isomer yielded the same product, but it is very probable that it does so by first isomerizing to the cis compound.

The nature of the pinacolone formed when there is more than one R group that may migrate has received considerable attention. With a symmetrical pinacol it is necessary to consider only which of two possible groups will migrate. In these reactions it is found that if steric factors are unimportant, the "migration aptitude" of various groups is proportional to their electron-donating ability. Thus the p-anisyl group migrates in preference to the phenyl group.[21]

$$p\text{-MeOC}_6\text{H}_4 \quad \text{C}_6\text{H}_4\text{OMe-}p$$
$$\begin{matrix} | & | \\ \text{C}_6\text{H}_5-\text{C}-\text{C}-\text{C}_6\text{H}_5 \\ | & | \\ \text{HO} & \text{OH} \end{matrix}$$

$$\xrightarrow[\to]{\text{H}^+} 98.6\%$$

$$\overset{\text{O}}{\overset{\|}{\text{C}_6\text{H}_5-\text{C}}}-\overset{\text{C}_6\text{H}_5}{\underset{|}{\text{C}}}-(\text{C}_6\text{H}_4\text{OMe-}p)_2$$
$$+$$
$$1.4\% \quad \overset{\text{O}}{\overset{\|}{p\text{-MeOC}_6\text{H}_4-\text{C}}}-\overset{\text{C}_6\text{H}_4\text{OMe-}p}{\underset{|}{\text{C}}}-(\text{C}_6\text{H}_5)_2$$

Bachmann and Moser list the following order of migration aptitudes for various groups in the pinacol rearrangement: p-anisyl > p-tolyl > p-biphenyl > m-tolyl > p-fluorophenyl > phenyl > p-iodophenyl > p-bromophenyl, p-chlorophenyl > m-methoxyphenyl > o-tolyl, o- and m-bromophenyl, o- and m-chlorophenyl. While the order is about what would be expected for the meta- and para-substituted compounds, the ortho-substituted groups have a relatively low migration aptitude. This s probably the result of steric hindrance.

In discussing steric effects on the course of the pinacol rearrangement it should be pointed out that a symmetrical pinacol with two different types of R groups may exist in two isomeric forms, the meso and the dl,

[20] P. D. Bartlett and R. F. Brown, *J. Am. Chem. Soc.*, **62**, 2927 (1940).
[21] W. E. Bachmann and F. H. Moser, *J. Am. Chem. Soc.*, **54**, 1124 (1932).

and it may be necessary to state which is being studied since the preferred rotational conformation of the two isomers may not place the same group in the position trans to the departing group facilitating its migration. This point has been very effectively established by Curtin and Pollak in the related pinacolic deamination reaction.[22] With the amino alcohols studied in this reaction, there are two racemates (*dl* pairs). It was found that in the reaction of the α racemate of 1,2-diphenyl-1-*p*-chlorophenyl-2-aminoethanol with nitrous acid the phenyl group migrates, while with the β racemate the *p*-chlorophenyl group does.

$$C_6H_5$$
$$p\text{-}ClC_6H_4C\!\!-\!\!CHC_6H_5$$
$$HO \quad NH_2$$

$$\alpha \text{ racemate} \xrightarrow{\text{HNO}_2} p\text{-}ClC_6H_4CO\!\!-\!\!CH(C_6H_5)_2$$

$$C_6H_4Cl\text{-}p$$

$$\beta \text{ racemate} \xrightarrow{\text{HNO}_2} C_6H_5CO\!\!-\!\!CHC_6H_5$$

Pollak and Curtin point out that the most stable rotational conformation for each of the racemates will be the one which places the larger (aryl) groups attached to the hydroxylated carbon atom on either side of the smallest group (a hydrogen atom) on the amino carbon atom. In one racemate this will place the phenyl group trans to the amino group—ready to migrate when the amino group is changed to a diazonium ion group and then lost as nitrogen. In the most stable rotational form of the other racemate it is the *p*-chlorophenyl group that is trans to the amino group.

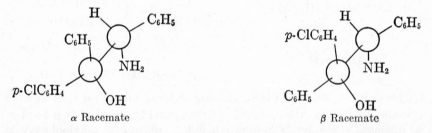

α Racemate β Racemate

The configurations assigned these two diastereomeric racemates on the basis of this interpretation were subsequently confirmed by independent means. This explanation, of course, depends on the assumption that the intermediate which rearranges (the diazonium ion in this case) does so at a rate which is rapid compared to the rate of interconversion of the different rotational conformations of a given species. While this assumption is plausible in the present case, it may not be in certain others, and

[22] D. Y. Curtin and P. I. Pollak, *J. Am. Chem. Soc.*, **73**, 992 (1951); cf. P. I. Pollak and D. Y. Curtin, *J. Am. Chem. Soc.*, **72**, 961 (1950); D. Y. Curtin, E. E. Harris, and P. I. Pollak, *J. Am. Chem. Soc.*, **73**, 3453 (1951).

when it is not, the extent of migration of the two groups will depend only on the stability of the two possible transition states for aryl-group migration.[23]

With unsymmetrical pinacols

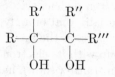

the situation is more complicated, since we must estimate the relative tendency of the two hydroxyl groups to be removed by acid as well as the relative migration aptitudes of various R groups.

14-2. The Benzilic Acid Rearrangement. The benzilic acid rearrangement is the base-catalyzed rearrangement of α-diketones to the salts of α-hydroxy acids, the most familiar example being the reaction of benzil.

$$C_6H_5COCOC_6H_5 + OH^- \rightarrow (C_6H_5)_2\overset{\displaystyle OH}{\underset{\displaystyle |}{C}}-CO_2^-$$

Westheimer has shown that this reaction is first-order in benzil and first-order in hydroxide ion and that it is not subject to *general* base catalysis.[24] Roberts and Urey found that benzil undergoes base-catalyzed O^{18} exchange at a rate which is much faster than its rearrangement.[25] These workers point out that their observations are consistent with the assumption that benzil reversibly and relatively rapidly adds a hydroxide ion to give an intermediate which undergoes a rate-controlling rearrangement.

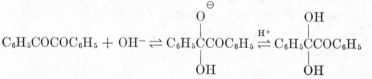

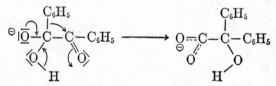

Whether the rate-controlling step of the rearrangement involves an internal proton transfer, as shown, or whether this occurs subsequently is a question which requires further consideration. There are certainly

[23] D. Y. Curtin and M. C. Crew, *J. Am. Chem. Soc.*, **77**, 356 (1955).

[24] F. H. Westheimer, *J. Am. Chem. Soc.*, **58**, 2209 (1936).

[25] I. Roberts and H. C. Urey, *J. Am. Chem. Soc.*, **60**, 880 (1938).

several reasons why such a proton transfer should facilitate the reaction. First, the reaction may be seen to resemble a carbonium-ion rearrangement in that the phenyl group is migrating to a (somewhat) electron-deficient carbon atom. The donation of a proton to the carbonyl oxygen atom will increase this electron deficiency. Second, the reaction is like a Cannizzaro reaction (especially that of a glyoxal, see Sec. 11-4a) except that the unshared electron pairs on the negatively charged oxygen atom are displacing a phenyl group with its electron pair rather than a hydride ion. In so far as the proton transfer shown has occurred in the transition state, there are two negatively charged oxygen atoms to displace the phenyl group. In addition to these permissive arguments, however, there is more direct evidence that the hydrogen atom is taking part in the rate-controlling step of the reaction. This is the fact that the reaction takes a different course when alkoxide ions are substituted for hydroxide ions. Lachman showed that with ethanolic sodium ethoxide, benzil yields benzaldehyde and ethyl benzoate,[26] perhaps by the mechanism

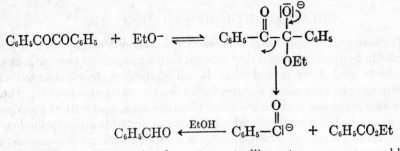

Similar proton transfers in the rate-controlling step may reasonably be suggested for at least some Cannizzaro reactions.

[26] A. Lachman, *J. Am. Chem. Soc.*, **45**, 1509 (1923).

CHAPTER 15

REARRANGEMENTS DUE TO ELECTRON-DEFICIENT NITROGEN AND OXYGEN ATOMS

15-1. Rearrangements Due to Electron-deficient Nitrogen Atoms.
15-1a. *The Hofmann Reaction of Amides.* Nitrogen compounds may rearrange just as their carbon analogs do when a group attached to the nitrogen atom is removed with a pair of bonding electrons. This similarity of the Hofmann and related reactions to many carbon-skeleton rearrangements appears to have been pointed out first by Whitmore in the initial paper of his important series "The Common Basis of Intramolecular Rearrangements."[1]

The Hofmann degradation of amides by the action of halogen and alkali almost certainly involves the initial formation of a N-haloamide, since these intermediates have been isolated in a number of cases and found to undergo the rearrangement in the presence of alkali. The removal of a halide anion is facilitated by transformation of the N-haloamide to its conjugate base (compare the basic hydrolysis of chloroform, Sec. 5-6). However, as Hauser and Kantor point out, it is not likely that there is a true intermediate in which a nitrogen atom has only a sextet of electrons.[2] It is more probable that the migration of the R group occurs simultaneously with the loss of the halide ion.

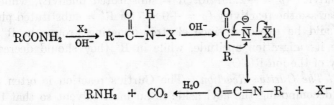

This concerted mechanism explains the absence of hydroxamic acids in the product[2] and the marked accelerating effect of electron-donating groups on the reaction ($\rho = -2.50$ for N-bromobenzamides).[3]

A number of workers have shown that in the Hofmann reaction, as

[1] F. C. Whitmore, *J. Am. Chem. Soc.*, **54**, 3274 (1932).
[2] C. R. Hauser and S. W. Kantor, *J. Am. Chem. Soc.*, **72**, 4284 (1950).
[3] C. R. Hauser and W. B. Renfrow, Jr., *J. Am. Chem. Soc.*, **59**, 121 (1937).

well as in the related Lossen, Curtius, and Schmidt reactions, the R group migrates with complete retention of configuration. For example, Noyes found that β-camphoramic acid (known to be cis from its relation to the anhydride-forming camphoric acid, prepared by the oxidation of camphor) undergoes the Hofmann reaction to give an amino acid whose

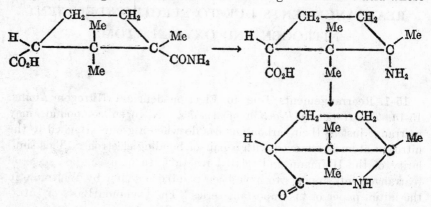

cis configuration is shown by its ability to form a lactam.[4] Wallis and Nagel showed that active α-benzylpropionamide gives optically pure α-benzylethylamine.[5]

The Lossen rearrangement of acyl derivatives of hydroxamic acids is very similar to the Hofmann reaction.

$$\underset{R-C-NHOC-R'}{\overset{O\quad\ O}{\parallel\quad\ \parallel}} \rightarrow \underset{R-C-N-OC-R'}{\overset{O\ \ominus\ O}{\parallel\quad\quad\parallel}}$$
$$\rightarrow R-N{=}C{=}O + R'CO_2^- \rightarrow \text{etc.}$$

Renfrow and Hauser[6] find that electron-donating groups in R increase the reactivity ($\rho = -2.597$ for R = substituted phenyl[7]), while in R′ they decrease the reactivity ($\rho = +0.865$ for R′ = substituted phenyl[7]). This would be expected since electron-donating groups in R should increase its migration aptitude, while in R′ they should decrease the stability of the ion R′CO$_2^-$.

15-1b. *The Curtius Reaction.* The Curtius reaction is often carried out by decomposing the acyl azide in an inert solvent so that the iso-cyanate, which is usually produced only as an intermediate in the Hofmann, Lossen, and Schmidt reactions, may in this case be isolated. The reaction may be written as involving a preliminary loss of nitrogen to

[4] W. A. Noyes and R. S. Potter, *J. Am. Chem. Soc.*, **34**, 1067 (1912); **37**, 189 (1915).

[5] E. S. Wallis and S. C. Nagel, *J. Am. Chem. Soc.*, **53**, 2787 (1931).

[6] W. B. Renfrow, Jr. and C. R. Hauser, *J. Am. Chem. Soc.*, **59**, 2308 (1937).

[7] L. P. Hammett, "Physical Organic Chemistry," pp. 190–191, McGraw-Hill Book Company, Inc., New York, 1940.

give an intermediate (I), in which the R group migrates from carbon to the nitrogen atom with only six electrons in its outer shell.

$$R-\overset{\overset{\text{O}}{\|}}{C}-\underline{\overline{N}}-N\equiv N| \longrightarrow N_2 + R-\overset{\overset{\text{O}}{\|}}{C}-\overline{N} \longrightarrow R-N=C=O$$

$$\text{I}$$

Actually, though, the intermediate I is the same one which would have been written in the Hofmann reaction if the migration of R had been suggested to occur subsequent to, rather than simultaneously with, the loss of halogen. It is about equally improbable as an intermediate in the Curtius reaction.[2] That is, the loss of nitrogen and the migration of R probably occur simultaneously.

After a consideration of the mechanism of the Schmidt reaction of carboxylic acids, Newman and Gildenhorn made and verified the prediction that the decomposition of acyl azides should be subject to acid catalysis.[8] This catalysis may be due to the fact that the bond between the two terminal nitrogen atoms has more triple-bond character in the conjugate acid of the azide (where the contributing structure written is the only one which does not involve charge separation) than in the azide itself.

$$R-\overset{\overset{\text{I}\overline{\text{O}}}{\|}}{C}-\overset{\ominus}{\underline{\overline{N}}}-\overset{\oplus}{N}\equiv N \rightleftharpoons \overset{\overset{\text{I}\text{O}\text{I}}{\overset{\text{H}}{|}}}{\underset{\underset{\text{R}}{|}}{C}}=\overline{N}-\overset{\oplus}{N}\equiv N| \longrightarrow N_2 + R-\overset{\oplus}{\overset{.}{N}}\equiv C-\overline{\underline{O}}-H$$

$$R-\overset{\overset{\text{I}\overline{\text{O}}}{\|}}{C}-\overset{\oplus}{\overline{N}}=\overset{\ominus}{N}=\overline{N}| \qquad\qquad R-\overline{N}=C=\overline{O}|$$

Newman and Gildenhorn suggest that the azide is protonated at nitrogen to give

$$R-\overset{\overset{\text{I}\overline{\text{O}}}{\|}}{C}-\overset{\overset{\text{H}}{|}}{\underline{N}}-\overset{\oplus}{N}\equiv N|$$

While this possibility has not been disproved, the alternate interpretation given seems preferable for reasons to be described in the next section.

15-1c. *The Schmidt Reaction.* The Schmidt reaction is usually considered to include the transformation of acids to amines and of ketones to amides by the action of hydrazoic acid and a strong acid catalyst,

[8] M. S. Newman and H. L. Gildenhorn, *J. Am. Chem. Soc.*, **70**, 317 (1948); R. A. Coleman, M. S. Newman, and A. B. Garrett, *J. Am. Chem. Soc.*, **76**, 4534 (1954).

as well as certain related reactions. Smith has proposed the most plausible mechanism for the reaction of ketones.[9] In this mechanism the conjugate acid of the ketone coordinates with a molecule of hydrazoic acid to give II, which is dehydrated to III; III then rearranges in a manner analogous to the Beckmann rearrangement.

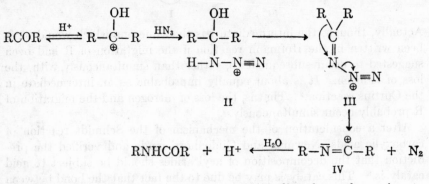

Although II could be written as rearranging directly to the conjugate acid of the amide,

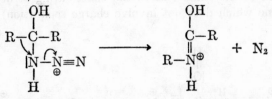

there are several reasons for believing that this does not occur. One reason is that intermediate III explains why alkyl azides usually may not be substituted for hydrazoic acid in this reaction.[9,10] The most convincing reason is the fact that if excess hydrazoic acid is used, tetrazoles are formed, although it has been shown that these could not have been formed by the subsequent reaction of the amides which are the initial products.[11] This fact is explained by the intermediate IV, which may combine with hydrazoic acid to yield a tetrazole.

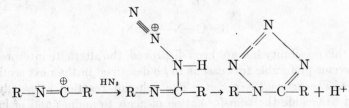

[9] P. A. S. Smith, *J. Am. Chem. Soc.*, **70**, 320 (1948).

[10] L. H. Briggs, G. C. De Ath, and S. R. Ellis, *J. Chem. Soc.*, 61 (1942); J. H. Boyer and J. Hamer, *J. Am. Chem. Soc.*, **77**, 951 (1955).

[11] K. F. Schmidt, *Ber.*, **57**, 707 (1924); *Chem. Abstr.*, **19**, 3248 (1925); M. A. Spielman and F. L. Austin, *J. Am. Chem. Soc.*, **59**, 2658 (1937).

Under the conditions used for the reaction an amide would be expected to be transformed to its conjugate acid but not to an ion like IV.

Newman and Gildenhorn found that 2,4,6-trimethylbenzoic acid undergoes the Schmidt reaction in sulfuric acid readily at 0° although benzoic acid requires a reaction temperature of 25° or more. It is certainly reasonable to ascribe the reactivity of the trimethyl compound to the ease with which it forms an oxocarbonium ion (see Sec. 12-1c). The reaction mechanism then appears to be

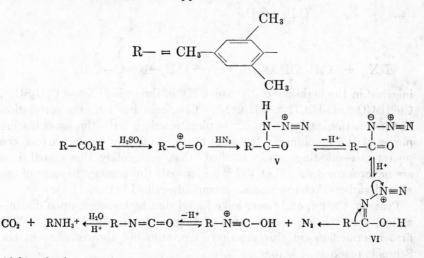

Although the reaction could have been written as involving the direct rearrangement of V, VI seems a better choice because its structure is more nearly analogous to III (the established intermediate for the ketone reaction).

It is difficult to tell whether the reaction of benzoic acid goes through some very small amount of the oxocarbonium ion or whether it involves the less reactive but more plentiful conjugate acid $C_6H_5C(OH)_2{}^+$.

15-1d. *The Beckmann Rearrangement.* Some of the first evidence that it is trans R groups which migrate most readily in rearrangement reactions was obtained in studies of the Beckmann rearrangement. This fact became obvious from a great many previously published data when Meisenheimer and others finally correctly established the configuration of oximes.[12] The reaction mechanism involves the removal of the hydroxyl group with its bonding electron pair and the simultaneous migration of the R group trans to it. This mechanism explains why the reaction is brought about by conditions favoring the removal of the hydroxyl group in this way. Acid catalysts are effective, as are

[12] J. Meisenheimer, *Ber.*, **54**, 3206 (1921); J. Meisenheimer, P. Zimmermann, and U. v. Kummer, *Ann.*, **446**, 205 (1926); O. L. Brady and G. Bishop, *J. Chem. Soc.*, **127**, 1357 (1925).

acyl halides. The latter often give intermediate esters which can be isolated and the subsequent rearrangement of which can be studied. Kuhara and coworkers pointed out the increase in rearrangement rate with

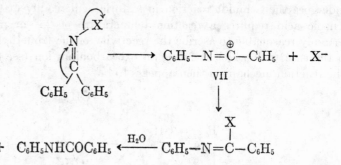

increase in the stability of the anion X^- in the series[13] $X^- = C_6H_5SO_3^-$, $ClCH_2CO_2^-$, $C_6H_5CO_2^-$, $CH_3CO_2^-$. Chapman has found a correlation of the reaction rate (where $X^- =$ picrate anion) with the ion-solvating power of the medium.[14] It seems likely, especially in the case of the poorer ion-solvating media studied, that completely dissociated ions are never formed, i.e., that VII is an ion pair (by analogy to some of the related carbon-skeleton rearrangements described in Sec. 14-1).

Pearson, Carter, and Greer have found that hydrazones, upon diazotization, undergo a rearrangement analogous to the Beckmann.[15] The first intermediate in this reaction is presumably the same as in the Schmidt reaction of ketones.

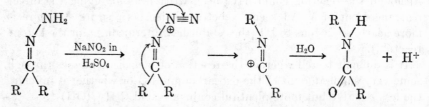

15-2. Rearrangements Due to Electron-deficient Oxygen Atoms.[16]

15-2a. Rearrangements of Esters of Peracids. Criegee has studied the rearrangement of the 9-decalyl esters of perbenzoic acid and *p*-nitroperbenzoic acid.[17] The facts that the rearrangement rate increases with

[13] M. Kuhara, K. Matsumiya, and N. Matsunami, *Mem. Coll. Sci. Kyoto Imp. Univ.*, 1, 105 (1914); M. Kuhara and H. Watanabe, *Mem. Coll. Sci. Kyoto Imp. Univ.*, 1(9), 349 (1916); *Chem. Abstr.*, 9, 1613 (1915); 11, 579 (1917).

[14] A. W. Chapman and C. C. Howis, *J. Chem. Soc.*, 806 (1933); A. W. Chapman, *J. Chem. Soc.*, 1550 (1934).

[15] D. E. Pearson and C. M. Greer, *J. Am. Chem. Soc.*, 71, 1895 (1949); D. E. Pearson, K. N. Carter, and C. M. Greer, *J. Am. Chem. Soc.*, 75, 5905 (1953).

[16] For a review of this subject see J. E. Leffler, *Chem. Rev.*, 45, 385 (1949).

[17] R. Criegee, *Ann.*, 560, 127 (1948).

the ion-solvating ability of the solvent and that the p-nitroperbenzoate reacts much more rapidly than the unsubstituted compound show that this is a polar reaction quite analogous to the rearrangements due to electron-deficient carbon and nitrogen atoms. Criegee's work was subsequently extended by Bartlett and Kice[18] and by Goering and Olson.[19] Both groups of workers showed that the rearrangement does not involve the formation of any significant fraction of free ions (in methanol solution) but presumably proceeds through an ion-pair intermediate instead.

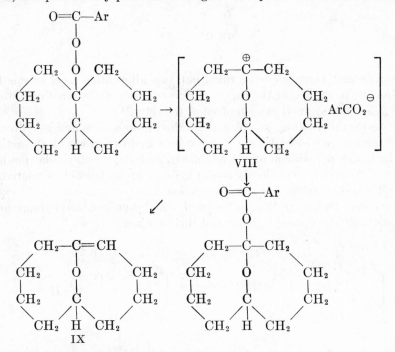

Bartlett and Kice isolated the by-product IX. It seems very unlikely that the reaction involves the intermediate formation of an ion containing an oxygen with only six electrons in its outer shell, since such an intermediate (of the type $RO^{\oplus}$) should be much less stable than even a primary carbonium ion. It therefore seems more probable that the rearrangement to the cation VIII occurs simultaneously with the removal of the $ArCO_2^-$ group. Denney has shown that the RCO_2^- never becomes entirely free by observing that when the starting perester is labeled in the carbonyl group with O^{18}, all of the O^{18} in the product was in the carbonyl group.[19a]

[18] P. D. Bartlett and J. L. Kice, *J. Am. Chem. Soc.*, **75**, 5591 (1953).
[19] Harlan L. Goering and A. C. Olson, *J. Am. Chem. Soc.*, **75**, 5853 (1953).
[19a] D. B. Denney, *J. Am. Chem. Soc.*, **77**, 1706 (1955).

15-2b. *Reaction of Ketones with Peracids*. The reaction of ketones with peracids to give esters probably has a mechanism of the type suggested by Criegee[17] and extended by Friess,[20] in which there is a rate-controlling addition of the peracid to the carbonyl group followed by a rapid rearrangement.

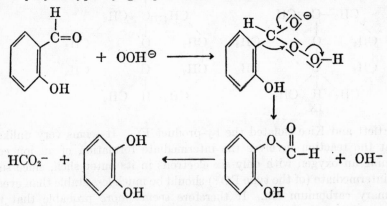

Doering and Dorfman have ruled out two alternative mechanisms by using O^{18} to show that the carbonyl oxygen atom of the reacting ketone becomes the carbonyl oxygen atom of the ester.[21]

The Dakin reaction, in which the formyl groups of *o*- and *p*-hydroxy- and -aminobenzaldehydes are replaced by a hydroxy group by the action of hydrogen peroxide in alkaline solution, probably has a similar mechanism. Although a covalently bound hydroxy group has only a relatively small tendency to become a hydroxide ion, this factor is counterbalanced by the very high migration aptitudes of *o*- and *p*-aminophenyl groups and *o*- and *p*-hydroxyphenyl groups and their conjugate bases.

Mislow and Brenner have found that in the reaction of optically active methyl α-phenylethyl ketone with peracetic acid,

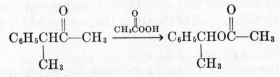

[20] S. L. Friess, *J. Am. Chem. Soc.*, **71**, 2571 (1949).
[21] W. von E. Doering and E. Dorfman, *J. Am. Chem. Soc.*, **75**, 5595 (1953).

the α-phenylethyl group migrates with complete retention of its stereochemical configuration.[22] This, of course, would be expected from analogy with the Hofmann, Curtius, Schmidt, and other reactions.

15-2c. *Rearrangements and Decompositions of Peroxides.* Leffler found that although p-methoxy-p'-nitrobenzoyl peroxide, like most acyl peroxides (Sec. 21-1a), decomposes by a free-radical mechanism in nonpolar solvents, the reaction rate is much faster in better ion-solvating media, suggesting the incursion of a polar decomposition.[23] The fact that the decomposition of the methoxynitroperoxide is vastly more sensitive to acid catalysis than that of the unsubstituted compound in benzene shows that a polar decomposition may be brought about even in a hydrocarbon solvent. In the relatively polar solvent thionyl chloride the reaction yields a rearrangement product—a mixed ester and anhydride of carbonic acid.

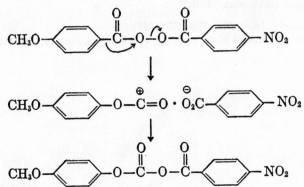

While an intermediate cation of bridged structure

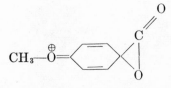

may possibly be formed, and analogous intermediates in other rearrangements described in this chapter, there appears to be no compelling evidence for such an intermediate, although it provides a good explanation for the effect of the p-methoxy group.

Bartlett and Leffler have presented evidence that both free-radical and polar reaction paths may be used in the decomposition of phenylacetyl peroxide.[24]

[22] K. Mislow and J. Brenner, *J. Am. Chem. Soc.*, **75**, 2318 (1953).

[23] J. E. Leffler, *J. Am. Chem. Soc.*, **72**, 67 (1950).

[24] P. D. Bartlett and J. E. Leffler, *J. Am. Chem. Soc.*, **72**, 3030 (1950).

One of the commercial methods for preparing phenol, the acid-catalyzed decomposition of cumene hydroperoxide,[25] probably has a mechanism

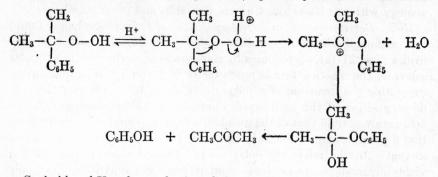

as Seubold and Vaughan, who found the reaction to be subject to specific acid catalysis, have suggested.[26]

[25] H. Hock and S. Lang, *Ber.*, **77B**, 257 (1944).
[26] F. H. Seubold, Jr. and W. E. Vaughan, *J. Am. Chem. Soc.*, **75**, 3790 (1953).

CHAPTER 16

ELECTROPHILIC AROMATIC SUBSTITUTION

Because most of the common aromatic substitution reactions—nitration, halogenation, sulfonation, and the Friedel-Crafts reaction—involve the attack of electrophilic species on the aromatic ring, we shall discuss *electrophilic* aromatic substitutions before the nucleophilic or free-radical varieties. Since orientation is a part of the larger problem of reactivity and since reactivity is best discussed in terms of the reaction mechanism, we shall begin our discussion by considering the mechanisms of these reactions.

16-1. Mechanism of Aromatic Nitration. *16-1a. Nitration in Sulfuric Acid Solution.* Nitration has probably received the most careful study, from a mechanistic viewpoint, of any aromatic substitution reaction. The exact nature of the mechanism varies considerably with the type of nitrating reagent used and with the character of the compound being nitrated. An example which is, in certain respects, relatively simple and which has received considerable attention is the nitration of nitrobenzene by nitric acid in sulfuric acid solution. Martinsen studied this reaction kinetically in 1905 and found agreement with the rate equation

$$v = k[C_6H_5NO_2][HNO_3]$$

where the bracketed expressions refer to the *formal* concentrations of the reagents without regard to the nature and relative concentrations of the various forms in which they may exist in sulfuric acid solution.[1] Second-order kinetics of this type were subsequently found by several other groups of workers in studies of the nitration of relatively unreactive aromatic compounds in sulfuric acid solution.[2] As Westheimer and Kharasch[3] and also Bennett, Brand, and Williams[4] pointed out, previous cryoscopic measurements by Hantzsch[5] show that the number of particles

---

[1] H. Martinsen, *Z. physik. Chem.*, **50**, 385 (1905); **59**, 605 (1907).

[2] A. Klemenc and R. Schöller, *Z. anorg. u. allgem. Chem.*, **141**, 231 (1924); K. Lauer and R. Oda, *J. prakt. Chem.*, **144**, 176 (1936); *Ber.*, **69**, 1061 (1936).

[3] F. H. Westheimer and M. S. Kharasch, *J. Am. Chem. Soc.*, **68**, 1871 (1946).

[4] G. M. Bennett, J. C. D. Brand, and G. Williams, *J. Chem. Soc.*, 869, 875 (1946).

[5] A. Hantzsch, *Z. physik. Chem.*, **61**, 257 (1907); **65**, 41 (1908).

formed from a nitric acid molecule in sulfuric acid solution approaches four, suggesting ionization by the equation

$$HNO_3 + 2H_2SO_4 \rightarrow NO_2^+ + H_3O^+ + 2HSO_4^- \qquad (16\text{-}1)$$

The latter investigators note other work, including spectral data and their own electrolytic demonstration that nitrogen is in a cationic form, in support of this suggestion that sulfuric acid produces nitronium ions (NO_2^+) from nitric acid. They also point out that these nitronium ions are very probably the actual nitrating species in the reactions studied. The activating and orienting influences of substituents upon new groups entering the ring, the catalytic effect of acids, and other factors reveal the electrophilic character of the reagent which attacks the aromatic ring. The nitronium ion should be the most electrophilic nitrating agent possible, and in pure sulfuric acid it appears to be the principal form in which nitric acid exists. It therefore seems likely that it is the effective nitrating agent. Westheimer and Kharasch have presented a more direct argument that this is the case. They note that the second-order rate constant for the nitration of nitrobenzene increases by about 3,000-fold as the concentration of sulfuric acid is increased from 80 to 90 per cent. This increase in rate may be attributed to an increase in the fraction of the nitric acid present as nitronium ions due to the shift of the equilibrium (16-1) to the right. However, it might also be suggested that the nitration is due to the nitric acidium ion, $H_2ONO_2^+$, whose relative concentration should also increase with the acidity of the medium.

$$HONO_2 + H_2SO_4 \rightleftharpoons H_2\overset{\oplus}{O}NO_2 + HSO_4\overset{\ominus}{} \qquad (16\text{-}2)$$

It was found possible to distinguish between these two alternatives by use of two indicators.[3] One, anthraquinone, ionizes in sulfuric acid simply by the addition of a proton, as suggested in Eq. (16-2) for nitric acid.

$$C_{14}H_8O_2 + H_2SO_4 \rightleftharpoons C_{14}H_8O_2\overset{\oplus}{H} + HSO_4\overset{\ominus}{} \qquad (16\text{-}3)$$

The other, tris-(p-nitrophenyl)methanol ionizes in a manner like that shown for nitric acid in Eq. (16-1).

$$(p\text{-}O_2NC_6H_4)_3COH + 2H_2SO_4 \rightleftharpoons (O_2NC_6H_4)_3\overset{\oplus}{C} + H_3\overset{\oplus}{O} + 2HSO_4\overset{\ominus}{}$$

The effect of sulfuric acid concentration on the positions of the equilibria shown was determined for the two indicators. It was then seen that the rate constant for nitration varied with the sulfuric acid concentration in very nearly the same way as did the fraction of tris-(p-nitrophenyl)-methanol present as the carbonium ion and not at all like the fraction of anthraquinone present as its conjugate acid (this fraction changed by less than a factor of 10 between 80 and 90 per cent sulfuric acid).

Hughes, Ingold, and coworkers have made the evidence for the nitronium ion overwhelming: by more accurate cryoscopic measurements in sulfuric acid solution;[6] by isolation of nitronium perchlorate, nitronium disulfate, and other nitronium salts;[7] and by spectral studies of nitronium salts and of solutions of nitric acid and related compounds.[8]

16-1b. *Nitration in Nitromethane and Acetic Acid Solutions.* A series of investigations which have added greatly to our knowledge of nitration and of aromatic substitution reactions in general was begun by Benford and Ingold with a study of nitration in nitromethane solution.[9] Some such solvent capable of dissolving both nitric acid and relatively nonpolar organic compounds is necessary to study the nitration of aromatic hydrocarbons whose rate of nitration in sulfuric acid solution is usually controlled by the rate of solution therein. Since the water formed in the reaction enters into certain equilibria involving nitric acid, the effect of this complication was minimized by using the nitric acid in large excess (about 5 M) over the aromatic compound (about 0.1 M). Under these conditions it was found that the nitration of benzene was a *zero-order reaction*,

$$v = k$$

the rate simply remaining constant until all of the benzene had reacted. The value of the rate constant did depend upon the concentration of nitric acid used, but this did not change significantly during the course of a given run. The nitrations of toluene and ethylbenzene were also found to be zero-order and to have the same rate constant as benzene. This independence of the concentration and even the nature of the aromatic compound suggests that the reactions all have the same rate-controlling step(s) and that this step(s) does not involve the aromatic compound. Hughes, Ingold, and Reed have found the same zero-order kinetics for the nitration of toluene, p-xylene, mesitylene, ethylbenzene, and (under some conditions) benzene in acetic acid solution, and they have shown that the rate of reaction in all cases is controlled by the rate of formation of nitronium ions as shown in the scheme below.[10]

---

[6] R. J. Gillespie, J. Graham, E. D. Hughes, C. K. Ingold, and E. R. A. Peeling, *J. Chem. Soc.*, 2504 (1950).

[7] D. R. Goddard, E. D. Hughes, and C. K. Ingold, *J. Chem. Soc.*, 2559 (1950).

[8] C. K. Ingold, D. J. Millen, and H. G. Poole, *J. Chem. Soc.*, 2576 (1950); D. J. Millen, *J. Chem. Soc.*, 2589, 2600, 2606 (1950).

[9] G. A. Benford and C. K. Ingold, *J. Chem. Soc.*, 929 (1938).

[10] E. D. Hughes, C. K. Ingold, and R. I. Reed, *J. Chem. Soc.*, 2400 (1950).

$$HNO_3 + HNO_3 \rightleftharpoons H_2\overset{\oplus}{O}NO_2 + \overset{\ominus}{NO_3}$$

$$H_2\overset{\oplus}{O}NO_2 \rightleftharpoons H_2O + \overset{\oplus}{NO_2} \qquad (16\text{-}4)$$

$$\overset{\oplus}{NO_2} + ArH \rightarrow ArNO_2 + \overset{\oplus}{H}$$

Nitronium-ion formation will be rate-controlling only if the nitronium ions react with the aromatic compound more rapidly than they recombine with water. This fact permits a test of the proposed mechanism. With the less reactive halobenzenes the reaction was between zero- and first-order in aromatic compound and with the still less reactive compounds, o-, m-, and p-dichlorobenzene, 1,2,4-trichlorobenzene, and ethyl benzoate, the nitration in acetic acid solution was definitely first-order. This would be predicted from the steady-state approximation if the nitronium ions recombine with water much more rapidly than they attack the aromatic reactant. The first-order rate constants obtained *were*, of course, dependent on the nature of the aromatic compound.

The mechanism (16-4) was subjected to a large number of other experimental tests, all of which supported it. Sulfuric acid was found to increase and potassium nitrate to decrease the rates of both the zero- and first-order nitrations without appreciably changing their kinetic form. The effects of these two reagents are on the rapid and reversible first step. These effects are quantitatively as well as qualitatively in agreement with theory. Small amounts of water have relatively little effect on the rate, but larger amounts considerably slow the reaction and may change a zero-order reaction over to a first-order one (by making the second step reversible).

Although the nitronium ion itself has been found to be the active nitrating reagent in the examples described, we cannot exclude the possibility that nitronium-ion donors such as $H_2\overset{\oplus}{O}NO_2$, $AcONO_2$, O_2NONO_2, $HONO_2$, etc., may be responsible for nitration in some other cases.

16-1c. *Mechanism of the Attack of the Nitrating Agent on the Aromatic Ring*. Martinsen[1] and later workers[2,3] found that although nitration rates in sulfuric acid increase with the sulfuric acid concentration up to 90 per cent sulfuric acid, a rate maximum is reached between 90 and 95 per cent sulfuric acid, and in more concentrated sulfuric acid the reaction proceeds more slowly. The nitration of 2,4-dinitrotoluene in 100 per cent sulfuric acid proceeds at less than one-third the maximum rate (in 92 per cent sulfuric acid).[11] The increase in nitration rate between 80 and 90 per cent sulfuric acid has been attributed to the increase in the fraction of nitric acid present as nitronium ion. It seems

[11] G. M. Bennett, J. C. D. Brand, D. M. James, T. G. Saunders, and G. Williams, *J. Chem. Soc.*, 474 (1947).

to be agreed that this increase stops in 90 to 92 per cent sulfuric acid because in acid of this strength almost all of the nitric acid is present as nitronium ions. There is disagreement, however, as to why the rate decreases in stronger acid.

Part of the decrease in nitration rate of aromatic nitro compounds is due to the partial conversion to their conjugate acids, which would certainly be expected to be less reactive than the unprotonated molecules in electrophilic substitution reactions. Gillespie's determinations of the ionization constants of certain aromatic nitro compounds as bases in sulfuric acid show that this is an important factor, but not the largest one, in bringing about the decrease in nitration rate between 90 to 92 and 100 per cent sulfuric acid.[12] With stronger bases such as benzoic acid this factor may become the major one. To aid in the examination of other explanations of these solvent effects on the rate, let us consider possible mechanisms for the replacement of a hydrogen atom by a nitro group in the attack of a nitronium ion. We may assume that the mechanism is concerted, with the introduction of the nitro group and the removal of the hydrogen as a proton (the task of a base) occurring in a single step.

$$O_2\overset{\oplus}{N} + Ar—H + B \to ArNO_2 + B\overset{\oplus}{H} \qquad (16\text{-}5)$$

Alternately, we may assume that there is a definite intermediate in the reaction, as Pfeiffer and Wizinger have suggested.[13] Such an intermediate may be formed rapidly and reversibly (16-6), or it may be formed in the rate-controlling step and then rapidly deprotonated (16-7).

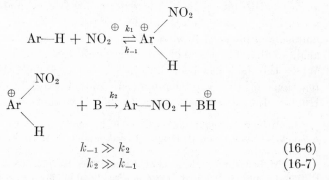

$$k_{-1} \gg k_2 \qquad\qquad (16\text{-}6)$$
or
$$k_2 \gg k_{-1} \qquad\qquad (16\text{-}7)$$

It has been suggested that the decrease in nitration rate between 92 and 100 per cent sulfuric acid is due to a decrease in the concentration of the strongest base present, the bisulfate ion.[11] This explanation requires that the proton removal be a part of the rate-controlling step of the

[12] R. J. Gillespie, *J. Chem. Soc.*, 2542 (1950).
[13] P. Pfeiffer and R. Wizinger, *Ann.*, **461**, 132 (1928).

reaction, as in mechanisms (16-5) and (16-6). Melander has pointed out that reactions with rate-controlling proton transfers are almost always slowed by the replacement of the hydrogen atom involved by deuterium or tritium and has taken advantage of this fact to demonstrate the probability of mechanism (16-7).[14] In the nitration of tritiated samples of benzene, nitrobenzene, toluene, bromobenzene, and naphthalene he found that tritium atoms were replaced to just the same extent and therefore at just the same rate as protium atoms (hydrogen atoms of mass one). Mechanisms (16-5) and (16-6), involving proton transfers in the rate-controlling step, are therefore unlikely. Other workers have reached this conclusion by similar studies using deuterium.[15]

Solvent effects on nitration rates in the region of 100 per cent sulfuric acid have been discussed in terms of the strength of hydrogen bonding to the aromatic compound, the ion-solvating power of the medium, and other factors.[10,15,16]

16-1d. *Nitrations Involving Prior Nitrosation.* A number of aromatic nitration reactions have been found to be slowed by nitrous acid.[10] This appears to be partly due to the action of nitrous acid as a base

$$HNO_2 + 2H_2SO_4 \rightleftharpoons NO^+ + H_3O^+ + 2HSO_4^-$$

and partly to its ability to transform nitric acid to dinitrogen tetroxide.

$$HNO_2 + HNO_3 \rightarrow N_2O_4 + H_2O$$

In certain nitration reactions oxidation of the aromatic compound is a significant side reaction. Since this oxidation transforms some of the nitric acid to nitrous acid and oxides of nitrogen, many such nitrations are greatly slowed by this side reaction. The nitration of aromatic amines and phenols, however, has been found to be catalyzed by nitrous acid, so that nitrous acid–producing side reactions cause autocatalysis. While this fact has been known for a long time,[1] the mechanisms of reactions of this type have been studied carefully only recently by Hughes, Ingold, and coworkers.[17] These workers show that the nitrous

[14] L. Melander, *Nature,* **163,** 599 (1949); *Acta Chem. Scand.,* **3,** 95 (1949); *Arkiv Kemi,* **2,** 211 (1951); cf. U. Berglund-Larsson and L. Melander, *Arkiv Kemi,* **6,** 219 (1953).

[15] W. M. Lauer and W. E. Noland, *J. Am. Chem. Soc.,* **75,** 3689 (1953); T. G. Bonner, F. Bowyer, and G. Williams, *J. Chem. Soc.,* 2650 (1953).

[16] T. G. Bonner, F. Bowyer, and G. Williams, *J. Chem. Soc.,* 3274 (1952); R. J. Gillespie and D. G. Norton, *J. Chem. Soc.,* 971 (1953); G. S. Hammond and F. J. Modic, *J. Am. Chem. Soc.,* **75,** 1385 (1953).

[17] C. A. Bunton, E. D. Hughes, C. K. Ingold, D. I. H. Jacobs, M. H. Jones, G. J. Minkoff, and R. I. Reed, *J. Chem. Soc.,* 2628 (1950); J. Glazer, E. D. Hughes, C. K. Ingold, A. T. James, G. T. Jones, and E. Roberts, *J. Chem. Soc.,* 2657 (1950). See also R. M. Schramm and F. H. Westheimer, *J. Am. Chem. Soc.,* **70,** 1782 (1948).

acid catalysis is due to the occurrence of a nitrosation reaction to yield a nitroso compound which is subsequently oxidized to the nitro compound usually observed as the product.   The nitrosation is due both to the action of the nitrosonium ion, NO^+, and to dinitrogen tetroxide, which, although less active, is present in much greater concentrations.[17,18] Even the more reactive nitrosonium ion is not nearly so strong an electrophilic reagent as the nitronium ion.   For this reason it is capable of attacking only the most reactive aromatic compounds, such as amines, phenols, phenol ethers, etc., and thus it is only these compounds whose nitrations are catalyzed by nitrous acid.   For the same reason, the nitrosonium ion is capable of existence in much more weakly acidic solutions than is the nitronium ion.   In relatively dilute acid solutions, where nitronium ions have very little tendency to be formed, practically all the nitration involves nitrosation and oxidation.   On the other hand, in strongly acidic solutions the nitration of even amines and phenols may be due to nitronium ions, and under these conditions nitrous acid, which interferes with nitronium-ion formation, is a negative rather than a positive catalyst.[17]

16-2. Mechanisms of Other Electrophilic Aromatic Substitution Reactions.   16-2a. *Deuterium Exchange.*   Since Lowry-Brønsted acids are electrophilic reagents, they would be expected to be capable of performing an aromatic substitution reaction by donating a proton to the ring to replace one already there.   This symmetrical substitution reaction will be observable only by the use of deuterium or tritium tracers.

Ingold, Raisin, and Wilson showed that benzene could be deuterated by shaking with deuterium sulfate.[19]   They further observed that the rate of deuterium exchange decreases as the strength of the catalyzing acid decreases but may be greatly increased by the presence of electron-donating groups on the aromatic ring.   Thus, while aqueous hydrochloric acid is essentially incapable of catalyzing the deuterium exchange of benzene at room temperature, it is quite effective with anisole and dimethylaniline, even though the latter compound must be changed largely to its unreactive salt under the reaction conditions.   The nuclear deuterium exchange of phenol, unlike that of most aromatic compounds, is base-catalyzed.   This is due to the transformation of the —OH group to the much more strongly electron-donating —O⁻ group.   The ortho and para hydrogen atoms of the phenoxide anion are thus reactive enough to be replaced by the action of the weak acid, water.   We know that it is the positions activated toward ordinary electrophilic aromatic substitution which are active in these acid-catalyzed deuterium exchanges,

[18] E. L. Blackall, E. D. Hughes, and C. K. Ingold, *J. Chem. Soc.*, 28 (1952).
[19] C. K. Ingold, C. G. Raisin, and C. L. Wilson, *Nature*, **134,** 734 (1934); *J. Chem Soc.*, 1637 (1936).

not only because phenol, aniline, anisole, dimethylaniline, etc., exchange three carbon-bound hydrogen atoms fairly readily and any others much more difficultly (if at all), but also because deuterium has been shown to enter only the ortho and para positions of aniline and phenol.[20]   This was established by Best and Wilson, who showed that deuterated samples of these compounds lost all of their deuterium when transformed to their 2,4,6-tribromo derivatives.

16-2b. *Sulfonation.*   A study of the mechanism of aromatic sulfonation reactions reveals certain complications not found in some of the other electrophilic aromatic substitution reactions. For example, Melander has shown that in the sulfonation of tritium-labeled benzene and bromobenzene by oleum the tritium atoms are replaced considerably more slowly than protium.[14]   The observation reveals the improbability of a mechanism like (16-7), in which a rate-controlling attack of the substituting agent on the aromatic ring is followed by a relatively rapid loss of a hydrogen cation to restore aromaticity to the ring.   Since there appears to be no particular evidence in favor of a concerted mechanism like (16-5), we shall assume by analogy with other aromatic substitutions that the reaction proceeds by a two-step mechanism but that in the case of sulfonation the intermediate reverts to reactant at a rate at least comparable with its transformation to product.

Hinshelwood and coworkers have studied the sulfonation of nitrobenzene, p-nitrotoluene, chlorobenzene, m-dichlorobenzene, bromobenzene, α-nitronaphthalene, p-nitroanisole, and benzene by sulfur trioxide in nitrobenzene solution.[21]   In all cases the reaction was found to be first-order in aromatic compound and second-order in sulfur trioxide. This suggests that the reaction may be due to a small amount of sulfur trioxide dimer, S_2O_6, in mobile equilibrium with the monomer.   The two-stage nature of the reaction also opens up the possibility that one sulfur trioxide molecule is involved in the first step and one in the second.   It is not likely, however, that sulfur trioxide acts as a base to remove the proton in the second step, since the solvent, nitrobenzene, is a much stronger base and is present in a much larger concentration.   Brand has described evidence that $HOSO_2^+$, or some sulfuric acid solvate thereof, such as $H_3S_2O_7^+$, is the active agent in sulfonations in oleum.[22] This intermediate, the conjugate acid of sulfur trioxide, is rather analogous to S_2O_6, in which sulfur trioxide has coordinated with the Lewis

[20] A. P. Best and C. L. Wilson, *J. Chem. Soc.*, 28 (1938).

[21] D. R. Vicary and C. N. Hinshelwood, *J. Chem. Soc.*, 1372 (1939); K. D. Wadsworth and C. N. Hinshelwood, *J. Chem. Soc.*, 469 (1944); E. Dresel and C. N. Hinshelwood, *J. Chem. Soc.*, 649 (1944).

[22] J. C. D. Brand, *J. Chem. Soc.*, 997, 1004 (1950); J. C. D. Brand and W. C. Horning, *J. Chem. Soc.*, 3922 (1952).

acid, SO_3. In sulfuric acid of less than 100 per cent strength the reaction rate has been said to be proportional to the first power of the sulfur trioxide concentration.[23]

16-2c. *Friedel-Crafts Alkylation.* Carbonium ions appear to be relatively effective at attacking aromatic nuclei to introduce alkyl groups. This fact is, no doubt, the basis of many Friedel-Crafts alkylation reactions involving alkyl halides, olefins, alcohols, esters, and other reactants capable of forming carbonium ions. A carbonium-ion mechanism gives an explanation for the many rearrangements which have been found to accompany the reaction. While carbonium ions may be reaction intermediates, there is evidence that they need not always be so. The reaction of *d*-sec-butyl alcohol with benzene in the presence of boron fluoride, hydrogen fluoride, phosphoric acid, or sulfuric acid gives *sec*-butylbenzene which is largely (> 99 per cent) racemized but which definitely has *some* optical activity.[24] If the reaction is regarded as a nucleophilic substitution on carbon, it may be considered an S_N1 reaction in which racemization is not quite complete because of the operation of a shielding effect (Sec. 5-2c). The reaction may alternately be considered S_N1 with a little S_N2 character. One way of increasing the S_N2 character would be to increase the nucleophilicity of the nucleophilic reagent (the aromatic reactant) as by adding electron-donating groups. This has been done by Hart and Eleuterio, who obtained ring-alkylated products of relatively high optical purity in the reaction of active α-phenylethyl chloride with phenols in alkaline solutions.[25] These workers demonstrated the S_N2 character of their reaction by showing it to be first-order in each reactant and to lead to inversion in configuration at the asymmetric carbon atom and also by showing that the aryl ether is not an intermediate in the formation of the ring-alkylated product. Of course, this example was hardly a typical Friedel-Crafts reaction.

Hart, Spliethoff, and Eleuterio have described evidence for aromatic substitution by the S_Ni mechanism.[26] They found that the para-alkylated product of the reaction of phenol and of 2,6-xylenol with optically active α-phenylethyl chloride had undergone inversion of configuration at the asymmetric carbon atom, presumably because of an S_N2-type reaction. The products of the ortho alkylations of phenol, *p*-cresol, and *p*-chlorophenol all had the same configuration as the starting α-phenylethyl chloride. This retention of configuration that occurs only for substitution ortho to the hydroxy group suggests an S_Ni-type

[23] W. A. Cowdrey and D. S. Davies, *J. Chem. Soc.*, 1871 (1949).

[24] C. C. Price and M. Lund, *J. Am. Chem. Soc.*, **62**, 3105 (1940); R. L. Burwell, Jr. and S. Archer, *J. Am. Chem. Soc.*, **64**, 1032 (1942).

[25] H. Hart and H. S. Eleuterio, *J. Am. Chem. Soc.*, **76**, 516, 519 (1954).

[26] H. Hart, W. L. Spliethoff, and H. S. Eleuterio, *J. Am. Chem. Soc.*, **76**, 4547 (1954).

mechanism in which the hydroxy group solvates the chloride ion as it is displaced.

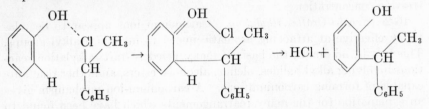

The kinetics of a more representative Friedel-Crafts alkylation have been investigated by Ulich and Heyne, who studied the condensation of benzene with n-propyl chloride, using a gallium trichloride catalyst in carbon disulfide solution.[27] They report that the reaction rate is proportional to the concentration of benzene and to that of the gallium chloride–propyl chloride complex,

$$v = k[C_6H_6][C_3H_7Cl \cdot GaCl_3]$$

or, alternately third-order

$$v = k'[C_6H_6][C_3H_7Cl][GaCl_3]$$

since $\quad [C_3H_7Cl][GaCl_3] = K[C_3H_7Cl \cdot GaCl_3]$

Brown and Grayson report analogous third-order kinetics for the condensations of several benzyl chlorides with aromatic compounds in the presence of aluminum chloride in nitrobenzene solution.[28] There are conductimetric[29] and spectroscopic[30] data, as well as dipole-moment determinations[31] and radioactive-halogen-exchange[32] and vapor pressure–composition phase studies,[33] which show that several Friedel-Crafts catalysts may coordinate with the halogen atom of alkyl halides and in some cases thus promote their ionization. It therefore seems most reasonable to explain the observed third-order kinetics by assuming a reversible and relatively rapid reaction between the alkyl halide and the Friedel-Crafts catalyst to give a small concentration of an intermediate which then reacts with the aromatic compound in the rate-controlling step. Depending upon the exact nature of all of the constituents of the reaction mixture, this intermediate may be an alkyl halide–catalyst

[27] H. Ulich and G. Heyne, Z. Elektrochem., 41, 509 (1935).

[28] H. C. Brown and M. Grayson, J. Am. Chem. Soc., 75, 6285 (1953).

[29] P. Walden, Ber., 35, 2018 (1902).

[30] V. V. Korshak and N. N. Lebedev, Zhur. Obshchei Khim., 18, 1766 (1948); F. Fairbrother and B. Wright, J. Chem. Soc., 1058 (1949).

[31] F. Fairbrother, Trans. Faraday Soc., 37, 763 (1941); J. Chem. Soc., 503 (1945).

[32] F. Fairbrother, J. Chem. Soc., 503 (1937).

[33] H. C. Brown, L. P. Eddy, and R. Wong, J. Am. Chem. Soc., 75, 6275 (1953); H. C. Brown and W. J. Wallace, J. Am. Chem. Soc., 75, 6279 (1953).

complex, which undergoes an S_N2-type attack by the aromatic compound, or it may be a carbonium ion (perhaps as part of an ion pair), which subsequently replaces a proton on the aromatic ring. Furthermore there will be a gradual and continuous transition between the S_N1 and S_N2 extremes, as described in Secs. 5-2e and 6-3b.

Brown and Grayson suggest that their reactions of benzyl chlorides are of the S_N2 type and state that their data appear to eliminate the possibilities of a carbonium-ion mechanism. Thus the mechanism

$$ArCH_2Cl + AlCl_3 \underset{k_{-1}}{\overset{k_1}{\rightleftharpoons}} \overset{\oplus}{ArCH_2} + \overset{\ominus}{AlCl_4}$$

$$\overset{\oplus}{ArCH_2} + Ar'H \overset{k_2}{\rightarrow} ArCH_2Ar'\overset{\oplus}{H}$$

$$ArCH_2Ar'\overset{\oplus}{H} + \overset{\ominus}{AlCl_4} \overset{k_3}{\rightarrow} ArCH_2Ar' + HCl + AlCl_3$$

$$k_{-1} \gg k_2; \; k_3 \gg k_2$$

involving a rate-controlling attack of the carbonium ion (or ion pair) on the aromatic ring is said to be unacceptable because it predicts that p-nitrobenzyl chloride should react more rapidly than benzyl chloride, since it will form a more reactive carbonium ion. It is certainly true that k_2 should be larger for the p-nitro compound, but it is the fraction k_1k_2/k_{-1} upon which the rate depends, and the rest of this fraction, k_1/k_{-1} (the equilibrium constant for the formation of the carbonium ion), must be much larger for the unsubstituted compound. In fact, since the side-chain carbon atom of the benzyl chloride must be considerably more positive in the transition state of the rate-controlling step of the reaction, a p-nitro group would be expected to decrease the reactivity, exactly as found.

It is also stated that reaction by the ionization mechanism should be powerfully affected by changes in the ionizing properties of the medium, while the observed reaction rate is merely cut in two by replacement of 60 per cent of the nitrobenzene solvent by methylcyclohexane.[28] However, this change in solvent probably affects the reaction rate in more ways than one. Since nitrobenzene forms a complex with aluminum chloride, a shift to a hydrocarbon solvent should increase the activity of the catalyst. In fact, as Brown and Grayson note, the reaction appears to go faster in benzene than in nitrobenzene solution.

As Brown and Grayson further note, the formation of n- (rather than iso-) propylbenzene and neopentyl- (rather than t-amyl-) benzene in the reactions of the corresponding alcohols with benzene in the presence of aluminum chloride suggests that these reactions proceed by the S_N2 mechanism. It appears, however, that Friedel-Crafts alkylations rarely, if ever, acquire enough S_N2 character to cause the *making* of the new carbon-carbon bond to have more effect on the reactivity than the *breaking* of the carbon-halogen (or other) bond. Thus methyl halides undergo the reaction less readily than their ordinary primary alkyl counterparts[34] even though both may react by an S_N2 type of mechanism. Despite this fact, the continuous addition of electron-donating groups does not result in an interminable increase in reactivity, because sooner or later the point will be reached where a carbonium ion may be formed with the greatest of ease but, having been formed, will be too stable to react further. Thus, benzene may be alkylated with methyl chloride, or even more easily with benzyl chloride or benzhydryl chloride, but triphenylmethyl chloride fails to react. This is not due to the impossibility of the existence of the product, since tetraphenylmethane is a quite stable compound, boiling at 431° without decomposition.[35] Nor is it due to steric hindrance, since triphenylmethyl chloride and the more reactive aromatic compound phenol yield *p*-hydroxytetraphenylmethane with no Friedel-Crafts catalysts (except the anion-solvating reagents phenol and hydrogen chloride).[36]

16-2*d. Friedel-Crafts Acylation.* For the Friedel-Crafts acylation reaction we may postulate either a carbonyl addition mechanism

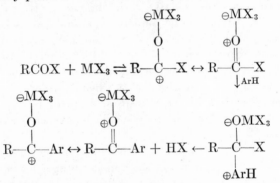

or an acyl carbonium-ion mechanism

$$RCOX + MX_3 \rightleftharpoons \overset{\ominus}{MX_4} + \overset{\oplus}{RCO}$$
$$\downarrow \text{ArH}$$

$$\underset{R-\overset{\|}{\underset{}{C}}-Ar \; + \; HX \; \xleftarrow{\;MX_4\ominus\;}}{\overset{O\cdot MX_3}{}} \overset{\oplus}{RCOArH}$$

Just as in Friedel-Crafts alkylation the prevalence of rearrangements

[34] C. C. Price, "Organic Reactions," vol. III, p. 4, John Wiley & Sons, Inc., New York, 1946.

[35] F. Ullmann and A. Münzhuber, *Ber.*, **36**, 404 (1903).

[36] H. Hart and F. A. Cassis, *J. Am. Chem. Soc.*, **76**, 1634 (1954).

in the reaction of primary halides and other facts suggest that the reaction tends to have more S_N1 character than most nucleophilic substitutions, so in the present case does the acyl carbonium-ion mechanism appear to be more common than in most acid halide and ester hydrolysis reactions.   This is probably due to the fact that most aromatic reactants are not very highly nucleophilic.

Burton and Praill have found considerable evidence that at least some Friedel-Crafts acetylation reactions are due to the "acetylium" ion, $CH_3CO^\oplus$.[37] These workers show that solutions of sulfuric or perchloric acid in acetic anhydride are capable of acetylating anisole, although similar solutions in acetic acid are inactive.   This fact could be explained by assuming the acetylating agent is either the acetylium ion or the conjugate acid of acetic anhydride, either of which should be more reactive than the conjugate acid of acetic acid.   Burton and Praill also found that a powerful acetylating agent could also be prepared by the reaction of acetyl chloride with silver perchlorate in nitromethane or acetic anhydride solution and postulated that this agent is the salt, acetylium perchlorate.[37]   It is reasonable that this compound should be ionized in such solvents, since Seel has shown conductimetrically that CH_3COBF_4, $CH_3COSbCl_6$, and $C_6H_5COSbCl_6$ are ionized in sulfur dioxide solution.[38,39]

16-2e. *Halogenation.* From our discussions of the mechanisms of other aromatic substitution reactions we should expect X^+ (where X is halogen) to be the most active halogenating agent possible and compounds of the type X—Y, where Y may be removed with the bonding electron pair, to be also capable of attacking aromatic rings.   The activity of reagents of the type X—Y should increase with the electron-withdrawing power of Y.   In a number of studies these expectations have been borne out (in so far as they have been investigated).

Soper and Smith studied the chlorination of phenol by hypochlorous acid and found that the rate data agreed with either of the equations[40]

$$v = k[OCl^-][C_6H_5OH]$$

or $\qquad v = k'[HOCl][C_6H_5O^-]$ \hfill (16-8)

which are kinetically indistinguishable, since

$$[OCl^-][C_6H_5OH] = \frac{K_a^{HOCl}}{K_a^{C_6H_5OH}} [HOCl][C_6H_5O^-] \qquad (16\text{-}9)$$

[37] H. Burton and P. F. G. Praill, *J. Chem. Soc.*, 1203, 2034 (1950); 522, 529, 726 (1951); 755 (1952); 827, 837 (1953).

[38] F. Seel, *Z. anorg. u. allgem. Chem.*, **250**, 331 (1943); **252**, 24 (1943).

[39] F. Seel and H. Bauer, *Z. Naturforsch.*, **2b**, 397 (1947).

[40] F. G. Soper and G. F. Smith, *J. Chem. Soc.*, 1582 (1926).

We may calculate from the ionization constants of hypochlorous acid and phenol that the concentration term, $[OCl^-][C_6H_5OH]$, for hypochlorite-ion chlorination will be about 100 times as large as $[HOCl][C_6H_5O^-]$, the term for hypochlorous acid chlorination. However, since hypochlorous acid should be a tremendously more powerful chlorinating agent than hypochlorite ion and since the phenoxide ion should be vastly more reactive than phenol, it is very likely that k' is, at least, millions of times larger than k. Hence the chlorination must be almost entirely due to hypochlorous acid. These workers also found that the reaction is specifically catalyzed by hydrochloric acid, which transforms hypochlorous acid to chlorine. This shows that chlorine is the more reactive species.

Analogously, Francis has shown that hypobromous acid is a less effective aromatic brominating agent than is bromine.[41]

Shilov and Kanyaev found that the hypobromous acid bromination of sodium m-anisolesulfonate is catalyzed by acids.[42]

$$v = k[ArH][HOBr][H^+]$$

The brominating agent here could be either H_2OBr^+ or Br^+. Wilson and Soper and Derbyshire and Waters have obtained similar results with other aromatic reactants.[43]

Berliner has investigated the iodination of aniline in aqueous solution in the presence of iodide ions and found the reaction rate to be proportional to the inverse square of the iodide-ion concentration.[44] Since most of the material titratable as iodine is in the form of the triiodide ion under the conditions used, iodination by iodine would have a rate varying with the reciprocal of the iodide concentration

$$I_3^- \rightleftharpoons I_2 + I^-$$

while reaction due to hypoiodous acid or its conjugate acid or to the iodine cation would have rates proportional to the inverse square of the iodide-ion concentration.

$$I_3^- + H_2O \rightleftharpoons HOI + H^+ + 2I^-$$
$$I_3^- + H_2O \rightleftharpoons H_2OI^+ + 2I^-$$
$$I_3^- \rightleftharpoons I^+ + 2I^-$$

The actual iodinating agent under the conditions used is therefore one

[41] A. W. Francis, *J. Am. Chem. Soc.*, **47**, 2340 (1925).

[42] E. Shilov and N. Kanyaev, *Compt. rend. acad. sci. U.R.S.S.*, **24**, 890 (1939); *Chem. Abstr.*, **34**, 4062 (1940).

[43] W. J. Wilson and F. G. Soper, *J. Chem. Soc.*, 3376 (1949); D. H. Derbyshire and W. A. Waters, *J. Chem. Soc.*, 564, 574 (1950).

[44] E. Berliner, *J. Am. Chem. Soc.*, **72**, 4003 (1950).

of these latter three. By studying the effect of pH on the reaction rate it is demonstrated that the reaction could either be a general base-catalyzed reaction of the anilinium ion with hypoiodous acid,

$$v = k[\text{HOI}][\text{C}_6\text{H}_5\text{NH}_3{}^+] \left(\sum_i [\text{B}_i] \right) \qquad (16\text{-}10)$$

a general acid-catalyzed reaction of hypoiodous acid with aniline,

$$v = k[\text{HOI}][\text{C}_6\text{H}_5\text{NH}_2] \left(\sum_i [\text{HB}_i] \right) \qquad (16\text{-}11)$$

or a general base-catalyzed reaction of either the iodine cation or its hydrate, the conjugate acid of hypoiodous acid, with aniline.

$$v = k[\text{I}^+][\text{C}_6\text{H}_5\text{NH}_2] \left(\sum_i [\text{B}_i] \right) \qquad (16\text{-}12)$$

As Berliner points out, the mechanism represented by Eq. (16-10) is quite unreasonable. The anilinium ion should be much too deactivated to react with such a weakly electrophilic reagent, and even if it did react, meta substitution should occur (actually more than 64 per cent of *p*-iodoaniline is formed). Equation (16-11) is applicable to a rate-controlling nucleophilic attack of the aromatic ring on iodine and electrophilic removal of the hydroxy group by HB, viz.,

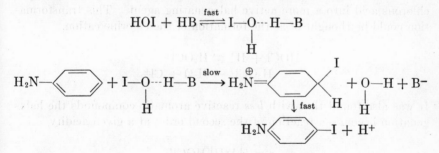

A mechanism in agreement with Eq. (16-12) may have the form

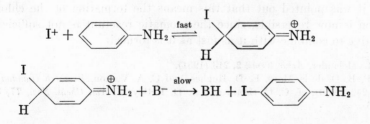

This mechanism (and the analogous one involving H_2OI^+) involves the removal of hydrogen as part of the rate-controlling step and therefore leads to the prediction that deuterium or tritium would be replaced more slowly than protium atoms in this position. Although there appears to be no kinetic hydrogen-isotope effect in aromatic bromination,[45] no test seems to have been made on iodination for which such an effect would appear to be much more likely (because of the greater stability of the iodine cation). Further work is needed to distinguish between these alternative mechanisms.

It has sometimes been considered hopeless to attempt to distinguish between those halogenations in aqueous solution due to X^+ and those due to XOH_2^+, and, indeed, it has been suggested that these two formulas could not even represent two different species. Nevertheless, a preliminary report has appeared of an investigation in which good evidence for such a distinction has been obtained. The investigators, de la Mare, Hughes, and Vernon, have studied the chlorinating action of hypochlorous acid in acidic solution.[46] For aromatic compounds of the proper degree of reactivity (e.g., anisole and phenol) and certain olefins (allyl ethyl ether and allyl fluoride) the reaction at a given acidity is first-order, being dependent only upon the concentration of hypochlorous acid. This result, reminiscent of the zero-order nitrations in nitromethane and acetic acid solution described in Sec. 16-1b, shows that the aromatic compound is not involved in the rate-controlling step of the reaction, which must therefore be some transformation of hypochlorous acid into a more active halogenating agent. This transformation could be thought of as the formation of the chlorine cation.

$$HOCl + H^+ \rightleftharpoons H_2OCl^+$$
$$H_2OCl^+ \rightarrow H_2O + Cl^+$$

It was also found that with *less* reactive aromatic compounds the halogenation becomes a reaction of the second order at a given acidity

$$v = k[\text{ArH}][\text{HOCl}]$$

and it was pointed out that this means the formation of the chlorine cation is now reversible, since the aromatic reactant is not sufficiently reactive to combine with it as fast as it is formed.

[45] L. Melander, *Arkiv Kemi*, **2**, 213 (1951).

[46] P. B. D. de la Mare, E. D. Hughes, and C. A. Vernon, *Research (London)*, **3**, 192, 242 (1950); cf. C. G. Swain and A. D. Ketley, *J. Am. Chem. Soc.*, **77**, 3410 (1955).

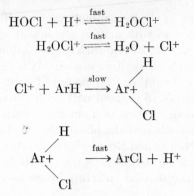

Similarly, with *more* reactive compounds (certain olefins) the first-order reaction is also changed to a second-order process. Here the compound is reactive enough to be halogenated by the conjugate acid of hypochlorous acid and therefore need not wait for the formation of chlorine cation.

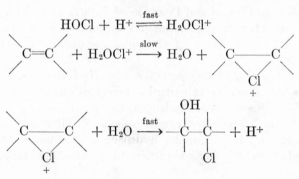

De la Mare, Hughes, and Vernon state that the rate-controlling step in the first-order halogenations must be the formation of the chlorine cation rather than merely the formation of the conjugate acid of hypochlorous acid, because the latter reaction, a proton donation from oxygen to oxygen, should occur too rapidly to measure. However, as described in Sec. 8-2b, it is not certain that we can make such an unequivocal statement about a proton transfer to a very weak base. Nevertheless, if the second-order reactions of both the more reactive and less reactive compounds are acid-catalyzed (this is implied, but not directly stated), then it would be difficult to explain all three types of reactions on the assumption that the first-order one involved a rate-controlling formation of H_2OCl^+.

16-2f. *Diazo Coupling.* Wistar and Bartlett have obtained good evidence that it is the aromatic diazonium ion which is the effective electrophilic reagent in diazo-coupling reactions.[47] Their kinetic data on the coupling reaction with amines eliminated all possibilities except the reaction of the diazohydroxide with the anilinium ion and the reaction of the diazonium ion with the free amine. It is certainly unreasonable that anilinium ion should be the preferred aromatic reactant, when diazo coupling is known to proceed only with activated aromatic nuclei and when the coupling reaction of amines is known to be oriented ortho and para. With phenols it is the phenoxide ion that undergoes electrophilic attack. As Hauser and Breslow have pointed out, the electrophilic character of aromatic diazonium ions may be thought of in terms of the contribution of the right-hand structure below to the total structure of the ion.[48]

$$\text{Ar} — \overset{\oplus}{\text{N}} \equiv \text{N}| \leftrightarrow \text{Ar} — \overline{\text{N}} = \overset{\oplus}{\text{N}}|$$

Electron-withdrawing groups would be expected to increase and electron-donating groups to decrease this electrophilicity. Hammett[49] has noted that according to Conant and Peterson's[50] data the relative reactivity of para-substituted benzenediazonium ions does decrease with the decreasing electron-withdrawing power of the substituent ($NO_2 > SO_3^- > Br > H > CH_3 > CH_3O$).

16-2g. *Replacement of Groups Other than Hydrogen.* Although all of the electrophilic aromatic substitution reactions discussed thus far have involved the replacement of hydrogen, there is no reason why all such reactions should. There are several reasons why it is usually hydrogen that is replaced. For example, hydrogen is the most common substituent and offers little steric hindrance to an attacking group. Another

important factor is that in most intermediates of the type Ar+ the ease

$$\text{Ar+} \overset{\displaystyle H}{\underset{\displaystyle X}{<}}$$

of proton transfer reactions usually makes it much easier to lose H+ than X+.

It would be expected, then, that the ease of replacement of a group X will depend on the stability of the species which is formed when X is expelled without its bonding electron pair. Since the stability of the halogen cations varies in the order $I > Br > Cl > F$, the same order of ease of electrophilic displacement would be expected, and it is found. Iodination reactions are quite subject to reversal due to the replacement

---

[47] R. Wistar and P. D. Bartlett, *J. Am. Chem. Soc.*, **63**, 413 (1941).

[48] C. R. Hauser and D. S. Breslow, *J. Am. Chem. Soc.*, **63**, 418 (1941).

[49] L. P. Hammett, "Physical Organic Chemistry," p. 314, McGraw-Hill Book Company, Inc., New York, 1940.

[50] J. B. Conant and W. D. Peterson, *J. Am. Chem. Soc.*, **52**, 1220 (1930).

of iodine by hydrogen by the action of the electrophilic reagent hydrogen iodide. Gold and Whittaker have pointed out that the effect of substituents on the reaction

$$ArI + HI \rightarrow ArH + I_2$$

is the same as a typical aromatic substitution reaction.[51] Aromatic brominations are not ordinarily sufficiently reversible to produce directly measurable amounts of bromine, but the occurrence of reactions like the following[52]

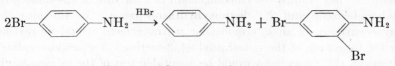

shows that some such reversal has probably taken place.

Kuivila and coworkers have studied the displacement of boron from benzeneboronic acid and its derivatives.[53] Nightingale has reviewed a number of reactions in which aromatic nitration occurs with the replacement of a group other than hydrogen.[54] Some of the acid-catalyzed decarboxylation reactions mentioned in Sec. 13-1*d* could have been discussed just as well in this section. The replacement of the sulfonic acid group by hydrogen is also familiar and is acid-catalyzed, as would be expected.

16-2*h*. *The Benzidine Rearrangement.* The benzidine rearrangement

has proved of great interest to theoretical organic chemists. A number of mechanisms and modifications of mechanisms have been proposed. Most of these are in agreement with the fact that the rearrangement is *intramolecular.* Jacobson pointed out that no rearrangement of an unsymmetrical hydrazobenzene ArNHNHAr' had ever been found to give any of either of the symmetrical benzidines, $H_2NArArNH_2$ or $H_2NAr'Ar'NH_2$.[55] Wheland and Schwartz used a radioactive-carbon-tracer technique to show that not more than 0.3 per cent of the symmetrical product, *o*-tolidine, was formed in the rearrangement of 2-methyl-2'-ethoxyhydrazobenzene.[56] These data show that the reaction is probably not a cleavage to two fragments of the same type (such as an

[51] V. Gold and M. Whittaker, *J. Chem. Soc.*, 1184 (1951).

[52] R. Baltzly and J. S. Buck, *J. Am. Chem. Soc.*, **63,** 1757 (1941).

[53] H. G. Kuivila and E. K. Easterbrook, *J. Am. Chem. Soc.*, **73,** 4629 (1951); H. G. Kuivila and A. R. Hendrickson, *J. Am. Chem. Soc.*, **74,** 5068 (1952); H. G. Kuivila, *J. Am. Chem. Soc.*, **76,** 870 (1954).

[54] D. V. Nightingale, *Chem. Rev.*, **40,** 117 (1947).

[55] P. Jacobson, *Ann.*, **428,** 76 (1922).

[56] G. W. Wheland and J. R. Schwartz, *J. Chem. Phys.*, **17,** 425 (1949); cf. G. J. Bloink and K. H. Pausacker, *J. Chem. Soc.*, 950 (1950).

ArNH· and an Ar'NH· radical) followed by their recombination in such a way as to yield the final product. It does not, however, rule out a mechanism in which cleavage yields two different types of fragments (such as ArNH⁺ and Ar'NH⁻), since if an unsymmetrical hydrazobenzene always cleaves in the same way, the combination of different types of fragments could never lead to the formation of a symmetrical benzidine.

Ingold and Kidd have obtained evidence of a more general nature to show that the hydrazobenzene never cleaves into two independent fragments. They studied the rearrangement of a mixture of 2,2′-dimethoxyhydrazobenzene and 2,2′-diethoxyhydrazobenzene with the idea that any occurrence of an intermolecular rearrangement would be revealed by the formation of the mixed product, 3-methoxy-3′-ethoxybenzidine.[57] However, this experiment would be a suitable test of the intramolecular character of the rearrangement only if both hydrazobenzenes undergo a considerable portion of their reaction at the same time; i.e., their rearrangement rates must be comparable. The methoxy compound was found to be about six times as reactive as the ethoxy compound, a difference in reactivity that was probably not excessive for the purpose. No mixed product was found, and rearrangement therefore appears to be intramolecular. Smith, Schwartz, and Wheland have carried out a study not differing greatly in principle from that of Ingold and Kidd but with features permitting much greater accuracy.[58] They studied the rearrangement of a mixture of 2-methylhydrazobenzene labeled in the methyl group with C^{14} (I) and 2,2′-dimethylhydrazobenzene (II), which rearranges only three times as fast.

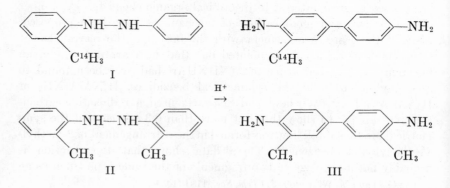

The o-tolidine (III) produced contained no excess C^{14} (over that present in ordinary carbon), and it was concluded that not more than 0.03 per cent

[57] C. K. Ingold and H. V. Kidd, *J. Chem. Soc.*, 984 (1933).

[58] D. H. Smith, J. R. Schwartz, and G. W. Wheland, *J. Am. Chem. Soc.*, **74**, 2282 (1952).

of a mixed product could have been formed (not more than about 5 per cent of mixed product could have been formed in Ingold and Kidd's study).

Although the reaction was known to be acid-catalyzed and the relative reactivities of a number of substituted hydrazobenzenes had been determined, it was not until 1950 that the kinetic order, one of the most important data upon which to base a reaction mechanism, was reported. This report is due to Hammond and Shine, who showed that the reaction is second-order in hydrogen ion rather than first-order, as had been commonly assumed.[59] The reaction had long been known to be first-order in hydrazobenzene. These kinetic data have been verified by Carlin, Nelb, and Odioso[60] and by Croce and Gettler.[61] More recently, Cohen and Hammond have shown the reaction to be subject to general acid catalysis.[62] This may mean that the doubly protonated form of hydrazobenzene rearranges as it is formed or immediately thereafter,

$$C_6H_5NHNHC_6H_5 + H^+ \underset{k_{-1}}{\overset{k_1}{\rightleftharpoons}} C_6H_5\overset{\oplus}{N}H_2NHC_6H_5$$

$$C_6H_5\overset{\oplus}{N}H_2NHC_6H_5 + HA \underset{k_{-2}}{\overset{k_2}{\rightleftharpoons}} C_6H_5\overset{\oplus}{N}H_2\overset{\oplus}{N}H_2C_6H_5$$

$$C_6H_5\overset{\oplus}{N}H_2\overset{\oplus}{N}H_2C_6H_5 \overset{k_3}{\rightarrow} H_2NC_6H_4C_6H_4NH_2 + 2H^+$$

$$k_{-1} \gg k_2; \ k_3 \gg k_{-2}$$

although mechanisms of the other types used to explain general acid catalysis (Sec. 8-2) could also be devised for this case. The rearrangement step of the reaction may involve a simultaneous cleavage of the

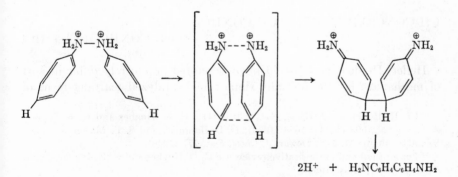

$$2H^+ \ + \ H_2NC_6H_4C_6H_4NH_2$$

[59] G. S. Hammond and H. J. Shine, *J. Am. Chem. Soc.*, **72**, 220 (1950).

[60] R. B. Carlin, R. G. Nelb, and R. C. Odioso, *J. Am. Chem. Soc.*, **73**, 1002 (1951).

[61] L. J. Croce and J. D. Gettler, *J. Am. Chem. Soc.*, **75**, 874 (1953).

[62] M. D. Cohen and G. S. Hammond, *J. Am. Chem. Soc.*, **75**, 880 (1953).

nitrogen-nitrogen bond, which has been weakened by the electrostatic repulsion between two like charges, and the formation of a new carbon-carbon bond.[62,63] The mechanism of the formation of the by-products in the benzidine rearrangement has also been considered.[60,63]

16-2i. *Other Aromatic Rearrangements.*[64] The benzidine rearrangement is one of a number of rearrangements of the type

$$\overset{\displaystyle R}{\underset{\displaystyle C_6H_5N}{|}}{-}X \overset{H^+}{\rightarrow} \text{o- and p-}XC_6H_4NHR$$

which have a considerable similarity in over-all result but which may differ widely in reaction mechanism. While the benzidine rearrangement has been well established as an intramolecular process, there are other examples that have equally well been shown to be intermolecular in that the X which becomes attached to the ring in the product is not necessarily the one attached to the side chain in the reactant.

One of the earliest and best established of these intermolecular rearrangements is the acid-catalyzed transformation of N-chloroacetanilide to o- and p-chloroacetanilide. Orton and coworkers pointed out that the reaction was catalyzed specifically by hydrochloric acid and succeeded in isolating both acetanilide and chlorine from the reaction mixture.[65] They also demonstrated that under a given set of conditions the hydrochloric acid–catalyzed reaction yielded the same ratio of o- to p-chloroacetanilide as did the reaction of acetanilide with chlorine.[66] These data strongly suggest that the "rearrangement" consists of the reaction of N-chloroacetanilide with hydrochloric acid to give acetanilide and chlorine.

$$CH_3CONClC_6H_5 + HCl \rightleftharpoons CH_3CONHC_6H_5 + Cl_2$$
$$\rightarrow CH_3CONHC_6H_4Cl + HCl$$

Heller, Hughes, and Ingold have suggested an entirely different sort of mechanism for the formally similar acid-catalyzed rearrangement of

[63] Cf. R. Robinson, *J. Chem. Soc.*, 220 (1941); E. D. Hughes and C. K. Ingold, *J. Chem. Soc.*, 608 (1941); 1638 (1950); D. L. Hammick and S. F. Mason, *J. Chem. Soc.*, 638 (1946); M. J. S. Dewar, *J. Chem. Soc.*, 777 (1946).

[64] For a recent and authoritative review see E. D. Hughes and C. K. Ingold, *Quart. Revs. (London)*, **6**, 34 (1952).

[65] K. J. P. Orton and W. J. Jones, *J. Chem. Soc.*, **95**, 1456 (1909); K. J. P. Orton and H. King, *J. Chem. Soc.*, **99**, 1185 (1911).

[66] K. J. P. Orton and A. E. Bradfield, *J. Chem. Soc.*, 986 (1927).

phenylhydroxylamine to o- and p-aminophenol.[67] They proposed the intermediate formation of a resonance-stabilized carbonium ion capable of combining with nucleophilic reagents in more than one way.

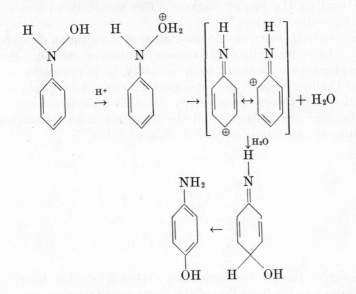

The reaction products may vary in the presence of other nucleophilic reagents. Thus in methanol and ethanol solutions the reaction yields methyl and ethyl ethers of o- and p-aminophenol. In the presence of phenol some p-$HOC_6H_4C_6H_4NH_2$-p was formed. A kinetic study shows the reaction rate to be proportional to the concentration of the conjugate acid of phenylhydroxylamine. The reaction probably proceeds through a discrete intermediate like the resonance-stabilized cation above rather than proceeding by a concerted mechanism of the S_N2' type (Sec. 5-5b), because the rate of the hydrochloric acid–catalyzed reaction, in which o- and p-chloroaniline are formed, is independent of the chloride-ion concentration.[67] The matter is being investigated more thoroughly in this regard, however.

16-3. Reactivity and Orientation in Electrophilic Aromatic Substitution. *16-3a. Basis for Electronic Effects in Orientation and Reactivity.* Modern concepts of physical organic chemistry offer a particularly satisfying qualitative explanation for the observed data on reactivity and orientation in electrophilic aromatic substitution reactions. This may be partly because aromatic substitution was the most widely used proving ground for many of these concepts when they were being devel-

[67] H. E. Heller, E. D. Hughes, and C. K. Ingold, *Nature*, **168**, 909 (1951).

oped by the English school of organic chemists during the 1920's. In accordance with a common practice, we shall discuss these concepts in terms of resonance instead of the T, M, E, etc., effects (Sec. 2-4e) generally used by the English workers. This should in no way obscure our debt to these workers.[68]

For *irreversible* reactions the orientation of substitution depends only on the relative reactivity of the various positions on the ring. Some of the complications introduced by reversibility, as in sulfonation and the Friedel-Crafts reaction, are considered in Sec. 16-3g. According to transition-state theory the reactivity depends on the free-energy difference between the reactants and the transition state. Assuming the formation of an intermediate like that shown below,

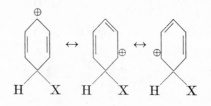

the transition state for the reaction as a whole will be either the transition state leading to the formation of the intermediate from reactant or the one leading from the intermediate to product. In either case, the transition state will differ from the reactant largely by looking much more like the intermediate. Therefore it is useful, if not rigorous, to discuss orientation and reactivity in terms of the stability of the intermediate (compared to that of the reactants). Since electron donation by the inductive effect should stabilize the positively charged ring of the intermediate and electron withdrawal should destabilize it, we should expect groups capable of inductive electron supply to increase reactivity and inductive electron-withdrawing groups to decrease reactivity in electrophilic aromatic substitutions. Of the common substituents only alkyl groups may be very definitely claimed to have an electron-donating inductive effect. Therefore the inductive effect of most groups would be expected to tend to decrease reactivity. With most groups, however, resonance effects also appear to be quite important. Thus for all groups in which the atom attached directly to the ring has an unshared electron pair (and does not have a formal positive charge) a fourth particularly stable structure (IV) may contribute to the resonance hybrid intermediate.

[68] J. Allan, A. E. Oxford, R. Robinson, and J. C. Smith, *J. Chem. Soc.*, 401 (1926); C. K. Ingold and E. H. Ingold, *J. Chem. Soc.*, 1310 (1926); C. K. Ingold, *Ann. Repts. on Progr. Chem.* (*Chem. Soc. London*), **23**, 129 (1926); *Rec. trav. chim.*, **48**, 797 (1929); *Chem. Rev.*, **15**, 225 (1934).

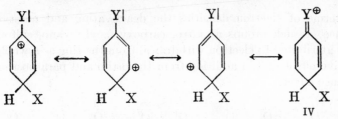

IV

This contributing structure (IV) has one more covalent bond than any of the others. A similar structure may be written for the intermediate for ortho (but not meta) substitution. This resonance factor causes an activation of the ortho and para positions which opposes the deactivation produced by the inductive effect. In the case of the halogen substituents the inductive effect appears to be more powerful than the resonance effect. That is, the inductive effect deactivates all positions, and while the resonance effect decreases this deactivation for the ortho and para position, it does not eliminate it. The halogens therefore bring about deactivation with ortho-para orientation. With alkoxy and amino groups the inductive effect is smaller, and because of the greater basicity of oxygen and nitrogen the resonance effect is larger. These two types of groups cause activation with ortho-para orientation. The negative σ constants of m-amino groups (Table 2-4) and observations by de la Mare and Vernon on the bromination of anisole derivatives[69] show that both types of groups may activate the meta position. This rather unexpected result, which has been attributed to a "second-order relay" to the meta position of the strong activation of the ortho and para positions,[69] is worthy of further investigation.

Orientation in aromatic substitution reactions has often been discussed in terms of the electron densities at the various positions of aromatic rings. The positions of high electron density are then said to be reactive in electrophilic substitution and those of low electron density reactive in nucleophilic substitution. However, this procedure is not rigorous from the viewpoint of transition-state theory, and while it usually gives the right answer (and is simpler to apply), there are several cases known in which orientation is incorrectly predicted. As Jaffé has pointed out, the 2 and 4 positions of pyridine N-oxide and azobenzene, for example, are more reactive than the 3 position toward both electrophilic and nucleophilic substitution.[70] Thus in one of the two types of reactions the reactivity is not dependent on the electron density alone. There will be a tendency toward this type of behavior in the case of any compound with a substituent group capable of both tautomeric electron donation and withdrawal.

[69] P. B. D. de la Mare and C. A. Vernon, *J. Chem. Soc.*, 1764 (1951).
[70] H. H. Jaffé, *J. Am. Chem. Soc.*, **76**, 3527 (1954).

In terms of electron densities the deactivating and meta-orienting influence of such groups as nitro, carboxy, acyl, cyano, sulfonic acid, etc., is attributed to electron withdrawal from the ring as a whole by the inductive effect and in addition from the ortho and para positions by a resonance effect.

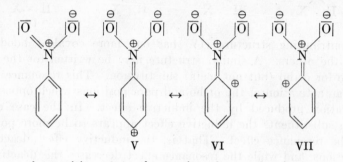

In terms of transition state theory, ignoring no-bond structures and structures with like charges on adjacent atoms, there are no contributing structures of the type of V, VI, and VII for the intermediate for para substitution of nitrobenzene and only one for ortho. Thus the strong deactivation of the ortho position and the *greater* deactivation of the para position may be explained by the existence of only three structures for the ortho intermediate, and for the para only the following two.

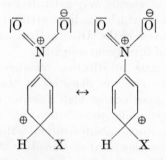

Five structures contribute to the intermediate for meta substitution.

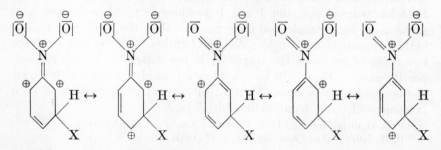

16-3b. *Correlation of Electrophilic Aromatic Substitution with the Hammett Equation.* Since Hammett's σ constants are quantitative measures of the electron density on given positions of aromatic rings, the usual qualitative agreement between electron density and reactivity in aromatic substitution creates interest as to whether a quantitative

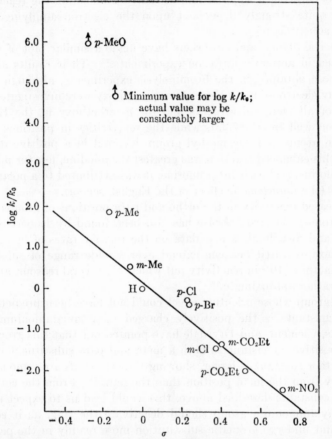

FIG. 16-1. Hammett-equation plot for the brominolysis of substituted benzeneboronic acids. The values of σ are from Table 2-4 and are slightly different from those used by Kuivila and Hendrickson.[71]

relationship holds. The data of Kuivila and Hendrickson on the rates of brominolysis of substituted benzeneboronic acids[71] are among the most suitable for this purpose. Although it is the —B(OH)$_2$ group that is replaced in their reaction, the effect of substituents is essentially the same as in the replacement of hydrogen. A Hammett-equation plot for the reaction is shown in Fig. 16-1. The points lie near a straight

[71] H. G. Kuivila and A. R. Hendrickson, *J. Am. Chem. Soc.*, **74**, 5068 (1952).

line for all substituents except those capable of supplying electrons to the ring by resonance. These groups, p-Cl, p-Br, p-Me, and p-MeO, are all more reactive than would be expected, the relative magnitudes of the deviations increasing with the ability of the groups to donate electrons by resonance. The ρ constant for the reaction is large, the line in Fig. 16-1 having a slope of almost four. This shows the reaction rate to be quite strongly dependent upon the electron-supplying abilities of the substituents.

Roberts, Sixma, and coworkers have made a similar plot of the data obtained in aromatic nitration experiments.[72] Their results are much like those obtained in the brominolysis experiments, although no such strongly electron-donating groups as p-methoxy were investigated. The data for all meta substituents and for p-carbethoxy fit the Hammett equation well ($\rho = -7.22$), while the reactivities in positions para to halogen atoms and the methyl group deviated in a positive direction. Since this enhanced reaction was greatest for p-iodine, less for p-bromine and chlorine, and least for p-fluorine, it was attributed to a polarizibility effect[72] (the *inductomeric* effect of the English school).

Increased reactivity in the ortho and para positions of groups capable of tautomeric electron release has also been found by Robertson, de la Mare, and Swedlund, whose data on the relative rates of halogenation of monosubstituted benzene extend over a wide range of substituents and a factor of 10^{24} in reactivity but which, for several reasons, are necessarily rather approximate.[73]

One group whose orienting effect could not have been predicted from its σ constants is the positively charged trimethylammonium group. Roberts, Clement, and Drysdale have pointed out that this group has a large positive σ constant as both a meta and para substituent but that the meta σ constant is larger, showing that electrons are removed more strongly from the meta position than the para.[74] From the correlation with σ constants described above, this would lead us to expect that the trimethylammonium group should deactivate the ring, as it certainly does, and undergo aromatic substitution more readily in the para than in the meta position, as it certainly does not. Roberts and coworkers point out that the observed meta orientation may be explained in a manner similar to that suggested by Pfeiffer and Wizinger.[75] The transition state for meta substitution will be described by structures VIII,

[72] J. D. Roberts, J. K. Sanford, F. L. J. Sixma, H. Cerfontain, and R. Zagt, *J. Am. Chem. Soc.*, **76**, 4525 (1954); F. L. J. Sixma, *Rec. trav. chim.*, **73**, 243 (1954). Cf. C. W. McGary, Jr., Y. Okamoto, and H. C. Brown, *J. Am. Chem. Soc.*, **77**, 3037 (1955).

[73] P. W. Robertson, P. B. D. de la Mare, and B. E. Swedlund, *J. Chem. Soc.*, 782 (1953).

[74] J. D. Roberts, R. A. Clement, and J. J. Drysdale, *J. Am. Chem. Soc.*, **73**, 2181 (1951).

[75] P. Pfeiffer and R. Wizinger, *Ann.*, **461**, 132 (1928).

IX, and X and that for para substitution by XI, XII, and XIII (among others).

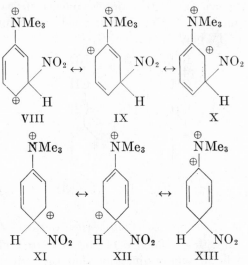

VIII   IX   X

XI   XII   XIII

However, structure XIII, having like charges on adjacent atoms, will have such a high energy content as to decrease greatly its contribution to the total structure of the transition state for para substitution. Therefore the transition state for meta substitution will be more stable. This type of argument may be used to explain the fact that meta substitution always occurs when the atom directly attached to the ring bears a formal positive charge. This generalization has alternately been explained[68,76] by the suggestion that the inductive effect removes electrons more effectively from the ortho and para than from the meta positions due to the contributions of structures like

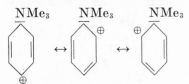

This explanation requires a new interpretation of the σ constants of the trimethylammonium group in terms of an electrostatic effect operating directly through space.[76]

Other compounds that appear to have a smaller electron density in the ortho and para positions than in the meta position but which nevertheless undergo substitution (less readily than benzene, however) in the ortho and para positions are $C_6H_5CH{=}CHCO_2H$, $C_6H_5CH{=}CHNO_2$,

[76] C. K. Ingold, "Structure and Mechanism in Organic Chemistry," sec. 19b, Cornell University Press, Ithaca, N.Y., 1953.

and $C_6H_5CH{=}CHSO_2Cl$.[77]   This suggests that although structure XIV contributes less to the transition state for para substitution than do the other structures shown, its contribution is sufficient to cause this transition state to be more stable than that for meta substitution, for which no structure like XIV may be written.[77]

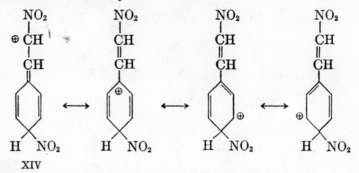

XIV

16-3c. *Effect of Alkyl and Substituted Alkyl Groups.*   The activating and ortho-para directing influence of unsubstituted alkyl groups is probably due to both hyperconjugation and the inductive effect.   It appears that the relative importance of these two factors may vary from reaction to reaction.   Thus the methyl group, for which hyperconjugation should be greater, usually, but not always, activates the para position more strongly than does the *t*-butyl group, which should have a larger inductive effect.[78]   Berliner and Berliner have studied the relative rates of bromination of a number of alkylbenzenes.[79]

When halogen atoms are substituted on a saturated aliphatic side chain, they cannot donate electrons by a resonance effect because they are not conjugated (for this purpose) with the ring.   Their electron-withdrawing inductive effect may still operate, however, resulting in a kind of hyperconjugation in the case of benzyl-type halides.

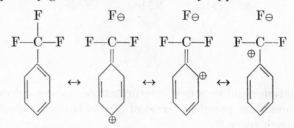

[77] F. G. Bordwell and K. Rohde, *J. Am. Chem. Soc.*, **70,** 1191 (1948).

[78] P. B. D. de la Mare and P. W. Robertson, *J. Chem. Soc.*, 279 (1943); E. Berliner and F. J. Bondhus, *J. Am. Chem. Soc.*, **68,** 2355 (1946); **70,** 854 (1948); K. L. Nelson and H. C. Brown, *J. Am. Chem. Soc.*, **73,** 5605 (1951); H. Cohn, E. D. Hughes, M. H. Jones, and M. G. Peeling, *Nature*, **169,** 291 (1952).

[79] E. Berliner and F. Berliner, *J. Am. Chem. Soc.*, **72, 222,** 3417 (1950).

It is resonance of this sort that has been said to cause the p-CF_3 σ constant to have a larger positive value than that for m-CF_3.[80] The tendency of groups capable of strong electron withdrawal by the inductive effect to cause *meta* substitution, increases with the number and electron-withdrawing power of these groups and decreases with their distance from the aromatic ring. This is shown by the data in Table 16-1.

TABLE 16-1. PERCENTAGE OF META SUBSTITUTION IN THE NITRATION OF
VARIOUS NEGATIVELY SUBSTITUTED ALKYLBENZENES

Compound	Meta, %	Compound	Meta, %
$C_6H_5CH_3$	3[a]	$C_6H_5CH_2CH_2NO_2$	13[d]
$C_6H_5CH_2Cl$	14[b]	$C_6H_5CH_2NMe_3^{\oplus}$	88[e]
$C_6H_5CHCl_2$	34[a]	$C_6H_5CH_2CH_2NMe_3^{\oplus}$	19[e]
$C_6H_5CCl_3$	64[a]	$C_6H_5(CH_2)_3NMe_3^{\oplus}$	5[f]
$C_6H_5CH_2NO_2$	67[c]		

[a] A. F. Holleman, J. Vermeulen, and W. J. de Mooy, *Rec. trav. chim.*, **33**, 1 (1914).
[b] C. K. Ingold and F. R. Shaw, *J. Chem. Soc.*, 575 (1949).
[c] J. W. Baker, *J. Chem. Soc.*, 2257 (1929).
[d] J. W. Baker and I. S. Wilson, *J. Chem. Soc.*, 842 (1927).
[e] F. R. Goss, W. Hanhart, and C. K. Ingold, *J. Chem. Soc.*, 250 (1927).
[f] C. K. Ingold and I. S. Wilson, *J. Chem. Soc.*, 810 (1927).

16-3d. *Orientation and Reactivity in Nonbenzenoid Aromatic Rings.* Orientation and reactivity in the electrophilic aromatic substitution reactions of nonbenzenoid compounds may be treated in a manner similar to that we have used for benzene derivatives. Thus since furan, pyrrole, and thiophene are resonance hybrids of structures of the type

we should expect these compounds to be more reactive than benzene because of the considerable contribution of structures with unshared electrons at the various carbon atoms of the ring. While it is not easy to predict the type of orientation expected from the structures above, it may be seen that more relatively stable contributing structures may be written for the intermediate for alpha substitution

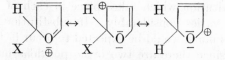

than for the intermediate for beta substitution.

[80] J. D. Roberts, R. L. Webb, and E. A. McElhill, *J. Am. Chem. Soc.*, **72**, 408 (1950).

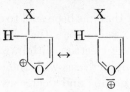

Since the corresponding transition states will be rather similarly stabilized, activated alpha substitution would be expected and is found.

For the intermediate in the alpha substitution of naphthalene, the
positive charge may be distributed between two different atoms without
disturbing the benzenoid resonance of the nonreacting ring,

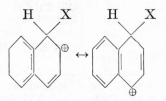

and a total of seven relatively stable contributing structures may be
written.   For beta substitution there are only six relatively stable contributing structures and only one atom on which the positive charge
may be placed without disturbing the benzene ring.

For pyridine the principal contributing structures would be expected
to be

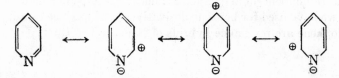

From these structures and the electronegativity of the nitrogen atom
we would expect all positions on the ring to be deactivated and the α
and γ positions even more so than the β.   There is evidence that this
is the case, but the great unreactivity of pyridine and the fact that under
the acidic conditions used for aromatic substitution it is changed into
its even less reactive conjugate acid, have made it difficult to study the
electrophilic aromatic substitution reactions of this compound.

16-3e. *The Ortho-Para Ratio.*   With ortho-para directing groups the
fraction of substitution which takes place in each of the two types of
active positions varies considerably.   If substitution were completely
random, twice as much would be expected to occur in the ortho position
as in the para, since there are two ortho positions but only one para.
Actually it appears that there is usually less than twice as much ortho
as para substitution.   One reason for the general preference for para

substitution is steric. The nitration of toluene gives 56.5 per cent ortho, 3.5 per cent meta, and 40 per cent para substitution, while t-butylbenzene gives 12 per cent ortho, 8.5 per cent meta, and 79.5 per cent para substitution. Thus the ratio of ortho to para substitution is almost 10 times as large for toluene as for t-butylbenzene, while the ratios of meta to para substitution hardly differ beyond the experimental error.[81] Steric inhibition of ortho substitution is also reflected in the decreases of the ortho-para ratio which have been found to accompany increasing size of the new group being introduced into the aromatic ring. Thus Holleman has pointed out that the ortho-para ratio is smaller in the case of bromination than in chlorination and that it is still smaller in sulfonation.[82]

There are certain data which make it obvious, however, that the ortho-para ratio is influenced by electronic as well as steric factors. Holleman reports that the nitration of fluorobenzene gives 12 per cent ortho substitution, chlorobenzene 30 per cent, bromobenzene 38 per cent, and iodobenzene 41 per cent (none of these halobenzenes give an appreciable amount of meta substitution).[82] While this order is the reverse of that expected from steric hindrance, it seems capable of explanation by the factors that we used originally to explain the deactivating but ortho-para-directing effect of the halogens. The inductive effect decreases with the distance from the halogen, deactivating the ortho position most and the para position least. The electron-supplying resonance effect of the halogens, however, makes it just as possible to write a given type of contributing structure for para as for ortho substitution. Indeed, such facts as the greater stability of para compared to ortho quinones have been used as evidence for the innately greater stability of a structure like XV compared to one like XVI.

XV   XVI

Since the inductive effect decreases with distance while the resonance effect does not, we should expect the deactivation of the ortho position

[81] H. Cohn, E. D. Hughes, M. H. Jones, and M. G. Peeling, *Nature*, **169**, 291 (1952); cf. K. L. Nelson and H. C. Brown, *J. Am. Chem. Soc.*, **73**, 5605 (1951).

[82] A. F. Holleman, *Chem. Rev.*, **1**, 218 (1925).

relative to the para to increase with increasing electronegativity of the halogen.

16-3f. Effect of Several Substituents. When both an ortho-para- and a meta-directing group are in an aromatic ring it is almost invariably the ortho-para-directing group that largely controls the orientation, if there is any conflict. In the terms of the electromeric (E) effect of the English school, perhaps this is because the electron-donating ortho-para-directing group is caused to donate electrons even more strongly during the reaction, due to the powerful electron withdrawal of the substituting reagent. The electron withdrawal of the meta-directing group is, if anything, decreased during the reaction.

With two ortho-para-directing groups the more strongly electron-withdrawing one usually controls the orientation. When cases of this sort involve amino groups, however, as with aromatic substitution of amines in general, it should be kept in mind that in many of the reaction mixtures used amino compounds will exist largely as ammonium ions. With two meta-directing groups, the one more strongly electron-withdrawing usually dominates.

16-3g. Effect of Reversibility on Orientation in Aromatic Substitution. Many sulfonation, Friedel-Crafts, iodination, and other aromatic substitution reactions are appreciably reversible under the conditions under which they are usually run. When this occurs, the ordinary orientation rules we have described will not necessarily be followed. These rules are for determining the *kinetically controlled product*, i.e., the one formed most rapidly. However, if reversal is fast enough, the various products will form in amounts proportional to their stabilities. That is, we shall obtain most of the *thermodynamically controlled product*. Since the reverse of an electrophilic aromatic substitution is simply another electrophilic aromatic substitution, the product formed most rapidly is almost always the one which also reverts to starting material most rapidly. Therefore it is impossible to predict the thermodynamically controlled product simply from a knowledge of the kinetically controlled one.

The data on the sulfonation of naphthalene may be explained in these terms. It is well known that the reaction at about 80° yields practically pure α-naphthalenesulfonic acid, while at 160° the β isomer is the predominant product. Studies of the reaction[83] show that it makes no difference whether the α sulfonation occurring below 100° is reversible or not, since the rate of β sulfonation is negligible below about 110°. Above this temperature the sulfonation of naphthalene yields largely

[83] R. Lantz, *Compt. rend.*, **201**, 149 (1935); *Bull. soc. chim. France* [5], **2**, 2092 (1935); A. A. Spryskov, *Zhur. Obshchei Khim.*, **14**, 833 (1944); **16**, 1057. 2126 (1946); **17**, 591, 1309 (1947); *Chem. Abstr.*, **40**, 1821 (1946); **41**, 2720 (1947); **42**, 894, 1921 (1948); **43**, 471 (1949).

the β isomer if the reaction is allowed to proceed to equilibrium (quite rapidly attained at 160°). Under these conditions the α isomer is believed to be formed faster, just as it is at lower temperatures, but it is also hydrolyzed faster, so that in time it is the slower but less reversible β sulfonation that yields the predominant product. The greater thermodynamic stability of this product is probably at least partly due to the less sterically hindered nature of the β position.

There are a number of Friedel-Crafts reactions which under mild conditions give largely the more rapidly formed o- and p-dialkyl- or 1,2,4-trialkylbenzenes. However, at higher temperatures or with longer reaction times or larger amounts of catalyst they yield the more stable m-di- or 1,3,5-trisubstituted compounds. While data of this sort could be explained by postulating the reversal of the alkylation reaction (and this explanation is probably correct for certain alkylbenzenes), McCaulay and Lien have shown that another mechanism may operate in the formation of the isomeric xylenes.[84] These workers studied the isomerization of xylenes in a hydrogen fluoride solution containing boron trifluoride. They showed that in the initial phases of the isomerization of o-xylene considerable meta but very little para isomer was formed. If the reaction involved toluene formation and remethylation, p-xylene should initially be formed more rapidly than the meta isomer. It therefore appears that the reaction is an internal rearrangement, probably with a mechanism like that of certain carbonium-ion rearrangements.

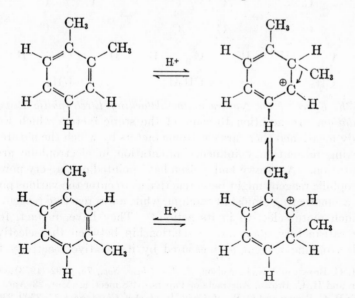

A similar mechanism may operate for the Jacobsen rearrangement.

[84] D. A. McCaulay and A. P. Lien, *J. Am. Chem. Soc.*, **74**, 6246 (1952).

It is not always easy to predict the relative stability of various possible isomers and hence the nature of the thermodynamically controlled product. The number of relevant data available is not large. However, when one of the two groups on the ring is capable of electron supply and the other of electron withdrawal by resonance (as in the nitroanilines), the ortho and para isomers, in which these groups are conjugated, will be the more stable isomers.

We should remember that it is the relative stability of the various isomers in the *actual reaction mixture* which determines the thermo-dynamically controlled product. This has been emphasized in McCaulay and Lien's study of the isomeric xylenes.[84] The equilibrium mixture in the presence of hydrogen fluoride and a catalytic concentration of boron fluoride contains about 60 per cent of the meta isomer and about 20 per cent of each of the others. In the presence of a large excess of boron fluoride, however, the equilibrium mixture was more than 99 per cent meta. Since the xylenes exist as their salts in the presence of excess boron trifluoride, the equilibrium is shifted toward the more basic meta isomer, for whose protonated forms the most resonance structures, including hyperconjugation structures, may be written

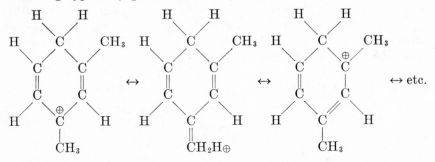

16-3h. *Effect of the Nature of the Attacking Electrophilic Reagent on Orientation.* In addition to some of the steric factors which we have already mentioned there are electronic factors by which the nature of the attacking reagent may influence orientation in electrophilic aromatic substitution. As Brown and Nelson have pointed out, a very powerfully electrophilic reagent might be so reactive as to enter the various positions of an aromatic ring almost at random, while a less reactive reagent would be much more selective in its action.[85] They have, in fact, found a fairly satisfactory quantitative relationship between the selectivity of an electrophilic reagent as measured by its relative reactivity toward

[85] H. C. Brown and K. L. Nelson, *J. Am. Chem. Soc.*, **75**, 6292 (1953); cf. K. L. Nelson and H. C. Brown, Abstracts of Papers, ACS meeting, Mar. 23–Apr. 1, 1954, p. 13P; H. C. Brown and C. W. McGary, Jr., *J. Am. Chem. Soc.*, **77**, 2300, 2306, 2310 (1955).

two different aromatic compounds and the selectivity as measured by its relative reactivity toward two different positions on the ring of a given aromatic compound. In order to avoid complications due to steric effects, only data on meta and para substitution are considered. Because of reliable data available the "activity" of an electrophilic reagent is measured in terms of the *partial rate factor* for substitution in the para position of toluene. This partial rate factor is the reactivity of a given position of an aromatic ring relative to the reactivity of a position on benzene. Thus the partial rate factor for toluene is equal to the rate constant for reaction of toluene with the electrophilic reagent multiplied by the fraction of para substitution occurring, all divided by one-sixth (since there are six positions on the benzene ring) of the rate constant for the reaction of benzene with the electrophilic reagent. When the logarithms of the partial rate factors for the para substitution of toluene in chlorination, nitration, mercuration, chloromethylation, sulfonation, Friedel-Crafts isopropylation, and sulfonylation are plotted against the logarithms of the ratio of para to meta substitution, a reasonably straight line is obtained. This relationship promises to be very useful and important and is being investigated more thoroughly.

CHAPTER 17

NUCLEOPHILIC AROMATIC SUBSTITUTION[1]

17-1. Aromatic Diazonium Salts. Because of the great stability of elemental nitrogen, its formation in a reaction may add tremendously to the driving force for the reaction. It is for this reason, no doubt, that aromatic diazonium salts undergo nucleophilic displacement reactions so much more easily than aromatic halides. Before we discuss the reactions of these compounds, though, we shall discuss the mechanism of their formation by the diazotization of amines, since this topic has not yet been considered.

17-1a. Mechanism of Diazotization of Amines. Taylor showed that the rate of reaction of primary amines with nitrous acid follows the rate equation[2]

$$v = k[\text{RNH}_2][\text{HNO}_2]^2$$

where the bracketed expressions refer to the actual (rather than formal) concentrations of the enclosed species. This observation was confirmed by Schmid and Muhr[3] and most reasonably interpreted by Hammett, who suggested that the amine performs a nucleophilic attack on nitrogen trioxide present in equilibrium with the nitrous acid.[4] Such a nucleophilic attack could lead to the conjugate acid of a nitrosamine and further proton transfers to the diazo hydroxide, which reacts with acid to give the diazonium ion (17-1). This mechanism involving the intermediate formation of nitrogen trioxide has been supported further by Hughes, Ingold, and Ridd, who studied the reaction in considerably less acidic solution.[5] The change in pH so decreased the nitrous acid concentration and increased the amine concentration as to make the first rather than the second step of mechanism (17-1) rate-controlling; i.e., the kinetic equation had the form

[1] For a comprehensive review of this subject see J. F. Bunnett and R. E. Zahler, *Chem. Rev.*, **49**, 273 (1951).

[2] T. W. J. Taylor, *J. Chem. Soc.*, 1099, 1897 (1928).

[3] H. Schmid and G. Muhr, *Ber.*, **70**, 421 (1937).

[4] L. P. Hammett, "Physical Organic Chemistry," p. 294, McGraw-Hill Book Company, Inc., New York, 1940.

[5] E. D. Hughes, C. K. Ingold, and J. H. Ridd, *Nature*, **166**, 642 (1950); cf. C. A. Bunton, D. R. Llewellyn, and G. Stedman, *Nature*, **175**, 83 (1955).

$$v = k[\text{HNO}_2]^2$$

It is found that in acidic solutions containing enough chloride ion the kinetic equation has an additional term involving the first powers of the hydrogen-ion, chloride-ion, and nitrous acid concentrations.[3] This is apparently due to the assumption by nitrosyl chloride of the function of nitrogen trioxide in mechanism (17-1).[4]

$$2\text{HNO}_2 \rightleftharpoons \text{H}_2\text{O} + \text{N}_2\text{O}_3$$

(17-1)

17-1b. Decomposition of Diazonium Salts. The transformation of benzenediazonium salts and that of a number of nuclear-substituted derivatives to phenols have been found to be first-order in aqueous solution, the rate being independent of the nature and concentrations of the anion in dilute solutions.[6] Waters[7] has suggested that the reaction proceeds by the S_N1 mechanism, although he points out that a nucleophilic attack by water may be occurring. The fact that the decomposition of benzenediazonium chloride proceeds only about 20 per cent faster in 12 N hydrochloric acid (where 60 per cent of the reaction product is chlorobenzene) than in dilute solution[8] has been quoted in support of the S_N1 mechanism. In this concentrated a solution, however, we cannot discount the possibility that the accelerating effect of an additional nucleophilic attack by chloride ions may be partially offset by a solvent effect, decreasing the rate of nucleophilic attack by water. The fact that p-nitrobenzenediazonium chloride hydrolyzes more slowly than

[6] H. Euler, *Ann.*, **325**, 292 (1902); J. C. Cain, *Ber.*, **38**, 2511 (1905); H. A. H. Pray, *J. Phys. Chem.*, **30**, 1417, 1477 (1926); J. E. Taylor and T. J. Feltis, *J. Am. Chem. Soc.*, **74**, 1331 (1952); E. A. Moelwyn-Hughes and P. Johnson, *Trans. Faraday Soc.*, **36**, 948 (1940).

[7] W. A. Waters, *J. Chem. Soc.*, 266 (1942).

[8] M. L. Crossley, R. H. Kienle, and C. H. Benbrook, *J. Am. Chem. Soc.*, **62**, 1400 (1940).

the unsubstituted compound supports the carbonium-ion mechanism for the latter, at least, since the p-nitro group should greatly increase the rate of nucleophilic attack by water, as it does the rate of other aromatic nucleophilic displacements. Assuming an S_N1 mechanism, it is certainly reasonable that the reactivity should be decreased, as it has been found to be,[8] by the nitro and other electron-withdrawing groups. Electron-donor groups in the meta position increase the reactivity as expected, but, surprisingly, in the para position they decrease the reactivity.[8,9] Hughes, however, has pointed out that this is consistent with the S_N1 mechanism, since groups capable of supplying electrons by resonance from the para position should stabilize the diazonium ion,[1]

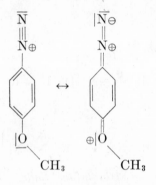

even though such resonance stabilization is impossible for the carbonium ion.

Lewis and Hinds have shown that with the p-nitro compound reactivity toward bimolecular nucleophilic attack is sufficiently developed to be observable.[10] They found the increase in the rate of decomposition of the diazonium ion in the presence of bromide ion to be proportional to the bromide-ion concentration, as was the ratio of p-nitrobromobenzene to p-nitrophenol in the product. They also found the reaction to be very sensitive to catalysis by copper, its effect being noticeable at a concentration of 10^{-5} M. This catalysis is probably related to the Sandmeyer reaction, but there appears to be no generally accepted explanation for it.

17-2. Bimolecular Nucleophilic Displacements on Aromatic Rings. *17-2a. Mechanism of Aromatic Bimolecular Nucleophilic Displacement.* While the aromatic bimolecular nucleophilic displacement reaction

$$Y| + Ar—X \rightarrow Ar—Y + X|$$

bears a considerable formal resemblance to the S_N2 mechanism for sub-

[9] E. S. Lewis and E. B. Miller, *J. Am. Chem. Soc.*, **75**, 429 (1953).
[10] E. S. Lewis and W. H. Hinds, *J. Am. Chem. Soc.*, **74**, 304 (1952).

stitution at saturated carbon atoms, in the present case, as in ester hydrolysis (Sec. 12-1b), the carbon atom undergoing nucleophilic attack is never bonded to more than four other atoms at once. This greatly facilitates the stability of a discrete reaction intermediate in which both the entering and departing groups are covalently bound to carbon. In certain cases such an intermediate may be observed directly. For example, a number of aromatic polynitro compounds are known to form adducts with metal alkoxides, cyanides, and amines. Meisenheimer has shown that the adduct formed from potassium ethoxide and trinitro-anisole and that from potassium methoxide and trinitrophenetole are identical, the same mixture of trinitroanisole and trinitrophenetole being obtained from each on acidification.[11] This is convincing evidence that the adduct has structure I.

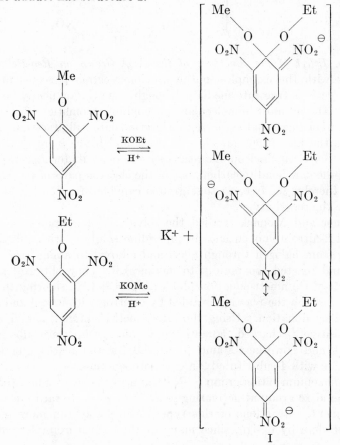

Farr, Bard, and Wheland have shown that solution of m-dinitrobenzene

[11] J. Meisenheimer, Ann., **323**, 205 (1902).

in liquid ammonia to give a purple solution capable of conducting an electric current is probably due to the formation of the anion II.[12]

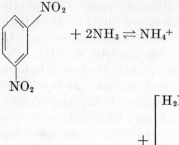

$+ 2NH_3 \rightleftharpoons NH_4^+$

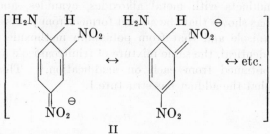

II

17-2b. Effect of the Structure of the Aryl Group on Reactivity. By analogy with the examples in the previous section it seems probable that there is a true intermediate (though usually not nearly so stable as I or II) in most bimolecular nucleophilic aromatic substitutions. Structural changes that stabilize this intermediate will practically always stabilize the transition state leading to it and hence increase the reactivity. Since the nucleophilic reagent uses one of its own electron pairs to form the new bond to carbon, one of the electron pairs of the aromatic ring is thereby set free, so that groups capable of accepting electrons increase the reactivity.

Berliner and Monack studied the solvolysis of a number of 4-substituted 2-nitrobromobenzenes in piperidine solution, with substituents ranging from halogen through alkyl and alkoxyl to amino (the 4-nitro compound reacted too rapidly to measure).[13] They obtained a fairly satisfactory Hammett-equation plot with $\rho = +4.95$, showing the great extent to which the reaction is aided by electron withdrawal and slowed by electron donation. Using the nitro, methylsulfonyl, acetyl, chloro, and positively charged trimethylammonio groups as substituents, Bunnett and coworkers found $\rho = +3.9$ for the reaction of sodium methoxide with 4-substituted 2-nitrochlorobenzenes.[14]

The diazonium cation group ($-N_2^{\oplus}$) appears to be even more effective than the nitro group at activating o- and p-halogen toward nucleophilic replacement. Reactions of this type are probably run more often by accident than by design, since many of the known examples were dis-

[12] J. D. Farr, C. C. Bard, and G. W. Wheland, *J. Am. Chem. Soc.*, **71**, 2013 (1949).

[13] E. Berliner and L. C. Monack, *J. Am. Chem. Soc.*, **74**, 1574 (1952).

[14] J. F. Bunnett, F. Draper, Jr., P. R. Ryason, P. Noble, Jr., R. G. Tonkyn, and R. E. Zahler, *J. Am. Chem. Soc.*, **75**, 642 (1953).

covered when a reaction series involving the diazotization of an aromatic amine yielded an unexpected product. For example, when 1-nitro-2-naphthylamine is diazotized in hydrochloric acid solution the nitro group is replaced by a chlorine atom.[15]

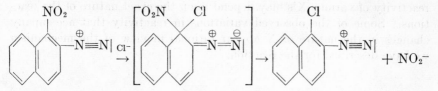

Halogen atoms in the α and γ positions of pyridine rings are also activated to nucleophilic attack.

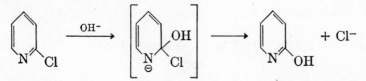

From comparisons of the reactivity of 2-chloro-5-nitropyridine and 2,4-dinitrochlorobenzene toward various nucleophilic reagents, the activation of these positions appears to be less than that due to an o- or p-nitro group.[16]

Banks has found that the nucleophilic substitution reactions of halides of the type of α- and γ-halopyridines are acid-catalyzed.[17] As he points out, this behavior might be expected since the protonation of a hetero-nitrogen atom should increase its electron-withdrawing power.

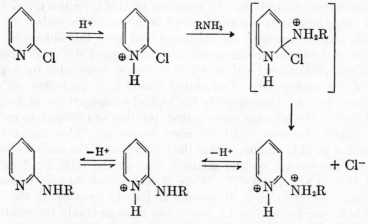

[15] N. N. Vorozhtsov, V. V. Kozlov, and I. S. Travkin, *Zhur. Obshchei Khim.*, **9**, 522 (1939); *Chem. Abstr.*, **34**, 410 (1940).

[16] A. Mangini and B. Frenguelli, *Gazz. chim. ital.*, **69**, 86 (1939); R. R. Bishop, E. A. S. Cavell, and N. B. Chapman, *J. Chem. Soc.*, 437 (1952).

[17] C K. Banks, *J. Am. Chem. Soc.*, **66**, 1127 (1944).

17-2c. *Effect of the Nature of the Displaced Group on Reactivity.* The effect of the nature of X on the rate of nucleophilic substitution reactions of Ar—X is rather different from the effect in the analogous aliphatic substitution reactions. As in the aliphatic cases, however, the relative reactivity of various X's may depend upon the exact nature of the reactions. Some of the observed variations in reactivity that accompany changes in the nature of X appear rational in view of the mechanism we have described for the reaction.

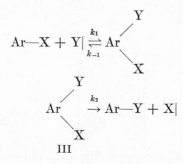

$$\text{III}$$

If k_{-1} is negligible in comparison to k_2, the first step of the reaction is rate-controlling; otherwise, the second step is. Other things being equal, we should expect the intermediate III to lose preferentially whichever of X or Y represents the more stable (less basic) species. In most of the aromatic nucleophilic displacements that have been studied kinetically, Y was an amine or alkoxide or hydroxide ion and X a halogen atom. It therefore seems likely that in these cases the first step of the reaction is rate-controlling. In reactions of this type the C—X bond is not being broken to any great extent in the transition state, although there is interference with the resonance that gives this linkage a small amount of double-bond character. For this reason the great strength of the carbon-fluorine bond, which is probably responsible for a great deal of the unreactivity of saturated fluorides, is no longer such an important factor. Consequently the high electronegativity of fluorine, which makes the adjacent carbon atom positive and subject to nucleophilic attack, becomes relatively more important. This may explain the data of Bevan, who found that the reactivities of the various *p*-nitrohalobenzenes toward sodium ethoxide were in the ratio F:Cl:Br:I:: 3,100:13.6:11.8:1 at 90.8°.[18] While it seems that fluorine is usually the most reactive halogen, Hammond and Parks have shown that it is possible to change the reaction conditions so as to obtain the reactivity sequence ArBr > ArCl > ArF.[19] This was done by changes designed to increase the extent to which the carbon-halogen bond is broken in the

---

[18] C. W. L. Bevan, *J. Chem. Soc.*, 2340 (1951).
[19] G. S. Hammond and L. R. Parks, *J. Am. Chem. Soc.*, **77**, 340 (1955).

transition state. The variation in the relative ease of nucleophilic displacement of groups that may accompany a change in nucleophilic reagent has been shown quite strikingly by Loudon and Robson.[20] These workers found that by use of the proper nucleophilic reagent, any one of the three substituents of 3-chloro-4-(p-toluenesulfonyl)nitrobenzene could be preferentially displaced.

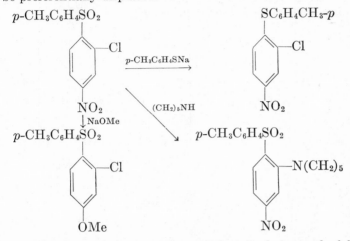

Despite the existence of cases of the type described above, the following order of mobilities listed by Bunnett and Zahler[1] has considerable utility:

—F > —NO₂ > —Cl ∼ —Br ∼ —I > —OSO₂R > —NR₃⁺ > —OAr > —OR > —SAr ∼ —SR > —SO₂R > —NR₂ > —H.

The Chichibabin method of amination of pyridine and related compounds[21] is an example of a nucleophilic displacement of hydrogen (as a hydride ion).

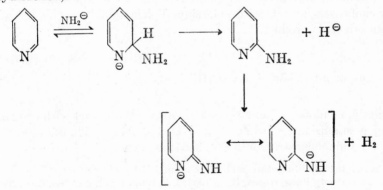

²⁰ J. D. Loudon and T. D. Robson, *J. Chem. Soc.*, 242 (1937); cf. J. D. Loudon and N. Shulman, *J. Chem. Soc.*, 722 (1941).

²¹ A. E. Chichibabin and O. A. Seide, *Zhur. Russ. Fiz.-Khim. Obshchestva*, **46**, 1216 (1914); *Chem. Abstr.*, **9**, 1901 (1915); M. T. Leffler, "Organic Reactions," vol. I, chap. 4. John Wiley & Sons, Inc., New York, 1942.

17-3. Other Mechanisms for Aromatic Nucleophilic Substitution.

17-3a. Some Reactions of Cyanide Ions. There are a number of reactions known in which sodium or potassium cyanide reacts with an aromatic nitro compound to give rearranged products. The reaction with *p*-nitrobromobenzene, for example, gives *m*-bromobenzoic acid rather than *p*-nitrobenzonitrile, as might be expected. The most reasonable reaction mechanism appears to be the following:[1,22]

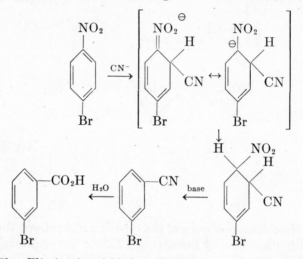

17-3b. The Elimination-Addition Mechanism. A large number of instances have been recorded in which an alkali-metal amide reacts with an aromatic halide to replace the halogen atom by hydrogen and to introduce the amino group into the ortho position. In one of the earliest cases studied, Haeussermann showed that each of the three isomeric dibromobenzenes reacts with potassium diphenylamide to give the same (meta-oriented) product.[23]

$$o\text{-, } m\text{-, or } p\text{-}C_6H_4Br_2 + KN(C_6H_5)_2 \rightarrow \quad (C_6H_5)_2N{-}\bigcirc{-}N(C_6H_5)_2$$

Similarly, *o*-chloro-, *o*-bromo-, and *o*-iodoanisole all react with sodamide to give *m*-anisidine,[24] while *o*- and *m*-chlorobenzotrifluoride react to give *m*-aminobenzotrifluoride.[25] The most convincing evidence con-

[22] C. K. Ingold, "Structure and Mechanism in Organic Chemistry," sec. 50*C*, Cornell University Press, Ithaca, N.Y., 1953; J. F. Bunnett, M. M. Rauhut, D. Knutson, and G. E. Bussell, *J. Am. Chem. Soc.*, **76**, 5755 (1954).

[23] C. Haeussermann, *Ber.*, **33**, 939 (1900); **34**, 38 (1901).

[24] H. Gilman and S. Avakian, *J. Am. Chem. Soc.*, **67**, 349 (1945).

[25] R. A. Benkeser and R. G. Severson, *J. Am. Chem. Soc.*, **71**, 3838 (1949).

cerning the mechanism of these reactions has been obtained by Roberts and coworkers. They found that chlorobenzene labeled at the chlorine-bearing carbon atom with C^{14} reacted with potassium amide in liquid ammonia to give aniline in which only half of the original C^{14} was still at the carbon atom bearing the functional group.[26] They therefore suggested that the reaction consists of a rate-controlling dehydro-halogenation to give an electrically neutral "benzyne" intermediate to which ammonia may add in two possible ways.

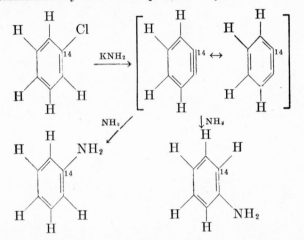

It is pointed out that this mechanism agrees with the fact that: (1) the entering amino group never appears more than one carbon atom away from the location of the displaced halogen; (2) the starting halides and resulting anilines are not isomerized under the reaction conditions; (3) halides (such as bromomesitylene and bromodurene) having no o-hydrogen do not react; (4) o-deuterochlorobenzene reacts more slowly than its protium analog.[26,27]

There are certain other reactions, such as the formation of resorcinol by the alkali fusion of o-, m-, or p-bromophenol or p-hydroxybenzene-sulfonic acid, which may proceed by the elimination-addition mechanism but for which other mechanisms are also quite possible.[1,22]

[26] J. D. Roberts, H. E. Simmons, Jr., L. A. Carlsmith, and C. W. Vaughan, *J. Am. Chem. Soc.*, **75**, 3290 (1953).

[27] J. D. Roberts, Abstracts of Papers, ACS meeting, Mar. 23–Apr. 1, 1954, Kansas City, Mo., p. 19N.

PART III

FREE-RADICAL REACTIONS

CHAPTER 18

RELATIVELY STABLE FREE RADICALS

18-1. The Triphenylmethyl and Related Radicals. 18-1*a. The Triphenylmethyl Radical.* The first molecule to be recognized as a free organic radical was synthesized by Gomberg.[1] In attempting to prepare hexaphenylethane, he treated triphenylmethyl chloride with finely divided silver in benzene solution. When the resultant white crystalline solid was found to be triphenylmethyl peroxide, the experiment was repeated in the absence of air. There then resulted a yellow solution, which upon evaporation yielded a white crystalline solid. The solid was originally thought to be triphenylmethyl on the basis of the great reactivity of its solutions. It combined very rapidly with chlorine, bromine, and iodine to form the corresponding triphenylmethyl halides, with nitric oxide to yield triphenylnitrosomethane, $(C_6H_5)_3CNO$, and with oxygen to yield the peroxide. It was later shown, however, that the white solid was hexaphenylethane, which in solution dissociates reversibly into the yellow free triphenylmethyl radical. This equilibrium and the dissociation of other hexaarylethanes have been studied most often by spectroscopic measurements,[2] by molecular-weight determinations,[3] and by magnetic-susceptibility measurements[4] (free radicals tend to be paramagnetic, while nonradicals are diamagnetic). Each of the methods has its weaknesses. The spectroscopic method is often rendered inaccurate by side reactions that yield colored products. The molecular-weight method often depends upon a small difference between two large numbers, one of which cannot be determined too accurately. It is also somewhat restricted to specific temperatures, such as the melting point and boiling point of the solvent. The magnetic method was long thought to be relatively reliable, but it has since been shown that previously

---

[1] M. Gomberg, *Ber.*, **33**, 3150 (1900); *J. Am. Chem. Soc.*, **22**, 757 (1900).

[2] J. Piccard, *Ann.*, **381**, 347 (1911); K. Ziegler and L. Ewald, *Ann.*, **473**, 163 (1929).

[3] M. Gomberg and L. H. Cone, *Ber.*, **37**, 2037 (1904); W. Schlenk, T. Weickel, and A. Herzenstein, *Ann.*, **372**, 1 (1910); M. Gomberg and C. S. Schoepfle, *J. Am. Chem. Soc.*, **39**, 1652 (1917); **41**, 1655 (1919).

[4] (*a*) N. W. Taylor, *J. Am. Chem. Soc.*, **48**, 854 (1926); (*b*) E. Müller, I. Müller-Rodloff, and W. Bunge, *Ann.*, **520**, 235 (1935); (*c*) M. F. Roy and C. S. Marvel, *J. Am. Chem. Soc.*, **59**, 2622 (1937).

used corrections for the diamagnetic contributions to the susceptibility are very probably much too low and that it would be extremely difficult to make an accurate correction.[5] Independently of the method of measurement, there are a large number of experimental precautions that should be taken in studies of this sort if the results are to be dependable. In most of the reported investigations not all of these precautions were taken.

The ease of dissociation of hexaarylethanes (compared, say, to that of ethane itself) may be described in terms of two factors. One of these, the resonance stabilization of the triarylmethyl radicals, results in a reluctance of these radicals to form a covalent bond to any atom or radical. The other, presumably a steric hindrance factor, results in an added reluctance of triarylmethyl radicals to form covalent bonds to themselves (or other bulky groups). We shall discuss the factors by comparison of the triphenylmethyl radical with the unsubstituted methyl radical as a standard. Bent and Cuthbertson have found the hydrogenolysis of hexaphenylethane to be exothermic by about 35 kcal/mole in solution.[6] When this thermochemical equation is combined with

$$(C_6H_5)_3CC(C_6H_5)_3 + H_2 \rightarrow 2(C_6H_5)_3CH \qquad \Delta H = -35 \text{ kcal}$$

those for the association of triphenylmethyl radicals and of hydrogen atoms,

$$
\begin{array}{ll}
2(C_6H_5)_3C\cdot \rightarrow (C_6H_5)_3CC(C_6H_5)_3 & \Delta H = -10 \text{ kcal} \\
2H\cdot \rightarrow H_2 & \Delta H = -103 \text{ kcal}
\end{array}
$$

we get
$$
\begin{array}{ll}
2(C_6H_5)_3C\cdot + 2H\cdot \rightarrow 2(C_6H_5)_3CH & \Delta H = -148 \text{ kcal} \\
(C_6H_5)_3C\cdot + H\cdot \rightarrow (C_6H_5)_3CH & \Delta H = -74 \text{ kcal}
\end{array}
$$

Thus the tertiary carbon-hydrogen bond–dissociation energy is found to be 74 kcal/mole, or 28 kcal smaller than the value (102 kcal[7]) for the formation of our standard methyl radical from methane.

Further data by Bent and coworkers show that the heat of combination of triphenylmethyl radicals with oxygen to form triphenylmethyl peroxide is −50 kcal/mole (of peroxide).[8] If we assume that the single bond

[5] P. W. Selwood and R. M. Dobres, *J. Am. Chem. Soc.*, **72**, 3860 (1950); T. L. Chu and S. I. Weissman, *J. Am. Chem. Soc.*, **73**, 4462 (1951).

[6] H. E. Bent and G. R. Cuthbertson, *J. Am. Chem. Soc.*, **58**, 170 (1936).

[7] H. C. Andersen and G. B. Kistiakowsky, *J. Chem. Phys.*, **11**, 10 (1943); G. B. Kistiakowsky and E. R. Van Artsdalen, *J. Chem. Phys.*, **12**, 469 (1944).

[8] H. E. Bent, G. R. Cuthbertson, M. Dorfman, and R. E. Leary, *J. Am. Chem. Soc.*, **58**, 165 (1936).

energies of Table 1-4 are applicable to dimethyl peroxide, we may calculate that the combination of two methyl radicals with an oxygen molecule should be exothermic by about 81 kcal/mole, or 31 kcal more so than triphenylmethyl radicals. In contrast to these figures of 28 and 31 kcal, the heat of dimerization of methyl radicals (85 kcal) is 74 kcal greater than that of triphenylmethyl radicals. Thus, of the 74 kcal greater ease of dissociation of hexaphenylethane compared to ethane, it seems reasonable to attribute rather more than half to steric interactions between bulky phenyl groups on adjacent carbon atoms and somewhat less than half to resonance stabilization of the triphenylmethyl radicals.

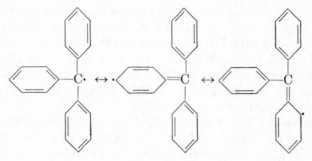

The resonance stabilization of this radical would probably be much greater if coplanarity of the molecule were not prevented by steric interference between the o-hydrogen atoms of the phenyl groups.

Further support for a steric contribution to the ease of dissociation of hexaarylethanes is found in the observation that while methyl substituents in any position increase the extent of dissociation, those in the ortho position do so best.[9]   Also the observation that the carbon-carbon single bond is about 1.58 A in hexaphenylethane rather than the usual length of 1.54 A suggests that it is stretched by steric repulsions.[10]

Ziegler, Orth, and Weber have studied the rate of dissociation of hexaphenylethane by measuring its rate of combination with nitric oxide.[11] With a sufficiently high concentration of nitric oxide the reaction rate is independent of its concentration and simply first-order in hexaphenylethane. The rate-controlling step, then, must be dissociation to triphenylmethyl radicals, which combine with nitric oxide much more rapidly than they dimerize.

[9] C. S. Marvel, M. B. Mueller, C. M. Himel, and J. F. Kaplan, *J. Am. Chem. Soc.*, **61**, 2771 (1939); C. S. Marvel, J. F. Kaplan, and C. M. Himel, *J. Am. Chem. Soc.*, **63**, 1892 (1941).

[10] S. H. Bauer and J. Y. Beach, *J. Am. Chem. Soc.*, **64**, 1142 (1942).

[11] K. Ziegler, P. Orth, and K. Weber, *Ann.*, **504**, 131 (1933).

$$(C_6H_5)_3CC(C_6H_5)_3 \rightarrow 2(C_6H_5)_3C\cdot$$
$$(C_6H_5)_3C\cdot + NO \rightarrow (C_6H_5)_3C—NO$$

The rate constants thus found are in satisfactory agreement with ones obtained by somewhat similar methods involving the reaction of hexaphenylethane with iodine and with oxygen.[12] The reaction rate was measured in each of the following solvents: CCl_4, $CHCl_3$, $C_2H_4Br_2$, $C_6H_5NH_2$, C_2H_5OH, $C_6H_5CH_3$, $C_6H_5NO_2$, $C_6H_5N(CH_3)_2$, ClC_2H_4OH, $CH_2(CO_2C_2H_5)_2$, $NCCH_2CO_2C_2H_5$, $o\text{-}HOC_6H_4CO_2CH_3$, C_5H_5N, CH_3CN, and CS_2.[11,12] None of the rate constants determined differed from a mean value by as much as a factor of two. This striking independence of the nature of the solvent is found in most free-radical reactions except those (a large number) in which the solvent enters directly into the reaction by being attacked by an intermediate radical. The rate constants for a typical polar reaction would vary by a factor of millions or more in a range of solvents like that listed above. The nature of the solvent has also been found to have little effect on the magnitude of the *equilibrium* constant for dissociation.[13]

It is interesting that the *heat of activation* for dissociation of hexaphenylethane has been found to be about 20 kcal, considerably larger than the *heat of reaction* (about 10 kcal).[12] This shows that the recombination of triphenylmethyl radicals requires about 10 kcal of activation. Apparently the central carbon atom of the radical, having all three valences in the same plane, must begin to assume a tetrahedral configuration in order to form the new carbon-carbon bond; and this deviation from planarity results in a loss of resonance stabilization.

18-1b. Effect of Structure on the Dissociation of Hexaarylethanes and Related Compounds. Marvel and coworkers have used the magnetic method to determine the dissociation constants for a large number of hexaarylethanes and have found that alkyl, cyclohexyl, methoxy, and phenyl substituents all increase the extent of dissociation.[9,14] Since all of these groups are capable of electron donation, it is somewhat surprising to learn that electron-withdrawing groups also appear to increase radical stability. Tris-(p-nitrophenyl)methyl, for example, exists as a radical in the solid state.[15] Nevertheless, the presence of either type of substituent may permit extra contributing structures to be written. Those for p-alkyl groups show the operation of a type of hyperconjugation.

[12] K. Ziegler, L. Ewald, and P. Orth, *Ann.*, **479**, 277 (1930); K. Ziegler, A. Seib, F. Knoevenagel, P. Herte, and F. Andrews, *Ann.*, **551**, 150 (1942).

[13] K. Ziegler and L. Ewald, *Ann.*, **473**, 163 (1929).

[14] C. S. Marvel and coworkers, *J. Am. Chem. Soc.*, **59**, 2622 (1937); **61**, 2008, 2769 (1939); **62**, 1550 (1940); **66**, 415, 914 (1944).

[15] F. L. Allen and S. Sugden, *J. Chem. Soc.*, 440 (1936).

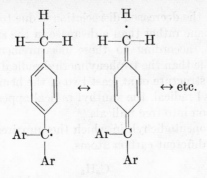

With *p*-nitro groups we may write structures of the type

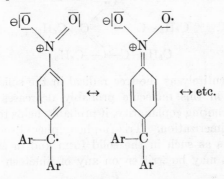

Dipole-dipole repulsions are also probably important in promoting dissociation of hexaarylethanes.

The effect of certain fused-ring systems on radical stability has also been studied. The dimer of the 9-phenylfluoryl radical,

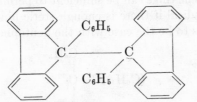

is colorless and hence presumably undissociated in solution at room temperature. The brown color formed reversibly upon heating suggests that dissociation does occur at higher temperatures. It has been stated that the decrease in dissociation (compared to hexaphenylethane) is due to a smaller amount of resonance energy in the radical.[16] On the other hand, according to the measurements of Bent and Cline, who find that the heat of reaction with oxygen is about 20 kcal less than it is for

[16] L. C. Pauling and G. W. Wheland, *J. Chem. Phys.*, **1**, 362 (1933).

hexaphenylethane, the decreased dissociation is due to an increase in the stability of the ethane rather than a decrease in the stability of the free radical.[17] In fact, according to these measurements the radical is probably *more* stable than the triphenylmethyl radical (it has the advantage of a coplanar structure of at least two of the benzene rings).

Unlike the fluoryl radical, the xanthyl radical appears to increase the extent of dissociation into free radicals.[18]

Pentaphenylcyclopentadienyl, in which the unpaired electron may be written on twenty different carbon atoms,

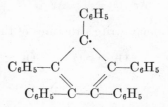

appears to exist entirely as the free radical in the solid form.[19] While steric hindrance in this molecule probably decreases the amount of resonance by preventing coplanarity, it probably helps to aid dissociation by hampering dimerization. Tris-(*p*-phenylphenyl)methyl is another radical that exists as such in the solid form and in solution.[4b,5] The unpaired electron may be written on any of nineteen different carbon atoms.

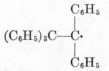

The resonance stabilization due to distribution of the unpaired electron over only two benzene rings can be sufficient to permit the formation of a fairly stable free radical if there is enough steric hindrance to dimerization. This appears to be the case with the pentaphenylethyl radical,

$$(C_6H_5)_3C—\overset{\displaystyle C_6H_5}{\underset{\displaystyle C_6H_5}{C}}\cdot$$

which exists (according to molecular weight determinations) entirely as the free radical in benzene solution.[20] This is probably due to a large extent to the large size of the triphenylmethyl group. Even a

[17] H. E. Bent and J. E. Cline, *J. Am. Chem. Soc.*, **58**, 1624 (1936).

[18] J. B. Conant and coworkers, *J. Am. Chem. Soc.*, **47**, 572, 3068 (1925); **48**, 1743 (1926); **49**, 2080 (1927); **51**, 1925 (1929).

[19] E. Müller and I. Müller-Rodloff, *Ber.*, **69B**, 665 (1936).

[20] W. Schlenk and H. Mark, *Ber.*, **55B**, 2285 (1922).

t-butyl group can be effective in this position. Conant and Bigelow observed that tetraphenyldi-*t*-butylethane forms a yellow color reversibly when its benzene solution is heated to about 50°.[21] That this represents dissociation to radicals is also shown by the rapid absorption of the theoretical amount of oxygen even at room temperature (where a slight yellow color is present).

There are a number of compounds which do not dissociate sufficiently under ordinary conditions to yield a directly measurable concentration of free radicals but which may be shown by somewhat less direct methods to dissociate under fairly mild conditions. Conant and Evans have found that a number of 9,9'-dialkyl derivatives of bixanthyl react with oxygen at room temperature at a rate which is independent of the oxygen concentration and which is first-order in the bixanthyl.[22] The rate-controlling step of the reaction is presumably a dissociation to two 9-alkylxanthyl radicals. Bachmann and Wiselogle observed that penta-arylethanes, upon heating, disproportionate to hexaarylethanes and tetraarylethanes, probably by the mechanism[23]

$$(C_6H_5)_3CCH(C_6H_5)_2 \rightleftharpoons (C_6H_5)_3C\cdot + (C_6H_5)_2CH\cdot$$
$$2(C_6H_5)_3C\cdot \rightleftharpoons (C_6H_5)_3CC(C_6H_5)_3$$
$$2(C_6H_5)_2CH\cdot \rightarrow (C_6H_5)_2CHCH(C_6H_5)_2$$

The rate of reaction has been determined for a number of derivatives, and the effect of structure on reactivity has been discussed.[23,24]

18-1c. Diradicals of the Triphenylmethyl Type. A considerable amount of research has been directed toward learning whether certain compounds have the diradical structure I or the quinoid structure II.

I and II cannot simply be two contributing structures for the same molecule, since I has two unpaired electrons and II has none (Sec. 1-1*a*, rule 5). Structure II is favored by having one more covalent bond than I. However I has the advantage of the resonance stabilization of *n* more benzene rings. We would therefore expect an increase in *n* to favor I. This appears to be the case.

[21] J. B. Conant and N. M. Bigelow, *J. Am. Chem. Soc.*, **50**, 2041 (1928).
[22] J. B. Conant and M. W. Evans, *J. Am. Chem. Soc.*, **51**, 1925 (1929).
[23] W. E. Bachmann and F. Y. Wiselogle, *J. Org. Chem.*, **1**, 354 (1936).
[24] J. Coops, H. Galenkamp, J. Haantjes, H. L. Luirink, and W. T. Nauta, *Rec. trav. chim.*, **67**, 469 (1948).

According to magnetic-susceptibility measurements the compound for which $n = 1$ and the one (known as the Chichibabin hydrocarbon) for which $n = 2$ do not have structure I to any detectable extent,[25,26] but for $n = 3$ and 4 there is a detectable fraction of material with structure I in equilibrium with the more stable II.[27] Schwab and Agliardi studied some of these compounds by a more sensitive and probably more reliable method based on the fact that free radicals catalyze the conversion of p- to o-hydrogen.[28] They found that not more than 0.2 per cent of the compound where $n = 1$ was present as a diradical but that about 10 per cent of the Chichibabin hydrocarbon ($n = 2$) was.

By the method of paramagnetic resonance absorption the Chichibabin hydrocarbon has been found to be 4 to 5 per cent diradical in character.[29]

Diradicals may also be favored by making quinoid structures impossible, as in the Schlenk hydrocarbon,

$$(C_6H_5)_2\overset{\bullet}{C}\!-\!-\overset{\bullet}{C}(C_6H_5)_2$$

whose diradical character is readily detectable even by magnetic-susceptibility measurements.[26]

The diradical structure may also be favored by steric interference with the coplanarity necessary for the maximum stability of the quinoid form. Müller and Neuhoff have shown this to be the case by synthesizing the compound

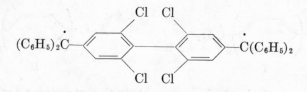

and observing that it has enough diradical character to detect by magnetic measurements.[30]

[25] E. Müller, Z. Elektrochem., **45,** 593 (1939).

[26] E. Müller and I. Müller-Rodloff, Ann., **517,** 134 (1935).

[27] E. Müller and H. Pfanz, Ber., **74B,** 1051, 1075 (1941).

[28] G.-M. Schwab and N. Agliardi, Ber., **73B,** 95 (1940).

[29] C. A. Hutchison, Jr., A. Kowalsky, R. C. Pastor, and G. W. Wheland, J. Chem. Phys., **20,** 1485 (1952).

[30] E. Müller and H. Neuhoff, Ber., **72B,** 2063 (1939); cf. E. Müller and E. Tietz, Ber., **74B,** 807 (1941).

18-2. Nitrogen, Oxygen, and Sulfur Free Radicals. *18-2a. Radicals with the Unpaired Electron on Nitrogen.* Wieland found that when the colorless solution of tetraphenylhydrazine in toluene is heated, a greenish-brown color is formed reversibly.[31] This is attributed to dissociation to the diphenylamino radical.

$$(C_6H_5)_2NN(C_6H_5)_2 \rightleftharpoons 2(C_6H_5)_2N\cdot$$

In agreement with this suggestion, Cain and Wiselogle have found that at a pressure of greater than 0.2 atm nitric oxide reacts with tetraphenylhydrazine to give diphenylnitrosoamine at a rate independent of the nitric oxide concentration and first-order in that of the hydrazine.[32] The rate-controlling step of this reaction is apparently a dissociation to the diphenylamino radical, which then reacts with nitric oxide more rapidly than it dimerizes. It has also been found that tetraphenylhydrazine and hexaphenylethane, each of which is considerably dissociated at 90°, react at about this temperature to yield the tertiary amines expected from a coupling of unlike radicals.[31]

$$(C_6H_5)_3CC(C_6H_5)_3 + (C_6H_5)_2NN(C_6H_5)_2 \rightarrow 2(C_6H_5)_3CN(C_6H_5)_2 \quad (18\text{-}1)$$

This amine is not dissociated even at considerably higher temperatures. Analogous to the fact that bonds between unlike atoms tend to be stronger than those between like atoms (Sec. 1-3c), it is rather generally found that unlike radicals couple to form stronger bonds than identical radicals. With regard to reaction (18-1) we may see from Table 1-4 that two typical carbon-nitrogen bonds should have a greater combined strength than one carbon-carbon and one nitrogen-nitrogen bond. This greater strength of the bond between unlike radicals may be found even when the bond joins identical (but differently substituted) atoms, as when both are carbon, and presumably has the same source as that for bonds between unlike atoms, viz., the added resonance contribution of ionic structures. Wieland reports that the electron-withdrawing *p*-nitro group decreases the ease of dissociation of tetraphenylhydrazine, while the *p*-methoxy and *p*-dimethylamino groups increase it.[31] Molecular-weight determinations show that tetra-(*p*-dimethylaminophenyl)hydrazine is appreciably dissociated in benzene and nitrobenzene solutions even at room temperature.

Tetrazane derivatives are in general even more highly dissociated than the related hydrazines. The white crystalline hexaphenyltetrazane (III) gives blue solutions that disobey Beer's law, become more deeply

[31] H. Wieland, *Ann.*, **381**, 200 (1911); *Ber.*, **48**, 1078 (1915); "Die Hydrazine," pp. 71ff., Ferd. Enke Verlag, Stuttgart, 1913.

[32] C. K. Cain and F. Y. Wiselogle, *J. Am. Chem. Soc.*, **62**, 1163 (1940).

colored at higher temperatures, and react with nitric oxide and with triphenylmethyl to yield the expected products.[33]   This radical may be

$$(C_6H_5)_2N—N—N—N(C_6H_5)_2 \rightleftharpoons 2(C_6H_5)_2\overset{\cdot}{N}—NC_6H_5$$

$$\underset{C_6H_5}{\diagup} \qquad \underset{C_6H_5}{\diagdown}$$

III

stabilized by electron-withdrawing groups on the lone phenyl group. The compound 1,1-diphenyl-2-picrylhydrazyl (IV), for example, exists entirely as a free radical, both in solution and in the solid state.   This has been established both by molecular-weight determinations[34] and magnetic-susceptibility studies.[4b,35]   Some of the contributing structures below show how the electron-withdrawing power of the nitro group may aid in the stabilization of this radical.

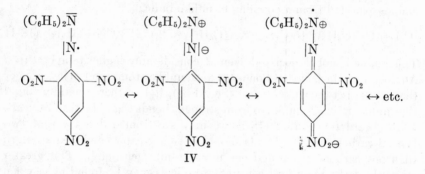

IV

Goldschmidt and coworkers have found that the dissociation of the tetraphenyldibenzoyltetrazane, V, is increased by electron-donating substituents on the phenyl groups and decreased by electron-withdrawing substituents there.[36]

$$(C_6H_5)_2N—N—N—N(C_6H_5)_2 \rightleftharpoons 2(C_6H_5)_2\overset{\cdot}{N}—NCOC_6H_5$$

$$\underset{C_6H_5CO}{|} \qquad \underset{COC_6H_5}{|}$$

V

[33] S. Goldschmidt, *Ber.*, **53**, 44 (1920).

[34] S. Goldschmidt and K. Renn, *Ber.*, **55**, 628 (1922).

[35] (a) H. Katz, *Z. Physik.*, **87**, 238 (1933); (b) J. Turkevich and P. W. Selwood, *J. Am. Chem. Soc.*, **63**, 1077 (1941).

[36] S. Goldschmidt, A. Wolf, E. Wolffhardt, I. Drimmer, and S. Nathan, *Ann.*, **437**, 194 (1924); S. Goldschmidt and J. Bader, *Ann.*, **473**, 137 (1929).

Schwartz and Wilmarth have pointed out that the data obey the Hammett equation, with ρ being -2.6.[37]

Trivalent nitrogen free radicals are also known.   One type includes the so-called Würster salts which are prepared by the oxidation of p-phenylenediamine derivatives at the proper pH.   The formation of the resonance-stabilized radical shown below has been proved by study of the oxidation-reduction curves at various pH's, spectroscopic measurements, and magnetic-susceptibility determinations.[38]   This species is,

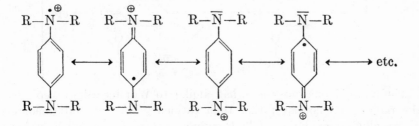

of course, both an ion and a free radical.   The tri-p-tolylaminium ion, which may be prepared by the oxidation of tri-p-tolylamine, is also in this category.[35a,39]   The oxidation of N,N-diphenylhydroxylamine yields

$$(p\text{-}CH_3C_6H_4)_3\overset{\oplus}{N} \cdot \leftrightarrow \text{etc.}$$

a radical[4a,35a,40] that is perhaps as much an oxygen as a nitrogen free radical.

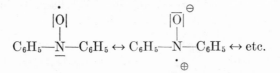

18-2b. Oxygen and Sulfur Free Radicals.   Bis-(9-ethoxy-10-phenanthryl) peroxide has been shown by magnetic methods to undergo a light-catalyzed dissociation to the 9-ethoxy-10-phenanthroxy radical.[41]

[37] N. Schwartz and W. K. Wilmarth, *J. Chem. Phys.*, **20**, 748 (1952).

[38] L. Michaelis, *Chem. Rev.*, **16**, 243 (1935).

[39] P. Rumpf and F. Trombe, *Compt. rend.*, **206**, 671 (1938); *J. chim. phys.*, **35**, 110 (1938).

[40] L. Cambi, *Gazz. chim. ital.*, **63**, 579 (1933).

[41] H. G. Cutforth and P. W. Selwood, *J. Am. Chem. Soc.*, **70**, 278 (1948).

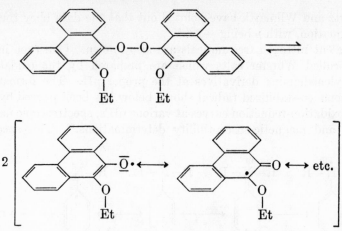

The semiquinones are somewhat similar to Würster salts except that the radicals are anions rather than cations. They are intermediates in the alkaline oxidation of hydroquinones to quinones and have been investigated thoroughly by Michaelis.[38,42]

Schlenk and Weickel found that the blue solution formed by the reaction of benzophenone with sodium in ether reacted rapidly with iodine or oxygen to regenerate the ketone.[43] From this and other evidence they suggested that the metal ketyl, VI, a salt whose anion is also a radical, is formed. Magnetic measurements have shown that an equilibrium is established between the metal ketyl and its dimer, a metal pinacolate.[44]

$$(C_6H_5)_2 - C - \overset{\ominus}{O} \overset{\oplus}{Na}$$
$$| \rightleftharpoons$$
$$(C_6H_5)_2 - C - \overset{\ominus}{O} \overset{\oplus}{Na}$$

$$2Na^+ + 2\left[\ C_6H_5 - \overset{\overset{\displaystyle \cdot}{|O|}}{\underset{\ominus}{C}} - C_6H_5 \leftrightarrow C_6H_5 - \overset{\overset{\displaystyle \ominus}{|\overline{O}|}}{\underset{\cdot}{C}} - C_6H_5 \leftrightarrow etc.\ \right]$$

VI

[42] L. Michaelis and M. P. Schubert, *Chem. Rev.*, **22**, 437 (1938).

[43] W. Schlenk and T. Weickel, *Ber.*, **44**, 1182 (1911).

[44] S. Sugden, *Trans. Faraday Soc.*, **30**, 18 (1934); R. N. Doescher and G. W. Wheland, *J. Am. Chem. Soc.*, **56**, 2011 (1934).

Cutforth and Selwood have shown by means of magnetic methods that bis-(2-benzothiazolyl) disulfide dissociates reversibly to form measurable concentrations of free radicals at 100° and above.[41]

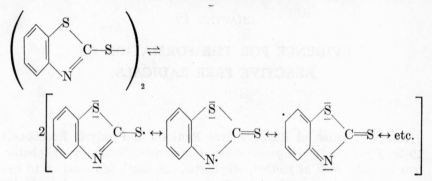

CHAPTER 19

EVIDENCE FOR THE FORMATION OF
REACTIVE FREE RADICALS

19-1. Formation of Reactive Free Radicals in Pyrolysis Reactions.
19-1a. Pyrolysis of Organometallic Compounds. Ordinary aliphatic
free radicals, such as methyl, ethyl, etc., are much too reactive to be
produced and kept at the fairly high concentrations required for their
study by the methods used for triphenylmethyl and related radicals.
Accordingly, it has been necessary to adopt other techniques.

The first work to yield good evidence for the formation of radicals of
this type was that of Paneth and Hofeditz,[1] who used a modification of a
method by which atomic hydrogen had been previously studied.[2] A

Pb(CH$_3$)$_4$ in H$_2$ →   → To liquid air
trap and pump

B   *A*

FIG. 19-1. Schematic diagram of apparatus used by Paneth and Hofeditz to study
tetramethyllead decomposition.

stream of an inert gas, such as hydrogen or nitrogen, containing some
tetramethyllead vapor was allowed to flow through a glass tube. If the
tube was heated strongly at any point *A* (Fig. 19-1), a lead mirror was
deposited on the wall of the tube at this point. Thus the heat had
caused the decomposition of the tetramethyllead to yield metallic lead
as one product. Evidence as to the nature of another product was
obtained by subsequently heating the tube at a point *B* upstream from
the lead mirror deposited at *A*. When this was done, a new mirror was
deposited at *B* and the old mirror at *A* was removed. It seemed reasonable that it was methyl radicals formed by the decomposition of tetra-
methyl lead at *B* that combined with and removed the lead at *A*. This
hypothesis was confirmed when it was shown that the product of the
removal of lead at *A* could be caught in a liquid air trap and identified
as tetramethyllead. It was further shown that removal of bismuth,
zinc, and antimony mirrors could be brought about with the formation

[1] F. A. Paneth and W. Hofeditz, *Ber.*, **62**, 1335 (1929).
[2] K. F. Bonhoeffer, *Z. physik. Chem.*, **113**, 199 (1924).

of their methyl derivatives. Mirrors were not removed by the carrier gases, hydrogen, nitrogen, etc., nor by possible decomposition products such as methane, ethane, ethylene, and acetylene. Under given conditions, the rate of disappearance of the metal at A was found to decrease as the distance between A and B increased. This showed that the methyl radicals disappeared rather rapidly after they were formed. When hydrogen was used as the carrier gas, most of the methyl radicals appeared as methane, but when the carrier was nitrogen or helium, the principal product was ethane.

By the same technique tetraethyllead was shown to yield ethyl radicals.[3] Tetrabenzyltin similarly yielded benzyl radicals, but the gaseous products of the decomposition of tetra-n-propyllead and tetraisobutyllead removed zinc and antimony mirrors to form dimethylzinc and $(CH_3)_2Sb$—$Sb(CH_3)_2$, respectively.[4] Apparently if any n-propyl or isobutyl radicals are formed, they decompose very rapidly.

19-1b. *Pyrolysis of Other Types of Organic Compounds.* The formation of free radicals upon heating is not a special characteristic of certain types of compounds. It appears that essentially all organic compounds will decompose to give radicals if heated to a high enough temperature. Rice, Johnston, and Evering secured the first good evidence that this is true.[5] They found that a large number of different organic compounds, including hydrocarbons, alcohols, aldehydes, ketones, ethers, and acids, removed metallic mirrors following pyrolysis at 800 to 1000° in an apparatus of the type used by Paneth. No organometallic compounds containing other than methyl or ethyl groups could be detected in the products of reaction with metallic mirrors. It is suggested that at the pyrolysis temperature higher radicals decompose to lower radicals and olefins, e.g.,[6]

$$CH_3CH_2CH_2\cdot \rightarrow CH_3\cdot + CH_2{=}CH_2$$
$$(CH_3)_2CHCH_2\cdot \rightarrow CH_3\cdot + CH_3CH{=}CH_2$$

Although most compounds will give radicals when heated to high enough temperatures, it does not follow that *all* high-temperature vapor-phase reactions are free-radical in character. Some have been shown to be reactions of the four-center type (Chap. 24). The mechanisms of high-temperature vapor-phase pyrolysis reactions have been studied with great care by a number of capable investigators. Steacie has written an authoritative and comprehensive monograph on this work.[7] In later

---

[3] F. A. Paneth and W. Lautsch, *Ber.*, **64B**, 2702 (1931).

[4] F. A. Paneth and W. Lautsch, *J. Chem. Soc.*, 380 (1935).

[5] F. O. Rice, W. R. Johnston, and B. L. Evering, *J. Am. Chem. Soc.*, **54**, 3529 (1932).

[6] F. O. Rice, *J. Am. Chem. Soc.*, **53**, 1959 (1931).

[7] E. W. R. Steacie, "Atomic and Free Radical Reactions," 2d ed., Reinhold Publishing Corporation, New York, 1954.

sections we shall discuss the mechanisms of the free-radical decompositions of a number of classes of compounds in more detail, particularly for certain compounds which decompose in solution at temperatures below 200° and which are therefore useful as initiators in free-radical-catalyzed reactions.

19-2. Other Methods of Forming Free Radicals. 19-2a. Photolysis.

By removing metallic mirrors with the radicals formed, Pearson[8] verified earlier suggestions that the photolysis of acetone involves the intermediate formation of free radicals. Analysis of the organometallic compounds formed in mirror removals shows that photolysis produces methyl radicals from acetone,[9] ethyl radicals from diethyl ketone,[9] and both phenyl and methyl radicals from acetophenone.[10] Since biacetyl has been found in the photolysis reaction mixture from acetone, it appears likely that acetyl radicals are also an intermediate in the reaction.[11,12] From the sharp decrease in the yield of biacetyl which accompanies an increase in the reaction temperature, it seems that the acetyl radicals are easily decarbonylated. Methane, ethane, carbon monoxide, biacetyl, methyl ethyl ketone, and acetonyl acetone have been found as reaction products under conditions where only a small fraction of the acetone used was allowed to decompose. The relative amounts of these products formed depend on the reaction temperature, the acetone concentration, and other variables. Noyes and Dorfman have considered these and other data in summarizing the evidence for the following reaction mechanism.[13]

$$CH_3COCH_3 \xrightarrow{h\nu} CH_3\cdot + CH_3CO\cdot$$
$$CH_3\cdot + CH_3CO\cdot \rightarrow CH_3COCH_3$$
$$CH_3CO\cdot \rightarrow CH_3\cdot + CO$$
$$2CH_3\cdot \rightarrow CH_3CH_3$$
$$2CH_3CO\cdot \rightarrow CH_3COCOCH_3 \qquad (19\text{-}1)$$
$$CH_3\cdot + CH_3COCH_3 \rightarrow CH_4 + CH_3COCH_2\cdot$$
$$CH_3\cdot + CH_3COCH_2\cdot \rightarrow CH_3COCH_2CH_3$$
$$2CH_3COCH_2\cdot \rightarrow CH_3COCH_2CH_2COCH_3$$
$$CH_3CO\cdot + CH_3COCH_2\cdot \rightarrow CH_3COCH_2COCH_3$$

The situation would become even more complicated if the reaction were allowed to proceed long enough for a significant amount of attack by the various free radicals on the products shown.

[8] T. G. Pearson, *J. Chem. Soc.*, 1718 (1934).

[9] T. G. Pearson and R. H. Purcell, *J. Chem. Soc.*, 1151 (1935).

[10] H. H. Glazebrook and T. G. Pearson, *J. Chem. Soc.*, 589 (1939).

[11] M. Barak and D. W. G. Style, *Nature*, **135**, 307 (1935).

[12] R. Spence and W. Wild, *Nature*, **138**, 206 (1936); *J. Chem. Soc.*, 352 (1937).

[13] W. A. Noyes, Jr. and L. M. Dorfman, *J. Chem. Phys.*, **16**, 788 (1948).

Under certain conditions the principal reaction products are carbon monoxide and ethane. It has been suggested that the reaction involves a direct rearrangement of the acetone into these two products without the intermediate formation of radicals. Dorfman and Noyes, however, have shown that such a mechanism cannot contribute significantly to the total reaction, since the ratio of methane to ethane formed increases as the intensity of catalyzing light is decreased, and at sufficiently low intensities considerably more methane than ethane is produced.[14] The direct mechanism, which offers no explanation for these data, is apparently not of great importance, if it occurs at all. Mechanism (19-1) provides a good explanation of the data, since ethane is formed by a reaction second-order in radicals and methane by one first-order in radicals and since the radical concentrations should decrease with decreasing light intensity. The mechanism has met other tests which Noyes and Dorfman describe.[13]

It might be thought that the large amount of energy given off by the pairing of electrons might make the pairing of radicals occur with great ease. This is often so (allowing for the fact that the concentration of reactive radicals can never be very large), but in the case of atoms and some very simple radicals it is just this energy which proves the reaction's undoing. The energy remains in the molecule and is usually not lost readily as a quantum of light. In a complex molecule the energy is distributed over the whole molecule, adding to the energy of a number of internal vibrations and rotations. It is very improbable that all of the energy will be concentrated in one bond so as to cause its rupture before the molecule is energetically equilibrated with the rest of the system by collisions with other molecules and the walls of the container. In a diatomic molecule, however, the energy must be transferred by collision *very* quickly after the molecule is formed or it will dissociate again. For this reason most atom- and some simple radical-pairing reactions occur only at walls or in the gas phase at termolecular collisions where the third colliding molecule may absorb some of the energy given off.

19-2b. *Reaction of Organic Halides with Sodium Vapor.*[15] Von Hartel and Polanyi studied the vapor-phase reaction between sodium and certain organic halides by a technique that has been used a great deal subsequently. At elevated temperatures and reduced pressures they let sodium vapor in an inert carrier gas, such as hydrogen or nitrogen, flow through a nozzle into a reaction vessel containing an organic halide and carrier gas.[16] The reaction appears to involve radical formation. With

[14] L. M. Dorfman and W. A. Noyes, Jr., *J. Chem. Phys.*, **16**, 557 (1948).

[15] Much of the work on this subject has been summarized by E. Warhurst, *Quart. Revs. (London)*, **5**, 44 (1951).

[16] H. von Hartel and M. Polanyi, *Z. physik. Chem.*, **11B**, 97 (1930).

hydrogen as a carrier gas methyl halides yield methane. The best evidence for radical formation in this reaction is due to Horn, Polanyi, and Style, who used a reactor like that shown in Fig. 19-2, in which the effluent gases from the Na-RX reaction chamber, A, flowed into a second vessel, B, containing iodine vapor.[17] Under these conditions the reaction of methyl chloride yielded some methyl iodide. The reaction scheme must have been

$$CH_3Cl + Na \rightarrow NaCl + CH_3 \cdot \overset{I_2}{\rightarrow} CH_3I$$

since methyl chloride does not react with iodine under the conditions used and since the methyl iodide cannot be formed from a sodium compound because all of the sodium is used up in reaction vessel A, where

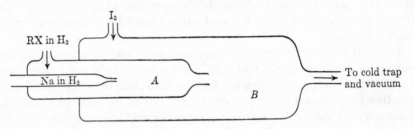

Fig. 19-2. Schematic diagram of apparatus for reaction of organic halides with sodium in the vapor phase.

it is deposited on the wall as sodium chloride. No sodium salts are deposited in vessel B or subsequently. Similar evidence has been obtained for the formation of the ethyl[17] and phenyl[18] radicals.

Von Hartel, Polanyi, and Meer determined the rate of reaction of a number of organic halides with sodium vapor.[16,19] This was done by using a sodium lamp to illuminate the transparent apparatus at the point where the sodium vapor flowed into an excess of organic halide. Since the sodium vapor was visible under the sodium lamp, it was possible to estimate how far the average sodium atom penetrated the halide vapor before reaction. From this distance the collision yield (the average number of collisions required to bring about reaction) was calculated. Some of the data obtained by these workers and by Warhurst[15] are shown in Table 19-1.

From the results shown it appears that radical stability is of importance in determining the reactivity but that polar effects (see Sec. 20-1c) are also present, electron-withdrawing groups increasing the reactivity

[17] E. Horn, M. Polanyi, and D. W. G. Style, *Z. physik. Chem.*, **23B**, 291 (1933); *Trans. Faraday Soc.*, **30**, 189 (1934).

[18] E. Horn and M. Polanyi, *Z. physik. Chem.*, **25B**, 151 (1934).

[19] H. von Hartel, N. Meer, and M. Polanyi, *Z. physik. Chem.*, **19B**, 139 (1932).

TABLE 19-1. REACTIVITIES OF ORGANIC HALIDES TOWARD SODIUM VAPOR AT 275°C[15,16,19]

Organic halide	Collision yield[a]	Organic halide	Collision yield[a]
CH_3F	$>10^6$	$CHCl_3$	100
CH_3Cl	10,000	CCl_4	25
CH_3Br	50	$CH_2{=}CHCl$	11,000
CH_3I	1	$CH_2{=}CHCH_2Cl$	250
C_2H_5Cl	7,000	$C_6H_5CH_2Cl$	~1
$n\text{-}C_3H_7Cl$	4,400	CH_3OCH_2Cl	2,780
$n\text{-}C_4H_9Cl$	3,300	C_2H_5OCOCl	1,220
$n\text{-}C_5H_{11}Cl$	2,200	CH_3COCl	20
$i\text{-}C_3H_7Cl$	3,300	$C_2H_5OCOCH_2Cl$	36
$t\text{-}C_4H_9Cl$	1,500	CH_3COCH_2Cl	5
CH_2Cl_2	900	$HOCH_2CH_2Cl$	980

[a] Average number of collisions required to bring about reaction.

toward the electron-donating sodium atom. No satisfying explanation has been advanced for the continued increase in reactivity with increasing length of the aliphatic chain.

19-2c. *Electrolysis.* It seems likely that a number of electrolysis reactions involve the formation of free radicals. Clusius and coworkers have described some of the evidence that the first step of the Kolbe electrolysis of salts of carboxylic acids is the loss of an electron by the carboxylate anion.[20] The observed products in the case of sodium propionate, for example, are explained on the basis of the following reactions:

$$CH_3CH_2CO_2^{\ominus} \xrightarrow{-e} CH_3CH_2CO_2\cdot$$
$$CH_3CH_2CO_2\cdot \rightarrow CH_3CH_2\cdot$$
$$2CH_3CH_2\cdot \rightarrow CH_2{=}CH_2 + CH_3CH_3 \qquad (19\text{-}2)$$
$$2CH_3CH_2\cdot \rightarrow CH_3CH_2CH_2CH_3$$
$$CH_3CH_2CO_2\cdot + CH_3CH_2\cdot \rightarrow CH_3CH_2CO_2CH_2CH_3 \qquad \text{etc.}$$

Such reactions as the methylation of trinitrotoluene, which takes place in the presence of electrolyzing sodium acetate,[21] probably involve the action of a methyl radical formed by decarboxylation of an acetoxy radical.

Free radicals also appear to be produced by the electrolysis of solutions of certain organometallic compounds. The electrolysis of solutions of ethylsodium in diethylzinc yields, at the anode, mostly ethane and

[20] P. Hölemann and K. Clusius, *Z. physik. Chem.*, **35B**, 261 (1937); W. Schanzer and K. Clusius, *Z. physik. Chem.*, **190A**, 241 (1941); **192A**, 273 (1943).
[21] L. F. Fieser, R. C. Clapp, and W. H. Daudt, *J. Am. Chem. Soc.*, **64**, 2052 (1942)

ethylene but also some methane, propane, and butane.[22] The first two compounds are probably formed by disproportionation and the latter by dimerization of ethyl radicals, as shown in the third and fourth equations of scheme (19-2). No explanation for methane and propane formation is apparent. Additional evidence for the formation of ethyl radicals is provided by the fact that tetraethyllead is formed if a lead anode is used. In view of the ability of zinc to increase its coordination number beyond two, it seems likely that in diethylzinc solution ethylsodium may exist as Na^+ and $Zn(C_2H_5)_4^=$ ions.

Evans and coworkers have explained the results of Grignard electrolysis experiments in terms of a free-radical mechanism.[23]

There is also evidence for the formation of free radicals in the bombardment of alkyl halides with neutrons,[24] alpha particles,[25] and X rays.[25]

19-2d. *Methylene Radicals.* The methylene radical, CH_2, appears to be formed in the pyrolysis of diazomethane.[26] When the pyrolysis is carried out by the technique used by Paneth with tetraalkyllead compounds, it is found that tellurium, selenium, antimony, and arsenic mirrors are removed, but zinc, cadmium, lead, thallium, and bismuth mirrors are not. These data show that it is not methyl radicals which are formed, because these would remove any of the mirrors described. The methylene radicals were further characterized by the identification of polytelluroformaldehyde, $(CH_2Te)_x$, as the product of removal of tellurium mirrors. The isolation of polytelluroformaldehyde has also been used as evidence for the formation of methylene radicals in the photolysis of diazomethane and of ketene.[27] In most of the experiments in which the methylene radical has been produced its principal reaction has been dimerization to ethylene.

In the methylene radical, two of carbon's four orbitals are used for bonding to hydrogen. From Hund's rules (Sec. 1-2) we should expect one of the two remaining electrons to be in each of the other two orbitals and these two electrons to be unpaired.[28]

[22] F. Hein, E. Petzchner, K. Wagler, and F. A. Segitz, *Z. anorg. u. allgem. Chem.,* **141,** 161 (1924).

[23] W. V. Evans and coworkers, *J. Am. Chem. Soc.,* **56,** 654 (1934); **58,** 720, 2284 (1936); **61,** 898 (1939); **62,** 534 (1940); **63,** 2574 (1941).

[24] E. Glückauf and J. W. J. Fay, *J. Chem. Soc.,* 390 (1936); C. S. Lu and S. Sugden, *J. Chem. Soc.,* 1273 (1939).

[25] H. Eyring, J. O. Hirschfelder, and H. S. Taylor, *J. Chem. Phys.,* **4,** 479 (1936); C. B. Allsopp, *Trans. Faraday Soc.,* **40,** 79 (1944); J. Weiss, *Nature,* **153,** 748 (1944).

[26] F. O. Rice and A. L. Glasebrook, *J. Am. Chem. Soc.,* **56,** 2381 (1934).

[27] T. G. Pearson, R. H. Purcell, and G. S. Saigh, *J. Chem. Soc.,* 409 (1938).

[28] Cf. K. J. Laidler and E. J. Casey, *J. Chem. Phys.,* **17,** 213 (1949).

CHAPTER 20

ADDITION OF FREE RADICALS TO OLEFINS

20-1. Vinyl Polymerization. *20-1a. Mechanism of Vinyl Polymerization.* Since the addition of a carbonium ion, carbanion, or free radical to an olefin should yield another intermediate of the same type, it is not surprising that vinyl polymerization may be catalyzed by either acids, bases, or free radicals.

$$R \overset{\oplus}{} + CH_2=CHX \rightarrow R CH_2 \overset{\oplus}{C}HX \overset{CH_2=CHX}{\longrightarrow} RCH_2CHXCH_2\overset{\oplus}{C}HX \rightarrow etc.$$

$$R \overset{\ominus}{} + CH_2=CHX \rightarrow R CH_2 \overset{\ominus}{C}HX \overset{CH_2=CHX}{\longrightarrow} RCH_2CHXCH_2\overset{\ominus}{C}HX \rightarrow etc.$$

$$R\cdot + CH_2=CHX \rightarrow R CH_2\overset{.}{C}HX \overset{CH_2=CHX}{\longrightarrow} RCH_2CHXCH_2\overset{.}{C}HX \rightarrow etc.$$

Of these three possible methods of polymerization the free-radical type is by far the most important.

There is good evidence that certain vinyl polymerizations proceed by a free-radical mechanism. Schulz and Wittig[1] found that tetraphenylsuccinonitrile, known to be about 1 per cent dissociated into free radicals, initiated the polymerization of styrene. The kinetics of the polymerization could be readily explained by a free-radical mechanism. Vinyl polymerizations have been found to be brought about by benzoyl peroxide,[2] triphenylmethylazobenzene,[3] N-nitrosoacylarylamines,[4] and several aliphatic azo compounds.[5] There is other evidence that all of these compounds decompose readily by a free-radical mechanism. Schulz showed that in the tetraphenylsuccinonitrile-initiated polymerization of styrene and methyl methacrylate[6] and the triphenylmethylazobenzene-initiated polymerization of styrene[3,6] approximately one polymer chain was formed per molecule of initiator used. The actual participation of the initiator in the reaction has been shown by the

[1] G. V. Schulz and G. Wittig, *Naturwissenschaften*, **27**, 387 (1939).

[2] G. V. Schulz and E. Husemann, *Z. physik. Chem.*, **39B**, 246 (1938).

[3] G. V. Schulz, *Naturwissenschaften*, **27**, 659 (1939).

[4] A. T. Blomquist, J. R. Johnson, and H. J. Sykes, *J. Am. Chem. Soc.*, **65**, 2446 (1943).

[5] F. M. Lewis and M. S. Matheson, *J. Am. Chem. Soc.*, **71**, 747 (1949).

[6] G. V. Schulz, *Z. Elektrochem.*, **47**, 265 (1941).

detection of chlorine in the polystyrene formed by chloroacetyl peroxide[7] and *p*-chlorobenzoyl peroxide initiation,[8] and of bromine in the polystyrene formed under the influence of *p*-bromobenzoyl peroxide,[7,8] 3,4,5-tribromobenzoyl peroxide,[9] and *m*-bromobenzoyl peroxide.[10] Fraenkel, Hirshon, and Walling have even identified free radicals formed during vinyl polymerization directly by paramagnetic resonance-absorption spectroscopy.[11] A number of structural studies on polymers[12] have verified the mechanistically probable hypothesis that vinyl monomers undergo, at least predominantly, head-to-tail polymerization as shown above rather than head-to-head and tail-to-tail polymerization to give

$$\cdots CH_2CHX-CHXCH_2-CH_2CHX-CHXCH_2 \cdots$$

Probably the principal reason why radicals almost always add to $CH_2=CHX$ to form the new radical on the substituted carbon atom is that practically all X groups stabilize radicals better than hydrogen does.

Free-radical polymerizations have mechanisms of the following general type.

$$I \rightarrow R\cdot \qquad (20\text{-}1)$$

$$R\cdot + CH_2{=}CHX \rightarrow RCH_2\dot{C}HX$$
$$RCH_2\dot{C}HX + CH_2{=}CHX \rightarrow R(CH_2CHX)_2\cdot \qquad (20\text{-}2)$$
$$R(CH_2CHX)_n\cdot + CH_2{=}CHX \rightarrow R(CH_2CHX)\cdot_{n+1}$$

$$R(CH_2CHX)_n\cdot + R\cdot \rightarrow R(CH_2CHX)_nR$$
$$R(CH_2CHX)_n\cdot + R(CH_2CHX)_m\cdot \rightarrow R(CH_2CHX)_n(CHXCH_2)_mR$$
$$\downarrow \qquad (20\text{-}3)$$
$$R(CH_2CHX)_nH + R(CH_2CHX)_{m-1}CH{=}CHX$$
$$R(CH_2CHX)_n\cdot + HS \rightarrow R(CH_2CHX)_nH + S\cdot$$

The reaction starts by what is known as the *initiation step* (20-1) in which the *initiator*, I, in some way yields a free radical (R·). In the *propagation*, or *chain-carrying*, steps (20-2) the free radical adds to an olefinic double bond to yield a new radical, which then adds to another molecule of olefin, etc., so that the polymer chain may become hundreds of monomer units long. This process may be interrupted by any of

[7] C. C. Price, R. W. Kell, and E. Krebs, *J. Am. Chem. Soc.*, **64**, 1103 (1942).

[8] P. D. Bartlett and S. G. Cohen, *J. Am. Chem. Soc.*, **65**, 543 (1943).

[9] C. C. Price and B. E. Tate, *J. Am. Chem. Soc.*, **65**, 517 (1943).

[10] H. F. Pfann, D. J. Salley, and H. Mark, *J. Am. Chem. Soc.*, **66**, 983 (1944).

[11] G. K. Fraenkel, J. M. Hirshon, and C. Walling, *J. Am. Chem. Soc.*, **76**, 3606 (1954).

[12] C. S. Marvel and E. C. Horning in H. Gilman, "Organic Chemistry," 2d ed., vol. 1, chap. 8, John Wiley & Sons, Inc., New York, 1943, and references given therein; cf. C. S. Marvel, E. D. Weil, L. B. Wakefield, and C. W. Fairbanks, *J. Am. Chem. Soc.*, **75**, 2326 (1953).

several types of *termination steps* (20-3). In the initiation step a reactive radical is created; in each propagation step one radical is used up and one is formed with no net change; while in the termination step one or more reactive radicals is destroyed. Termination may occur by the pairing of two radicals or by a disproportionation reaction between two radicals. In addition, there may be present in the reaction mixture an *inhibitor* like HS that is very reactive toward free radicals. This inhibitor may react with a *growing-chain radical* to yield a radical, S·, which is relatively incapable of adding to a monomer molecule and which thereby inhibits polymerization. Since the propagation step may occur hundreds of times to every occurrence of an initiation, termination, or inhibition step, the free-radical chain mechanism gives a very satisfactory explanation of how a few molecules of initiator may cause the polymerization of a large number of molecules of monomer, and similarly how a small amount of inhibitor may prevent the polymerization of a large amount of monomer. The action of inhibitor also explains the existence of an *induction period*, a period at the beginning of the reaction when no polymerization occurs, due to inhibition. Since the inhibitor is being used up during this period, the reaction begins to pick up speed as the inhibitor supply becomes exhausted.

Most of the italicized terms in the preceding paragraph are used generally not only in discussions of polymerization but in all types of chain-reaction mechanisms.

Many of the effects of changes in reactants and reaction conditions on the properties of the polymer produced may be explained in terms of a mechanism of the type just described. For example, an increase in the concentration of initiator causes a decrease in the average molecular weight of the resultant polymer. The increase in initiator concentration causes an increase in the number of growing-chain radicals. Since the rate of the polymerization (propagation) reaction is first-order in these radicals, there is an increase in polymerization rate. However, since the termination reaction is second-order in these radicals, its rate increases faster, and thus the average length of the polymer chains is shorter.[2]

The chain length, and hence molecular weight, of polymers formed by a free-radical mechanism may also be influenced by a process known as *chain transfer*. This reaction involves the abstraction, by the radical end of a growing-chain polymer, of an atom from another molecule to terminate the polymer chain but to create a new radical capable of bringing about further polymerization. The net result is that there may be a decrease in the average molecular weight of the polymer but no necessary decrease in the rate of polymerization. Chain-transfer agents (mercaptans are often used) are frequently introduced deliberately in order to control the molecular weight of the polymer and are sometimes called *regulators*. However, chain transfer may occur to many of the solvents in which polymerization has been studied, to unchanged monomer, or to previously formed polymer chains. In the latter case, of course, no decrease in average molecular weight occurs, since the process terminates one chain but adds to the length of another.

20-1*b*. *Absolute Rate Constants for Vinyl Polymerization.* Let us consider the mechanism of the benzoyl peroxide–catalyzed polymerization of vinyl acetate.[13] The benzoyl peroxide (P) acts as an initiator by decomposing to yield two free radicals (B) (Sec. 21-1*a*). We shall assume that essentially all of these radicals add to vinyl acetate monomer molecules (M) to form a growing-chain radical (R), that the rate constant for the addition of the growing-chain radical to monomer is independent of the chain length, and that termination is due to a bimolecular reaction between growing-chain radicals.

$$P \xrightarrow{k_1} 2B$$
$$B + M \rightarrow R$$
$$R + M \xrightarrow{k_2} R$$
$$R + R \xrightarrow{k_3} R—R \qquad \text{or disproportionation products}$$

Since vinyl acetate forms a polymer with fairly long chains, we may describe its polymerization rate, as measured by the rate of disappearance of monomer, by the equation

$$-\frac{dM}{dt} = k_2 RM \qquad (20\text{-}4)$$

ignoring the relatively small amount of monomer used up by reaction with the initiating radical B. Since the growing-chain radical should be quite reactive, we may use the steady-state treatment (Sec. 3-1*a*), in which we equate its rate of formation to its rate of disappearance. Having postulated that every initiating radical forms a growing-chain radical, we may say

$$2k_1 P = 2k_3 R^2 \qquad \text{or} \qquad R = \sqrt{\frac{k_1 P}{k_3}}$$

Substituting in (20-4),

$$-\frac{dM}{dt} = k_2 \sqrt{\frac{k_1}{k_3}} \, MP^{1/2} \qquad (20\text{-}5)$$

Nozaki and Bartlett[13] have found that the reaction is first-order in vinyl acetate and one-half-order in benzoyl peroxide, as required by Eq. (20-5) and the mechanism leading to it. The rate constant they obtain for the reaction will be equal to $k_2 \sqrt{k_1/k_3}$ in terms of the rate constants for

[13] K. Nozaki and P. D. Bartlett, *J. Am. Chem. Soc.*, **68**, 2377 (1946).

individual steps.   From separate experiments on benzoyl peroxide the value of k_1 may be determined.   From this a value of $k_2/\sqrt{k_3}$ may be determined, but by none of the ordinary methods of measuring polymerization rates has it been possible to obtain a rate constant (like k_2 or k_3) governing a reaction of a reactive growing-chain radical.

However, by use of a special technique known as the *rotating-sector method*, Melville determined the average life of intermediate radicals in the vapor-phase polymerization of methyl methacrylate.[14]   It appears that this method was first applied accurately to a liquid-phase polymerization by Bartlett and Swain,[15] who studied the radical-induced polymerization of vinyl acetate.   When the rotating-sector method is employed, an initiator is used whose decomposition to radicals is light-catalyzed.   The reaction vessel is illuminated by a beam of the catalyzing light.   This beam is required to pass through the area swept by a rotating opaque disk from which a sector has been cut.   Thus by rotation of the disk the reaction mixture may be subjected to alternate periods of light and dark of known duration.   Since the rate of decomposition of the initiator is directly proportional to the light intensity, we see from Eq. (20-5) that the polymerization rate will be proportional to the square root of the light intensity.

Let us consider the case where one-fourth of the opaque disk has been cut out, so that the dark periods are three times as long as the light periods.   When the disk is rotated slowly so that the periods of light and dark are relatively long, the concentration of growing-chain radicals (and therefore the rate, which is proportional to this concentration) will quickly increase at the beginning of a light period until the steady state is reached, where the rate of termination has become equal to the rate of initiation.   At the beginning of a dark period the rate will quickly fall to zero.   This situation is depicted in the plot of rate (or concentration of growing chains) vs. time shown in Fig. 20-1a.   When the disk is rotated more rapidly (Fig. 20-1b), the light period is too short for the reaction rate to approach the steady state closely, and the dark period is too short for the rate to fall very close to zero.   As the disk-rotation rate continues to increase, we begin (Fig. 20-1c) to approach the situation in which the light is uninterrupted but only one-fourth as intense.   Under these conditions the reaction will proceed one-half as fast as

[14] H. W. Melville, *Proc. Roy. Soc. (London)*, **163A,** 511 (1937).

[15] P. D. Bartlett and C. G. Swain, *J. Am. Chem. Soc.*, **67,** 2273 (1945); **68,** 2381 (1946); cf. G. M. Burnett and H. W. Melville, *Nature*, **156,** 661 (1945); *Proc. Roy. Soc. (London)*, **189A,** 456 (1947); G. M. Burnett, H. W. Melville, and L. Valentine, *Trans. Faraday Soc.*, **45,** 960 (1949); M. S. Matheson, E. E. Auer, E. B. Bevilacqua, and E. J. Hart, *J. Am. Chem. Soc.*, **71,** 2610 (1949); H. Kwart, H. S. Broadbent, and P. D. Bartlett, *J. Am. Chem. Soc.*, **72,** 1060 (1950).

during the light periods with slow disk rotation. Thus, from comparison of Figs. 20-1a and c, we see that as the rate of disk rotation is increased, the average polymerization rate over a full cycle of light and dark will double. Flory had shown that the rate of approach to the steady state is directly related to the ratio k_3/k_2.[16] Therefore k_3/k_2 may be determined from the rate of disk rotation at which the polymerization rate

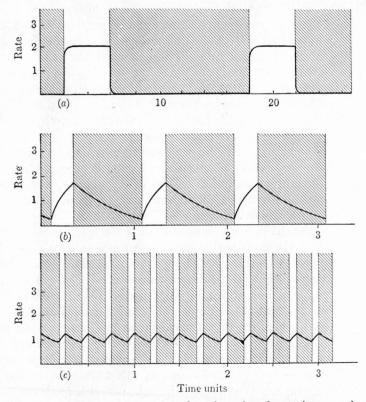

Fig. 20-1. Rate of polymerization plotted against time for various speeds of the rotating disk. Shaded areas represent dark periods; unshaded areas represent periods of illumination.

is the mean between the rate it approaches at slow rotation and that which it approaches at rapid rotation. From this value of k_3/k_2 and the value of $k_2/\sqrt{k_3}$, determined from ordinary methods of following polymerization rates, the individual values of k_2 and k_3 are obtained. The value of k_2 appears to be about 10^3 liters mole^{-1} sec^{-1} and that of k_3 about 3×10^7 liters mole^{-1} sec^{-1} for vinyl acetate at 25°.[15]

The rotating-sector method has been used to determine the absolute rate constants and steady-state concentration of growing-chain radicals

[16] P. J. Flory. *J. Am. Chem. Soc.*, **59**, 241 (1937).

for other polymerizations. This and other methods for obtaining such data have been reviewed by Burnett and Melville.[17]

20-1c. *Copolymerization.*[18] The polymerization of a mixture of two or more monomers, giving a polymer chain in which both monomers become units, is of great interest from the standpoint of theoretical organic chemistry as well as being of considerable commercial importance.

A satisfactory theoretical basis for comparing the behavior of monomers in copolymerization was published by three different groups of workers in 1944.[19-21] Expressed in the symbols later agreed upon by all three groups of workers,[22] this treatment may be stated as follows: In the copolymerization of the two monomers M_1 and M_2, the growing-chain radicals can be of only two kinds, those ending in an M_1 unit (designated $M_1\cdot$) and those ending in an M_2 unit ($M_2\cdot$). If we make the reasonable approximation that the reactivity of the growing-chain radical depends only upon the nature of the radical end, the polymer chain is seen to be propagated by only four types of reactions.

$$
\begin{aligned}
M_1\cdot + M_1 &\xrightarrow{k_{11}} M_1\cdot \\
M_1\cdot + M_2 &\xrightarrow{k_{12}} M_2\cdot \\
M_2\cdot + M_1 &\xrightarrow{k_{21}} M_1\cdot \\
M_2\cdot + M_2 &\xrightarrow{k_{22}} M_2\cdot
\end{aligned}
\tag{20-6}
$$

In the formation of polymers of relatively high molecular weight the amount of monomer consumed in initiation may be neglected. Thus the rate of disappearance of M_1 and M_2 is

$$
-\frac{d[M_1]}{dt} = k_{11}[M_1\cdot][M_1] + k_{21}[M_2\cdot][M_1]
$$

$$
-\frac{d[M_2]}{dt} = k_{12}[M_1\cdot][M_2] + k_{22}[M_2\cdot][M_2]
$$

and the relative rate of disappearance is

$$
\frac{d[M_1]}{d[M_2]} = \frac{k_{11}[M_1\cdot][M_1] + k_{21}[M_2\cdot][M_1]}{k_{12}[M_1\cdot][M_2] + k_{22}[M_2\cdot][M_2]}
\tag{20-7}
$$

[17] G. M. Burnett, *Quart. Revs. (London)*, **4**, 292 (1950); G. M. Burnett and H. W. Melville, *Chem. Rev.*, **54**, 225 (1954).

[18] For comprehensive and authoritative reviews of this topic see F. R. Mayo and C. Walling, *Chem. Rev.*, **46**, 191 (1950), and T. Alfrey, J. J. Bohrer, and H. Mark, "Copolymerization," Interscience Publishers, Inc., New York, 1952.

[19] T. Alfrey and G. Goldfinger, *J. Chem. Phys.*, **12**, 205 (1944).

[20] F. R. Mayo and F. M. Lewis, *J. Am. Chem. Soc.*, **66**, 1594 (1944).

[21] F. T. Wall, *J. Am. Chem. Soc.*, **66**, 2050 (1944).

[22] T. Alfrey, F. R. Mayo, and F. T. Wall, *J. Polymer Sci.*, **1**, 581 (1946).

We may assume that a steady state is soon reached at which the rate of conversion of $M_1 \cdot$ radicals to $M_2 \cdot$ radicals is equal to the rate of the reverse reaction.

$$k_{12}[M_1 \cdot][M_2] = k_{21}[M_2 \cdot][M_1] \tag{20-8}$$

Substituting the value of $[M_1 \cdot]$ from (20-8) into (20-7) and multiplying numerator and denominator by $[M_2]/k_{21}[M_2 \cdot]$, we obtain

$$\frac{d[M_1]}{d[M_2]} = \frac{[M_1]}{[M_2]} \frac{(k_{11}/k_{12})[M_1] + [M_2]}{(k_{22}/k_{21})[M_2] + [M_1]}$$

If we define r_1 as k_{11}/k_{12} and r_2 as k_{22}/k_{21}, this becomes

$$\frac{d[M_1]}{d[M_2]} = \frac{[M_1]}{[M_2]} \frac{r_1[M_1] + [M_2]}{r_2[M_2] + [M_1]} \tag{20-9}$$

The constants r_1 and r_2 are referred to as *monomer reactivity ratios*, since each is the ratio of the rate constant for the combination of the given type of radical with the corresponding monomer to its rate constant for combination with the other monomer.

Equation (20-9), which describes the relative rate at which two monomers enter the polymer chain in terms of their concentrations and of their monomer reactivity ratios, may be used in the differential form shown when the relative concentration of the monomers does not change greatly. The integration of (20-9) yields a more generally applicable (but considerably more complex) expression. The use of the integrated expression to obtain values for r_1 and r_2 is described by Mayo and Lewis[20] for the copolymerization of styrene and methyl methacrylate. The equations fit the experimental results quite satisfactorily, and Alfrey, Bohrer, and Mark have tabulated monomer reactivity ratios for 275 different pairs of monomers.[18] Equations developed to treat the copolymerization of three[23] and of n monomers[24] have also been found to give satisfactory results.[24,25]

In the case of the copolymerization of styrene and methyl methacrylate, Mayo and Lewis[20] obtained the values

$$r_1 = 0.50 \pm 0.02 \qquad r_2 = 0.50 \pm 0.02$$

These values mean that a growing-chain radical ending with a styrene unit has twice the tendency to combine with methyl methacrylate molecules that it has to combine with styrene. The methyl methacrylate–type radicals, on the other hand, show a preference for combination

[23] T. Alfrey and G. Goldfinger, *J. Chem. Phys.*, **12**, 322 (1944).

[24] C. Walling and E. R. Briggs, *J. Am. Chem. Soc.*, **67**, 1774 (1945).

[25] E. C. Chapin, G. E. Ham, and R. G. Fordyce, *J. Am. Chem. Soc.*, **70**, 538 (1948).

with styrene. Thus there will be a considerable tendency for the units in the copolymer chain to alternate between styrene and methyl methacrylate (the *alternating effect*). It seems reasonable to expect that the rate at which radicals combine with a given monomer to form a new radical would depend upon the stability of the radical being formed. For the values of r_1 and r_2 found, however, it is obvious that this is, at least, not the *only* factor of importance. If it were, both types of radicals would prefer to react with the same monomer, and this preference would be of the same magnitude for both; i.e., it would be expected that $k_{11}/k_{12} = k_{21}/k_{22}$ or $r_1 r_2 = 1$. Actually $r_1 r_2$ is usually considerably less than unity and is never significantly more. In other words, the tendency of radical $M_1 \cdot$ to react with M_1 as compared to its tendency to react with M_2 is never more and usually less than would have been predicted from the relative reactivities of M_1 and M_2 toward radical $M_2 \cdot$. The accumulation of a large number of monomer reactivity ratios led to the explanation of these facts by the development of a theory of polar effects on free-radical reactions, which has proved very useful in the interpretation of data on other radical reactions. Mayo and Walling have pointed out a few of the areas of applicability.[18]

The importance of polar factors was first discussed by Price,[26] who pointed out that the magnitude of the alternating effect in copolymerization increased with an increasing difference in the electron-donating ability of the substituents on the two monomers. Alfrey and Price have described the copolymerization behavior of olefins in terms of two factors: Q, a measure of the stability of the radical formed when the olefin adds to a growing polymer chain, and e, a measure of the sum of the electron-withdrawing power of the substituents on the double bond.[27,28] Each olefin has its characteristic value of Q, the general monomer reactivity factor, and e, the polar factor. From these two values for two olefins there may be calculated, by the equations of Alfrey and Price, values to be expected for r_1 and r_2 in copolymerization. The agreement of these r values with those determined experimentally is only fair. At least part of the deviation from experimental values is no doubt due to the complete neglect of steric factors. From a tabulation of the Q and e values that have been obtained[18] it appears that radical-stabilizing ability varies approximately as follows: $p\text{-}Me_2NC_6H_4 \sim p\text{-}O_2NC_6H_4 > C_6H_5 > CN \sim CO_2Me > Cl \sim Me > H$, while as electron withdrawers, $CN > CO_2Me > p\text{-}O_2NC_6H_4 > Cl > H > Me > C_6H_5 > p\text{-}Me_2NC_6H_4$. Instead of attributing the polar effect to a coulombic attraction between two dipoles, as Alfrey and Price do, Walling

[26] C. C. Price, *J. Polymer Sci.*, **1**, 83 (1946).

[27] T. Alfrey and C. C. Price, *J. Polymer Sci.*, **2**, 101 (1947).

[28] C. C. Price, *J. Polymer Sci.*, **3**, 772 (1948).

and Mayo[29] suggest that it is due to stabilization of the transition state by resonance structures involving electron donation and acceptance. For example, in the transition state of the addition of a methyl acrylate molecule to a growing polymer chain ending in a styrene unit, the following resonance structure may be considered:

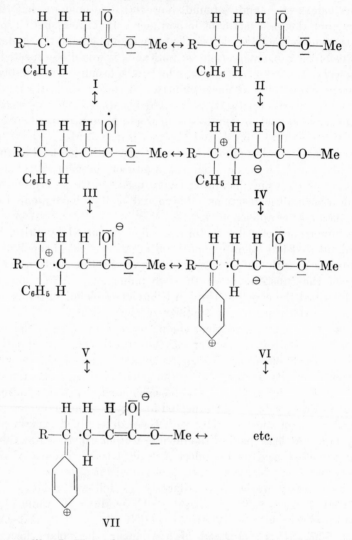

Structures like I, II, and IV may be written for the addition of any olefin to any free radical, and those of the type of III and V could explain the reactivity of methyl acrylate toward the addition of free radicals

[29] C. Walling and F. R. Mayo, *J. Polymer Sci.*, **3**, 895 (1948).

in general.   Structures like VI could contribute in the addition of styrene-type radicals to any olefin.   It is structures like VII, and similar ones that could be written, which explain the particularly great reactivity of electron-donor radicals toward electron-acceptor olefins.   If we define an electron-donor radical as one that could form an especially stable cation upon loss of its unpaired electron and an electron-acceptor radical as one that forms an especially stable anion upon gaining an electron, we may say that added reactivity will be found at any time a donor radical adds to an olefin to form an acceptor radical or vice versa.   This added reactivity is in addition to that which would be expected from radical-stability considerations.   We should expect the reactivity of a series of radicals toward a given olefin to decrease with increasing radical stability and the reactivity of a series of olefins toward a given radical to increase with increasing stability of the radical being formed.

20-2. Other Free-radical Additions to Olefins.   *20-2a. Radical Additions of Halogen.*   When bromine and ethylene are mixed in the gas phase in a glass vessel, it appears that much, if not all, of the ensuing addition reaction occurs on the glass walls of the container, since coating these walls with paraffin decreases the reaction rate more than tenfold.[30] An even larger difference is found in the reaction of chlorine and ethylene.[31]   The reaction goes faster when the container is coated with cetyl alcohol than when it is paraffin-coated and still faster when coated with stearic acid.   From this fact, together with the fact that small amounts of water vapor catalyze the reaction in glass (on which the water could be adsorbed) but not in a paraffin-coated vessel, it appears most likely that this surface reaction has a polar mechanism.   In investigating reaction rates and mechanisms, it is important to keep the possibility of surface reactions in mind.

However, despite the frequency of polar addition, there is good evidence that it is often possible to bring about the addition of halogen to olefinic double bonds by a free-radical chain reaction.   For example, the addition of chlorine to tetrachloroethylene in the vapor phase[32] and in carbon tetrachloride solution[33] has been found to be catalyzed by light (with high quantum yields) and strongly inhibited by oxygen. Bromine and cinnamic acid in carbon tetrachloride solution combine very rapidly, even in the dark, if oxygen is excluded.   In the presence of oxygen the reaction is very slow in the dark but occurs readily in the light.[34]   The addition of chlorine to benzene[35] and of bromine to phenan-

[30] R. G. W. Norrish, *J. Chem. Soc.*, **123**, 3006 (1923).
[31] R. G. W. Norrish and G. G. Jones, *J. Chem. Soc.*, 55 (1926).
[32] R. G. Dickinson and J. L. Carrico, *J. Am. Chem. Soc.*, **56**, 1473 (1934).
[33] R. G. Dickinson and J. A. Leermakers, *J. Am. Chem. Soc.*, **54**, 3852, 4648 (1932).
[34] W. H. Bauer and F. Daniels, *J. Am. Chem. Soc.*, **56**, 2014 (1934).
[35] H. P. Smith, W. A. Noyes, Jr., and E. J. Hart, *J. Am. Chem. Soc.*, **55**, 4444 (1933)

threne[36] are also light-catalyzed, and the latter is slowed by certain inhibitors. These data may be explained by a mechanism of the type

$$Cl_2 \xrightarrow{h\nu} 2Cl\cdot$$

$$Cl\cdot + Cl_2C{=}CCl_2 \rightarrow Cl_3C{-}\overset{\cdot}{C}Cl_2$$

$$Cl_3C{-}\overset{\cdot}{C}Cl_2 + Cl_2 \rightarrow Cl_3C{-}CCl_3 + Cl\cdot$$

That oxygen functions as an inhibitor by combining with the chain-propagating pentachloroethyl radicals is evidenced by the production of trichloroacetyl chloride in the oxygen-inhibited chlorination of tetrachloroethylene.[33]

20-2b. *Radical Additions of Hydrogen Halides.* The addition of hydrogen bromide to unsymmetrical olefins is a reaction which is of particular interest because it was used extensively in testing older theories of physical organic chemistry. Many anomalous results obtained earlier were explained by the observation of Kharasch and Mayo that while the addition of hydrogen bromide to allyl bromide under "ordinary" conditions occurs rapidly to yield largely 1,3-dibromopropane, the reaction of the carefully purified reactants in the absence of air occurs slowly and yields almost entirely 1,2-dibromopropane.[37] That the predominant formation of the 1,3-dibromide is due to the presence of peroxides was shown by the following facts: On standing in the presence of air in either the light or dark, allyl bromide becomes contaminated with peroxides. This peroxide-containing allyl bromide reacts rapidly and yields largely 1,3-dibromide in either the presence or absence of air. Even carefully purified allyl bromide in the absence of air may be made to yield largely the 1,3-dibromide if a little benzoyl peroxide is added. It seems likely that hydrogen bromide does add to allyl bromide by a polar mechanism to give mostly 1,2-dibromopropane. While the presence of peroxides has no effect upon this reaction, the peroxides serve as initiators for a rapid free-radical chain reaction which produces largely 1,3-dibromopropane. In agreement with this explanation are the facts that the formation of 1,3-dibromide is largely eliminated by inhibitors such as hydroquinone, diphenylamine, etc., and that the formation of the 1,3-dibromide is catalyzed by light.[37] The mechanism suggested for the free-radical part of the reaction is as follows:[38,39]

[36] C. C. Price, *J. Am. Chem. Soc.*, **58**, 1835 (1936).

[37] M. S. Kharasch and F. R. Mayo, *J. Am. Chem. Soc.*, **55**, 2468 (1933).

[38] M. S. Kharasch, H. Engelmann, and F. R. Mayo, *J. Org. Chem.*, **2**, 288 (1937).

[39] D. H. Hey and W. A. Waters, *Chem. Rev.*, **21**, 202 (1937).

Peroxide → R·

R· + HBr → RH + Br·

$$Br· + CH_2=CHCH_2Br → BrCH_2\overset{·}{C}HCH_2Br \qquad (20\text{-}10)$$

$$BrCH_2\overset{·}{C}HCH_2Br + HBr → BrCH_2CH_2CH_2Br + Br· \qquad (20\text{-}11)$$

The nature of the product is determined by the chain-propagating steps (20-10) and (20-11). In step (20-10) the bromine atom would be expected to add to the end rather than the middle carbon atom, since a secondary radical is more stable than a primary one. Hydrogen bromide is unique among the hydrogen halides in its tendency to undergo reversal in the mode of its addition to olefins in the presence of peroxides. This fact may be rationalized in terms of the bond energies listed in Table 1-4.

First we must argue that if the free-radical mechanism is to be effective, both of the propagation steps must be rapid, since if they are not, the intermediate radicals will tend to accumulate, and termination will be facilitated. The activation energy for these steps must be at least equal to the energy of reaction, and therefore it would be best if both steps were exothermic. This is the case with hydrogen bromide. In step (20-10) the difference in energy between a double bond and a single bond (about 63 kcal) is offset by the energy of the new carbon-bromine bond (65 kcal) that is formed. In (20-11) an 87-kcal hydrogen-bromine bond is broken, but a 98-kcal carbon-hydrogen bond is formed. Hydrogen fluoride does not react because its bond (energy about 135 kcal) is too strong to be easily broken by a radical. The failure with hydrogen iodide is apparently due to the unreactivity of the iodine atom, which does not form a strong enough bond to carbon to compensate for breaking a double bond. The situation with regard to hydrogen chloride is rather delicately balanced. Raley, Rust, and Vaughan have shown that hydrogen chloride may be added to ethylene by a free-radical chain mechanism.[40] However, in this case the reaction analogous to (20-11) involves the attack of a reactive *primary* radical. The more stable secondary radicals are evidently not reactive enough, since propylene is relatively unreactive toward free-radical addition of hydrogen chloride.[40] This rationalization would be more convincing, of course, if it were based on bond-dissociation energies rather than just average bond energies. Unfortunately, the necessary data of the former type are less readily available.

Even with hydrogen bromide the presence of peroxides does not always result in a reversal in the direction of addition. In some cases the polar addition proceeds so rapidly that the free-radical reaction cannot be made to compete with it. In other cases each of the two mechanisms

[40] J. H. Raley, F. F. Rust, and W. E. Vaughan, *J. Am. Chem. Soc.*, **70**, 2767 (1948).

would be expected to give the same product. Thus methyl methacrylate would be expected to yield a primary bromide by the free-radical as well as a polar mechanism.

$$\underset{\substack{| \\ \text{CH}_2{=}\text{C}{-}\text{CO}_2\text{Me}}}{\overset{\text{Me}}{}} \xrightarrow{\text{Br·}} \underset{\substack{| \\ \cdot}}{\overset{\text{Me}}{\text{BrCH}_2{-}\text{C}{-}\text{CO}_2\text{Me}}} \xrightarrow{\text{HBr}}$$

$$\underset{\substack{| \\ \text{BrCH}_2{-}\text{CH}{-}\text{CO}_2\text{Me} + \text{Br·}}}{\overset{\text{Me}}{}}$$

This reaction has been found to yield the product shown,[41] although we do not know which of the two possible explanations described is correct.

Goering, Abell, and Aycock have shown that the free-radical addition of hydrogen bromide goes trans.[42] They found that addition to 1-bromo-cyclohexene yielded cis-1,2-dibromocyclohexane and that addition to 1-methylcyclohexene gave cis-1-bromo-2-methylcyclohexane. It was suggested that the trans orientation is due to the formation of an intermediate radical with a bridged structure (VIII) like that of a bromonium ion to which an electron has been added.

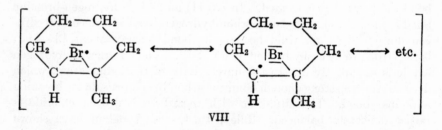

VIII

20-2c. *Miscellaneous Free-radical Additions to Olefins.* There are a wide variety of organic compounds that have been found to add to olefins by a free-radical mechanism. A large number of these reactions were discovered by Kharasch and coworkers. Many of the additions proceed well only with terminal olefins. A number of polyhalomethanes have been found to react in the presence of a diacyl peroxide or ultra-violet light.[43] The mechanism, illustrated for the case of carbon tetra-

---

[41] C. C. Price and E. C. Coyner, *J. Am. Chem. Soc.*, **62**, 1306 (1940).

[42] Harlan L. Goering, P. I. Abell, and B. F. Aycock, *J. Am. Chem. Soc.*, **74**, 3588 (1952).

[43] M. S. Kharasch, E. V. Jensen, and W. H. Urry, *J. Am. Chem. Soc.*, **69**, 1100 (1947); M. S. Kharasch, O. Reinmuth, and W. H. Urry, *J. Am. Chem. Soc.*, **69**, 1105 (1947).

chloride, is

Initiator $\rightarrow$ R·

R· + CCl$_4$ $\rightarrow$ RCl + ·CCl$_3$

R—CH=CH$_2$ + ·CCl$_3$ $\rightarrow$ R—$\overset{\bullet}{\text{CH}}$—CH$_2CCl_3$

R—$\overset{\bullet}{\text{CH}}$—CH$_2CCl_3$ + CCl$_4$ $\rightarrow$ R—CHCl—CH$_2$CCl$_3$ + ·CCl$_3$

Other types of compounds probably add by an analogous mechanism. Aldehydes add to give ketones,[44] secondary amines yield tertiary amines,[45] and primary alcohols are transformed to secondary alcohols.[46]

$$\text{RCHO} + \text{R}'\text{CH=CH}_2 \rightarrow \text{R}'\text{CH}_2\text{CH}_2\text{COR}$$
$$\text{R}_2\text{NH} + \text{R}'\text{CH=CH}_2 \rightarrow \text{R}'\text{CH}_2\text{CH}_2\text{NR}_2$$
$$\text{RCH}_2\text{OH} + \text{R}'\text{CH=CH}_2 \rightarrow \text{R}'\text{CH}_2\text{CH}_2\text{CHOHR}$$

[44] M. S. Kharasch, W. H. Urry, and B. M. Kuderna, *J. Org. Chem.*, **14**, 248 (1949).

[45] W. H. Urry, O. O. Juveland, and F. W. Stacey, *J. Am. Chem. Soc.*, **74**, 6155 (1952).

[46] W. H. Urry, F. W. Stacey, O. O. Juveland, and C. H. McDonnell, *J. Am. Chem. Soc.*, **75**, 250 (1953); W. H. Urry, F. W. Stacey, E. S. Huyser, and O. O. Juveland, *J. Am. Chem. Soc.*, **76**, 450 (1954).

CHAPTER 21

DECOMPOSITION OF PEROXIDES AND AZO AND DIAZO COMPOUNDS

21-1. Decomposition of Peroxides. *21-1a. Mechanism of the Decomposition of Diacyl Peroxides.* There is good evidence that the decomposition of diacyl peroxides may proceed by a free-radical mechanism. Walker and Wild have shown that the decomposition of acetyl peroxide is catalyzed by light.[1] The decomposition of benzoyl peroxide is slowed by inhibitors and catalyzed by known radicals.[2] The decomposition of benzoyl peroxide in nitrobenzene solution brings about considerable para phenylation of the nitrobenzene, although substitution by electrophilic reagents gives almost entirely meta substitution.[3] Acyl peroxides are the most common catalysts for a large number of reactions for which there is much good evidence for a free-radical mechanism.

Since benzoyl peroxide has been investigated more thoroughly than any other acyl peroxide, its decomposition will be discussed in some detail. The reaction does not consist simply of a first-order decomposition of the peroxide. In addition, to an extent that varies widely with the solvent, it is a chain reaction in which the radicals formed initially attack benzoyl peroxide molecules to produce further decomposition. This is shown by the observations of Nozaki and Bartlett[2] that the reaction is inhibited by reagents such as oxygen, hydroquinone, and picric acid and accelerated by free radicals such as triphenylmethyl and diphenylamino. Further evidence is the fact that in many solvents the kinetic order of the reaction is greater than one. The fact that the reaction rate varies widely with the solvent suggests that the solvent is participating in the rate-controlling step of the reaction. The order of reactivity in various solvents (see Table 21-1) would be utterly inexplicable for a polar reaction, and it would not be reasonable to expect such large variation in the rate of cleavage of an uncharged molecule to neutral radicals. However, it can be rationalized fairly well by the assumption that the radicals originally formed from the peroxide decom-

---

[1] O. J. Walker and G. L. E. Wild, *J. Chem. Soc.*, 1132 (1937).

[2] K. Nozaki and P. D. Bartlett, *J. Am. Chem. Soc.*, **68**, 1686 (1946).

[3] D. H. Hey, *J. Chem. Soc.*, 1966 (1934).

position react with the various solvents to form radicals that differ widely in their ability to induce the further decomposition of benzoyl peroxide.[2]

Information about the "spontaneous," as distinguished from the "induced," decomposition of benzoyl peroxide has been obtained by Hammond and Soffer.[4]   These workers used the very effective inhibitor iodine in a solvent (carbon tetrachloride) which does not react with the initial product of inhibition, benzoyl hypoiodite.   Under anhydrous conditions iodobenzene from the decomposition of the hypoiodite was isolated as the reaction product in more than 80 per cent yield.   However, when a separate layer of water, which is known to hydrolyze benzoyl hypoiodite rapidly, was added to the reaction mixture, the product was benzoic acid in almost quantitative yield.   That the reaction studied was only the "spontaneous" decomposition seems assured because no further decrease in reaction rate was found when the inhibitor concentration was more than doubled.   The benzoic acid could not have been formed from water and benzoyl peroxide or some intermediate ordinarily present in the carbon tetrachloride decomposition of the peroxide since no benzoic acid was found among the products of the decomposition of benzoyl peroxide in carbon tetrachloride with no iodine but an excess of water present.   It was also shown that the water had no effect on the rate-controlling step of the reaction in which benzoic acid is produced quantitatively, because the reaction rate was identical to that in the absence of water.   Since the rate-controlling step of the spontaneous decomposition thus appears to produce intact benzoate groups quantitatively, it must be simply a fission of the peroxide into two benzoate radicals.

$$C_6H_5COO—OCOC_6H_5 \rightarrow 2C_6H_5COO\cdot$$

The evidence for this mechanism is of considerable interest in view of the fact that the mechanism

$$C_6H_5COO—OCOC_6H_5 \rightarrow C_6H_5\cdot + CO_2 + C_6H_5COO\cdot$$

had been suggested and used in the interpretation of many earlier data.

The mechanism of the "induced" decomposition of benzoyl peroxide is also of interest, since this is the principal reaction path in those solvents in which decomposition is rapid and even in the "slower" solvents if the solution is fairly concentrated.   Bartlett and Nozaki have studied the decomposition of benzoyl peroxide in n-butyl ether solution.[5]   The

[4] G. S. Hammond and L. M. Soffer, *J. Am. Chem. Soc.*, **72**, 4711 (1950).
[5] P. D. Bartlett and K. Nozaki, *J. Am. Chem. Soc.*, **69**, 2299 (1947).

relatively high rate of the reaction and the marked inhibition by oxygen show that the reaction is largely induced. In a 50 per cent solution of vinyl acetate in n-butyl ether containing 1 per cent benzoyl peroxide, there is more decomposition of benzoyl peroxide but less polymerization of vinyl acetate than in a similar solution in cyclohexane. This shows, among other things, that the additional decomposition of benzoyl peroxide (induced decomposition) does not cause any additional polymerization and hence that it probably does not involve the formation of additional radicals. This is in agreement with an induced decom-

TABLE 21-1. PERCENTAGE DECOMPOSITION OF BENZOYL PEROXIDE IN VARIOUS SOLVENTS[a] AT 79.8°[2,5]

Solvent	Time, min	De-compn., %	Solvent	Time, min	De-compn., %
Carbon tetrachloride....	60	13.0	t-Butylbenzene.........	60	28.5
Cyclohexene...........	60	14.0	Acetic anhydride.......	60	48.5
Anisole...............	60	14.0	Cyclohexane..........	60	51.0
Methyl benzoate........	60	14.5	Ethyl acetate..........	60	53.5
Chloroform...........	60	14.5	Acetic acid...........	60	59.3
Nitrobenzene..........	60	15.5	Dioxane..............	60	82.4
Benzene..............	60	15.5	Diethyl ether..........	10	75.2
Toluene..............	60	17.4	Ethyl alcohol..........	10	81.8
Chlorobenzene..........	60	18.0	m-Cresol..............	10	87.6
Styrene...............	60	19.0	Isopropyl alcohol.......	10	95.1
Ethyl iodide...........	60	23.4	2,4,6-Trimethylphenol..	10	98.8[b]
Acetone..............	60	28.5			

[a] Aniline, triethylamine, dimethylaniline, and n-butylamine all reacted explosively.
[b] At 60.0°.

position in which only one radical is created for every radical destroyed. The principal products of the decomposition in n-butyl ether solution are benzoic acid (almost 1 mole per mole of peroxide decomposed) and high-boiling material that is probably largely α-butoxybutyl benzoate (by analogy with the work of Cass,[6] who isolated more than 0.8 mole of α-ethoxyethyl benzoate per mole of benzoyl peroxide in a similar peroxide decomposition in diethyl ether solution). The nature of the product makes it most likely that it is the α-butoxybutyl radical which is responsible for the induced decomposition of the peroxide and hence that the mechanism of the major portion[7] of the reaction is

[6] W. E. Cass, J. Am. Chem. Soc., **69**, 500 (1947).
[7] The decomposition must also consist to a minor extent of a simultaneous carbon dioxide–producing reaction since some carbon dioxide is obtained.

$$C_6H_5COO-OCOC_6H_5 \xrightarrow{k_1} 2C_6H_5COO\cdot$$

$$C_6H_5COO\cdot + C_3H_7CH_2OC_4H_9 \xrightarrow{k_2} C_6H_5CO_2H + C_3H_7\overset{\cdot}{C}HOC_4H_9$$

$$C_3H_7\overset{\cdot}{C}HOC_4H_9 + C_6H_5COO-OCOC_6H_5$$

$$\xrightarrow{k_3} C_3H_7CH\overset{\displaystyle OCOC_6H_5}{\underset{\displaystyle OC_4H_9}{\Big\langle}} + C_6H_5COO\cdot$$

Some possible termination reactions are:
1. Recombination of benzoate radicals to give benzoyl peroxide.

$$2C_6H_5COO\cdot \xrightarrow{k_4} C_6H_5COO-OCOC_6H_5$$

2. Combination of benzoate radicals to give phenyl benzoate or some other molecule not likely to reenter the reaction.

$$2C_6H_5COO\cdot \xrightarrow{k_5} C_6H_5COOC_6H_5 + CO_2$$

3. Crossed termination between a benzoate and an α-butoxybutyl radical to give the principal reaction product (or other nonradicals).

$$C_6H_5COO\cdot + C_3H_7\overset{\cdot}{C}HOC_4H_9 \xrightarrow{k_6} C_3H_7CH\overset{\displaystyle OCOC_6H_5}{\underset{\displaystyle OC_4H_9}{\Big\langle}}$$

4 Dimerization or disproportionation of the α-butoxybutyl radicals.

$$2C_3H_7\overset{\cdot}{C}HOC_4H_9 \xrightarrow{k_7} C_4H_9OCH-CHOC_4H_9 \atop \quad\ \ \overset{|}{C_3H_7} \ \ \overset{|}{C_3H_7}$$

In the case of each of these possibilities the kinetic order of the reaction may be ascertained by assuming that the given possibility is the only termination step and by applying the steady-state assumption (Sec. 3-1a) to the resultant mechanism.

Using the symbols

$$P = [C_6H_5COO-OCOC_6H_5] \qquad SH = n\text{-}C_4H_9OC_4H_9\text{-}n$$

$$R = [C_6H_5COO\cdot] \qquad\qquad S = [n\text{-}C_3H_7\overset{\cdot}{C}HOC_4H_9\text{-}n]$$

and assuming termination mechanism 3, crossed termination, we get the reaction mechanism

$$P \xrightarrow{k_1} 2R$$

$$R + SH \xrightarrow{k_2} RH + S$$

$$S + P \xrightarrow{k_3} R\text{---}S + R$$

$$R + S \xrightarrow{k_6} R\text{---}S$$

Therefore $-\dfrac{dP}{dt} = k_1P + k_3PS$ (21-1)

From the steady-state assumption (and ignoring the large and hence essentially constant concentration of solvent),

$$\frac{dR}{dt} = 2k_1P - k_2R + k_3PS - k_6RS = 0 \qquad (21\text{-}2)$$

and $$\frac{dS}{dt} = k_2R - k_3PS - k_6RS = 0 \qquad (21\text{-}3)$$

From Eq. (21-3) $$R = \frac{k_3PS}{k_2 - k_6S}$$

Substitution in (21-2) and solution of the quadratic gives

$$S = \frac{k_c}{k_3}$$

where $$k_c = \frac{-k_1k_6 + \sqrt{k_1{}^2k_6{}^2 + 4k_1k_2k_3k_6}}{2k_6}$$

Therefore, $-\dfrac{dP}{dt} = k_1P + k_cP = (k_1 + k_c)P$

Thus, if mechanism 3 is the only mechanism for termination, the entire reaction, induced as well as spontaneous, will be first-order.

Termination mechanism 1 leads to the kinetic equation

$$-\frac{dP}{dt} = k_2\sqrt{\frac{k_1}{k_4}}\,P^{1/2}$$

in which the entire reaction is one-half-order in peroxide.

From 2, the equation

$$-\frac{dP}{dt} = k_1P + k_2\sqrt{\frac{k_1}{k_5}}\,P^{1/2}$$

is obtained, in which the induced part of the reaction is one-half-order.

Mechanism 4 yields the relation

$$-\frac{dP}{dt} = k_1P + k_3\sqrt{\frac{k_1}{k_7}}\,P^{3/2}$$

in which the induced part of the reaction is three-halves-order with respect to peroxide. Bartlett and Nozaki found the reaction to be first-order.[5] Since the reaction is apparently very largely induced and since only termination mechanism 3 yields first-order kinetics for the induced part of the reaction, they concluded that termination probably occurs, at least largely, by reaction between the two unlike radicals. They also point out that there is considerable precedent for such a tendency of unlike radicals to prefer reaction with each other to dimerization (cf. Sec. 18-2a). In the present case it is noteworthy that the α-butoxybutyl radical would be a strongly electron-donating radical, while the benzoate radical should be electron-accepting.

It appears that in alcoholic solutions the benzoate radicals attack the α-hydrogens and perhaps also the hydroxyl hydrogens to form radicals that induce the further decomposition of benzoyl peroxide.[5] With phenols, phenoxy radicals are thought to be produced.[5] There are several possible ways in which amines may be attacked.[5,8]

In the solvents in which the decomposition of benzoyl peroxide is relatively slow (see Table 21-1), the reaction mechanism appears to be somewhat different. In some cases there are simultaneous first- and three-halves-order reactions, and in others simultaneous first- and second-order reactions. Nozaki and Bartlett discuss the mechanistic implications of these and other data.[2] In these solvents a considerable portion of the induced reaction is due to the radicals originally produced from the benzoyl peroxide, although some induced decomposition due to radicals from the solvent still occurs.

21-1b. *Effect of Structure on the Rate of Decomposition of Diaroyl Peroxides.* Swain, Stockmayer, and Clarke have investigated the effect of structure on the rate of the *spontaneous* thermal decomposition of meta- and para-substituted benzoyl peroxides in dioxane solution.[9] They used 3,4-dichlorostyrene to inhibit the *induced* decomposition of the peroxide. By neglecting the relative stability of the radicals formed and attributing the influence of substituents on rate to a polar factor, fair agreement with experimental results was obtained.

A benzoyl peroxide molecule may be considered to be two dipoles joined at their negative ends.

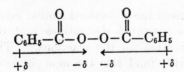

If the reaction is thought of as due to this repulsion, the rate would be expected to be proportional to the magnitude of the dipoles. Therefore

[8] J. E. Leffler, *J. Am. Chem. Soc.*, **72**, 3809 (1950); C. E. Boozer and G. S. Hammond, *J. Am. Chem. Soc.*, **76**, 3861 (1954).

[9] C. G. Swain, W. H. Stockmayer, and J. T. Clarke, *J. Am. Chem. Soc.*, **72**, 5426 (1950).

electron-donating groups, which would increase the size of the dipoles, should increase the reaction rate. In general, this is found to be the case, while electron-withdrawing groups slow the reaction. In fact, the data agree fairly well with the Hammett equation, where ρ has the value -0.38 for this reaction, and σ is the sum of the σ values for the substituents on both rings (e.g., since $\sigma = -0.268$ for the p-methoxy group, this value is used for p-methoxybenzoyl peroxide, and the value -0.536 is used for p,p'-dimethoxybenzoyl peroxide). The experimental values of the rate constants are compared with those predicted from the Hammett equation in Table 21-2.

TABLE 21-2. RATES OF SPONTANEOUS DECOMPOSITION OF SUBSTITUTED
BENZOYL PEROXIDES IN DIOXANE AT 80°[9]

Substituents	σ	10^3k		Deviation, %[a]
		Predicted	Actual	
p,p'-Di-MeO	-0.536	4.03	7.06	75
p-MeO	-0.268	3.18	4.54	43
p,p'-Di-Me	-0.340	3.40	3.68	8
p,p'-Di-t-Bu	-0.394	3.56	3.65	2.5
m,m'-Di-MeO	$+0.230$	2.06	3.45	67
m-MeO	$+0.115$	2.28	2.89	27
p-Me, m'-Br	$+0.221$	2.08	2.66	28
m,m'-Di-Me	-0.138	2.84	2.64	7
None	0.000	2.52	2.52	0
p,p'-Di-Cl	$+0.454$	1.69	2.17	28
p,p'-Di-Br	$+0.464$	1.68	1.94	15
m-CN	$+0.517$	1.60	1.64	2.5
m,m'-Di-Cl	$+0.746$	1.31	1.58	21
m,m'-Di-Br	$+0.782$	1.27	1.54	21
p,p'-Di-CN	$+1.30$	0.81	1.22	51
m,m'-Di-CN	$+1.03$	1.02	1.02	0
Median...........	....	....	....	21

[a] Percentage by which the actual deviated from the predicted.

Blomquist and Buselli have obtained similar results; in addition they studied five ortho-substituted derivatives and determined entropies and energies of activation for the reactions.[10] They found that p,p'-dinitrobenzoyl peroxide (and also the m,m' isomer) decomposed much more rapidly than would be expected from Hammett's equation; they pointed out that this may be due to the nitro group's being such a strong electron-withdrawing group that it has reversed the direction of the dipole. There is a possibility, however, that the large rate of the nitro compounds is due to the difficulty in suppressing the *induced* part of the decomposition. The effect of substituents on the rate of the induced

[10] A. T. Blomquist and A. J. Buselli, *J. Am. Chem. Soc.*, **73**, 3883 (1951).

decomposition is the opposite of that on the spontaneous decomposition. Since electron-donor radicals are most active at inducing decomposition, it is not surprising that electron-withdrawing groups in the peroxide molecule should aid the reaction.[9]

21-1c. *Decomposition of Dialkyl Peroxides.* The decomposition of di-*t*-butyl peroxide has been studied in some detail. The reaction is catalyzed by ultraviolet radiation.[11] It has been studied kinetically in the vapor phase at temperatures around 150° by Raley, Rust, and Vaughan.[12] These workers showed that packing the reaction vessel with enough glass rodding to change the surface-volume ratio by more than elevenfold had no detectable effect on the rate of reaction of the peroxide and hence that the rate-controlling step must occur in the gas phase. The reaction appeared to be entirely spontaneous, with no noticeable amount of induced chain decomposition, since it followed good first-order kinetics and was not slowed by such inhibitors as oxygen, nitric oxide, and propylene. When run in a vessel packed with glass wool, the reaction products are entirely acetone and ethane and are believed to be formed by the mechanism[13]

$$(CH_3)_3COOC(CH_3)_3 \rightarrow 2(CH_3)_3CO\cdot$$
$$(CH_3)_3CO\cdot \rightarrow (CH_3)_2CO + CH_3\cdot$$
$$2CH_3\cdot \rightarrow CH_3CH_3$$

Apparently the dimerization of the methyl radicals is at least partially a surface reaction, for when the reaction is run in a large unpacked vessel, some methane and methyl ethyl and higher ketones are formed,[12] presumably because the methyl radicals now enter into reactions other than dimerization.[12]

$$CH_3\cdot + CH_3COCH_3 \rightarrow CH_4 + CH_3COCH_2\cdot$$
$$CH_3COCH_2\cdot + CH_3\cdot \rightarrow CH_3COCH_2CH_3 \quad \text{etc.}$$

The rate-controlling step in the decomposition of di-*t*-butyl peroxide in cumene, *t*-butylbenzene, or tri-*n*-butylamine solution is apparently the same as in the vapor-phase reaction, since the reaction proceeds at the same rate (within experimental error) in all three solvents, and only about 30 per cent slower in the gas phase.[14] The decomposition of benzoyl peroxide, a compound sensitive to induced decomposition, is slow in *t*-butylbenzene solution at 80° but explosive in amine (e.g., aniline and triethylamine) solutions at room temperature.[2] Although the formation of *t*-butoxy radicals occurs at about the same rate in these

[11] (a) E. R. Bell, F. F. Rust, and W. E. Vaughan, *J. Am. Chem. Soc.*, **72**, 337 (1950); (b) L. M. Dorfman and Z. W. Salsburg, *J. Am. Chem. Soc.*, **73**, 255 (1951).

[12] J. H. Raley, F. F. Rust, and W. E. Vaughan, *J. Am. Chem. Soc.*, **70**, 88 (1948).

[13] N. A. Milas and D. M. Surgenor, *J. Am. Chem. Soc.*, **68**, 205 (1946).

[14] J. H. Raley, F. F. Rust, and W. E. Vaughan, *J. Am. Chem. Soc.*, **70**, 1336 (1948).

different solvents, their fate, which is settled after the rate-controlling step of the reaction, varies considerably. At 125° in tri-*n*-butylamine, where the donor element nitrogen makes the α-hydrogen atoms very susceptible to attack by an acceptor alkoxy radical, about 95 per cent of the *t*-butoxy radicals form *t*-butyl alcohol.[15] At the same temperature in cumene, where a benzyl-type radical, $C_6H_5\dot{C}(CH_3)_2$, may be formed, about 80 per cent of the *t*-butoxy radicals form alcohol, and in *t*-butylbenzene, where the resultant radical is not so stabilized by resonance, only 37 per cent form *t*-butyl alcohol. As previously stated, in the vapor phase, where the butoxy radical collides with other molecules only relatively rarely, no *t*-butyl alcohol was found. In cumene and *t*-butylbenzene it is noted that as the reaction temperature is increased, the yield of *t*-butyl alcohol decreases and that of acetone and methane increases. This shows that the activation energy for the decomposition of the radical is higher than for its abstraction of a hydrogen atom from solvent. Under certain conditions the reaction may become partly induced. This appears to be the case with the decomposition of the pure liquid. In the first place, the reaction is about three times as fast as would be expected from the rate constants in the other solvents studied.[11a] Also, from the nature of the products it appears certain that di-*t*-butyl peroxide molecules have been attacked by intermediate radicals. This would certainly be expected to cause chain decomposition. Under these conditions isobutylene oxide becomes a principal reaction product. The following mechanism explains these facts.

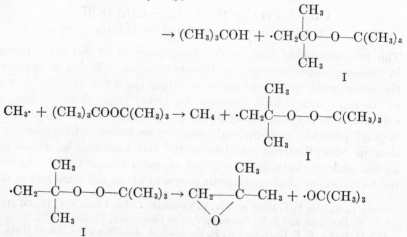

$$(CH_3)_3COOC(CH_3)_3 \rightarrow 2(CH_3)_3CO\cdot$$

$$(CH_3)_3CO\cdot \rightarrow CH_3COCH_3 + CH_3\cdot$$

$$(CH_3)_3CO\cdot + (CH_3)_3COOC(CH_3)_3$$

$$CH_3$$
$$|$$
$$\rightarrow (CH_3)_3COH + \cdot CH_2CO\!-\!O\!-\!C(CH_3)_2$$
$$|$$
$$CH_3$$
$$\qquad\qquad I$$

$$CH_3$$
$$|$$
$$CH_3\cdot + (CH_3)_3COOC(CH_3)_3 \rightarrow CH_4 + \cdot CH_2C\!-\!O\!-\!O\!-\!C(CH_3)_3$$
$$|$$
$$CH_3$$
$$\qquad\qquad I$$

$$CH_3 \qquad\qquad\qquad CH_3$$
$$| \qquad\qquad\qquad\qquad |$$
$$\cdot CH_2\!-\!C\!-\!O\!-\!O\!-\!C(CH_3)_3 \rightarrow CH_2\!-\!C\!-\!CH_3 + \cdot OC(CH_3)_3$$
$$| \qquad\qquad\qquad\qquad\quad \diagdown\ \diagup$$
$$CH_3 \qquad\qquad\qquad\quad O$$
$$I$$

---

[15] This fact, incidentally, shows that the initial, rate-controlling cleavage is indeed into two butoxy radicals rather than directly to $CH_3\cdot + CH_3COCH_3 + (CH_3)_3CO\cdot$.

By a similar mechanism, small amounts of hydrogen chloride can cause induced chain decomposition. The addition of about 30 mm of HCl causes the initial rate of the vapor phase decomposition of 180 mm of di-t-butyl peroxide at about 140° to become at least 10 times as fast.[16] This may be attributed to chain induction by chlorine atoms.[16]

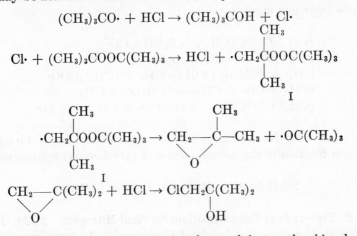

$$(CH_3)_3CO\cdot + HCl \rightarrow (CH_3)_3COH + Cl\cdot$$

$$Cl\cdot + (CH_3)_3COOC(CH_3)_3 \rightarrow HCl + \cdot CH_2\overset{\overset{\displaystyle CH_3}{|}}{\underset{\underset{\displaystyle CH_3}{|}}{C}}OOC(CH_3)_3$$

$$\text{I}$$

$$\cdot CH_2\overset{\overset{\displaystyle CH_3}{|}}{\underset{\underset{\displaystyle CH_3}{|}}{C}}OOC(CH_3)_3 \rightarrow CH_2\overset{\overset{\displaystyle CH_3}{|}}{\underset{\displaystyle O}{\diagdown}}C-CH_3 + \cdot OC(CH_3)_3$$

$$\text{I}$$

$$CH_2\underset{\displaystyle O}{\diagdown}C(CH_3)_2 + HCl \rightarrow ClCH_2\underset{\underset{\displaystyle OH}{|}}{C}(CH_3)_2$$

Here the isobutylene oxide is not isolated as such but as the chlorohydrin. Evidence that the radical (I) may have a separate existence, rather than decomposing at the same time it is formed, may be seen in the fact that di-t-butyl peroxide may be photochlorinated to $ClCH_2C(CH_3)_2$-$OOC(CH_3)_3$ at about 35°.[16] The radical (I) must have been an intermediate in this reaction. A study of the photolysis of di-t-butyl peroxide[11b] has given added evidence for certain of the conclusions drawn from thermal-decomposition data.

Studies on the decomposition of di-t-amyl peroxide suggest that the mechanism is very similar to that for the t-butyl isomer.[12] As might be expected, the decomposition of the t-amyloxy radical yields acetone and an ethyl radical rather than the less stable methyl radical (and methyl ethyl ketone). In general, it appears that the rate at which an alkoxy radical loses an alkyl radical (or hydrogen atom) depends upon the stability of the alkyl radical and the carbonyl compound formed. Hence the ease of decomposition (compared to the ease of abstraction of a hydrogen atom from solvent) of a series of alkoxy radicals was found to vary thus:[17] $CH_3—C(CH_3)_2O\cdot \sim (CH_3)_2CH—CH_2O\cdot > CH_3—CH(CH_3)O\cdot > n\text{-}C_3H_7—CH_2O\cdot > CH_3—CH_2O\cdot > CH_3O\cdot$.

21-1d. Decomposition of Alkyl Hydroperoxides. In contrast to dialkyl peroxides, alkyl hydroperoxides appear to be quite sensitive to induced

[16] J. H. Raley, F. F. Rust, and W. E. Vaughan, *J. Am. Chem. Soc.*, **70**, 2767 (1948).

[17] F. F. Rust, F. H. Seubold, Jr., and W. E. Vaughan, *J. Am. Chem. Soc.*, **72**, 338 (1950). For similar data see N. A. Milas and L. H. Perry, *J. Am. Chem. Soc.*, **68**, 1938 (1946).

chain decomposition. The decomposition of t-butyl hydroperoxide is strongly accelerated by that of 2,2′-azo-bis-isobutyronitrile, $Me_2C(CN)—N{=}N—(CN)CMe_2$,[18] a compound known to give free radicals (Sec. 21-2b), and also by that of di-t-butyl peroxide.[19] The mechanism of the latter induced decomposition appears to involve an attack on the hydroxylic hydrogen atom.[19]

$$(CH_3)_3COOC(CH_3)_3 \rightarrow 2(CH_3)_3CO\cdot$$
$$(CH_3)_3CO\cdot \rightarrow (CH_3)_2CO + CH_3\cdot$$
$$CH_3\cdot + (CH_3)_3COOH \rightarrow CH_4 + (CH_3)_3COO\cdot$$
$$(CH_3)_3COO\cdot + CH_3\cdot \rightarrow (CH_3)_3COOCH_3$$
$$(CH_3)_3COOCH_3 \rightarrow (CH_3)_3CO\cdot + CH_3O\cdot \qquad \text{etc.}$$

Bateman and Hughes have described evidence for a bimolecular initiation reaction in the decomposition of cyclohexenyl hydroperoxide.[20]

$$2C_6H_9OOH \rightarrow H_2O + C_6H_9O\cdot + C_6H_9OO\cdot$$

21-2. Free-radical Decompositions to Yield Nitrogen. *21-2a. Decomposition of Azomethane and Related Compounds.* In experiments of the Paneth type (Sec. 19-1a) Leermakers showed that the products of the decomposition of azomethane at 475° are capable of removing metallic mirrors.[21] This shows that free radicals are formed in the reaction but does not rule out the possibility that part of the reaction involves a rearrangement directly to ethane and nitrogen, the principal reaction products. However Davis, Jahn, and Burton have shown that in the closely related photolysis of azomethane no significant fraction of the reaction occurs by such a mechanism.[22] They found that the addition of nitric oxide to the reaction mixture prevented the formation of any gaseous alkanes. Nitric oxide, itself a free radical, is often a very effective reagent at "capturing" free alkyl radicals formed as reaction intermediates. From the quantum yield of unity,[22] unaffected by nitric oxide, and other facts it may be seen that the reaction does not consist to any appreciable extent of an induced chain decomposition.

The reaction appears to involve the transformation of azomethane into two methyl radicals and a nitrogen atom. However, this transformation may be depicted as occurring by a concerted mechanism[21]

---

[18] V. Stannett and R. B. Mesrobian, *J. Am. Chem. Soc.*, **72**, 4125 (1950).

[19] F. H. Seubold, Jr., F. F. Rust, and W. E. Vaughan, *J. Am. Chem. Soc.*, **73**, 18 (1951).

[20] L. Bateman and H. Hughes, *J. Chem. Soc.*, 4594 (1952).

[21] J. A. Leermakers, *J. Am. Chem. Soc.*, **55**, 3499 (1933).

[22] T. W. Davis, F. P. Jahn, and M. Burton, *J. Am. Chem. Soc.*, **60**, 10 (1938).

$$CH_3—N=N—CH_3 \rightarrow 2CH_3\cdot + N_2$$
$$2CH_3\cdot \rightarrow C_2H_6 \quad \text{etc.} \quad (21\text{-}4)$$

or by a stepwise process in which the $CH_3—N=N\cdot$ radical has an independent existence.[23]

$$CH_3—N=N—CH_3 \rightarrow CH_3—N=N\cdot + CH_3\cdot$$
$$CH_3—N=N\cdot \rightarrow CH_3\cdot + N_2 \quad\quad (21\text{-}5)$$
$$2CH_3\cdot \rightarrow C_2H_6 \quad \text{etc.}$$

No experiments have been reported in which the $CH_3—N=N\cdot$ radical has been "captured," but this cannot be construed as good evidence against mechanism (21-5) since it does not appear that any work has been carried out with this purpose and since the radical may just be intrinsically difficult to capture. However, Ramsperger has made a sound argument for mechanism (21-4) on the basis of the relative reactivities of $CH_3—N=N—CH_3$, $CH_3—N=N—CH(CH_3)_2$, and $(CH_3)_2$-$CH—N=N—CH(CH_3)_2$.[24] The diisopropyl compound is much more reactive than the dimethyl compound, as would be expected since the isopropyl radical is more stable than the methyl radical. If mechanism (21-5) operates, the methylisopropyl compound should be essentially as reactive as the diisopropyl compound, except for a statistical factor of two. On the other hand if mechanism (21-4) holds, the replacement of the second methyl by an isopropyl group should increase the reactivity by about the same factor as replacement of the first. This is found to be the case, the rate of decomposition of the mixed azo compound being about the geometric mean of the rates of the two simple compounds.

Jones and Steacie have discussed the mechanism of the photolysis of azomethane, including the formation of methane and minor products, in some detail.[25]

Cohen and Wang have compared the rates of decomposition of seven $p\text{-}XC_6H_4—N=N—C(C_6H_5)_3$ compounds, where X was H, CH_3, Br, NO_2, HO, CH_3O, and CH_3CONH.[26] Except for methyl, which had practically no effect, all substituents decreased the rate of reaction. It therefore appears that with all substituents there is resonance stabilization due to interaction with the azo group that may be either electron-

[23] M. Page, H. O. Pritchard, and A. F. Trotman-Dickenson, *J. Chem. Soc.*, 3878 (1953).

[24] H. C. Ramsperger, *J. Am. Chem. Soc.*, **49**, 912, 1495 (1927); **50**, 714 (1928); **51**, 2134 (1929); cf. S. G. Cohen and C. H. Wang, *J. Am. Chem. Soc.*, **77**, 2457, 3628 (1955).

[25] M. H. Jones and E. W. R. Steacie, *J. Chem. Phys.*, **21**, 1018 (1953).

[26] S. G. Cohen and C. H. Wang, *J. Am. Chem. Soc.*, **75**, 5504 (1953).

withdrawing or electron-donating and that this interaction, which is being destroyed in the transition state, is more important than any interaction with the unpaired electron on the radical being formed.[26]

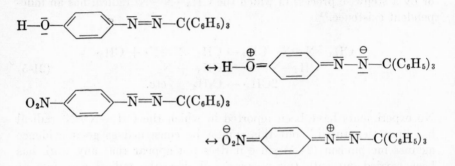

21-2b. Decomposition of Azo Nitriles. The azo nitriles comprise a class of azo compounds whose decomposition has been studied relatively thoroughly, partly because of the commercial use of some of them as initiators in free-radical polymerization. Lewis and Matheson showed that 2-azo-bis-isobutyronitrile decomposes at very nearly the same rate in a wide variety of solvents.[27] The reaction was cleanly first-order, and the rate was practically unaffected by the addition of an inhibitor. The reaction, then, like that of other azo compounds, has as its rate-controlling step a simple cleavage without a significant amount of induced chain decomposition.

Overberger and coworkers have studied the effect of structure on reactivity in these reactions.[28] Their results are summarized in Table 21-3. It was not known whether the various compounds studied had the meso or the *dl* configuration, but the cases where both diastereomers were studied show both to have about the same reactivity. It may be seen that most simple alkyl groups have about the same effect on the reactivity. The reaction-accelerating influence of the isobutyl and neopentyl groups is attributed to steric interference between the two groups attached to the azo nitrogen atoms. The reactivity of the cyclo-

[27] F. M. Lewis and M. S. Matheson, *J. Am. Chem. Soc.*, **71**, 747 (1949); cf. Ref. 28 and K. Ziegler, W. Deparade, and W. Meye, *Ann.*, **567**, 141 (1950); C. E. H. Bawn and S. F. Mellish, *Trans. Faraday Soc.*, **47**, 1216 (1951).

[28] C. G. Overberger, M. T. O'Shaughnessy, and H. Shalit, *J. Am. Chem. Soc.*, **71**, 2661 (1949); C. G. Overberger and M. B. Berenbaum, *J. Am. Chem. Soc.*, **73**, 2618 (1951); C. G. Overberger and H. Biletch, *J. Am. Chem. Soc.*, **73**, 4880 (1951); C. G. Overberger, H. Biletch, A. B. Finestone, J. Lilker, and J. Herbert, *J. Am. Chem. Soc.*, **75**, 2078 (1953); C. G. Overberger and A. Lebovits, *J. Am. Chem. Soc.*, **76**, 2722 (1954); C. G. Overberger, W. F. Hale, M. B. Berenbaum, and A. B. Finestone, *J. Am. Chem. Soc.*, **76**, 6185 (1954).

propyl compound may be rationalized in terms of the resemblance of the three-membered ring to a double bond. The radical formed upon decomposition of the azo compound is then seen to resemble an allyl radical, having resonance structures of the type

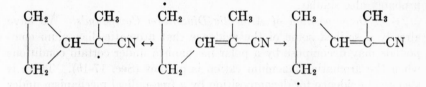

TABLE 21-3. RATE CONSTANTS, SEC^{-1}, FOR THE DECOMPOSITION OF AZO NITRILES IN TOLUENE AT 80°

I. Compounds of the type

$$R-\underset{\underset{CH_3}{|}}{\overset{\overset{CN}{|}}{C}}-N=N-\underset{\underset{CH_3}{|}}{\overset{\overset{CN}{|}}{C}}-R$$

R	$10^4 k$	R	$10^4 k$
Methyl	1.66	Benzyl	1.16
Ethyl	0.87	p-Chlorobenzyl	0.88
n-Propyl	1.70	p-Nitrobenzyl	1.00
Isopropyl	1.02	Cyclopropyl[a]	25
n-Butyl	1.58		33
Isobutyl[a]	7.1	Cyclobutyl[a]	1.51
	10		1.51
t-Butyl[a]	0.77	Cyclopentyl[a]	1.30
	1.09		1.31
Neopentyl[a]	136	Cyclohexyl	2.27
	158		

II. Alicyclic azo nitriles of the type $(CH_2)_n$ $\underset{\underset{CH_2}{\diagdown}}{\overset{\overset{CH_2}{\diagup}}{}}\underset{}{\overset{CN}{\diagup}}C-N=N-C\overset{NC}{\diagdown}\underset{\underset{CH_2}{\diagup}}{\overset{\overset{CH_2}{\diagdown}}{}}(CH_2)_n$

Alicyclic ring	$10^4 k$	Alicyclic ring	$10^4 k$
Cyclobutyl	0.0017	Cycloheptyl	12.2
Cyclopentyl	0.726	Cyclooctyl	83.5
Cyclohexyl	0.063	Cyclodecyl	18.4

[a] Both dl and meso isomers studied. It is not known which isomer has which structure.

and perhaps others in addition to structures involving the cyano group.[28] The relative ease with which free radicals are formed on alicyclic rings of various sizes was also studied (Table 21-3, II) and was found to resemble the relative ease of formation of carbonium ions on alicyclic rings (Sec. 6-3a). The reasons for this variation in reactivity are probably also similar.

21-2c. Decomposition of Aromatic Diazonium Compounds. We have already described some of the evidence that aromatic diazonium compounds may decompose by a polar mechanism under certain conditions when the aromatic diazonium cation is present (Sec. 17-1b). There is also good evidence for decomposition by a free-radical mechanism under some conditions where the diazonium compound is present in a covalent state. We do not imply, of course, that diazonium cations cannot react by a radical mechanism or the covalent compounds by a polar one.

Some of the first evidence for the free-radical mechanism was described by Grieve and Hey, who found that the decomposition of *N*-nitroso-acetanilide in several aromatic solvents led to the substitution of phenyl radicals into the aromatic ring.[29] Since the decomposition in nitrobenzene solution yields predominantly *o-* and *p*-nitrobiphenyl, it is obvious that the reaction is not an ordinary electrophilic aromatic substitution. These workers suggest that the reaction goes through phenyl diazoacetate, which decomposes to give nitrogen, acetoxy radicals, and phenyl radicals, which bring about the aromatic phenylation.

$$
\overset{\displaystyle NO}{\underset{\displaystyle |}{C_6H_5-N}}-Ac \rightarrow C_6H_5-N\!\!=\!\!N-OAc \rightarrow C_6H_5\cdot + N_2 + AcO\cdot
$$

$$
\downarrow C_6H_5NO_2
$$

$$
\text{mostly } o\text{- and } p\text{-}C_6H_5C_6H_4NO_2
$$

The exact mechanism of the aromatic substitution reaction will be discussed in Sec. 22-3a. Grieve and Hey also found the first-order reaction rate constants to be very little affected by the nature of the solvent over a range (viz., carbon tetrachloride, benzene, and nitrobenzene) for which the ion-solvating abilities should vary quite widely. Assuming the rate-controlling step of the reaction to be the decomposition of the diazoacetate, this insensitivity to solvent is very reasonable for a free-radical decomposition but not for a decomposition to ions. However, Huisgen and Horeld have shown that the rate of decomposition of nitroso-acetanilide in benzene, as measured by the rate of formation of nitrogen, is the same as the rate of formation of phenylazo-β-naphthol in the presence of β-naphthol, suggesting that the two reactions have a common rate-controlling step.[30]

[29] W. S. M. Grieve and D. H. Hey, *J. Chem. Soc.*, 1797 (1934).
[30] R. Huisgen and G. Horeld, *Ann.*, **562**, 137 (1949).

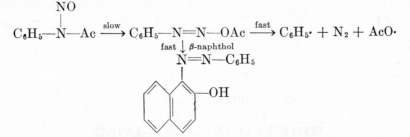

Considerable other evidence supports this explanation, according to which, the kinetic data give no evidence for or against the free-radical mechanism.[31] Nevertheless, there are many other data in support of the free-radical mechanism. DeTar has made strong arguments based on the fact that in several cases relatively small changes in the reaction conditions bring about a drastic change in the course of the reaction. In each case he points out how reasonable it is that the change in conditions should have brought about a change in reaction mechanism and how the change in mechanism should have changed the course of reaction in the manner found. Thus he finds that the decomposition of N-nitrosoacetanilide in methanol at 25° gives 25 to 30 per cent benzene and 5 to 10 per cent anisole.[32] The addition of sodium acetate increases the decomposition rate by about twentyfold and the yield of benzene to 40 to 45 per cent, while it decreases the yield of anisole to about 2 per cent. In the presence of 0.04 M sulfuric acid the yield of anisole increases to 55 to 75 per cent, while that of benzene drops to 10 per cent or less. It therefore appears that the nitrosoacetanilide rearranges to phenyl diazoacetate, which, in methanol, ionizes even faster than it decomposes. There is thus a small amount of the reactive covalent acetate in equilibrium with a larger amount of the more stable salt. The addition of acetate ions drives this equilibrium to the left, while sulfuric acid changes the acetate ions to acetic acid and drives the equilibrium to the right.

$$C_6H_5\text{—}N\text{=}N\text{—}OAc \rightleftharpoons C_6H_5\text{—}N_2^+ + OAc^-$$

$$\begin{array}{ccc} \downarrow & \downarrow & \uparrow\downarrow H^+ \\ C_6H_5\cdot & C_6H_5^+ & HOAc \\ \downarrow CH_3OH & \downarrow CH_3OH & \\ C_6H_6 & C_6H_5OCH_3 & \end{array}$$

The phenyl radical abstracts a hydrogen atom from methanol, preferring the more weakly bonded one attached to carbon, while the phenyl cation coordinates with the unshared electron pair of the oxygen atom. Huisgen and Nakaten have made observations similar to these.[33]

[31] R. Huisgen, *Ann.*, **573**, 163 (1951); D. H. Hey, J. Stuart-Webb, and G. H. Williams, *J. Chem. Soc.*, 4657 (1952).

[32] D. F. DeTar, *J. Am. Chem. Soc.*, **73**, 1446 (1951); cf. D. F. DeTar and M. N. Turetzky, *J. Am. Chem. Soc.*, **77**, 1745 (1955).

[33] R. Huisgen and H. Nakaten, *Ann.*, **573**, 181 (1951).

CHAPTER 22

SOME REACTIONS INVOLVING
RADICAL DISPLACEMENTS

22-1. Free-radical Halogenation. *22-1a. Mechanism of Radical Halogenations.* The chlorination and bromination of saturated hydrocarbons have long been known to be light-catalyzed. This fact shows that these reactions are very probably free-radical in nature, and the high quantum yields observed show that they are chain reactions of considerable chain length.

Vaughan and Rust showed that although chlorine and ethane alone react at a negligible rate at 120°, the reaction rapidly goes to completion if 0.002 mole per cent of tetraethyllead, which decomposes to give ethyl radicals at this temperature, is added.[1] They also found that hexaphenylethane is an effective catalyst of chlorinations in the liquid phase at lower temperatures. In the case of $Pb(C_2H_5)_4$ the reaction mechanism is presumably

$$Pb(C_2H_5)_4 \rightarrow Pb + 4C_2H_5\cdot$$
$$C_2H_5\cdot + Cl_2 \rightarrow C_2H_5Cl + Cl\cdot$$
$$Cl\cdot + C_2H_6 \rightarrow HCl + C_2H_5\cdot$$

A number of mechanisms of termination are possible. Some involve "wall reactions" and collisions with a third body to absorb the energy given off. Oxygen is a powerful inhibitor for the reaction, probably because of its great ability to combine with ethyl radicals to form C_2H_5—O—O·, a radical much less capable of removing hydrogen atoms from ethane than is Cl·.

From the nature of the products, we know that the chlorine atom attacks the hydrocarbon molecule to break a carbon-hydrogen bond rather than a carbon-carbon bond, although the latter type of bond is

---

[1] W. E. Vaughan and F. F. Rust, *J. Org. Chem.*, **5**, 449 (1940).

weaker. This is probably due partly to the possibility of forming the hydrogen-chlorine bond (stronger than carbon-chlorine) and partly to the fact that the carbon atoms are shielded, being surrounded entirely by hydrogen atoms.

The bromination of saturated hydrocarbons is rather similar to the chlorination, except that bromine atoms are less reactive than chlorine atoms. Iodine atoms are still less reactive, and for this reason the iodination of alkanes is not a synthetically useful reaction.

Steacie has discussed the kinetics and mechanisms of a number of vapor-phase halogenation reactions.[2]

22-1b. Halogenation with Reagents Other than Elemental Halogen. In addition to the elemental halogens there are a number of reagents that have been used in halogenation reactions that appear to be free-radical in character. One of the most widely used of these reagents is sulfuryl chloride. The extensive use of this compound stems from the studies of Kharasch and Brown, who found that in the presence of a benzoyl peroxide catalyst it is capable of replacing the hydrogen atoms attached to saturated carbon atoms in a wide variety of organic compounds.[3] Kharasch and Brown suggest the mechanism

$$R\cdot + SO_2Cl_2 \rightarrow RCl + \cdot SO_2Cl$$
$$\cdot SO_2Cl \rightarrow SO_2 + Cl\cdot$$
$$Cl\cdot + RH \rightarrow HCl + R\cdot$$

although it is possible that the $\cdot SO_2Cl$ radical may attack hydrocarbons in at least some cases.

Ziegler and coworkers have shown that N-bromosuccinimide is a particularly suitable reagent for the replacement of allylic hydrogen by bromine.[4] The fact that the reaction is catalyzed by light[5] and benzoyl peroxide[6] points to a free-radical mechanism. Although no study of the reaction kinetics appears to have been made the following mechanism has been suggested.[7]

[2] E. W. R. Steacie, "Atomic and Free Radical Reactions," 2d ed., pp. 657–747, Reinhold Publishing Corporation, New York, 1954.

[3] M. S. Kharasch and H. C. Brown, *J. Am. Chem. Soc.*, **61**, 2142, 3432 (1939); **62**, 925 (1940).

[4] K. Ziegler, A. Späth, E. Schaaf, W. Schumann, and E. Winkelmann, *Ann.*, **551**, 80 (1942).

[5] C. Meystre, L. Ehmann, R. Neher, and K. Miescher, *Helv. Chim. Acta*, **28**, 1252 (1945).

[6] H. Schmid and P. Karrer, *Helv. Chim. Acta*, **29**, 573 (1946).

[7] G. F. Bloomfield, *J. Chem. Soc.*, 114 (1944); cf. W. A. Waters, *Nature*, **154**, 772 (1944).

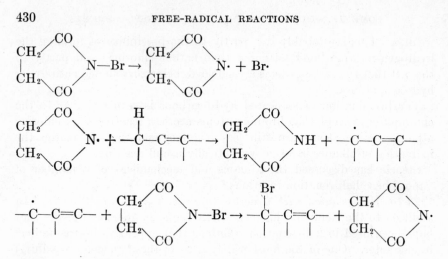

22-1c. Orientation in Radical Halogenations. Unless the intermediate radical rearranges (see Sec. 23-2 for the only such case which has been found), the nature of the product of a free-radical halogenation depends only on which hydrogen atom of the organic reactant is removed by the attacking halogen atom. As Mayo and Walling have pointed out, apparently both radical stability and polar factors are important here.[8] There will be a tendency for the most stable possible radical to be formed, but there will also be a tendency for the electron-withdrawing halogen atom to attack a point of high electron density and avoid a point of low electron density.

The existence of polar factors is perhaps most convincingly illustrated by certain correlations that have been obtained between Hammett's σ constants and reactivity in radical halogenations. Van Helden and Kooyman have studied the radical-catalyzed chlorination of the methyl group of a number of substituted toluenes by use of sulfuryl chloride.[9] Their data give a reasonable fit to the Hammett equation, with a ρ constant of -1.5. Comparison with their earlier data[10] shows that the sensitivity of the reactivity to the electron-withdrawing (or -donating) power of the substituent increases with the electron-withdrawing power of the attacking atom or radical. When the attacking radical is the succinimino radical, $\rho = -1.55$; when it is a bromine atom, $\rho = -1.05$; and for the trichloromethyl radical $\rho \sim 0$.[10] With aliphatic hydrocarbons these two effects appear to operate in the same direction. The order tertiary > secondary > primary would be expected for radical

[8] F. R. Mayo and C. Walling, *Chem. Rev.*, **46**, 269 (1950); cf. A. B. Ash and H. C. Brown, *Record Chem. Progr.* (*Kresge-Hooker Sci. Lib.*), **9**, 81 (1948).

[9] R. van Helden and E. C. Kooyman, *Rec. trav. chim.*, **73**, 269 (1954).

[10] E. C. Kooyman, R. van Helden, and A. F. Bickel, *Konikl. Ned. Akad. Wetenschav. Proc.*, **56B**, 75 (1953).

stability *and* electron density. This agrees with the experiments of Hass, McBee, and Weber on the thermal chlorination of propane, butane, isobutane, pentane, and isopentane.[11] By assuming that the relative reactivities of primary, secondary, and tertiary hydrogen atoms are 1.00 to 3.25 to 4.43, these workers were able to calculate the composition of the monochloride mixtures formed at 300° with the agreement seen in Table 22-1. The magnitude of these differences in ease

TABLE 22-1. CALCULATED AND EXPERIMENTAL COMPOSITION OF PRODUCTS OF MONOCHLORINATION OF FIVE LOWER HYDROCARBONS AT 300°[11]

Hydrocarbon	Monochlorides, %							
	Calculated				Experimental			
	1-Cl	2-Cl	3-Cl	4-Cl	1-Cl	2-Cl	3-Cl	4-Cl
Propane................	48	52	....	..	48	52		
Butane.................	32	68	....	..	32	68		
Isobutane..............	67	33	....	..	67	33		
2-Methylbutane.........	30	22	33	15	33.5	22	28	16.5
Pentane................	23.5	51	25.5	..	23.8	48.8	27.4	

of substitution varies with the reactivity of the halogen atom in the expected manner. Substitution becomes more nearly random at higher temperatures where many chlorine atoms have the ability to remove almost every hydrogen atom with which they collide.[11] Bromine atoms appear to have a stronger tendency to attack tertiary hydrogen than do the more reactive chlorine atoms. Roberts and Coraor, for example, have noted that the photobromination of isopentane yields almost entirely *t*-amyl bromide, while the chlorination reaction under the same conditions gave only a little of the tertiary chloride mixed with a large amount of other monochlorides.[12]

A chlorine atom would be expected to facilitate further chlorination on the same carbon atom by stabilization of the radical formed, but to inhibit reaction at this carbon atom (and to a lesser extent at adjacent carbons) by its electron-withdrawing inductive effect. Apparently the polar effect is more important than the radical stabilization effects. In most of the data that have been reported on free-radical chlorinations it appears that chlorine (compared to hydrogen) decreases the extent of chlorination on the same (α-) and adjacent (β-) carbon atoms and to a smaller extent on the γ-carbon atom. Thus Tishchenko has reported

[11] H. B. Hass, E. T. McBee, and P. Weber, *Ind. Eng. Chem.*, **28**, 333 (1936).
[12] J. D. Roberts and G. R. Coraor, *J. Am. Chem. Soc.*, **74**, 3586 (1952).

that the photochlorination of n-butyl chloride at 35 to 40° gives substitution on the various carbon atoms to the extent shown below.[13]

$$\overset{\delta}{CH_3}-\overset{\gamma}{CH_2}-\overset{\beta}{CH_2}-\overset{\alpha}{CH_2}-Cl$$
$$25\% \quad 50\% \quad 17\% \quad 3\%$$

The decreased reactivity of the α- compared to the β-carbon atom is probably largely due to the fact that the α-carbon is primary and the β- secondary. It is true that the α-carbon should be more highly deactivated by the inductive effect, but this factor should be at least partially offset by the increased stability of a radical on the same carbon as a chlorine atom. According to Rust and Vaughan, as the reaction temperature is increased, the deactivating influence of chlorine on the α-carbon atom is decreased, while the deactivation of the β-carbon atom is increased.[14] At 380°, they report, the dichlorides from the chlorination of n-butyl chloride contain about 22 per cent of the 1,1 isomer; 53 per cent 1,3; 25 per cent 1,4; and only a negligible fraction of the 1,2-dichloride. Ash and Brown, however, point out that the decrease in the yield of the 1,2 isomer may be due to the decomposition of the intermediate radical at the high temperature used.[8]

$$C_2H_5CH_2CH_2Cl + Cl\cdot \rightarrow HCl + C_2H_5\overset{\cdot}{C}HCH_2Cl \rightarrow C_2H_5CH{=}CH_2 + Cl\cdot$$

The interplay of radical stability and polar factors may be seen in many of the data of Henne and coworkers on the chlorination of aliphatic fluoride derivatives. The following results were obtained from chlorinations in the presence of sunlight.[15]

$$F_3CCH_2CH_2CH_3 \rightarrow 44\% \; F_3CCH_2\underset{\underset{Cl}{|}}{C}HCH_3, \; 56\% \; F_3CCH_2CH_2CH_2Cl$$

$F_3CCH_2CH_3 \rightarrow F_3CCH_2CH_2Cl$ (only monochloride isolated)

$F_2CHCH_3 \rightarrow 70\% \; F_2CClCH_3, \; 6\% \; F_2CClCH_2Cl$, but no F_2CHCH_2Cl

$F_3CH \rightarrow F_3CCl$ (very slowly)

$F_3CCH_2CF_3 \rightarrow$ no reaction

Some of the observed data are difficult to explain, however. For example, while CH_3CF_3 is chlorinated with difficulty, as expected, the only product isolated was Cl_3CCF_3, showing that $ClCH_2CF_3$ is more reactive toward chlorination than is CH_3CF_3.[15] This tendency of the hydrogen atoms

---

[13] D. V. Tishchenko, *Zhur. Obshchei Khim.*, **7**, 658 (1937); *Chem. Abstr.*, **31**, 5755 (1937); cf. M. S. Kharasch and H. C. Brown, *J. Am. Chem. Soc.*, **61**, 2142 (1939).

[14] F. F. Rust and W. E. Vaughan, *J. Org. Chem.*, **6**, 479 (1941).

[15] A. L. Henne and J. B. Hinkamp, *J. Am. Chem. Soc.*, **67**, 1197 (1945); A. L. Henne and A. M. Whaley, *J. Am. Chem. Soc.*, **64**, 1157 (1942); A. L. Henne, J. B. Hinkamp, and W. J. Zimmerschied, *J. Am. Chem. Soc.*, **67**, 1906 (1945).

next to a —CF_3 group to be deactivated but to be completely replaced once chlorination has started has been observed with a number of other compounds. Perhaps the inductive effect of the fluorine atoms is so great that the inductive effect added by the chlorine is relatively small. In this way the radical-stabilizing ability of chlorine becomes the more important factor. Another unexpected result has been found by Henne and Whaley, who reported that the chlorination of $CH_3CH_2CCl_3$ yields more $CH_3CHClCCl_3$ than $ClCH_2CH_2CCl_3$.

There are a number of possible explanations for these anomalous reactions that have not received careful mechanistic study. A related anomaly that seems to have a reasonable explanation appears in the chlorination of diethyl ether at room temperature, where α-hydrogen is replaced first, then the three β-hydrogens successively, and only then is the α'-hydrogen attacked. This is apparently due to the loss of hydrogen chloride by the α-chloro ether under the reaction conditions,

$$\text{Et}_2\text{O} \xrightarrow{\text{Cl}_2} \underset{\underset{\text{Cl}}{|}}{\text{CH}_3\text{CHOEt}} \xrightarrow{-\text{HCl}} \text{CH}_2{=}\text{CHOEt} \xrightarrow{\text{Cl}_2} \underset{\underset{\text{Cl Cl}}{|\ \ |}}{\text{CH}_2\text{CHOEt}}$$

$$\Big\downarrow -\text{HCl}$$

$$\underset{\underset{\text{Cl}}{|}}{\text{Cl}_3\text{CCHOEt}} \xleftarrow{\text{etc.}} \underset{\underset{\text{Cl}}{|}}{\text{Cl}_2\text{CHCHOEt}} \xleftarrow{\text{Cl}_2} \underset{\underset{\text{Cl}}{|}}{\text{CH}{=}\text{CHOEt}}$$

since chlorination at -25 to $-30°$ yields the α,α'-dichloride.[16]

In the free-radical halogenation of a n-alkylbenzene such as n-propylbenzene there are seen to be three types of hydrogens which could be removed by the attack of a halogen atom. These are the aromatic hydrogens, the benzyl hydrogens, and the others which we shall call aliphatic hydrogen. Only by removal of a benzyl hydrogen may a resonance-stabilized radical be formed. It is therefore not surprising that the free-radical halogenation of n-alkylbenzenes ordinarily yields benzyl-type halides. Evidently the slight electron-withdrawing power of the aromatic ring has a smaller effect than radical stabilization. For the removal of an aromatic hydrogen this polar factor should be stronger, and there is evidence that the phenyl radical is less stable than ordinary aliphatic radicals. As an illustration of the fact that aliphatic-type hydrogens are replaced in preference to aromatic ones, the chlorination of t-butylbenzene (which has no benzyl hydrogens) to 1-chloro-2-methyl-2-phenylpropane[3,17] may be mentioned. The difficulty of replacing an aromatic hydrogen

[16] G. E. Hall and F. M. Ubertini, *J. Org. Chem.*, **15**, 715 (1950).

[17] W. E. Truce, E. T. McBee, and C. C. Alfieri, *J. Am. Chem. Soc.*, **71**, 752 (1949).

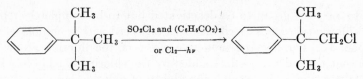

atom is seen in the radical chlorination of benzene, which yields the addition product benzene hexachloride at ordinary temperatures and gives substitution only at considerably elevated temperatures.

By letting a small amount of chlorine react with an excess of a hydrocarbon mixture and analyzing the organic chloride mixture formed, Brown and Russell showed that the hydrogen atoms in cyclohexane are about four times as reactive as the side-chain hydrogens in toluene toward photochlorination at 80°.[18] This is a surprising result even though the hydrogen atoms in cyclohexane are secondary and those in toluene are primary. Judging from the relative rates of decomposition of azo nitriles (Table 21-3, II), a radical on the cyclohexane ring would be expected to be slightly less stable, if anything, than on an aliphatic chain. By using deuterium-labeled hydrocarbons, it was shown that the situation was not being complicated by the attack of hydrocarbon radicals on hydrocarbon molecules.[18]

The polar effect on radical halogenation is perhaps found most strikingly in the reactions of compounds with such strongly electron-withdrawing substituents as the carboxyl group and its derivatives. In the radical chlorination of aliphatic acids and their derivatives the α-hydrogen atoms appear to be relatively inactive.[3]   In the chlorination of isobutyryl chloride with sulfuryl chloride in the presence of benzoyl peroxide, 80 per cent β-chloro- and 20 per cent α-chloroisobutyryl chloride are formed.[3]   It appears that neutral or electron-donating radicals preferentially remove α-hydrogen atoms because of the greater stability of the radicals formed. At least this is the interpretation given[8] the observation of Kharasch and Gladstone that the decompositions of acyl peroxides in aliphatic acid solutions yield succinic acid derivatives.[19]   For instance,

$$(CH_3CO_2)_2 \rightarrow 2CH_3CO_2\cdot \rightarrow 2CH_3\cdot + CO_2$$

$$CH_3\cdot + (CH_3)_2CHCO_2H \rightarrow CH_4 + (CH_3)_2\overset{\cdot}{C}CO_2H$$

$$2(CH_3)_2\overset{\cdot}{C}CO_2H \rightarrow \begin{matrix} (CH_3)_2C-CO_2H \\ | \\ (CH_3)_2C-CO_2H \end{matrix}$$

It has been suggested that the reaction above involves the formation of radicals on the β-carbon and that these then remove an α-hydrogen atom

[18] H. C. Brown and G. A. Russell, *J. Am. Chem. Soc.*, **74**, 3995 (1952).

[19] M. S. Kharasch and M. T. Gladstone, *J. Am. Chem. Soc.*, **65**, 15 (1943).

from another molecule to give the radical on the α-carbon.[20]   Price and Morita, however, have shown that this does not occur to any large extent if it occurs at all.   They studied the decomposition of acetyl peroxide in α-deuteroisobutyryl chloride and found considerable quantities of deuteromethane in the gases produced.[21]   Their data show that methyl radicals attack α-hydrogen about 12 times as rapidly as they attack β-hydrogen atoms.   The orientation observed in the radical chlorination of acids and their derivatives makes it appear likely that such halogenation methods as the Hell-Volhard-Zelinski, which give preferential alpha-substitution, proceed by a different mechanism, probably one analogous to that of the acid-catalyzed halogenation of ketones.

Ash and Brown have discussed the effect of structure on reactivity and orientation in radical chlorinations and have concluded that various groups have the following net effect on the ease of replacement of a hydrogen atom attached to the same carbon atom: $C_6H_5 > CH_3 > H > AcO > ClCH_2 > Cl_2CH > Cl_3Si > CO_2H > Cl > COCl > Cl_3CCO_2 > CCl_3 > CF_3$.[20]

22-2. Autooxidation.   *22-2a. Mechanism of Autooxidation Reactions.* The autooxidation of benzaldehyde, like that of many other compounds, has been found to be a light-catalyzed reaction.   From this fact a free-radical mechanism appears probable, and since Bäckström has found quantum yields on the order of 10,000 for the reaction, a chain mechanism is likely.[22]   The light-catalyzed autooxidation reaction was found to be markedly inhibited by small concentrations of diphenylamine, phenol, and anthracene.[22]   Ziegler and Ewald showed that hexaphenylethane, known to dissociate to free radicals, catalyzes the autooxidation of aldehydes.[23]   This direct evidence for the intermediacy of free radicals and the chemical course of the reaction (hydrogen is replaced by the hydroperoxy group) suggest the following mechanism for initiation and chain propagation.

$$(C_6H_5)_3CC(C_6H_5)_3 \rightarrow (C_6H_5)_3C\cdot$$
$$(C_6H_5)_3C\cdot + O_2 \rightarrow (C_6H_5)_3COO\cdot$$
$$(C_6H_5)_3COO\cdot + C_6H_5CHO \rightarrow (C_6H_5)_3COOH + C_6H_5CO\cdot$$
$$C_6H_5CO\cdot + O_2 \rightarrow C_6H_5COO_2\cdot$$
$$C_6H_5COO_2\cdot + C_6H_5CHO \rightarrow C_6H_5COO_2H + C_6H_5CO\cdot$$

The oxygen molecule has two unpaired electrons and may thus be

[20] A. B. Ash and H. C. Brown, *Record Chem. Prog. (Kresge-Hooker Sci. Lib.)*, **9**, 81 (1948); *J. Am. Chem. Soc.*, **77**, 4019 (1955).

[21] C. C. Price and H. Morita, *J. Am. Chem. Soc.*, **75**, 3686 (1953).

[22] H. L. J. Bäckström, *J. Am. Chem. Soc.*, **49**, 1460 (1927).

[23] K. Ziegler and L. Ewald, *Ann.*, **504**, 162 (1933).

regarded as a sort of diradical. It is not a sufficiently reactive radical to attack most organic molecules under ordinary conditions, but it is very facile at combining with free radicals. The hydroperoxy radicals formed by the addition of oxygen to organic radicals are much more reactive than is oxygen, but they are only moderately reactive compared to most organic radicals.

The determination of the nature of the termination step or steps requires a more careful and quantitative study of the reaction. Such a study appears to have been carried out first in connection with the autooxidation of olefins and has been reviewed by Bolland[24] and by Bateman.[25] If we assume that all radicals formed from the initiator attack either oxygen or the hydrocarbon and that termination is due to a reaction between two chain-carrying radicals, we may write the mechanism

$$\text{Initiator} \rightarrow \text{radicals (R· and/or RO}_2\text{·)} \qquad \text{rate} = r_1$$

$$\text{R·} + \text{O}_2 \overset{k_2}{\rightarrow} \text{RO}_2\text{·} \tag{22-1}$$

$$\text{RO}_2\text{·} + \text{RH} \overset{k_3}{\rightarrow} \text{R·} + \text{RO}_2\text{H} \tag{22-2}$$

$$2\text{R·} \overset{k_4}{\rightarrow} \left.\begin{array}{c} \\ \\ \\ \end{array}\right\} \begin{array}{l} \text{products not} \\ \text{further entering} \\ \text{the reaction} \end{array} \tag{22-3}$$

$$\text{R·} + \text{RO}_2\text{·} \overset{k_5}{\rightarrow} \tag{22-4}$$

$$2\text{RO}_2\text{·} \overset{k_6}{\rightarrow} \tag{22-5}$$

If the chain length is long, so that the number of radicals produced in propagation steps is very large compared to those produced by initiation,

$$k_2[\text{R·}][\text{O}_2] = k_3[\text{RO}_2\text{·}][\text{RH}] \tag{22-6}$$

From the steady-state treatment the rate of formation of radicals is equal to their rate of disappearance

$$r_1 = k_4[\text{R·}]^2 + 2k_5[\text{R·}][\text{RO}_2\text{·}] + k_6[\text{RO}_2\text{·}]^2 \tag{22-7}$$

A value for $[\text{RO}_2\text{·}]$ from Eq. (22-6) may be substituted in (22-7) to give

$$[\text{R·}] = \frac{r_1^{1/2}[\text{RH}]}{(k_4[\text{RH}]^2 + 2k_2k_3^{-1}k_5[\text{O}_2][\text{RH}] + k_2^2k_3^{-2}k_6[\text{O}_2]^2)^{1/2}} \tag{22-8}$$

The rate of the over-all reaction is measured by the uptake of oxygen and may be taken to be equal to the rate of reaction (22-1). Substitution of Eq. (22-8) into the rate equation for (22-1) gives

$$v = \frac{r_1^{1/2}[\text{RH}][\text{O}_2]}{(k_2^{-2}k_4[\text{RH}]^2 + 2k_2^{-1}k_3^{-1}k_5[\text{O}_2][\text{RH}] + k_3^{-2}k_6[\text{O}_2]^2)^{1/2}} \tag{22-9}$$

[24] J. L. Bolland, *Quart. Revs. (London)*, **3**, 1 (1949).
[25] L. Bateman, *Quart. Revs. (London)*, **8**, 147 (1954).

Equation (22-9) has been simplified by some workers by assuming that $k_5{}^2 = k_4 k_6$, but this relationship would not be expected to hold in most cases, and, indeed, Bateman and coworkers have shown that it does not.[26] In agreement with the equation the reaction rate has, in a number of cases, been shown to be proportional to the square root of the initiation rate.   Thus the rate of the benzoyl peroxide–induced reaction is proportional to the square root of the initiator concentration,[27] while the light-catalyzed reaction has a rate proportional to the square root of the light intensity.[28]   Since k_2 is much larger than k_3, as expected, at fairly high oxygen concentrations $RO_2\cdot$ radicals tend to reach a concentration much higher than that of $R\cdot$ radicals.   Under these conditions termination occurs essentially entirely by mechanism (22-5), and the first two terms in the denominator of Eq. (22-9) may be neglected compared to the third.   Thus at high oxygen pressures the rate equation approaches the form

$$v = k_3 k_6^{-\frac{1}{2}} r_1^{\frac{1}{2}}[RH] \qquad (22\text{-}10)$$

For analogous reasons, at low oxygen pressures the reaction may become first-order in oxygen.

$$v = k_2 k_4^{-\frac{1}{2}} r_1^{\frac{1}{2}}[O_2]$$

The intermediate cases are also known, of course.

In a study of the autooxidation of n-decanal Cooper and Melville have suggested that initiation may take place by the attack of oxygen on the aldehyde.[29]   A similar initiation mechanism has been suggested for the vapor-phase oxidation of ethers.[30]

22-2b. *Reactivity in Autooxidations.*   The reactivity of organic compounds in autooxidation reactions is probably most commonly controlled by the rate of attack of radicals on the compound.

$$RO_2\cdot + RH \rightarrow RO_2H + R\cdot$$

The reactivity in this step of the reaction is rather similar to that in free-radical halogenations, being increased by increasing stability of the radical being formed and by the presence of electron-donating substituents.   Due to the relatively low reactivity of $RO_2\cdot$ radicals, many autooxidation reactions show considerable selectivity.

[26] L. Bateman, G. Gee, A. L. Morris, and W. F. Watson, *Discussions Faraday Soc.*, **10**, 250 (1951); L. Bateman and A. L. Morris, *Trans. Faraday Soc.*, **49**, 1026 (1953); L. Bateman and G. Gee, *Proc. Roy. Soc. (London)*, **195A**, 391 (1948).

[27] J. L. Bolland, *Proc. Roy. Soc. (London)*, **186A**, 218 (1946); *Trans. Faraday Soc.*, **44**, 669 (1948).

[28] L. Bateman, *Trans. Faraday Soc.*, **42**, 266 (1946); L. Bateman and G. Gee, *Proc. Roy. Soc. (London)*, **195A**, 376, 391 (1948).

[29] H. R. Cooper and H. W. Melville, *J. Chem. Soc.*, 1984 (1951).

[30] T. A. Eastwood and C. Hinshelwood, *J. Chem. Soc.*, 733 (1952).

Because of the greater reactivity of tertiary hydrogen atoms and probably also because of the greater stability of tertiary hydroperoxides, it is feasible to prepare hydroperoxides from saturated hydrocarbons only in the case of the tertiary compounds. Thus, 9-decalyl hydroperoxide may be prepared by the autooxidation of decalin, but only in poor yield.[31] The reaction is greatly facilitated when the hydrogen atoms replaced are of the benzyl type, cumene and tetralin giving good yields of hydroperoxides.[32]

The relative reactivity of olefins toward autooxidation has been studied rather carefully. Due to the intermediacy of resonance-stabilized allylic free radicals, these reactions may involve double-bond migrations. Indeed, the fact that the autooxidation of ethyl linoleate yields hydroperoxides with conjugated double bonds[33] has been quoted as evidence that organic free radicals are intermediates in autooxidation processes.

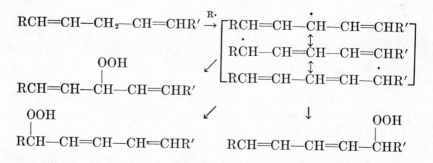

where $R = n\text{-}C_5H_{11}$; $R' = (CH_2)_7CO_2Et$

Bolland has pointed out some correlations between olefin structure and reactivity in the high oxygen pressure region where the kinetic Eq. (22-10) is obeyed, and the reactivity is controlled by step (22-2).[34] Taking propylene

$$\underset{\gamma}{CH_3}\text{---}\underset{\beta}{CH}\text{=}\underset{\alpha}{CH_2}$$

as a reference compound, he states that at 45°: (1) replacement of n hydrogen atoms at α or γ by alkyl groups increases the reactivity 3.3^n-fold; (2) replacement of an α-hydrogen by phenyl increases the reactivity

[31] A. C. Cope and G. Holzman, *J. Am. Chem. Soc.*, **72**, 3062 (1950).

[32] M. Hartmann and M. Seiberth, *Helv. Chim. Acta*, **15**, 1390 (1932); H. Hock and S. Lang, *Ber.*, **77B**, 257 (1944).

[33] J. L. Bolland and H. P. Koch, *J. Chem. Soc.*, 445 (1945); cf. E. H. Farmer, H. P. Koch, and D. A. Sutton, *J. Chem. Soc.*, 541 (1943).

[34] J. L. Bolland, *Trans. Faraday Soc.*, **46**, 358 (1950).

23-fold; (3) replacement of a γ-hydrogen by a 1-alkenyl group increases the reactivity 107-fold.

It should be pointed out that while we have discussed only the abstraction of hydrogen atoms from olefins, attacking peroxy radicals may also add to the double bonds, often with rather interesting results.[24,25]

Ethers are particularly sensitive to autooxidation, as might be expected, since the reaction involves attack by an electron-withdrawing radical. Diisopropyl ether has long been known to oxidize more easily than diethyl ether, and Eastwood and Hinshelwood have shown that dimethyl ether is particularly resistant to oxidation.[35] The ease of oxidation of aldehydes is probably due to the stability of the acyl radical. Walling and McElhill have shown that electron-donating substituents increase the reactivity of benzaldehydes toward a given perbenzoate radical.[36] It was found that n-butyraldehyde was several times as reactive as benzaldehyde, suggesting that the polar effect in this case is more important than the radical-stability effect.

22-3. Free-radical Aromatic Substitution.   *22-3a. Mechanism of Free-radical Aromatic Substitution.* It is likely that certain aromatic substitution reactions, such as high-temperature vapor-phase halogenations, proceed by a mechanism quite analogous to that of most free-radical aliphatic substitutions with such chain-propagating steps as

$$Cl\cdot + C_6H_6 \rightarrow HCl + C_6H_5\cdot$$
$$C_6H_5\cdot + Cl_2 \rightarrow C_6H_5Cl + Cl\cdot$$

For certain free-radical substitution reactions occurring in solution, however, there are reasons for considering other types of reaction mechanisms. The decomposition of phenyldiazoacetate (Sec. 21-2c), of benzoyl peroxide, and of several other compounds in aromatic solvents leads to the phenylation of the aromatic rings. The mechanism of these reactions was first considered carefully by Grieve and Hey, who suggested that a phenyl radical was simply displacing a hydrogen atom from the aromatic ring.[37]

$$C_6H_5\cdot + ArH \rightarrow C_6H_5\text{—}Ar + H\cdot \qquad (22\text{-}11)$$

However, as DeTar and Sagmanli have pointed out, no good evidence (such as the formation of certain reduction products) for the intermediacy of hydrogen atoms appears to have been found.[38] Furthermore, it does not seem likely that such a one-step displacement of a hydrogen atom would be a rapid enough reaction to compete with the possible competing reactions (such as dimerization) which must be very rapid,

[35] T. A. Eastwood and C. Hinshelwood, *J. Chem. Soc.*, 733 (1952).
[36] C. Walling and E. A. McElhill, *J. Am. Chem. Soc.*, **73**, 2927 (1951).
[37] W. S. M. Grieve and D. H. Hey, *J. Chem. Soc.*, 1797 (1934).
[38] D. F. DeTar and S. V. Sagmanli, *J. Am. Chem. Soc.*, **72**, 965 (1950).

since the phenyl radical is known from other studies to be quite reactive. The reaction simply involves the formation of a carbon-carbon bond while breaking a carbon-hydrogen bond, and it appears that carbon-hydrogen bonds are invariably much stronger than the corresponding carbon-carbon bonds. Therefore it seems that reaction (22-11) should have too high an activation energy to occur fast enough to explain the observed data. It could also be suggested that the aromatic substitution is part of an induced chain decomposition reaction,[38] in which radicals formed from the solvent attack the source of phenyl radicals.

$$C_6H_5-N=N-OAc \rightarrow C_6H_5\cdot + N_2 + AcO\cdot$$
$$C_6H_5\cdot + ArH \rightarrow C_6H_5H + Ar\cdot$$
$$Ar\cdot + C_6H_5-N=N-OAc \rightarrow Ar-C_6H_5 + N_2 + AcO\cdot$$

If this is the reaction mechanism, then the unsubstituted phenyl radical must be capable of bringing about induced decomposition in this way, since benzene is among the aromatic compounds which can be phenylated by the methods described. Yet biphenyl appears never to have been isolated as a by-product in the phenylation of other aromatic compounds.

The most probable mechanism seems to be a two-stage version of (22-11). The phenyl radical is depicted as adding to the aromatic ring to give a radical which may then lose a hydrogen atom.

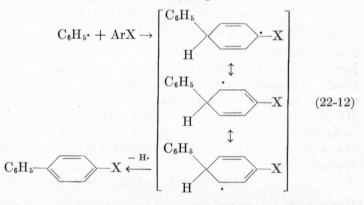

$$(22\text{-}12)$$

The hydrogen atom may be abstracted by another radical molecule, or it may be lost in an attack on the source of phenyl radicals.

Among the data in support of this mechanism we may mention the observation of Stockmayer and Peebles that benzene is incorporated into the polymer chain when used as a solvent for the polymerization of vinyl acetate.[39]

22-3b. Reactivity and Orientation in Free-radical Aromatic Substitution. The relative reactivities of the various positions on a given aromatic

[39] W. H. Stockmayer and L. H. Peebles, Jr., *J. Am. Chem. Soc.*, **75**, 2279 (1953).

ring toward free-radical aromatic substitution may be studied, of course, by determining the product ratios in the radical substitution of the appropriate aromatic compound.   In addition, the relative reactivities of different aromatic rings have been determined in a number of cases by "competition" experiments, in which phenyl radicals were generated in a mixture of two aromatic compounds and the comparative extent of phenylation of the two compounds determined.   Grieve and Hey[37] and other early investigators made such studies using product-isolation techniques, but these techniques do not yield nearly so accurate results as the spectroscopic and related methods which have been used more recently.

Using these improved methods of analyses, Hey, Nechvatal, and Robinson showed that essentially the same results were obtained whether N-nitrosoacetanilide, phenylazotriphenylmethane, phenyl azohydroxide, or benzoyl peroxide (the initially formed benzoate radicals are decarboxylated) is used as the source of phenyl radicals.[40]   Hey and coworkers have determined the relative reactivities of a number of aromatic compounds toward the phenyl radical.[41]   They have expressed their results in terms of the *reactivity relative to benzene*.   By determining the fraction of the various isomers produced they have also obtained the *partial rate factors* or reactivities of various positions relative to any one of the positions in the benzene ring.   Their results are listed in Table 22-2.

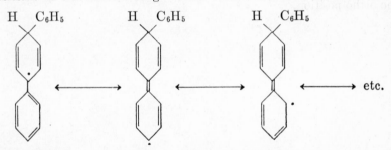

Also tabulated are some values calculated from the work of Dannley and coworkers.[42]   The larger partial rate factors observed, such as those for the ortho (2) and para (4) substitution of biphenyl, nitrobenzene, and

[40] D. H. Hey, A. Nechvatal, and T. S. Robinson, *J. Chem. Soc.*, 2892 (1951); cf. D. F. DeTar and H. J. Scheifele, Jr., *J. Am. Chem. Soc.*, **73**, 1442 (1951).

[41] D. R. Augood, D. H. Hey, and G. H. Williams, *J. Chem. Soc.*, 2094 (1952); 44 (1953); D. R. Augood, J. I. G. Cadogan, D. H. Hey, and G. H. Williams, *J. Chem. Soc.*, 3412 (1953); J. I. G. Cadogan, D. H. Hey, and G. H. Williams, *J. Chem. Soc.*, 794 (1954).

[42] R. L. Dannley, E. C. Gregg, Jr., R. E. Phelps, and C. B. Coleman, *J. Am. Chem. Soc.*, **76**, 445 (1954); R. L. Dannley and E. C. Gregg, Jr., *J. Am. Chem. Soc.*, **76**, 2997 (1954).

benzonitrile, are readily explained in terms of resonance stabilization of the intermediate radical of mechanism (22-12).

TABLE 22-2. RELATIVE REACTIVITIES AND PARTIAL RATE FACTORS FOR THE FREE-RADICAL PHENYLATION OF VARIOUS AROMATIC COMPOUNDS[40-42]

Compound	Relative reactivity	Partial rate factors		
		2 Substitution	3 Substitution	4 Substitution
C_6H_6	1.00	1.00	1.00	1.00
C_6H_5F	1.35	2.20	1.25	1.20
C_6H_5Cl	1.44	2.7	1.03	1.2
C_6H_5Br	1.75	2.59	1.75	1.83
C_6H_5I	1.80	2.79	1.70	1.80
$C_6H_5C_6H_5$	4.0	2.9	1.4	3.4
$C_6H_5NO_2$	4.0	7.0	1.2	7.9
C_6H_5CN	3.7	5.5	0.9	5.5
$C_6H_5SO_3CH_3$	1.5	2.0	1.2	1.0
C_5H_5N	1.5	2.2	1.0	1.0

Some of the smaller effects, such as the increased reactivity of practically all compounds in the meta position, are less easily explained. It may also be seen that there is in all cases a definite increase in reactivity in the ortho position.

CHAPTER 23

STEREOCHEMISTRY AND REARRANGEMENTS OF
FREE RADICALS

23-1. Stereochemistry of Free Radicals.   Brown, Kharasch, and Chao carried out an important investigation which has added greatly to our knowledge of the stereochemistry of free radicals.[1]   They studied the free-radical chlorination of optically active 2-methylbutyl chloride and found that the 1,2-dichloro-2-methylbutane formed was racemic.   This shows that the intermediate 1-chloro-2-methyl-2-butyl radicals racemized. This observation is also good evidence that the attack of a chlorine atom on the alkyl chloride does yield hydrogen chloride and an alkyl radical

$$CH_3CH_2\overset{\overset{\textstyle CH_3}{|}}{C}HCH_2Cl + Cl\cdot \rightarrow HCl + CH_3CH_2\overset{\overset{\textstyle CH_3}{|}}{\underset{\cdot}{C}}CH_2Cl$$

rather than the dichloride and a hydrogen atom

$$CH_3CH_2\overset{\overset{\textstyle CH_3}{|}}{C}HCH_2Cl + Cl\cdot \rightarrow CH_3CH_2\overset{\overset{\textstyle CH_3}{|}}{\underset{\underset{\textstyle Cl}{|}}{C}}CH_2Cl + H\cdot$$

since it would be a very improbable coincidence that the chlorine atom should attack the asymmetric carbon atom from the front and from the back at exactly the same rate.   While the radical is thus seen to have racemized, there are two possible explanations for this behavior.   On one hand, it may be that radicals are most stable when in a planar configuration, as carbonium ions appear to be (cf. Sec. 6-3a).   On the other hand, the radicals may prefer a pyramidal configuration, but, as in the case of amines, there may be a very rapid equilibrium between the two enantiomorphic pyramidal forms,

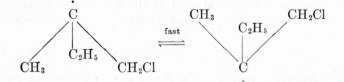

[1] H. C. Brown, M. S. Kharasch, and T. H. Chao, *J. Am. Chem. Soc.*, **62**, 3435 (1940).

The fact that the peroxide of 1-apocamphanecarboxylic acid

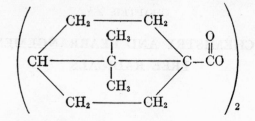

decomposes in carbon tetrachloride solution to give such probable products of the reaction of the 1-apocamphyl radical as 1-chloroapocamphane (36 per cent yield) shows that free radicals may exist at the bridgehead of small bicyclic ring systems, where they cannot reasonably have a planar configuration.[2] The formation of this chloride marks the apocamphyl radical as more reactive (less stable) than typical tertiary alkyl radicals, since the *t*-butyl radical, for example, has been shown to be insufficiently reactive to abstract chlorine atoms from carbon tetrachloride to any significant extent.[3] The lesser reactivity of the *t*-butyl radical may be due to an inherent greater stability of radicals in a planar configuration, but it may be due to certain other factors instead.

Since it is very likely that the vapor-phase nitration of saturated hydrocarbons proceeds by a free-radical mechanism, the observation of Blickenstaff and Hass that the nitration of bicyclo[2,2,1]heptane gives considerable bridgehead nitro compound[4] shows that the bridgehead (and hence nonplanar) radical probably has a stability comparable to the other (planar) radicals that may be formed from this hydrocarbon.

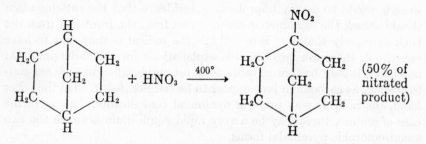

Overberger and Berenbaum studied the decomposition of both the meso and the *dl* forms of 2,2'-azo-bis-2,4-dimethylvaleronitrile and found

  [2] M. S. Kharasch, F. Engelmann, and W. H. Urry, *J. Am. Chem. Soc.*, **65**, 2428 (1943).
  [3] M. S. Kharasch, S. S. Kane, and H. C. Brown, *J. Am. Chem. Soc.*, **64**, 1621 (1942).
  [4] R. T. Blickenstaff and H. B. Hass, *J. Am. Chem. Soc.*, **68**, 1431 (1946).

that each isomer produced the same mixture of *meso-* and *dl-sym*-dimethyl-diisobutylsuccinonitriles.[5]

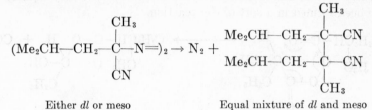

Either *dl* or meso   Equal mixture of *dl* and meso

This testifies not only to the racemization of the intermediate radicals but also to the fact that these radicals did indeed become *free* during the reaction.

Other workers have studied the stereochemistry of radicals by use of the free-radical-induced decarbonylation reaction of aldehydes. This reaction was first described by Winstein and Seubold, who found that around 130° and higher *t*-butyl peroxide causes aldehydes to lose carbon monoxide, presumably by the mechanism[6]

$$t\text{-BuO}\cdot + \text{RCHO} \rightarrow t\text{-BuOH} + \overset{\cdot}{\text{RCO}}$$

$$\overset{\cdot}{\text{RCO}} \rightarrow \text{R}\cdot + \text{CO}$$

$$\text{R}\cdot + \text{RCHO} \rightarrow \text{RH} + \overset{\cdot}{\text{RCO}}$$

Doering, Farber, Sprecher, and Wiberg obtained racemic 2,4-dimethyl-hexane from the decarbonylation of optically active methylethyliso-butylacetaldehyde, showing that the intermediate radical racemized.[7] They also obtained apocamphane in the decarbonylation of apocamphane-1-carboxaldehyde, showing that bridgehead radicals have a stability comparable to those for which a planar configuration is possible.

Bartlett and Greene have also studied a reaction in which a bridgehead radical was an intermediate in the decomposition of ditriptoyl peroxide.[8]

Kharasch, Kuderna, and Nudenberg have found that the decomposition of optically active methylethylacetyl peroxide yields, among other products, *sec*-butyl methylethylacetate, which may be hydrolyzed to optically active *sec*-butyl alcohol with the same configuration about its asymmetric carbon atom as the original peroxide had.[9] While it is

[5] C. G. Overberger and M. B. Berenbaum, *J. Am. Chem. Soc.*, **73**, 4883 (1951).

[6] S. Winstein and F. H. Seubold, Jr., *J. Am. Chem. Soc.*, **69**, 2916 (1947).

[7] W. von E. Doering, M. Farber, M. Sprecher, and K. B. Wiberg, *J. Am. Chem. Soc.*, **74**, 3000 (1952).

[8] P. D. Bartlett and F. D. Greene, *J. Am. Chem. Soc.*, **76**, 1088 (1954).

[9] M. S. Kharasch, J. Kuderna, and W. Nudenberg, *J. Org. Chem.*, **19**, 1283 (1954).

possible that the active ester may have resulted from the pairing of a
sec-butyl radical and a methylethylacetate radical, it may equally well
have been formed in a sort of S_Ni reaction.

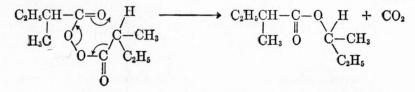

Due to the uncertainty of the reaction mechanism, it is difficult to draw
any definite conclusions from this observation.

23-2. Rearrangements of Free Radicals.   There are several reports in
the older literature of reactions that probably involved radical rearrangements.   In the electrolysis of potassium β,β-dimethylglutarate Walker
and Wood found a carbon-skeleton rearrangement to give 2-methyl-1-
butene.[10]   The most reasonable mechanism would appear to be

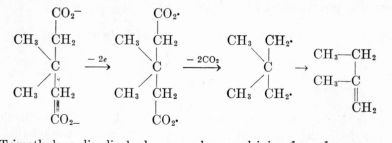

Trimethylene diradicals, however, have a driving force for rearrangement absent in a monoradical.   The migration of a group permits the
unpaired electrons to pair and form a new bond (although it is interesting
that they did not do so by forming a cyclopropane ring).   Rearrangements of ordinary radicals are not common, in contrast to carbonium-ion
rearrangements, whose occurrence is very widespread (Sec. 14-1).
Qualitatively there are some of the same driving forces for radical rearrangements as for carbonium-ion rearrangements.   Many primary
radicals produced as reaction intermediates could give more stable
tertiary radicals by the migration of a β substituent to the α-carbon atom.
The difference in stability between a primary and tertiary radical is
probably not so great as between a primary and tertiary carbonium ion.
This follows from the fact that the energy required to remove an electron
from a tertiary radical (its ionization potential) is probably less than for a
primary radical.   Thus it appears that in many of the cases where

[10] J. Walker and J. K. Wood, *J. Chem. Soc.*, **89**, 598 (1906); cf. L. Vanzetti, *Atti
accad. nazl. Lincei, Rend. Classe sci. fis. mat. e nat.*, [5], **13**, 112 (1904).

radical rearrangements have been sought, the increase in stability of the radical that would result from rearrangement is not so great as for the corresponding carbonium ion.   Nevertheless, it is not just the over-all change in stability which determines whether or not a rearrangement will occur but also the activation energy for the process.

The first good evidence for the rearrangement of an alkyl monoradical appears to be due to Urry and Kharasch.[11]   These workers treated neophyl chloride (2-methyl-2-phenyl-1-chloropropane) with phenyl-magnesium bromide in the presence of cobaltous chloride (there is no reaction in its absence), a reaction which earlier work showed would be expected to generate the neophyl radical.[12]   Among the reaction products were several, including 15 per cent isobutylbenzene, 9 per cent 2-methyl-3-phenyl-1-propene, and 4 per cent β,β-dimethylstyrene, which must have resulted from a carbon-skeleton rearrangement.   The following mechanism was suggested for the formation of the rearranged products.

$$C_6H_5MgBr + CoCl_2 \rightarrow MgBrCl + C_6H_5CoCl$$
$$2C_6H_5CoCl \rightarrow C_6H_5C_6H_5 + 2CoCl\cdot$$
$$C_6H_5C(CH_3)_2CH_2Cl + CoCl\cdot \rightarrow C_6H_5C(CH_3)_2CH_2\cdot + CoCl_2$$
$$C_6H_5C(CH_3)_2CH_2\cdot \rightarrow C_6H_5CH_2\overset{\bullet}{C}(CH_3)_2$$

$$2C_6H_5CH_2\overset{\bullet}{C}(CH_3)_2 \nearrow \begin{array}{l} C_6H_5CH_2CH(CH_3)_2 + C_6H_5CH{=}C(CH_3)_2 \\ \\ \text{or} \\ \\ C_6H_5CH_2CH(CH_3)_2 + C_6H_5CH_2C(CH_3){=}CH_2 \end{array}$$

The neophyl radical has been generated in other ways.   It is, no doubt, an intermediate in the radical chlorination of t-butylbenzene to neophyl chloride,[13] but in this case no rearrangement occurs.   It has also been produced in the t-butyl peroxide–induced decarbonylation of β-phenyl-isovaleraldehyde.   This was first done by Winstein and Seubold,[6] who isolated approximately equal amounts of the rearranged product, iso-butylbenzene, and the unrearranged product, t-butylbenzene, from the reaction mixture.   Seubold has described good evidence that the occurrence or nonoccurrence of rearrangement depends upon the lifetime of the neophyl radical.[14]   He isolated and analyzed the butylbenzene fraction from the decomposition in pure aldehyde solution (6.4 M) and in a 1.0 M solution of aldehyde in chlorobenzene.   He found 57 per cent isobutyl-

[11] W. H. Urry and M. S. Kharasch, *J. Am. Chem. Soc.*, **66**, 1438 (1944).

[12] M. S. Kharasch, D. W. Lewis, and W. B. Reynolds, *J. Am. Chem. Soc.*, **65**, 493 (1943); M. S. Kharasch, F. Engelmann, and W. H. Urry, *J. Am. Chem. Soc.*, **66**, 365 (1944).

[13] M. S. Kharasch and H. C. Brown, *J. Am. Chem. Soc.*, **61**, 2142 (1939); W. E. Truce, E. T. McBee, and C. C. Alfieri, *J. Am. Chem. Soc.*, **71**, 752 (1949).

[14] F. H. Seubold. Jr., *J. Am. Chem. Soc.*, **75**, 2532 (1953).

benzene (rearrangement) in the fraction from the pure aldehyde solution and 80 per cent isobutylbenzene in the fraction from the 1.0 M solution. The increase in extent of rearrangement with dilution of the aldehyde is very probably due to the fact that in the more dilute solution the neophyl radical collides with aldehyde molecules less frequently. Since the hydrogen-abstraction reaction is thus slowed, the rearrangement is relatively favored. In the chlorination reaction evidently the neophyl radicals attack chlorine more rapidly than they rearrange. Seubold has estimated that the activation energy of the rearrangement reaction is around 8 kcal. While the rearrangement may proceed through a radical (I) with a bridged structure rather similar to that of a "phenonium ion" (Sec. 14-1b),

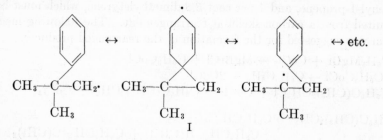

the evidence described shows that the radical formed initially does not have this structure. As a pathway through which the discrete intermediate neophyl radical rearranges, however, the radical I provides a reasonable explanation for why it is a phenyl rather than a methyl group that migrates in the rearrangement. This fact would appear to require some such explanation involving a *path* of low energy, since the migration of methyl would give a tertiary benzyl-type radical, a *product* of lower energy content.

Urry and Nicolaides have produced the *p*-methylneophyl radical, both by the reaction of the chloride with a Grignard reagent in the presence of cobaltous chloride and by the radical-induced decarbonylation of β-*p*-tolylisovaleraldehyde.[15] They found that the ability of the *p*-tolyl group to migrate in this radical rearrangement is about the same as that of a phenyl group. No evidence for the migration of an alkyl group was found, either with the *p*-methylneophyl radical or the 2,2-dimethylbutyl radical, which was generated by the Grignard method and which appeared to give no rearrangement at all.

Curtin and Hurwitz produced a number of related radicals by the decarbonylation of the appropriate aldehydes.[16] They found evidence

[15] W. H. Urry and N. Nicolaides, *J. Am. Chem. Soc.*, **74**, 5163 (1952).
[16] D. Y. Curtin and M. J. Hurwitz, *J. Am. Chem. Soc.*, **74**, 5381 (1952).

that the β,β,β-triphenylethyl (II), α-methyl-β,β,β-triphenylethyl (III), and β,β-diphenylpropyl (IV) radicals gave 100 per cent rearrangement.

$$(C_6H_5)_3CCH_2\cdot \qquad (C_6H_5)_3\overset{\cdot}{C}CHCH_3 \qquad (C_6H_5)_2\overset{\overset{\displaystyle CH_3}{|}}{C}CH_2\cdot$$
$$\text{II} \qquad\qquad\qquad \text{III} \qquad\qquad\qquad \text{IV}$$

In each case the rearrangement involved the migration of a phenyl group and the formation of a benzyl-type radical. With the β-phenyl-β-p-anisylethyl radical no carbon-skeleton rearrangement occurred, but the data do not show whether or not a hydrogen atom may have migrated.[16]

Bartlett and Cotman have presented evidence that the p-nitro-triphenylmethoxy radical rearranges with the predominant migration of the p-nitrophenyl group rather than an unsubstituted phenyl group.[17] Kharasch, Poshkus, Fono, and Nudenberg have similarly studied reactions in which substituted triphenylmethoxy radicals are produced; and they have shown that the p-phenylphenyl and the α-naphthyl groups migrate about six times as fast as the phenyl group, while the p-tolyl group migrates at about the same rate as phenyl.[18]

Kharasch, Liu, and Nudenberg obtained only the rearranged product, 2-bromo-2,3,4,4-tetramethylpentane, in the photobromination of 2,2,4,4-tetramethylpentane.[19] They therefore suspected that a radical rearrangement had occurred, although they realized that under the reaction conditions (200°) the bromide may have rearranged by a polar mechanism after it was formed. They therefore generated the di-t-butylmethyl radical (V) from the corresponding chloride by interaction with iso-propylmagnesium bromide and cobaltous bromide. The reaction product was found to be a mixture of 2,2,4,4-tetramethylpentane (VI) and 2,3,4,4-tetramethylpentene-1 (VII). These products may have been formed by a disproportionation reaction between the radical V and the rearranged radical VIII, or possibly by a disproportionation reaction between two radicals of the type of V, in which the abstraction of a hydrogen atom and rearrangement of a methyl group occur simultaneously.

$$\underset{\underset{\displaystyle Cl}{|}}{Me_3C-CH-CMe_3} \xrightarrow[CoBr_2]{i\text{-PrMgBr}} Me_3C-\overset{\cdot}{CH}-CMe_3$$
$$\text{V}$$

[17] P. D. Bartlett and J. D. Cotman, Jr., *J. Am. Chem. Soc.*, **72**, 3095 (1950).

[18] M. S. Kharasch, A. C. Poshkus, A. Fono, and W. Nudenberg, *J. Org. Chem.*, **16**, 1458 (1951).

[19] M. S. Kharasch, Y. C. Liu, and W. Nudenberg, *J. Org. Chem.*, **19**, 1150 (1954).

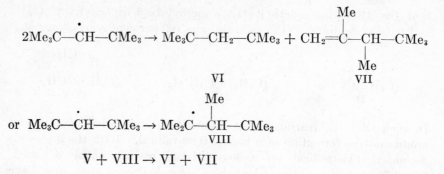

$$V + VIII \rightarrow VI + VII$$

In any event, this seems to be the first case in which a radical rearrangement involving the migration of an alkyl group has been reasonably well established.

PART IV

FOUR-CENTER-TYPE REACTIONS

CHAPTER 24

FOUR-CENTER-TYPE REACTIONS

According to the definition stated in Sec. 4-1c, four-center-type reactions are those in which the atoms in the reactant(s) simply change their configuration to that of the product(s) without electron pairing or unpairing and without the formation or destruction of ions. There are four (or more) key atoms, each of which is simultaneously forming a new bond and breaking an old one in the transition state. From this definition we should expect the following characteristics of reactions of this type: Their rates should not usually be greatly affected by the nature of the solvent, and in most cases they should proceed at a similar rate in the vapor phase as in solution. They should not be induced by initiators or slowed by inhibitors or have any of the other characteristics of chain reactions. They should not be light-catalyzed. They should not *require* acid or base catalysis, although cases are known which are *subject* to such catalysis.

24-1. Some Four-center-type Rearrangements. *24-1a. Cope Rearrangements.* Some excellent examples of four-center-type organic reactions are found in some of the rearrangements that have been discovered and studied most extensively by Cope and coworkers. They found that malononitriles, cyanoacetic esters, and malonic esters, all containing both an allyl and a vinyl substituent on the α-carbon atom, quite generally undergo a rearrangement reaction upon heating to give α,β-unsaturated compounds.[1]

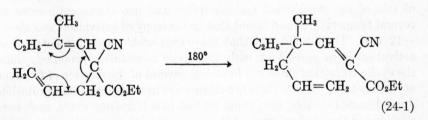

$$(24\text{-}1)$$

[1] A. C. Cope and E. M. Hardy, *J. Am. Chem. Soc.*, **62**, 441 (1940); A. C. Cope, K. E. Hoyle, and D. Heyl, *J. Am. Chem. Soc.*, **63**, 1843 (1941); A. C. Cope, C. M. Hofmann, and E. M. Hardy, *J. Am. Chem. Soc.*, **63**, 1852 (1941).

The conjugation of the α,β double bond with the cyano and carbethoxy groups is a driving force for the reaction. They suggested the mechanism shown above by analogy with the Claisen rearrangement. In agreement with the requirements of this mechanism, the reaction shown and a number of related ones were found to be kinetically first-order.[1] As also required, it was shown that the reaction is *intramolecular*. This was done by rearranging a mixture of ethyl (1-methyl-1-hexenyl)allyl-cyanoacetate (I) and diethyl isopropenylcrotylmalonate (II).

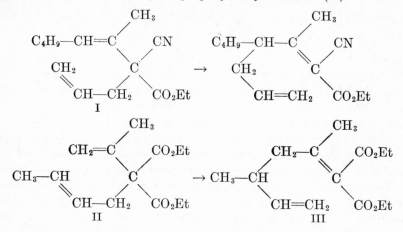

The reactions cleanly follow the equations above, showing that although both allyl and crotyl groups are migrating, evidently they do not become free, since no mixed products are formed.[1] The two groups were indeed migrating at the same time, since separate experiments on pure samples of I and II showed that their rearrangement rates are comparable. The rearrangement of II (which contains a crotyl group) to III (in which this has become an α-methylallyl group) is additional evidence for the mechanism (24-1), which requires that an allyl group "turn around" as it migrates.

Foster, Cope, and Daniels[2] studied the kinetics of the rearrangements of two of the substituted malononitriles and one cyanoacetic ester at several temperatures and found that the entropy of activation was about -12 e.u. They point out that this considerable negative entropy of activation is in agreement with the cyclic mechanism proposed, since the cyclic transition state will have lost several of the degrees of freedom of the reactant. While there are other ways in which freedom of rotation around various bonds, etc., could be lost in a transition state, such correlations of the configuration of the reactant in the transition state with the entropy of activation are certainly much more reliable for four-center-

[2] E. G. Foster, A. C. Cope. and F. Daniels, *J. Am. Chem. Soc.*, **69**, 1893 (1947).

type reactions than for reactions involving ions, because the entropy effects associated with ionic solvation may be large and not easily predictable.

Cope and coworkers studied the effect of structure on reactivity in these rearrangements and, among other things, found that the malononitriles rearranged faster than the corresponding cyanoacetic esters, which in turn were more reactive than the malonic esters.[1] This might be correlated with the greater electron-withdrawing power of the cyano group (compared to carbethoxy), or it might be that the cyano group better enters into conjugation with the α,β double bond being formed in the transition state. The latter explanation appears to be more probable (or more important). This follows from the fact that the phenyl group, which may conjugate with double bonds as effectively as cyano or carbethoxy but which is hardly comparable as an electron-withdrawing group, appears to be about as effective as a cyano or carbethoxy group at bringing about the Cope rearrangement. Thus Levy and Cope found that 3-phenyl-1,5-hexadiene rearranges to 1-phenyl-1,5-hexadiene smoothly at 177°.[3]

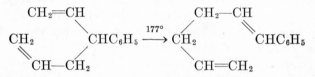

A methyl group was found to be definitely less effective than a phenyl group. 3-Methyl-1,5-hexadiene had to be heated to about 300° to rearrange, and even so the reaction was found to go only to about 95 per cent completion,[1] whereas all of the other rearrangements described were complete within the experimental error.

Rearrangements of amine oxides,[4] sulfoxides,[5] sulfones,[5] and sulfinates[5] have also been investigated.

24-1b. *The Claisen Rearrangement.* Claisen discovered that the allyl ethers of phenols rearrange cleanly at temperatures around 200°.[6] The product was found to be an *o*-allylphenol when an unsubstituted ortho position was present and a *p*-allylphenol when both ortho positions were blocked. The reaction is first-order and does not require a catalyst. The rearrangements of crotyl phenyl ethers give *o*-α-methylallylphenols. This does not prove that the reaction mechanism requires the allyl group

---

[3] H. Levy and A. C. Cope, *J. Am. Chem. Soc.*, **66**, 1684 (1944).

[4] A. C. Cope and P. H. Towle, *J. Am. Chem. Soc.*, **71**, 3423 (1949).

[5] A. C. Cope, D. E. Morrison, and L. Field, *J. Am. Chem. Soc.*, **72**, 59 (1950).

[6] For references to the earlier work described see D. S. Tarbell, The Claisen Rearrangement in R. Adams, "Organic Reactions," vol. II, chap. 1, John Wiley & Sons, Inc., New York, 1944.

to become inverted during the reaction. One could make the rationalization that an intermediate resonance-stabilized carbonium ion or radical preferred to recombine at its reactive secondary carbon atom. This alternate explanation, however, is rendered untenable by the observation that α-methylallyl phenyl ethers rearrange to *o*-crotylphenols. The rearrangement is intramolecular, since mixtures of ethers rearrange without the formation of any cross products. Thus the Claisen rearrangement is very similar to the Cope rearrangement, and it appears to have the following mechanism[7] (suggested earlier than that of the Cope rearrangement).

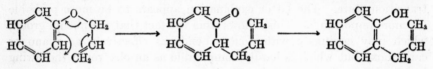

The second step, the enolization of a keto form of a phenol, may very well proceed by a polar mechanism, but since it appears to be much faster than the first step, it cannot be studied kinetically.

The study of the mechanism of the para Claisen rearrangement was complicated for some time by a report that allyl groups did not turn around in some cases but did in at least one other case. However, Rhoads, Raulins, and Reynolds have since shown that the report of inversion of an allyl group is incorrect and that the allyl group actually migrates without rearrangement.[8] These results, coupled with other observations of noninversion of allyl groups,[9] support the mechanism suggested by Hurd and Pollack.[7] According to this mechanism, the first step of an ordinary ortho Claisen rearrangement yields a product which cannot enolize to a phenol but which then undergoes a second four-center-type rearrangement to give a product which can enolize.

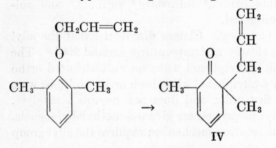

IV

[7] C. D. Hurd and M. A. Pollack, *J. Org. Chem.*, **3**, 550 (1939).

[8] S. J. Rhoads, R. Raulins, and R. D. Reynolds, *J. Am. Chem. Soc.*, **75**, 2531 (1953); **76**, 3456 (1954).

[9] J. P. Ryan and P. R. O'Connor, *J. Am. Chem. Soc.*, **74**, 5866 (1952); H. Schmid and K. Schmid, *Helv. Chim. Acta*, **36**, 489 (1953); E. N. Marvell, A. V. Logan, L. Friedman, and R. W. Ledeen, *J. Am. Chem. Soc.*, **76**, 1922 (1954).

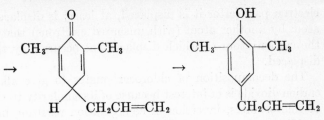

Perhaps more direct evidence for the mechanism above is furnished by Conroy and Firestone, who found that the intermediate IV, a diene, may be captured by reaction with the effective dieneophile, maleic anhydride.[10] Curtin and Johnson have presented additional evidence that the rearrangement proceeds through an intermediate of the type of IV and that the formation of IV is not merely an irrelevant side reaction.[11]

The Claisen rearrangement of allyl ethers is not limited to phenol ethers. Indeed, the first example that Claisen found was the rearrangement of the O-allyl ether of acetoacetic ester.[6] The reaction appears to be rather general for the allyl ethers of enols. Hurd and Pollack have found that the reaction proceeds satisfactorily for the simplest possible case, allyl vinyl ether rearranging to allyl acetaldehyde at about 250°.[12]

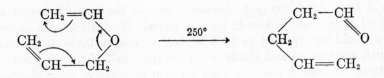

In a kinetic study Schuler and Murphy have found this rearrangement to be a homogeneous first-order gas-phase reaction with an entropy of activation of -7.7 e.u.[13]

24-1c. Some Four-center-type S_Ni Reactions. While it is not entirely clear how broad an area of reaction mechanisms Hughes, Ingold, and coworkers intended to include when they suggested the term S_Ni for certain internal nucleophilic substitution reactions,[14] we shall include under this heading those reactions in which an atom with an unshared

[10] H. Conroy and R. A. Firestone, *J. Am. Chem. Soc.*, **75**, 2530 (1953).

[11] D. Y. Curtin and H. W. Johnson, Jr., *J. Am. Chem. Soc.*, **76**, 2276 (1954).

[12] C. D. Hurd and M. A. Pollack, *J. Am. Chem. Soc.*, **60**, 1905 (1938).

[13] F. W. Schuler and G. W. Murphy, *J. Am. Chem. Soc.*, **72**, 3155 (1950); cf. L. Stein and G. W. Murphy, *J. Am. Chem. Soc.*, **74**, 1041 (1952).

[14] W. A. Cowdrey, E. D. Hughes, C. K. Ingold, S. Masterman, and A. D. Scott, *J. Chem. Soc.*, 1252 (1937); cf. Sec. 5-3.

electron pair (after it is displaced, at least) is displaced from a carbon atom by another atom (with unshared electrons) that was attached to the carbon atom at which displacement occurs only through the atom displaced.

The decomposition of chlorocarbonates to give alkyl chlorides and carbon dioxide is of interest because of its similarity to the decomposition of chlorosulfites, inversion of configuration resulting in the presence of pyridine and retention in its absence (Sec. 5-3).

Choppin, Frediani, and Kirby have shown that ethyl chlorocarbonate may decompose by a first-order reaction in the gas phase to yield ethyl chloride and carbon dioxide.[15] Thus there is apparently a four-center-type reaction possible for the decomposition of chlorocarbonates,

$$R \underset{Cl}{\overset{O}{\diagup}} C{=}O \longrightarrow R{-}Cl \ + \ CO_2 \qquad (24\text{-}2)$$

although we are not sure that it is this mechanism operating in those decompositions in solution which have been found to give retention of configuration. In so far as breaking of the R—O bond in mechanism (24-2) precedes the forming of the R—Cl bond, the mechanism is of the type suggested by Cram[16] and involves an ion-pair intermediate. It seems very unlikely that any intermediate in the vapor-phase reaction should have much ion-pair character, or else the reaction would not proceed at the rate it does in the gas phase. Nevertheless, in general, there would be expected to be a gradual transition between the polar ion-pair mechanism and the four-center-type mechanism. It would be arbitrary to draw a line (at some given percentage of ionic character for the transition state) between the two types of mechanisms.

Another reaction whose mechanism comes within the definition given at the beginning of this section is the decomposition of geminate diacyloxy compounds to aldehydes and anhydrides.

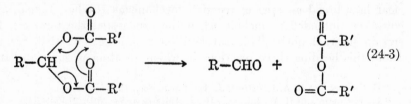

Coffin and coworkers have studied the kinetics of a number of reactions

[15] A. R. Choppin, H. A. Frediani, and G. F. Kirby, Jr., J. Am. Chem. Soc., 61, 3176 (1939).

[16] D. J. Cram, J. Am. Chem. Soc., 75, 332 (1953).

of this type in the vapor phase and have found all to be homogeneous first-order reactions.[17] The reaction in the liquid phase is subject to acid catalysis, but in the case of benzylidene diacetate and trichloro-ethylidene diacetate the liquid-phase reaction in the absence of catalysts has very nearly the same rate constant as the gas-phase reaction at the same temperature.[18] It therefore appears likely that the uncatalyzed reaction has a four-center-type mechanism like (24-3), while the acid-catalyzed reaction proceeds by a polar mechanism. The reactivity of $(R'CO_2)_2CHR$ compounds has been found to be little affected by changing R' from methyl to ethyl to propyl.[17-19] Variations in R gave relative reactivities that varied in the following order: C_6H_5[18] $\sim$ $o\text{-}ClC_6H_4$[18] $\sim$ $\alpha\text{-furyl}$[20] $\sim$ $CH_3CH{=}CH$[20] $>$ $n\text{-}C_6H_{13}$[21] $\sim$ $n\text{-}C_3H_7$[21] $\sim$ CH_3[17] $\sim$ CCl_3[18] $>$ $(AcO)_2CH$[22] $>$ H.[19] Thus, in general, the reactivity increases with the stability of the carbonyl group of the aldehyde being formed in the transition state. The position of the trichloromethyl and perhaps the diacetoxymethyl group seems anomalous, but steric factors are probably important in these cases.

24-2. Addition to Multiple Bonds. *24-2a. The Diels-Alder Reaction.* A number of examples of the Diels-Alder addition of unsaturated compounds to conjugated dienes have been found to be simple second-order reactions which have no induction period and whose rate is unaffected by initiators and inhibitors.[23] The reactivity of the diene is increased by electron-donating groups, while that of the dienophile is increased by electron-withdrawing groups.[24] Steric factors are also quite important. The reactivity of the diene is greatly increased when, as in the case of cyclopentadiene, the diene is held in a configuration in which the double bonds are oriented cis to each other with respect to rotation around the single bond between them.[24] The reaction appears to involve the formation of a complex (perhaps a reactive intermediate) like V, which may, by a relatively small change in the positions of the atoms, be transformed into the product.[23]

[17] C. C. Coffin, *Can. J. Research*, **5**, 636 (1931); **6**, 417 (1932), and subsequent articles.

[18] N. A. D. Parlee, J. R. Dacey, and C. C. Coffin, *Can. J. Research*, **15B**, 254 (1937); N. A. D. Parlee, J. C. Arnell, and C. C. Coffin, *Can. J. Research*, **18B**, 223 (1940).

[19] C. C. Coffin and W. B. Beazley, *Can. J. Research*, **15B**, 229 (1937).

[20] J. R. Dacey and C. C. Coffin, *Can. J. Research*, **15B**, 260 (1937).

[21] C. C. Coffin, J. R. Dacey, and N. A. D. Parlee, *Can. J. Research*, **15B**, 247 (1937).

[22] J. C. Arnell, J. R. Dacey, and C. C. Coffin, *Can. J. Research*, **18B**, 410 (1940).

[23] A. Wassermann, *J. Chem. Soc.*, 828 (1935); G. A. Benford, H. Kaufmann, B. S. Khambata, and A. Wassermann, *J. Chem. Soc.*, 381 (1939), and other sources cited therein.

[24] For some of the many data on reactivity, and the scope of the Diels-Alder reaction see Ref. 6, Adams, *op. cit.*, vol. IV, chaps. 1 and 2, vol. V, chap. 3.

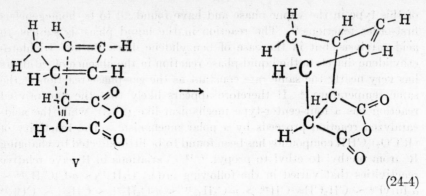

(24-4)

The reaction thus has a number of the characteristics of a four-center-type reaction. In some cases, however, it appears that the polar character of the transition state may be considerable.

The dimerization of cyclopentadiene is a homogeneous reaction in the gas phase,[25] and its rate in solution is not greatly affected by the ion-solvating power of the solvent.[26] On the other hand, the rate of reaction of cyclopentadiene with quinone in the vapor phase depends on the area of pyrex surface in the reaction vessel and is thus at least partly a heterogeneous reaction.[27] Furthermore, the rate of this reaction in solution shows a definite increase with increasing ion-solvating power.[28] Several Diels-Alder reactions have also been found to be subject to acid catalysis.[29] The acid catalysis is probably due to an increase in the electrophilicity of the dienophile resulting from its hydrogen-bonded association with the acid catalyst. So it is seen that under certain conditions the reaction has much of the character of a polar reaction. As we have stated before, no sharp line may be drawn between the two types of reaction mechanisms.

Among other suggestions for the detailed course of reaction along the general lines of mechanism (24-4) is the proposal that there is a reactive intermediate with a considerable resonance contribution of an electronic structure in which the diene has donated an electron to the dienophile, the former becoming a radical carbonium ion and the latter a radical carbanion.[30]

[25] G. A. Benford and A. Wassermann, *J. Chem. Soc.*, 362 (1939).

[26] H. Kaufmann and A. Wassermann, *J. Chem. Soc.*, 870 (1939).

[27] A. Wassermann, *J. Chem. Soc.*, 1089 (1946).

[28] *Ibid.*, 623 (1942).

[29] *Ibid.*, 618 (1942); W. Rubin, H. Steiner, and A. Wassermann, *J. Chem. Soc.*, 3046 (1949).

[30] R. B. Woodward, *J. Am. Chem. Soc.*, **64**, 3058 (1942); R. B. Woodward and H. Baer, *J. Am. Chem. Soc.*, **66**, 645 (1944).

Some of the observations on the reaction do not appear to have been explained in any reasonable fashion. For example, trimethylamine has been reported to be a catalyst, acetic acid has been said to be a catalyst for a reaction in the vapor phase, and phenol is a catalyst in the liquid phase, although the much more acidic iodoacetic acid is not.[29]

There are a number of other addition reactions that might be included under the present heading with a broad enough definition of the Diels-Alder reaction. These include the addition of vinyl ethers to α,β-unsaturated carbonyl compounds and related reactions involving carbon-oxygen double bonds,[31]

the addition of nitroso compounds to dienes,[32]

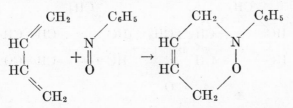

and a number of reactions involving carbon-nitrogen double and triple bonds.[24]

Also related is the addition reaction of sulfur dioxide to conjugated dienes,

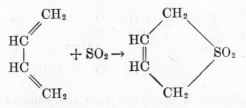

at least three examples of which have been found to be smooth second-order reactions.[33]

[31] R. I. Longley, Jr. and W. S. Emerson, *J. Am. Chem. Soc.*, **72**, 3079 (1950); C. W. Smith, D. G. Norton, and S. A. Ballard, *J. Am. Chem. Soc.*, **73**, 5267, 5270, 5273 (1951).

[32] Y. A. Arbuzov and coworkers, *Doklady Akad. Nauk S.S.S.R.*, **60**, 993, 1173 (1948); **76**, 681 (1951); *Chem. Abstr.*, **42**, 7299h (1948); **43**, 650c (1949); **45**, 8535e (1951).

[33] L. R. Drake, S. C. Stowe, and A. M. Partansky, *J. Am. Chem. Soc.*, **68**, 2521 (1946).

24-2b. Other Four-center-type Addition Reactions. Although the number of 1,4 addition reactions of olefins to conjugated dienes (the Diels-Alder reaction) is enormous, the 1,2 addition of one olefin to another occurs only rather infrequently. For one type of example the dimerization of certain fluoroolefins is known.

$$\begin{array}{ccc} CF_2 & CF_2 & CF_2\!-\!CF_2 \\ \| & + & \| & \to & | & | \\ CF_2 & CF_2 & CF_2\!-\!CF_2 \end{array}$$

Lacher, Tompkin, and Park have studied the kinetics of dimerization of tetrafluoroethylene and chlorotrifluoroethylene in the gas phase.[34] They found the reactions to be of the second order without an induction period and with no obvious demand for an initiator. Therefore it seems likely that they are of the four-center type.

Another 1,2 addition that may be of the four-center type is the addition of ketenes to cyclopentadiene.[35]

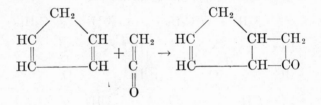

The dimerization of ketenes may also be a reaction of this type.

There are, too, a number of 1,3 additions known that may have four-center character[36]

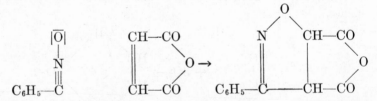

as well as the addition of azides and diazo compounds to olefinic double bonds.

24-3. Elimination Reactions. *24-3a. The Chugaev Reaction.* The Chugaev method of dehydrating an alcohol involves its transformation to a methyl xanthate, which upon pyrolysis yields methyl mercaptan, carbonyl sulfide, and the olefin. Hückel, Tappe, and Legutke suggested

[34] J. R. Lacher, G. W. Tompkin, and J. D. Park, *J. Am. Chem. Soc.*, **74**, 1693 (1952).
[35] A. T. Blomquist and J. Kwiatek, *J. Am. Chem. Soc.*, **73**, 2098 (1951).
[36] A. Quilico, G. S. d'Alcontres, and P. Grünanger, *Nature*, **166**, 226 (1950).

that the reaction involved a cyclic transition state in which the β-hydrogen atom was forming a bond to sulfur at the same time the α-carbon–oxygen bond was being broken.[37] Their mechanism was based to a considerable extent on the observation that the dehydration of menthols and α-decalols went predominantly cis. The mechanism was given a minor but reasonable modification by Stevens and Richmond, who suggested that it was the doubly bound sulfur atom that removed the β-hydrogen.[38]

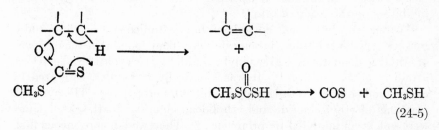

$$\text{CH}_3\text{SCSH} \longrightarrow \text{COS} + \text{CH}_3\text{SH}$$

(24-5)

These workers further observed that pinacolyl alcohol (3,3-dimethyl-2-butanol) gave the unrearranged olefin, t-butylethylene. Barton has noted that the reaction is probably of the four-center type,[39] and Alexander and Mudrak have added to the evidence for preferentially cis elimination.[40] O'Connor and Nace have studied the kinetics of several Chugaev reactions in the liquid phase.[41] They find the reaction to be first-order and unaffected by several ordinary free-radical inhibitors. The entropy of activation was negative. These data support a cyclic four-center-type mechanism such as (24-5), although, as O'Connor and Nace point out, there is no evidence that the electron pairs move as indicated by the arrows, or indeed that they move in pairs at all. These workers have also shown that when the methyl group attached to sulfur is replaced by a more strongly electron-withdrawing group, the reactivity of the xanthate increases.

24-3b. *Other Four-center-type Elimination Reactions.* The preparation of olefins by the pyrolysis of esters bears a strong resemblance to the Chugaev reaction, and, indeed, Hurd and Blunck proposed a four-center-type mechanism for the reaction before such a mechanism was suggested for the Chugaev reaction.[42]

---

[37] W. Hückel, W. Tappe, and G. Legutke, *Ann.*, **543**, 191 (1940).

[38] P. G. Stevens and J. H. Richmond, *J. Am. Chem. Soc.*, **63**, 3132 (1941).

[39] D. H. R. Barton, *J. Chem. Soc.*, 2174 (1949).

[40] E. R. Alexander and A. Mudrak, *J. Am. Chem. Soc.*, **72**, 1810, 3194 (1950).

[41] G. L. O'Connor and H. R. Nace, *J. Am. Chem. Soc.*, **74**, 5454 (1952); **75**, 2118 (1953).

[42] C. D. Hurd and F. H. Blunck, *J. Am. Chem. Soc.*, **60**, 2419 (1938); cf. Ref. 39.

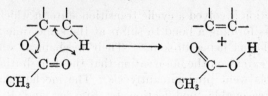

Evidence for the four-center-type mechanism in this case includes preferred cis orientation,[40,43] first-order kinetics,[41,44] a negative entropy of activation,[41,44] no induction period,[44] and no effect of surface area or inhibitors on the reaction rate.[44]

Barton, Howlett, and coworkers have studied the olefin-forming pyrolysis of alkyl chlorides in some detail. They found that the pyrolysis of ethylene dichloride (to give vinyl chloride) is, to a considerable extent, a radical chain reaction.[45] It was kinetically first-order, catalyzed by oxygen and chlorine, and strongly inhibited by propylene. The pyrolysis reactions of ethyl chloride and ethylidene chloride, on the other hand, were not at all inhibited by propylene.[46] They were homogeneous first-order reactions in the gas phase and gave excellent yields of the mono-dehydrochlorination products. These data suggest a four-center-type mechanism, and similar results have been obtained for *t*-butyl chloride,[47] isopropyl chloride,[48] propylene dichloride,[48] *n*-propyl chloride,[49] *n*-butyl chloride,[49] and 2,2-dichloropropane.[50] The fact that the pyrolysis of menthyl chloride is also homogeneous (in a reaction vessel with suitably coated walls), uninhibited (by propylene), and unimolecular in the vapor phase is of particular interest because the olefinic reaction products consist of about 25 per cent 2-menthene and 75 per cent 3-menthene.[51] The latter, major product must have been formed by a cis elimination, and the former, minor product may also have been formed by the same mechanism.

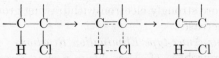

[43] R. T. Arnold, G. G. Smith, and R. M. Dodson, *J. Org. Chem.*, **15**, 1256 (1950); N. L. McNiven and J. Read, *J. Chem. Soc.*, 2067 (1952).

[44] D. H. R. Barton, A. J. Head, and R. J. Williams, *J. Chem. Soc.*, 1715 (1953); A. T. Blades, *Can. J. Chem.*, **32**, 366 (1954).

[45] D. H. R. Barton and K. E. Howlett, *J. Chem. Soc.*, 155 (1949).

[46] D. H. R. Barton and K. E. Howlett, *J. Chem. Soc.*, 165 (1949); K. E. Howlett, *J. Chem. Soc.*, 3695 (1952).

[47] D. H. R. Barton and P. F. Onyon, *Trans. Faraday Soc.*, **45**, 725 (1949).

[48] D. H. R. Barton and A. J. Head, *Trans. Faraday Soc.*, **46**, 114 (1950).

[49] D. H. R. Barton, A. J. Head, and R. J. Williams, *J. Chem. Soc.*, 2039 (1951).

[50] K. E. Howlett, *J. Chem. Soc.*, 945 (1953).

[51] D. H. R. Barton, A. J. Head, and R. J. Williams, *J. Chem. Soc.*, 453 (1952).

Each of the following chlorides is pyrolytically dehydrohalogenated, at least partly by a free-radical chain reaction: ethylene dichloride,[45] 1,1,1-trichloroethane,[52] *sym-* and *unsym-*tetrachloroethane,[53] 2,2′-dichloro diethyl ether,[49] 1,1-dichloropropane,[50] 1,4-dichlorobutane,[54] and 1,1,2-trichloroethane.[54] It is pointed out that part of the difference between the two classes of compounds described is that many in the former group either react to give radical inhibitors or are themselves inhibitors.

Another reaction that may be classified as an elimination is the decomposition of cyclobutane to ethylene. This decomposition is a first-order reaction unaffected by the surface area or by the addition of such free-radical inhibitors as propylene, nitric oxide, and toluene.[55] Thus it is reasonable to suggest a four-center mechanism for this reaction, too.

[52] D. H. R. Barton and P. F. Onyon, *J. Am. Chem. Soc.*, **72**, 988 (1950).
[53] D. H. R. Barton and K. E. Howlett, *J. Chem. Soc.*, 2033 (1951).
[54] R. J. Williams, *J. Chem. Soc.*, 113 (1953).
[55] C. T. Genaux, F. Kern, and W. D. Walters, *J. Am. Chem. Soc.*, **75**, 6196 (1953).

AUTHOR INDEX

467

SUBJECT INDEX

Acetaldehyde, aldol condensation, 252–254
cyanohydrin formation, 251
hydration, 240
NaHSO₃ addition to, 245
semicarbazone formation, 250
Acetals formation and hydrolysis, 244
Acetic acid, dielectric constant, 43
Acetic anhydride, dielectric constant, 43
hydrolysis, 301
Acetoacetic acid decarboxylation, 285
Acetoacetic ester condensation, 292–293
Acetone, aldol condensation, 253–254, 257–258
as base, 53
cyanohydrin formation, 251
dielectric constant, 43
enolization, 192, 198–199
extent of hydration, 240
ionization in water, 227
NaHSO₃ addition to, 245
O¹⁸ exchange, 241
percentage enol, 233
photolysis, 392–393
semicarbazone formation, 248–250
Acetonedicarboxylic acid decarboxylation, 287
Acetonitrile, as base, 53
dielectric constant, 43
Acetophenone, acidity, 50
condensation with benzaldehyde, 254
cyanohydrin formation, 251
photolysis, 392
semicarbazone formation, 248
Acetophenones, Hammett's ρ for semicarbazone formation, 250
Acetoxonium ions, 126–127
2-Acetoxycyclohexyl p-toluenesulfonate, neighboring group participation in, 127
Acetoxysuccinic acid, hydrolysis of active, 266
Acetylacetone, alkaline cleavage, 294–295
ionization in water, 227
percentage enol, 233
Acetyl chloride reactivity toward sodium vapor, 395
Acetylene acidity, 50
Acetylenes, additions of halogens to, 212
Acetylium ions, 339
Acetyl peroxide decomposition, 412
Acid anhydrides hydrolysis, 300–301

Acid and base catalysis, 190–201
general, 190–194
in acetaldehyde hydration, 240
in aromatic iodination, 341–342
in benzidine rearrangement, 347
in carbanion formation, 224–225
in cleavage of chloral, 295
in cyanohydrin formation, 251
in Curtius reaction, 319
in decarboxylation, 286
in Mannich reaction, 256
in mutarotation of glucose, 241–244
in O¹⁸ exchange of acetone, 241
in phenylhydrazone and oxime formation, 250
in semicarbazone formation, 246–248
reaction mechanisms and, 194–201
specific, 190–192
in acetal hydrolysis, 244
in benzilic acid rearrangement, 315
in cumene hydroperoxide decomposition, 326
Acid catalysis in halogen additions, 210
Acid halides, hydrolysis of, 300
Acidity, definitions, 46, 88
Acidity constants, 54
determination in certain mixed solvents, 56–59
Acidity functions, 59–61
correlation with reaction rates, 200
in decarbonylation, 292
in hydrations of olefins, 214–217
in lactone hydrolysis, 273
Acids and bases, 46–80
Arrhenius, 46
Lewis, 46
Lowry-Brønsted, 46
relative strengths, effect on, of resonance, 64
of solvent change, 54
of structure, 61–80
electrostatic effects, 68
inductive effects, 66
steric effects, 77–80
very weak, 50, 56–59
Acrolein addition to ethyl vinyl ether, 461
Additions, of acids to olefins, mechanism, 213–217
reactivity in, 217–219

481